Early British Quick Firing Artillery

Early British Quick Firing Artillery

(Field and Horse)

Len Trawin

Nexus Special Interests

Nexus Special Interests Ltd.
Nexus House
Boundary Way
Hemel Hempstead
Hertfordshire HP2 7ST
England

First published by Nexus Special Interests Ltd. 1997

ISBN 1-85486-154-9

Typeset by Kate Williams, London.
Printed and bound in Great Britain by Bookcraft (Bath) Ltd.

CONTENTS

AUTHOR'S NOTE

The material contained within this book has been gathered over a long period of time, from a wide variety of sources. The difficulty in bringing all the data to a common and accurate standard has been considerable and it follows that there are bound to be instances, hopefully isolated, where final achievement has not quite equalled original aspiration. For any such aberration I apologise unreservedly.

Imperial measurement has been retained, as has much of the original terminology. Metric conversion information and a glossary of terms can be found at the end of the book. Some of the plans shown are available separately as A3 scaled drawings. Please contact Nexus Special Interests Books Division (Tel: 01442 66551) for further details.

Acknowledgements and my grateful thanks are due to:

The Curator and Staff of The Museum of Artillery in the Rotunda, Woolwich, for their patience and willing assistance

The Royal Artillery Historical Trust, Woolwich

The Adjutant and C Sub Section, The King's Troop, Royal Horse Artillery, for their enthusiastic help and hospitality

The Imperial War Museum

The scholars and authors, too numerous to name, who, over many years, inspired a growing interest, and

a deep and special thanks to John Bradley, whose generosity laid the foundation for this work.

INTRODUCTION

Early historical records indicate that guns, of one form or another, were used by Edward III during the so-called Hundred Years War between England and France. Manuscripts record their use at the Battle of Crécy in 1346 and at the Siege of Calais. Those weapons were of little strategic use, however, as the weight of their structure meant that transporting them to the scene of battle was a laborious process, the gun carriage being a multi-axle cart drawn by large teams, generally of oxen. Being essentially either siege or garrison weapons, they were often cast at the location where they were to be used, which may sound improbable, but it must be remembered that a siege could last many years.

The first real attempt to bring mobility, in any practical sense of the word, to artillery, was made in the mid-1490s. Under the French king, Charles VIII, improvements in casting bronze and careful attention to barrel proportions, together with the introduction of trunnions, produced guns light enough to be mounted on two-wheeled carriages. The use of iron cannon balls instead of stone, plus the improved mobility of his artillery force, enabled Charles to sweep through Italy in only three months.

Those guns were still limited to the siege role however, and it was not until the mid-1750s, when a technique to fine bore barrels was developed, that further weight reductions, combined with improved ballistic performance, brought about a redesign of artillery carriages and limbers, once again by the French, which enabled draught teams to be reduced to six horses and made the gun a practical weapon for use in the field.

Britain had formed the Royal Artillery in 1716, but it was in 1793 that the Royal Horse Artillery was formed, its equipment by then considered sufficiently mobile to support cavalry in the field.

The Napoleonic Wars saw horse artillery used, with varying degrees of success, but it was the final act of that conflict, at Waterloo in 1815, which saw the use of horse artillery take the day, the French Horse Grenadiers being destroyed in the afternoon by Wellington's guns, which charged forward and unlimbered less than one hundred yards from the enemy. This was virtually the last of the classic uses of combined cavalry and horse artillery to occur on a battlefield.

With the ending of one revolution in Europe, another had been gathering momentum, initially fuelled by a thirst for knowledge, the results of which would have an impact of enormous importance on all aspects of life, both civil and military. The Industrial Revolution brought new materials and the means to fashion them, which changed the role of artillery from one of a close quarter support arm to a long range, unseen force, able to reach from beyond the sight of an enemy and destroy him.

Steel was the key material which made this change possible, shaped by new mechanical hammers into large forgings, then machined to tolerances hitherto impossible to achieve. Almost overnight barrels became lighter and stronger, they were rifled and loaded at the breech. Metallurgists devised alloys with steel and bronze and carriages became lighter and stronger.

Allied with these advances came a new substance to give vastly increased power. In 1864 a Swedish engineer and chemist, Dr. Alfred Nobel, produced nitroglycerine, in itself too violent for use as a propellant, but with nitrocellulose and mineral jelly, treated with acetone, it could be formed into any required shape. In string-like form it was cordite, destined to be the predominant propellant in the British Army's guns for three-quarters of a century. It was the absence of combustion residue, or fouling, from this 'smokeless' propellant, allied to accurately machined steel, which enabled a French engineer – M. de Bange – to design the first successful breech loading (BL) system to employ the interrupted thread principle. To this he married an obturator to render the breech gas-tight during detonation, but free to open and close at other times.

The increased rate of fire possible with the new loading system however, was offset by the continual need for a gun's crew to run-up and re-lay their gun consequent to the recoil of each round being fired. This was partially negated by the use of various additional brakes fitted to the carriage, on either the wheel naves or tyres, or by the use of dragshoes. These devices relied solely on the addition of resistance to the inertia of the carriage, which still needed to be run-up and the gun relaid for each round fired. In attempts to overcome this problem various types of spring spade were introduced. These are described in more detail later, but their function was to cushion the shock of recoil from gun to carriage, the whole still recoiling rearwards over the ground and still needing to be run-up and relaid.

The problems were solved, once again, by the French. Making use of developing engineering technology they interposed a pneumatic buffer and recuperator, between gun and carriage, to control the gun's recoil and return it to the loading position, the carriage being held stationary by a fixed spade. The result of their endeavours was the first practical quick firing (QF) gun. Introduced in 1897 as a 75mm field gun, it was to use 'fixed' ammunition to attain a sustained rate of fire of over twenty rounds per minute.

The introduction of fixed ammunition, where propellant and projectile were loaded as a single unit, marked the culmination of development of the projectile. The first cannon projectiles, loaded at the muzzle, were stones, often shaped on site by masons

travelling with the artillery. Iron cannon balls, it will be remembered, were introduced by the French king, Charles VIII, for use in his new style artillery. They were subsequently in general use, albeit in many and varied forms – together with grape and later, case shot – until rifled barrels made possible the change to cylindrical projectiles.

One of the few variations which had success in both geometric forms was first evolved experimentally during the siege of Gibraltar in 1778. At that time, small arms development had reached a stage where well-trained infantry could match the artillery of the day in range and accuracy. In an attempt to discourage this impertinence, Captain Mercier took to firing short fuzed mortar shells, before a reduced charge, from a howitzer. These exploded above the infantry, scouring the ground with fragments. Lieutenant Shrapnel, in 1784, improved on the idea with a thin-walled iron sphere, filled with musket balls and carrying a small charge of blackpowder, timed with a wooden fuze to explode above, or amongst, infantry. This was adopted as spherical case shot in 1792. At Woolwich Arsenal, in 1852, Captain Boxer adapted the Shrapnel principle to the new cylindrical form of projectile and fitted a fuze he had designed in 1849, to produce a form of aerial shotgun. Upon its introduction it was officially named as Shrapnel shell, in acknowledgement of its original inventor. Together with the well tried and tested, shorter range case shot, the shrapnel shell was the generally used projectile for light mobile artillery, until the large scale introduction of high explosive shells in the Great War of 1914.

Means to ignite explosive charges, whether for propellant or projectile, remained almost unchanged for centuries. Originally a flaming torch, later a piece of cord soaked in saltpetre and dried to make slow-match, which smouldered and glowed red hot, would be applied to priming powder at a cannon's touch-hole. The flint lock, developed originally for small arms, was adapted for use on some artillery of larger calibres in the mid-1750s.

At Waterloo, in 1815, the cannon were still touched-off with slow-match, although a more efficient system had been under development since 1805. It was the invention of a Scottish minister of the church, the Reverend Alexander Forsyth, and made use of the highly sensitive chemical, mercury fulminate, mixed with potassium chlorate. When dry, this mixture would detonate if struck and could be used to ignite the main powder charge in a weapon, with good reliability.

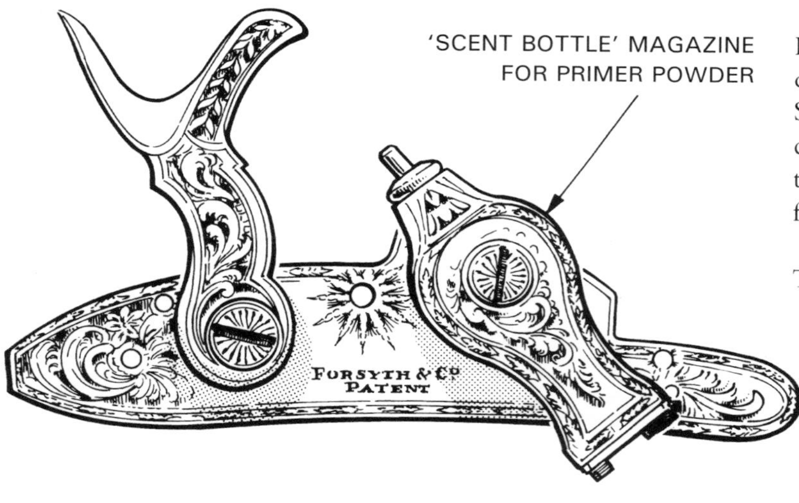

The invention was offered to the Board of Ordnance in 1807 and rejected. The wrangling and apparent vindictiveness that followed are already well documented and there is no need to repeat it here, however percussion cap ignition was adopted, for its small arms, by the British Army in 1838.

The ignition method used in artillery generally followed a friction system, where the sudden withdrawal of a roughened bar from a friction tube containing phosphorus, ignited the latter and the resultant flame ignited a charge of fine grain blackpowder in the body of the detonator tube, this in turn firing the propellant.

In 1866, Colonel Boxer adapted the percussion cap system to design the first successful centre-fire cartridge for use in the Snider rifle. His centre-fire cap was subsequently adapted for quick fire artillery ammunition in the late 1890s, being employed to ignite propellant charges and also in the time and percussion fuzes of projectiles.

This much abbreviated history of field artillery leads us to the time span which is the objective of this book. Other more learned students of the subject have provided excellent detailed literature on the uses and consequences of artillery use in campaigns throughout its history. Illustrations of artillery abound and, since the advent of photography, there are vivid and accurate images of its appearance and use. However, the rapid transition from recoiling carriage to quick firing gun deserves more than the usual passing reference.

Being, as weapon developments have always been, at the forward edge of emerging technology, it was a period that is of particular interest and worthy of much deeper attention which, in the following pages, I attempt to give.

GUN CARRIAGES

NOTES ON THEIR DESIGN AND CONSTRUCTION

Regardless of the stage in its development, a gun carriage had always to fulfil two functions. These were, first, to be a travelling support for the gun and secondly, a firing support for the gun in action. These two separate roles played by a gun carriage each presented many differing requirements. If we consider these individually, the problems confronting any carriage designer will become apparent.

As a travelling support for a gun, the carriage would need to have mobility, sufficient enough to be brought easily and rapidly into any required position. The degree of mobility would be influenced by several factors: by the amount of power required to move the carriage and maintain it in motion (the traction or draught); by its ability to move with equal ease either forwards or in reverse; and by its ability to overcome obstacles. These needs would demand that the carriage must be as light as possible commensurate with the weight of the gun and any additional equipment that had to be carried.

Any load would have to be correctly distributed about the axle (or axles, as we must include the limber as a factor in the design). The load distribution would depend upon the relative diameters of the pairs of wheels and the fact that the traction of the front wheels was generally more difficult than the rear, this being due to their having to create the tracks and partly reduce the height of any obstacles for the rear wheels.

This would indicate that the load on the front axle should be less than on the rear. However, if too much weight were on the rear axle, relative to the front, the rear wheels would sink in soft ground and increase the draught on the whole unit. So, for lightness of draught, the track would need to be the same for both sets of wheels, in order that the front wheels would assist the rear.

The wheel diameter would be a maximum and the axletree diameter a minimum. Various wheel diameters were used. Originally, five feet was the norm, but this was reduced to four feet six inches for the QF 15 pdr carriage, but a standard of four feet eight inches was adopted for all field wheels around 1910.

To keep the draught as light as possible the attachment for the traces would have to be at an ideal height from the ground in order to give the most advantageous inclination. Shafts were originally used for attachment of the draught animals, but were replaced with pole draught in 1895.

In addition to lightness of draught, the gun carriage would need to be able to manoeuvre 'very short', requiring a minimum overall length, turning within a minimum circle. This was attained by linking the gun and limber with a trail eye and limber hook allowing the unit to fold on itself, the turning circle being limited only by the wheel diameter and axle spacing. This arrangement also assisted the mobility over uneven ground, allowing the two axles to pivot independently and afford a degree of vertical flexibility to the unit, improving the ability to pass obstacles.

Some carriages were fitted with springs between the axles and body of the carriage. These were not widely adopted though, as the advantage of absorbing shocks was offset by a certain weakness introduced, plus the increase in height of the carriage. Springs were introduced into the limber and swingletree hooks of the 4.5 inch QF howitzer, to cushion the shocks in starting and when passing over rough ground.

An efficient system of braking was necessary for good mobility, a method of quickly checking the wheels being required to regulate the movement of the carriage. This was achieved with a simple system of levers or screws.

All of the foregoing comments on mobility would need to be tempered with a requirement for stability, this being influenced by the speed, weight, centre of gravity and track width; also a recognition that the capsizing angle of a field gun carriage was about thirty-five degrees. In general however, considerations of stability were of greater concern with the carriage in use as a firing platform than when travelling.

Further to mobility and stability, the carriage needed sufficient strength and durability to enable it to function reliably for a practical service life.

A further complication to any design was increasing complexity. As the gun became more efficient, various additional pieces of equipment were added to capitalise on, and compensate for, the performance.

The second requirement of the carriage was as a firing support for the gun in action. One function remained common with the foregoing remarks regarding mobility – that of the need to readily direct the gun onto any desired point.

Further to this, the carriage would have to provide a steady platform on which the gun could recoil axially and automatically return to the firing position. Provision was necessary for the attachment of sights and protection for the gun's crew in a manner that would not hinder the gun's operation.

The stability factor has already been mentioned, in as much as it was as equal a requirement when firing as when travelling.

It is advantageous here to make a closer study of the basic physical problems involved in producing a practical long recoil carriage design.

The first requirement was to render the carriage, to all intents, immobile during the firing cycle. This was achieved by means of a fixed trail spade which dug into the ground. Once this was done, there were two main forces acting on the carriage of a field gun firing point blank.

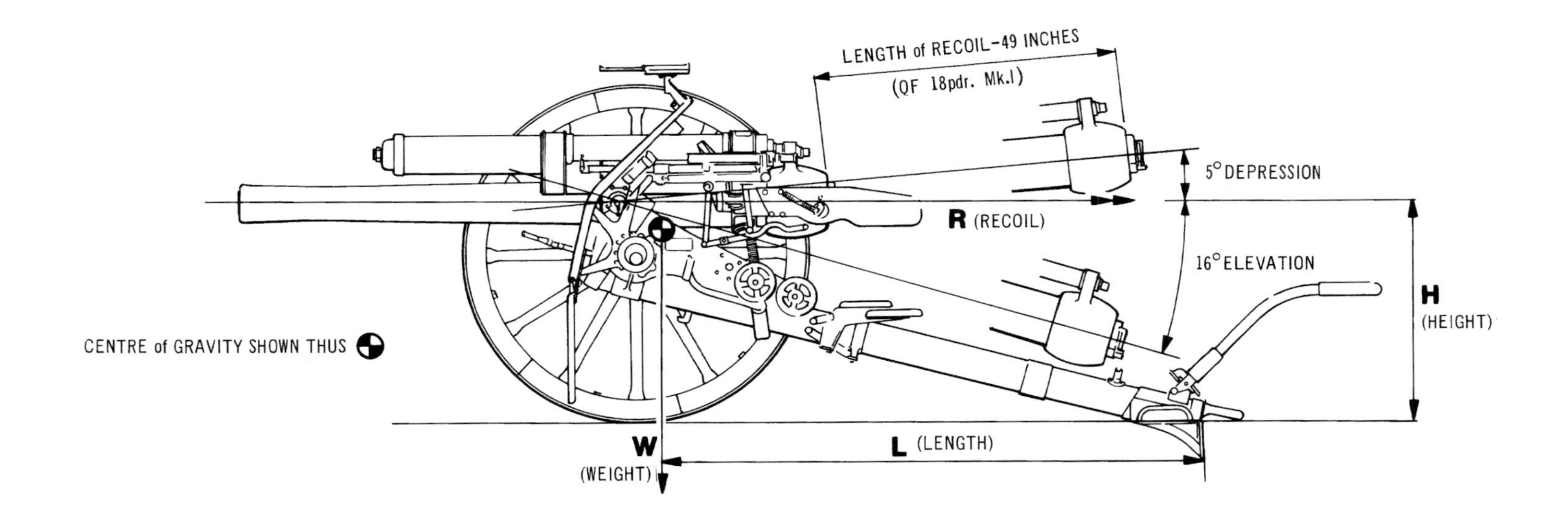

The **lifting force** (or **moment**) was a combination of the recoil force (**R**) and the height of the gun axis (**H**). The recoil was kept as small as practicable, but as it was dependent on the gun ballistics it could not be reduced. The gun height was kept as low as possible, but was limited by the practicalities of serving the gun.

The second force was the **stability moment**. This was a combination of the total weight of the gun plus carriage (**W**) and the length between the centre of gravity and the trail spade (**L**). For stability in the firing cycle the weight needed to be large, but, as we have already seen, the requirements of mobility precluded this to a large extent. The length needed to be as great as possible, but, once again, the requirements of mobility would inhibit this.

To prevent the carriage jumping under recoil, the lifting moment could not be allowed to equal, or exceed, the stability moment. This condition was made difficult to achieve due to the inconstant nature of some of the forces concerned.

By allowing the gun to move axially in a cradle during recoil, under the control of a hydraulic buffer and springs, the recoil energy could be absorbed. That was not as simple as it sounds however. The recoil represented energy, to be absorbed between gun and carriage by working. The work meant moving through distance (recoil) against resistance (hydraulic). It was immaterial which of these was the greater factor, as long as their product was the same the energy absorbed would be the same. By sufficiently

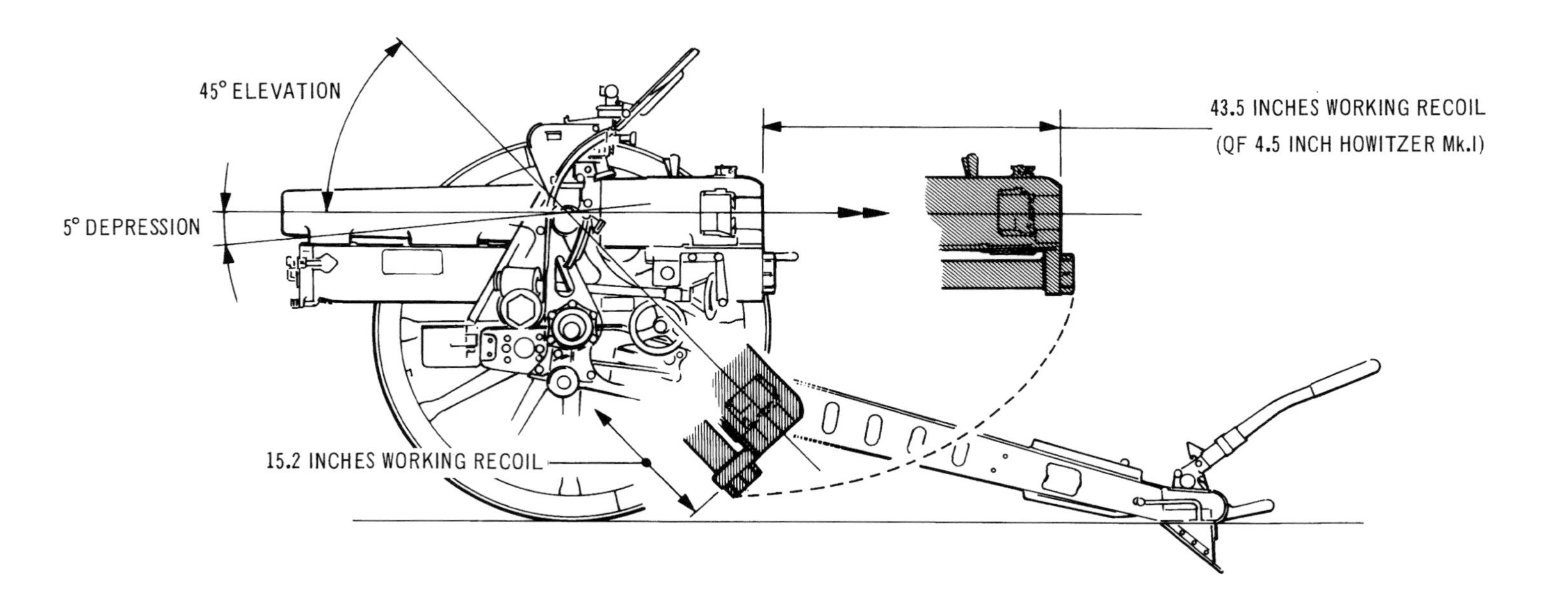

increasing the distance however, the resistance could be lowered in proportion and thus bring the carriage lifting moment below the stability moment to attain a stable condition. Unfortunately, once again, that was not as simple as it sounds. Because of the gun's movement during recoil, the centre of gravity moved rearwards along the gun's axis, decreasing the value of the carriage stability moment. In order to preserve stability of the carriage, the lifting moment had to be decreased in proportion by graduating the resistance of the hydraulic buffer, so as to be less at the end of recoil than at the beginning. This was achieved by cutting tapered channels into the buffer cylinder wall through which the hydraulic fluid was forced by the buffer piston.

The observations made thus far indicate that, within reason, to attain a non-recoiling carriage it was necessary to allow a long-recoiling gun.

This was a practical solution for a field gun, with its comparatively limited degree of elevation or depression. However, when the principles were applied to a field howitzer, the problems, although theoretically the same, were practically different.

When a field howitzer fired horizontally, it was practical to allow a recoil of forty-two to forty-eight inches, this being required to keep the pull on the buffer piston sufficiently low to provide a steady carriage. Such a length of recoil was impractical at large angles of elevation however, as the howitzer breech would, in all probability, strike the ground. This could have been avoided by mounting the gun with its axis higher on the carriage, but doing so would have increased the lifting moment and destabilised the carriage.

Another factor to be considered in howitzer design was the weight of the gun, which was greater than that of a field gun. This, and the greater angles of elevation, introduced gun weight as a factor, the effect of gravity increasing the recoil energy with the elevation.

The ingenious solution to this problem was to shorten the length of recoil as the angle of elevation became greater, by increasing the resistance to the buffer piston. This was achieved by a series of gears and a cam, connecting a valve on the buffer piston to the carriage. The increase in lifting moment at high elevation angles was fortunately a problem which solved itself. As the axis of the gun, when projected rearwards, moved towards the spade on increasing elevation, the lifting moment decreased in proportion until, upon the projected axis being at the spade centre, the lifting moment was, in theory, nil, and with further increased elevation became a negative factor.

To enable the springs to operate normally and return the gun barrel to position after recoil, it was necessary to provide a second valve, in order that the restricted, high elevation resistance for recoil did not inhibit the return springs during their function.

As the gun returned to the firing position after recoil, it would accelerate under the influence of the springs, and, unless checked, would come to the end of its travel with considerable violence. To prevent this, a small control plunger was introduced which displaced hydraulic fluid within the buffer cylinder, in a graduated way, at the conclusion of the gun's forward travel, bringing it to a controlled stop.

The methods of controlling recoil, returning the barrel and bringing about this cushioning effect varied in detail on different guns and will be described more fully within the relevant sections of the book.

SIGHTS

NOTES ON THEIR DEVELOPMENT

Introduction of the non-recoiling field gun carriage enabled the sight to be transferred from its earlier mounting, on the gun, to a carriage component which, although controlled by the elevating gear, remained unaffected by recoil.

Previous to this time, the tangent rearsight of a simple foresight and tangent arrangement had a straight vertical sight bar, with a deflection crosshead carrying the rearsight notch. This arrangement can be seen, as fitted to the Breech Loading 15 pdr Mk. IV on page 100.

At about the same time as the non-recoiling carriage was being developed, this sight was replaced by a tangent rearsight with a curved bar, or arc, the radius of which was centred on the foresight. With this feature it was possible to attach a spirit level to the tangent sight and a telescope on top of the arc, which provided a clinometer, telescopic sight and open sight on one assembly. This arrangement can be seen (minus the telescope), as fitted to the Quick Firing 15 pdr Mk. I on page 190.

Harsh experience during the Boer War taught that a shield was essential to protect a gun's crew from long-range small arms fire. In order for this shield to be fully effective, it was obvious that any sighting aperture in the shield must be kept to a minimum size. To achieve this, if a simple foresight and tangent were used, the foresight would need to be level with the shield, or as close as was practicable. Also, in order for the gun layer to gain maximum protection from the shield, the tangent rearsight had to move forward from its original position at the gun breech. The result of this was to shorten the sight radius, with a consequent loss of accuracy due to the magnification of any slight errors in aligning the sight onto a target.

To overcome this disadvantage, the foresight and top of the curved tangent rearsight were rigidly connected by a bar. This bar was pivoted to the cradle at the shield position, enabling the foresight and rearsight to be kept some distance apart. This **rocking bar sight** also provided a suitable mounting for a sighting telescope and open sights.

Deflection was achieved by the addition of a second sight bar, which would carry the telescope and open sights and was pivoted, towards the front end of the rocking bar, to move horizontally along a crosshead formed at the rear end of the rocking bar, controlled by screw or worm gearing. This arrangement can be seen, as fitted to the Quick Firing 18 pdr Mk. I on page 250. The functions of these two bars could also be performed by a single bar, in which case it was pivoted to the carriage by a ball and socket mounting. This arrangement can be seen, as fitted to the Breech Loading (Converted) 15 pdr Mk. I on page 154.

The sight was set by racking the sight arc up or down by means of a handwheel, the worm and wormwheel involved obviating the need for any extra sight locking device. The worm and wormwheel also usually incorporated the use of a graduated drum to display the range setting in yards.

Reciprocating sights

This feature of sighting gear was developed for the occasions on which artillery would operate on uneven ground. Before this time, any difference in the level of the gun carriage wheels would be offset by giving deflection towards the high side, the actual amount involving measurement and some calculation. The reciprocating sight allowed variations in wheel level to be automatically catered for by cross levelling the sight. The diagrams show the principles involved. It will be of help to study these in conjunction with the sections detailing rocking bar sights on page 154.

To shoot accurately, the line of sight had to be parallel to a vertical plane passing through the barrel axis at any angle of elevation.

With the gun on LEVEL GROUND and at point blank (VIEW 1), and through to full elevation (VIEW 2) it can be seen that the line of sight (**A**) did remain parallel to the vertical plane (**B**), with the barrel axis moving along this plane, the muzzle obviously upwards and the breech downwards.

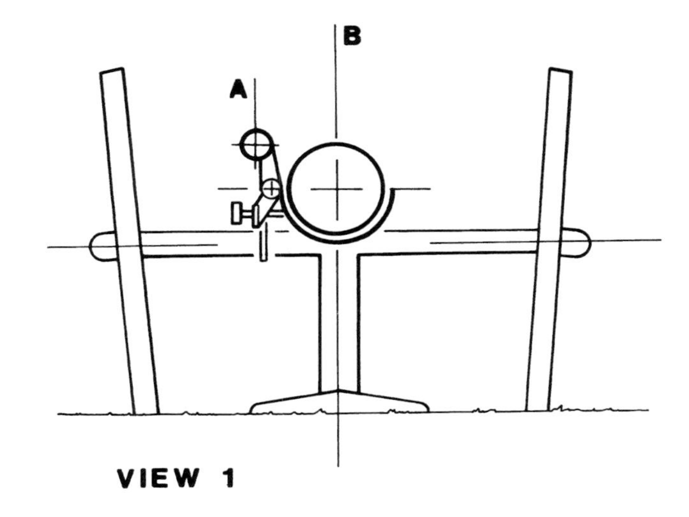

VIEW 1

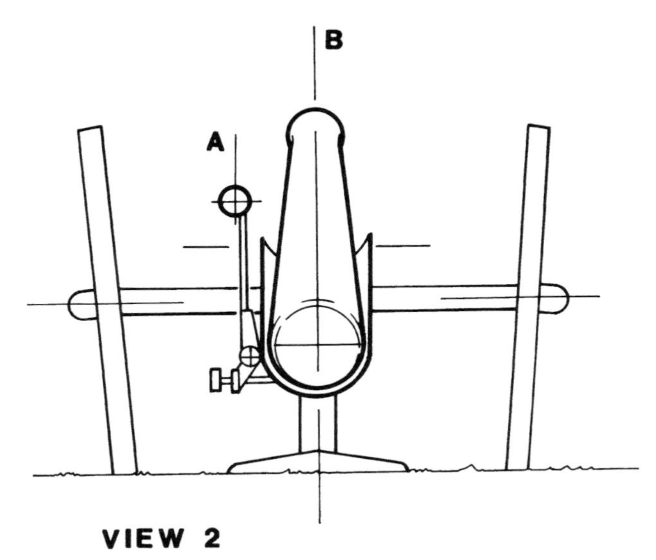

VIEW 2

THE GUN VIEWED DIRECTLY FROM THE REAR

If the gun was established on SLOPING GROUND at point blank (VIEW 3) and elevation then applied (VIEW 4), it will be seen that the barrel centre line (**CD**), being at right angles to the trunnion sloping centre line, moved away from the vertical plane (**B**) towards the right at the muzzle (**C**) and towards the left at the breech (**D**), throwing the point of aim to the right by an amount increasing with the elevation.

To restore the barrel centre line (**CD**) into the vertical plane (**B**), the sight was first cross levelled (VIEW 5) and the gun breech traversed right (VIEW 6) to realign the sight onto the target.

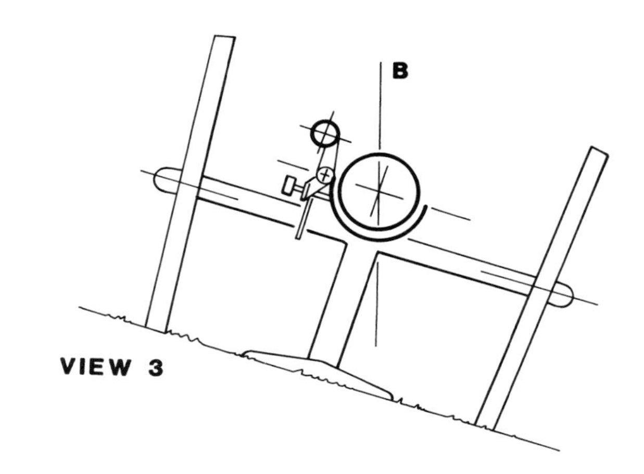

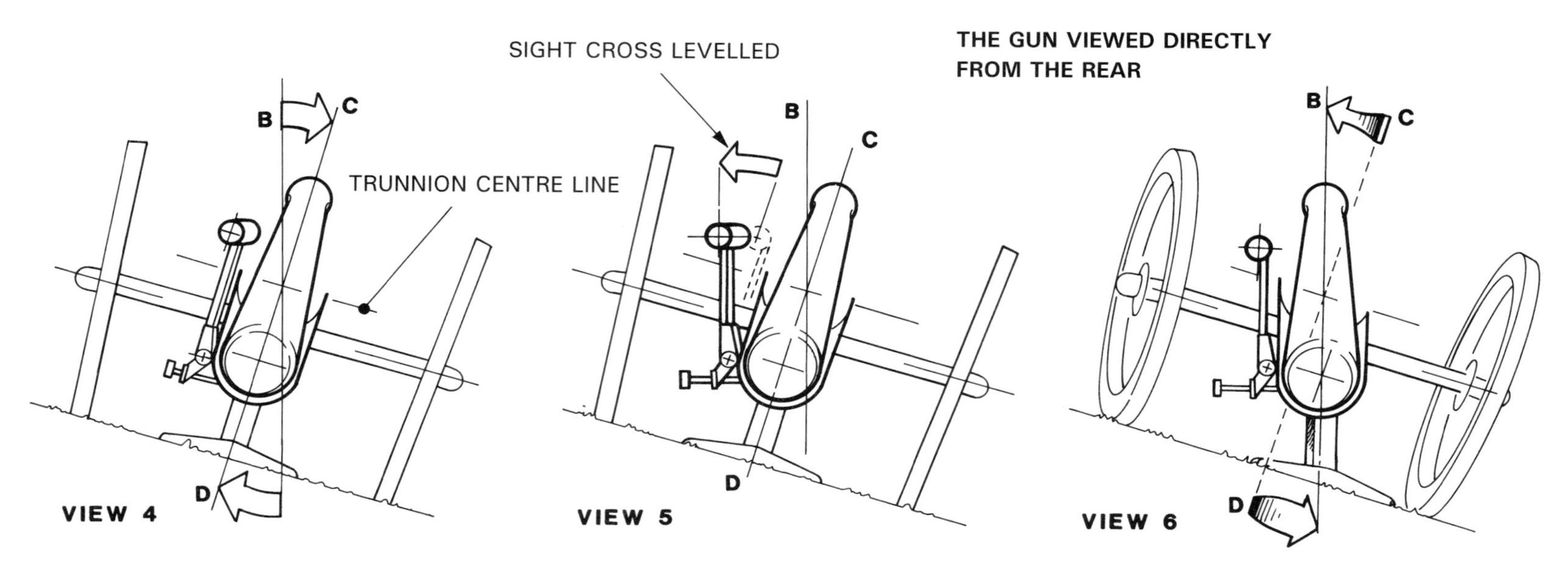

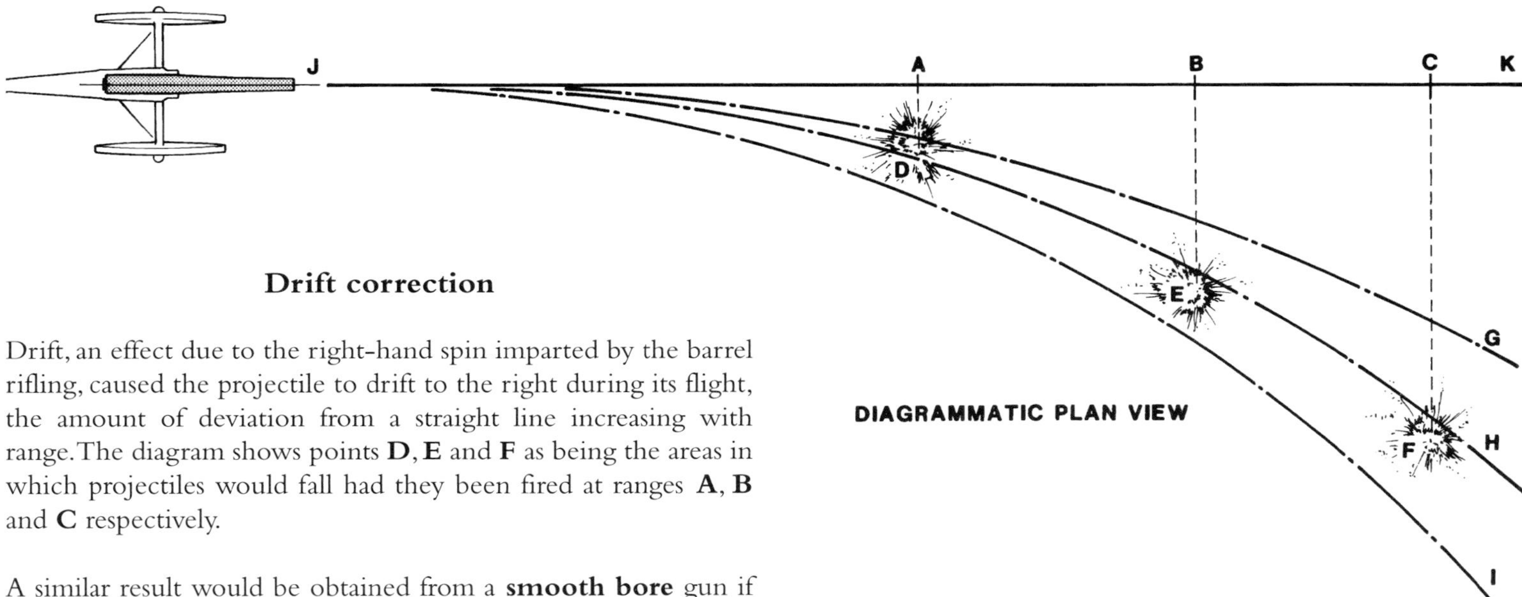

Drift correction

Drift, an effect due to the right-hand spin imparted by the barrel rifling, caused the projectile to drift to the right during its flight, the amount of deviation from a straight line increasing with range. The diagram shows points **D**, **E** and **F** as being the areas in which projectiles would fall had they been fired at ranges **A**, **B** and **C** respectively.

A similar result would be obtained from a **smooth bore** gun if the sight was tilted to the **right**, the resultant right deflection increasing with range as the sight was raised and the projectiles falling along the curved lines **G**, **H** or **I**, depending on the angle of tilt given to the sight.

From this, one can observe that should the sight on a **rifled gun** be tilted to the **left**, it should be possible to arrive at an angle of tilt for the sight that would produce a fall of projectiles along a roughly straight line **JK** to approximately counteract the effect of drift.

It was not possible to find an angle of tilt for the sight which would provide a precise correction at all ranges. This system, however, was a solution which was close enough to suffice for the purpose.

It was subsequently found that, should the sight be given an angle of tilt greater than that required for an average correction and then a permanent amount of right deflection applied, increased accuracy would result at medium ranges, any discrepancies occurring only at very short or very long ranges. This was due to the effect of permanent deflection overcoming that of the tilt and causing the projectile to fall to the right at short range, while at long range, the opposite effect would apply and the projectile would fall to the left.

To lay a gun using any of the foregoing sighting systems entailed two separate operations.

The first was to set a tangent or telescopic sight to the angle between the gun axis and the line of sight – the elevation. The second was to align the line of sight, or lay the gun, onto the target.

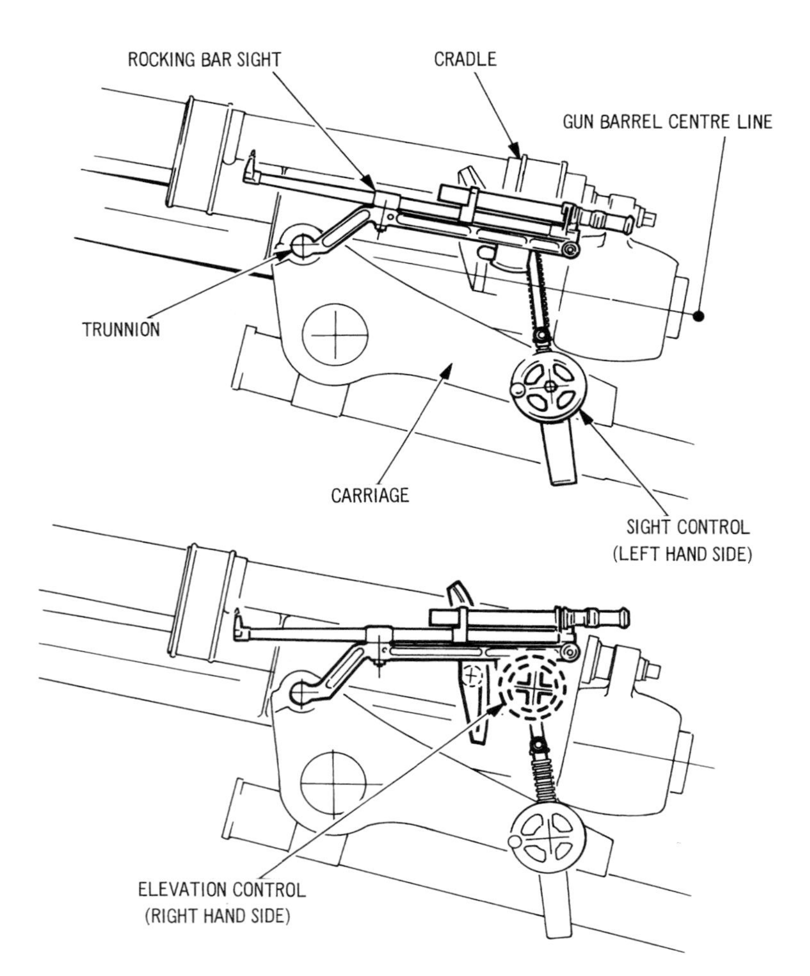

Independent line of sight

This system was developed to enable the two operations to be carried out, simultaneously or separately, by two members of the gun crew and two handwheels. This can be seen, as fitted to the Quick Firing 18 pdr Mk. I described on page 237.

The sight was of the rocking bar type, pivoted at the cradle left-hand trunnion, and incorporated three additional sets of gear, the functions of which were to move the sight relative to the carriage, to move cradle and gun together, relative to the sight and to measure the latter movement on a drum in either degrees or yards.

Sight control was performed by the gun layer, his sole function being to keep his sight centred on the target.

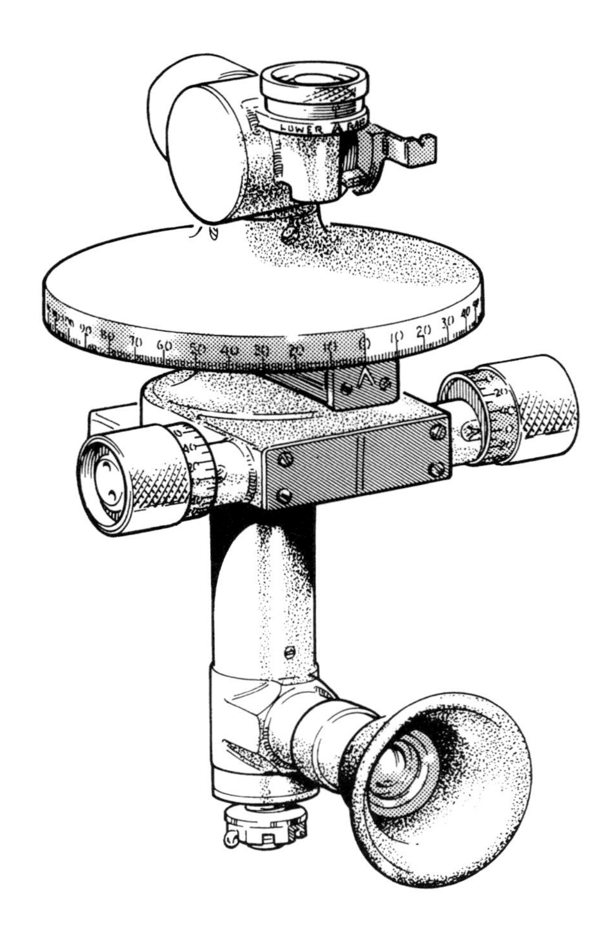

Elevation to any given range was controlled by a second gun crew member, who would elevate or depress the gun with a second handwheel and read the range on a drum indicator, with no disturbance to the line of sight.

With the elevation and sighting being independent, normal compensation for drift could not be incorporated on the sight, so the axis of the trunnions was tilted, left trunnion down, to give an average correction.

Also, on sloping ground, the reciprocating principle could not be employed and any slope had to be allowed for by applied deflection.

Dial sights

These were developed to enable the gun to be trained onto an unseen target, using aiming posts or a convenient landmark. Originally they were circular plates, graduated around the edge in degrees and having notched sight blades which could be adjusted for level. A description of this type of sight appears on page 152.

Later dial sights incorporated a magnification facility and enabled sighting to be done to any direction or elevation. A description of this sight type is on page 252.

MATERIALS

Wood

Various woods were employed by the Royal Carriage Department at Woolwich for the construction of transport vehicles, wheels, sidearm staves, levers, handspikes, rollers and platforms etc.

British wood

ASH A tough, quite elastic wood which does not tolerate exposure to weather well and, due to a lack of 'bitterness', is prone to worm damage in store. It was used for felloes, handspikes, levers, sidearm staves and spokes.

BEECH A hard, strong, pale wood which works to a clean and smooth finish. Although durable under water, it does not tolerate exposure to weather. It was used for ammunition box interior fittings and saddletrees.

ELM A very cross-grained wood, not prone to splintering, and particularly suited for work to be heavily nailed or shaped. It is very tolerant of damp but, being 'sweet', is prone to worm damage. It was used for footboards, deal box ends, rollers and scotches.

OAK A tough and durable wood, possessing great rigidity and stiffness. It contains an acid which corrodes iron, and is liable to crack or shake when exposed to extremes of dryness. It was used for spokes, skids, rollers, trail planks and the framework of some transport vehicles.

Foreign wood

BLACKWOOD (Australia and New Zealand) Similar in character to oak, but more brittle and resinous, it was often used for spokes.

GREENHEART (NW part of South America and the West Indies) A very heavy, hard, close-grained wood. It was used for spokes.

HICKORY (North America) A tough and elastic wood but not very durable when exposed to weather. It was used for sidearm staves and, sometimes, spokes.

PADOUK (East Indies) A very heavy, hard, red wood which was used for spokes and sometimes for felloes of heavy wheels.

PINE A general name applying to a range of coniferous woods from many locations. A resinous, light, elastic wood. As a general rule, the more turpentine there is in the wood, the stronger and more durable it is.

YELLOW (HARD) PINE (North America) This was used for the boarding of vehicles, such as the general service wagon.

COARSER GRAINED PINE, or FIR (Northern Europe) Used for large skidding and platforms. Spars for sheers were imported from Riga (Latvia).

ROCK (or HICKORY) ELM (Canada and central United States) Strong and elastic, similar to ash, it was used for poles, levers and sidearm staves.

SABICU (Cuba) A hard, heavy and durable wood, it was sometimes used for felloes of large wheels and for small rollers. (The staircases of the Great Exhibition of 1851 were of this wood. In 1910 it was listed as being expensive.)

WALNUT (Europe) Light and tough. It was used for shoulder pieces and gunstocks.

Metals

CAST IRON A cheap material due to the few processes involved in its manufacture. It cast well to shape and had great resistance to crushing. It could not be bent however, and was very brittle. Its tensile strength was only about one-third that of mild steel and it was used mainly for the pedestal mountings of garrison artillery.

MALLEABLE CAST IRON Cast iron could be made slightly malleable by extracting a certain amount of carbon from the outer surface. It was an expensive process, used until around 1900 in the manufacture of small items such as buckles and staples.

WROUGHT IRON Cast iron was treated to remove almost all carbon and other substances. During the process an amount of slag was trapped in the iron. Subsequent forging drew out the iron and slag particles into a parallel, fibrous structure with resultant high tensile strength. It could be forged to shape either hot or cold and was very easily welded. By 1900, due to the expense of manufacture, it had been largely superseded by mild steel but it was still used for parts of complex shape and ones which needed a large amount of welding.

REMANUFACTURED IRON Produced from wrought iron scrap, it lacked the parallel fibrous structure of wrought iron and was used for trail and perch eyes.

MILD STEEL A grade of iron containing about 0.3 per cent carbon, with added manganese and silicone. It was used for the majority of structural work, although it did not forge weld as readily as wrought iron.

CAST STEEL New material was usually used in the production of cast steel. It was used for the carriage brackets of heavy mountings, for cradles and some wheel flanges.

FORGED STEEL A substitute for wrought iron, it was also employed when components were too complex to be cast. Small articles (hooks, staples, eyes etc.) were produced from a very mild steel by drop-forging between shaped dies. Larger fittings (limber hooks, trail eyes etc.) were stamped to shape under a steam hammer. Some more complex shapes were produced by pressing the material into dies by hydraulic power.

NICKEL STEEL This was a good quality mild steel with a proportion of added nickel. The nickel raised the tensile strength and yield point without reducing the elongation. It did not weld easily.

SPRING STEEL A high carbon steel. After shaping, careful control of temperature during the hardening and tempering processes produced the elasticity.

BLISTER STEEL Wrought iron was heated in contact with a carbon rich material, such as charcoal. Carbon impregnated the iron producing a form of steel. A quantity of embodied slag remained however, and was a source of weakness.

SHEAR STEEL Bars of blister steel were welded together to make shear steel. Being very high in carbon it was used for tools and the soles of dragshoes.

CASE HARDENING An extra hard surface was required on some fittings, such as shields and the bearing faces of trail eyes, limber hooks etc. The part to be hardened was heated in contact with charcoal or a heavy hydro-carbon. The surface became impregnated with an excess of carbon, after which it was heated to a high temperature then quenched rapidly by water spray.

Alloys

GUNMETAL (BRONZE) An alloy of copper and tin, the proportions varying according to the qualities required. It possessed about half the strength of mild steel and did not corrode easily but it could not be forged to shape. It was used for bearings, wheel flanges, rollers, toothed wheels, some cradles and many small parts.

ALUMINIUM BRONZE Extremely tough and corrosion resistant and used for some valves and seatings.

MANGANESE BRONZE More truly a brass (copper and zinc) than bronze. One per cent manganese was added. Its mechanical properties were similar to those of mild steel, but it did not corrode. It could be forged to shape, but casting was more difficult due to the tendency of blow-holes to develop during pouring and contraction on cooling. It was used for some wheel flanges, rams, traversing racks, air cylinders, cradles and many small fittings.

PHOSPHOR BRONZE A true bronze (copper and tin), with a small amount of phosphorus added and was used where hardness and resistance to wear were more important than strength as it was very brittle. It was used for bearings and the pipeboxes of wheels.

PLASTIC METAL Composed mainly of tin, with some copper and lead. The fuzing temperature was only 482°F. Issued in strips, it was used generally as a coating on steel surfaces to prevent corrosion and seizure in bearings. It was also used for repairing the rams of hydraulic jacks and the repair of worn bearing surfaces on axletree arms etc. It would be applied to only one of two working surfaces.

SOLDER Composed of tin and lead, the proportions varying for different uses. Hard solder contained sixty per cent tin and would crackle when bent. Solder of less than fifty per cent tin would not crackle and would be considered deficient in quality.

Service hydraulic liquids

Recoil buffer oil

Under normal service conditions, a thin mineral oil would fulfil the requirements for hydraulic damping in recoil buffer cylinders. In an emergency, the following liquids could be used:

- Pure glycerine, or a mixture of glycerine and water in equal parts
- Any heavy lubricating oil
- Soapy water, or water with a proportion of added soda.

Under no circumstances would kerosene, paraffin or similar illuminating oils be used.

Under freezing conditions, recoil buffer cylinders could be filled with service hydraulic lift and Jack fluid.

Hydraulic lift and Jack fluid

Various fluids were employed on early hydraulic equipments. Glycerine and water, paraffin and buffer oil, distilled water and soft soap, ragosine oil (a Russian petroleum lubricating oil), and sugar and water were tried and discarded, until the following mixture was adopted as 'HP Fluid' or 'Fluid, lifts and jacks, hydraulic' in 1891. The formula was:

- Methylated spirit – seven gallons
- Distilled water – three and one quarter gallons
- Mineral oil – one quarter gallon
- Carbonate of soda – 250 grains.

This liquid performed at all temperatures met with in service. Very low temperatures would cause it to go pasty, but it would re-liquefy on passing rapidly through valves etc. It would cause steel equipment to corrode however, also leather seals and packings would degrade and need fairly frequent renewal. It would destroy India rubber items such as washers and seals.

Leather seals and stuffing box packings

L section leather seals were used on the inner end of some pipeboxes to prevent the ingress of dust and grit into the pipebox bearing areas.

Leather sealing rings of either L or U section were used to reinforce the sealing action of soft packing in stuffing boxes. This type of seal had the advantage of being self-tightening – the greater the liquid pressure, the tighter the seal became – providing that the feathered edges were in good and sharp condition. Two examples of typical hydraulic buffer stuffing boxes are illustrated here.

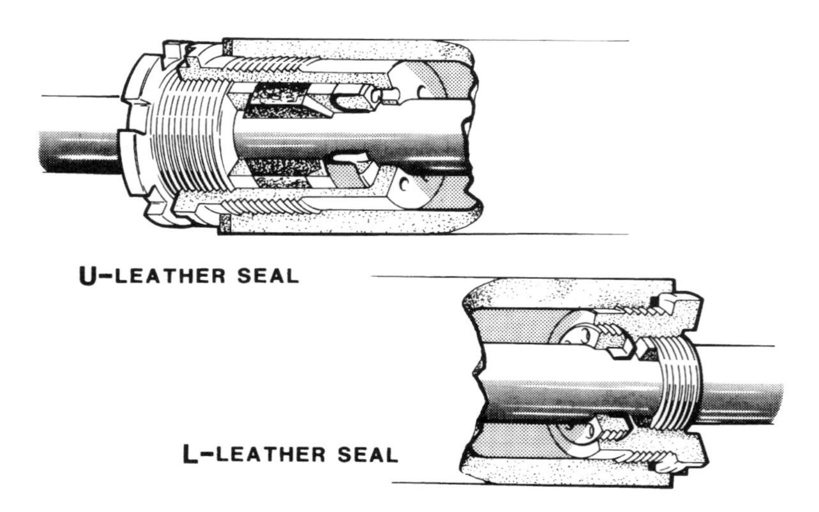

Leather seals could be manufactured locally, if required.

To make a U section leather seal, a disc of hide, known as hydraulic leather, would be cut to the dimensions shown. The disc would be soaked in water until quite soft, generally for about one and a half hours.

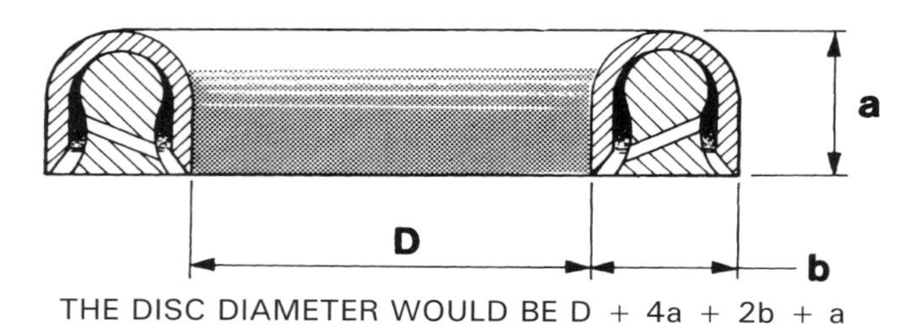

THE DISC DIAMETER WOULD BE D + 4a + 2b + a

It would next be pressed into a metal mould and heated to a temperature of 180°F, then allowed to cool until it could be handled, when the leather would be removed. Both leather and mould would be thoroughly wiped dry, the leather replaced into the mould and allowed to finish cooling completely. The leather was then removed from the mould and hung up until totally dry and hard.

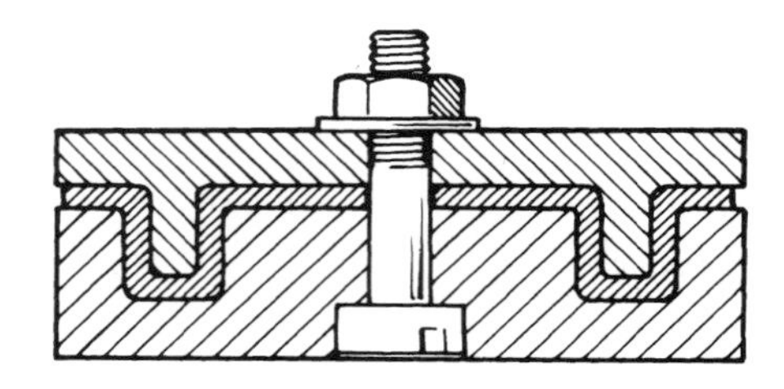

Next the leather was placed into a chuck, made from wood or soft metal, and mounted in a lathe to be turned and cut to the form shown in the diagram, with a sharp wood turning tool.

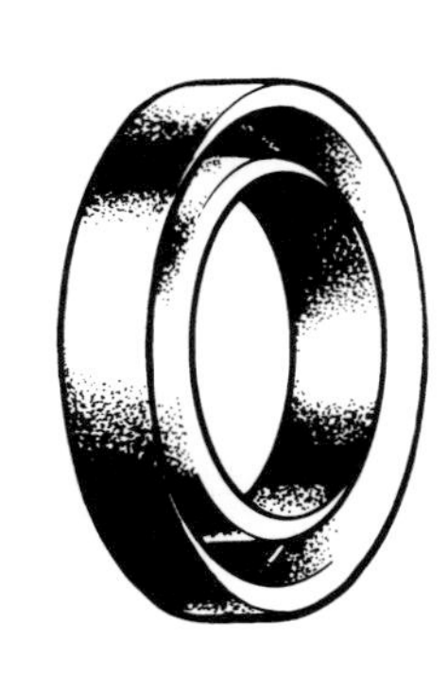

It was then burnished, while turning, with a smooth piece of hard wood and small quantity of soft soap, until perfectly smooth.

If the seal was not required for immediate use it would be coated with hot dubbing.

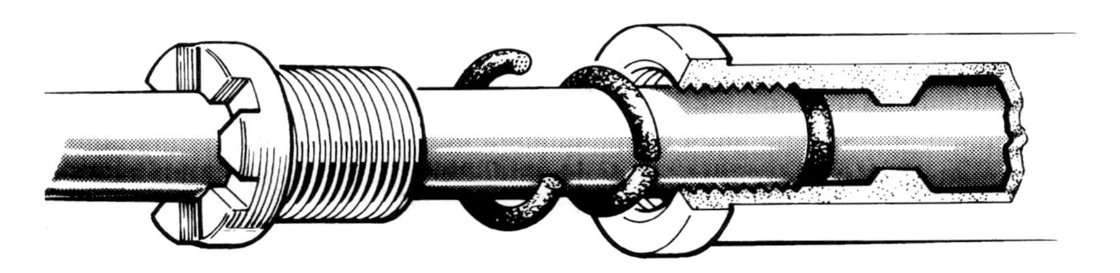

Stuffing box packings were of the following types:

Cotton rope

Hydraulic or greased packing, consisting of cotton rope plaited around a core of India rubber and soaked in melted tallow. This packing could be employed as an alternative to cotton rope, except when the liquid in use was thinner than ordinary buffer oil. Thin oil would dissolve out the tallow and the packing would become dry and hard, allowing leakage to occur.

Special packing, made in the Royal Carriage Department, consisting of plaited cotton soaked in melted paraffin wax. The wax would not dissolve out when oil was the liquid in use.

Asbestos, mixed with mutton fat and pressed hydraulically into the required shape, then enclosed in a stout canvas cover.

The first three of these packings were inserted into the stuffing box in the form of rings, the length of each piece being slightly more than needed to meet around the rod to be packed, the ends being placed in the stuffing box first, then the remainder of the ring being pressed in with a piece of wood. Successive rings would be inserted, ensuring that the joins were staggered from one another radially in order not to provide the liquid with a clear passage through the seal.

WHEEL CONSTRUCTION

A wheel generally consisted of the following components:

PIPEBOX A phosphor bronze cylinder, tapered internally to bear on the axletree arm. This internal taper was cannelured into one or two circumferential chambers which contained lubricating grease. The remaining lands or bearing surfaces were grooved spirally to distribute lubricant from these grease boxes.

The exterior surface of the pipebox was shaped to accommodate the particular flanges for that type of wheel.

FLANGES Produced in manganese bronze or steel these fitted onto the external surface of the pipebox.

The rear (inner) flange butted against a shoulder formed on the pipebox and was secured to the latter by a pin, bolt, or key, to ensure that the wheel rotated on the axletree arm and not on the pipebox. In some cases the rear (inner) flange was cast integrally with the pipebox.

The front (outer) flange was secured to the rear (inner) flange by bolts, which passed either through or between the feet of the spokes and were fitted with nuts. In some cases, there was additionally a ring nut which screwed onto a thread – cut at the outer end of the pipebox – to compress the front (outer) flange against the spokes. This pipebox nut was formed with a ratchet which was engaged by a spring catch to prevent the nut loosening in service.

Stamped on the front (outer) flange were the manufacturer's initials, the year of manufacture and the registered number.

The pipebox and flanges, together with the feet of the spokes comprised the centre or **nave** of the wheel.

SPOKES Usually produced in oak, these were twelve or fourteen in number, gripped at their feet between the flanges and radiating evenly from the pipebox to the felloes. Their outer ends were turned to form tongues which fitted into holes drilled radially through the felloes. The tongues were then secured by being split and having oak wedges driven in.

FELLOES Usually produced in ash, these were three, six or seven in number, cut or steamed to the circumference of the wheel and joined by cylindrical wood or trapezoidal steel plate dowels. Some later pattern wheels had steel slip plates bolted onto the bosom at the joints.

The smaller diameter face of a felloe was called the **bosom**, and the larger diameter face, the **sole**. The number of a wheel was always stamped on the backs of three of the felloes.

TYRE Early tyres were of wrought iron, later ones of mild steel. They were shrunk or pressed on while warm, around the sole of the felloes. Fitted through the tyre and felloes were countersunk bolts secured by nuts on the bosom.

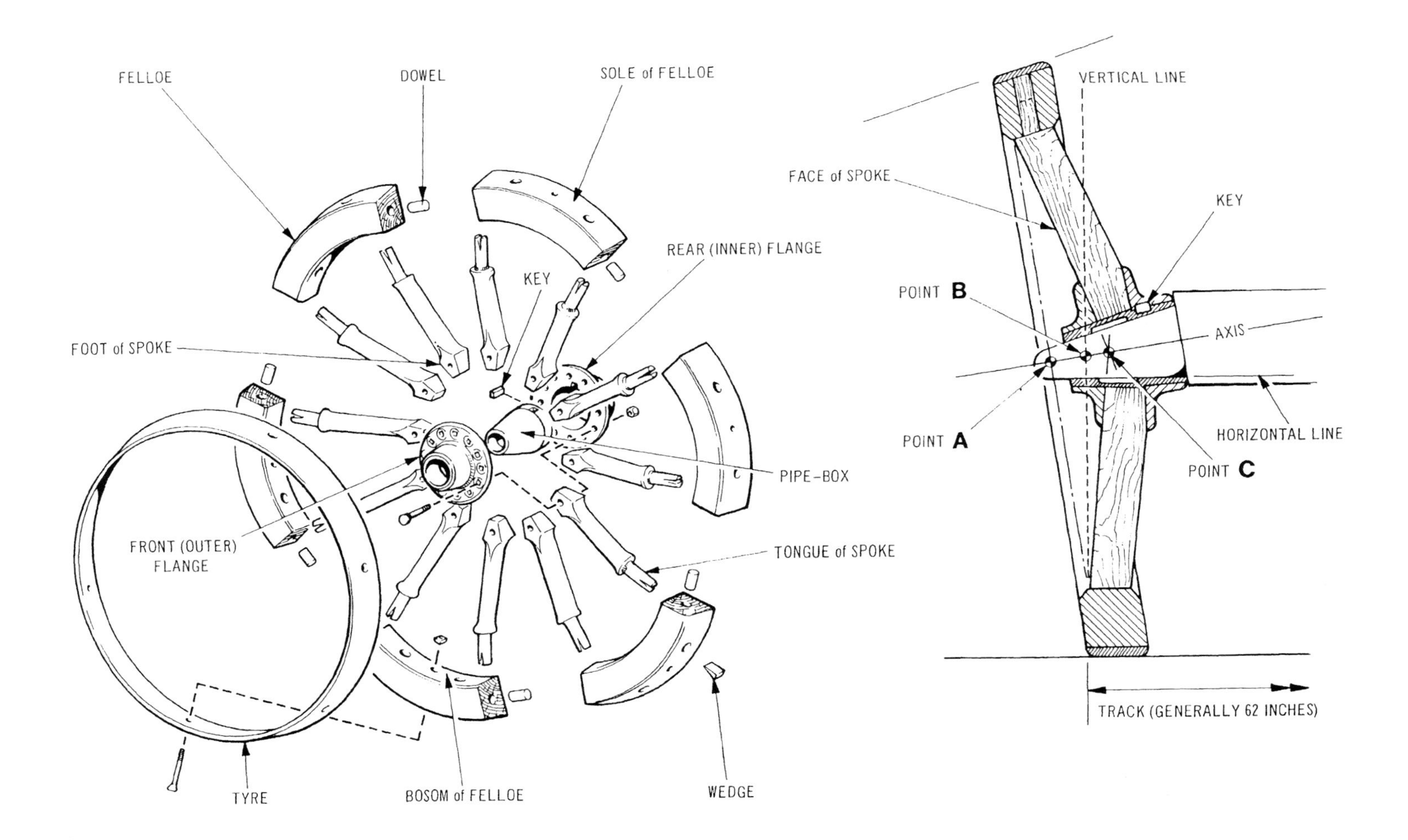
FELLOE
DOWEL
SOLE of FELLOE
REAR (INNER) FLANGE
KEY
FOOT of SPOKE
PIPE-BOX
FRONT (OUTER) FLANGE
TONGUE of SPOKE
TYRE
BOSOM of FELLOE
WEDGE
VERTICAL LINE
FACE of SPOKE
KEY
POINT B
AXIS
POINT A
HORIZONTAL LINE
POINT C
TRACK (GENERALLY 62 INCHES)

Wheel geometry (see page 25)

Terms used in describing the various factors met with in wheel geometry were DISH, HOLLOW, STRUT, BEVEL, LEAD and SET.

DISH (Diagram, point A to point C). In order to counteract the often severe side-loadings imposed on a wheel in military service the spokes were 'dished' as shown. The amount of dish in a 1st class wheel of five feet diameter was two and a half inches. Other five feet diameter wheels were dished two inches and wheels of lesser diameters were dished proportionally less in order to retain a constant angle of dish.

Single spoke wheels had all their spokes equally dished. Double spoke wheels had alternate spokes only dished, in order to retain a higher resistance to transverse loadings.

HOLLOW One effect of dish was to cause the lower supporting spoke to incline inwards from the vertical, thereby lowering the resistance to vertical loading. To counteract this, the axletree arm was given 'hollow' by being coned, with the underside kept horizontal, thus causing the wheel axis to angle downward and bring the lowest (working) spoke closer to the vertical.

STRUT (Diagram, point B to point C) The combined effect of dish and hollow caused the lower (working) spoke to be slightly inclined inwards towards the nave. The amount of this inclination, or 'strut', was generally half an inch for wheels of five feet diameter, decreasing proportionally in wheels of lesser diameter to keep the angle of strut constant. The effect of strut was to bring the lower (working) spoke to the vertical when running on a theoretical average slant.

BEVEL The outer diameter of the felloe sole was made less than the inner diameter. This 'bevel' ensured the full tyre width being in contact with the ground.

LEAD The effect of bevel made the wheel a frustum (slice) of a cone, which, if rolling unchecked would naturally follow a circular track about the theoretical apex of that cone. If forced to travel in a straight line the outer (lesser) diameter would slip, in order to keep pace with the inner (greater) diameter and thus apply continuous pressure to the washer and linch pin by trying to roll outwards from the axletree arm axis. In an attempt to minimise this effect the axletree arm was given 'lead' by being angled slightly forward. The amount was generally about one-sixteenth of an inch forward at a point ten inches along the arm axis from the shoulder.

SET The combination of hollow and lead gave the axletree arm its 'set'.

Dust excluders

Dust excluders were developed to prevent, or at least minimise, the entry of dust and grit into the pipebox bearing areas. They also prevented loss of lubricant from the grease boxes.

The outer end of the bearing area was protected by a dust cap,

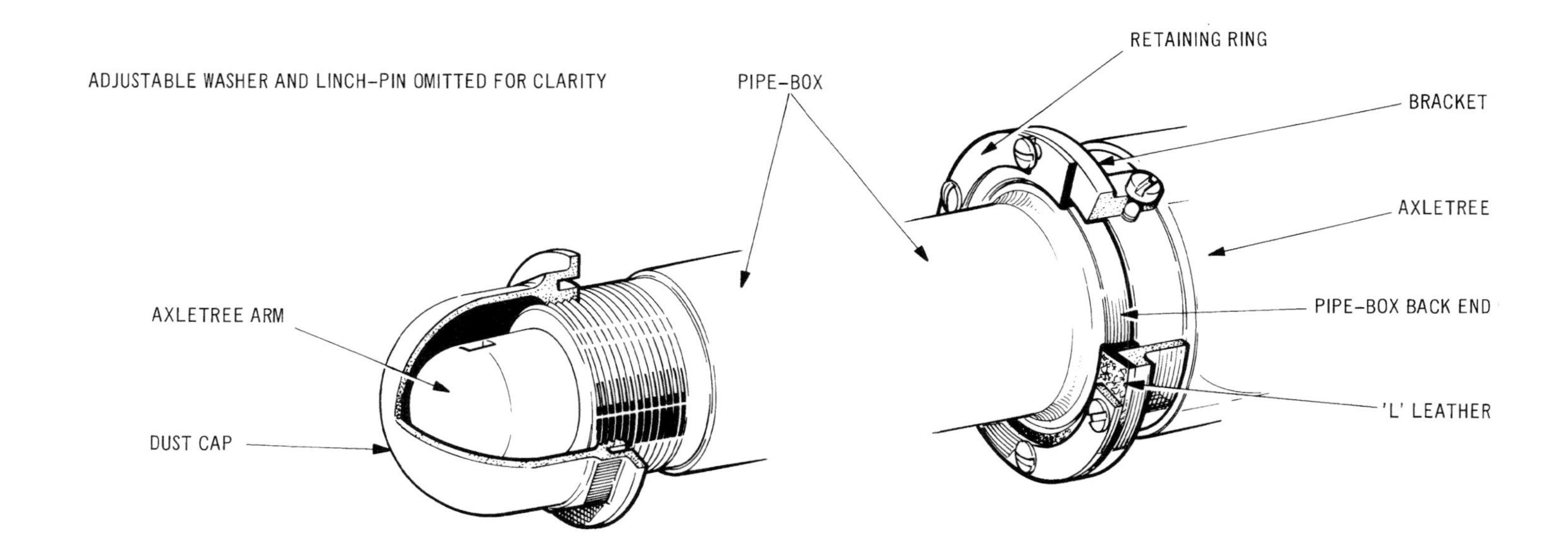

which screwed onto the pipebox thread and revolved with the wheel, clear of the adjustable washer and linch pin.

The inner end comprised a bracket, mounted on the axletree shoulder, into which fitted an L leather seal, held in place by a steel retaining ring. This formed a recess into which fitted the back end of the pipebox.

Wheel maintenance

Pipebox

Correct wheel lubrication was of prime importance. The intrusion of grit into the pipebox could be detected by the noise it produced as the wheel turned. Routine servicing involved

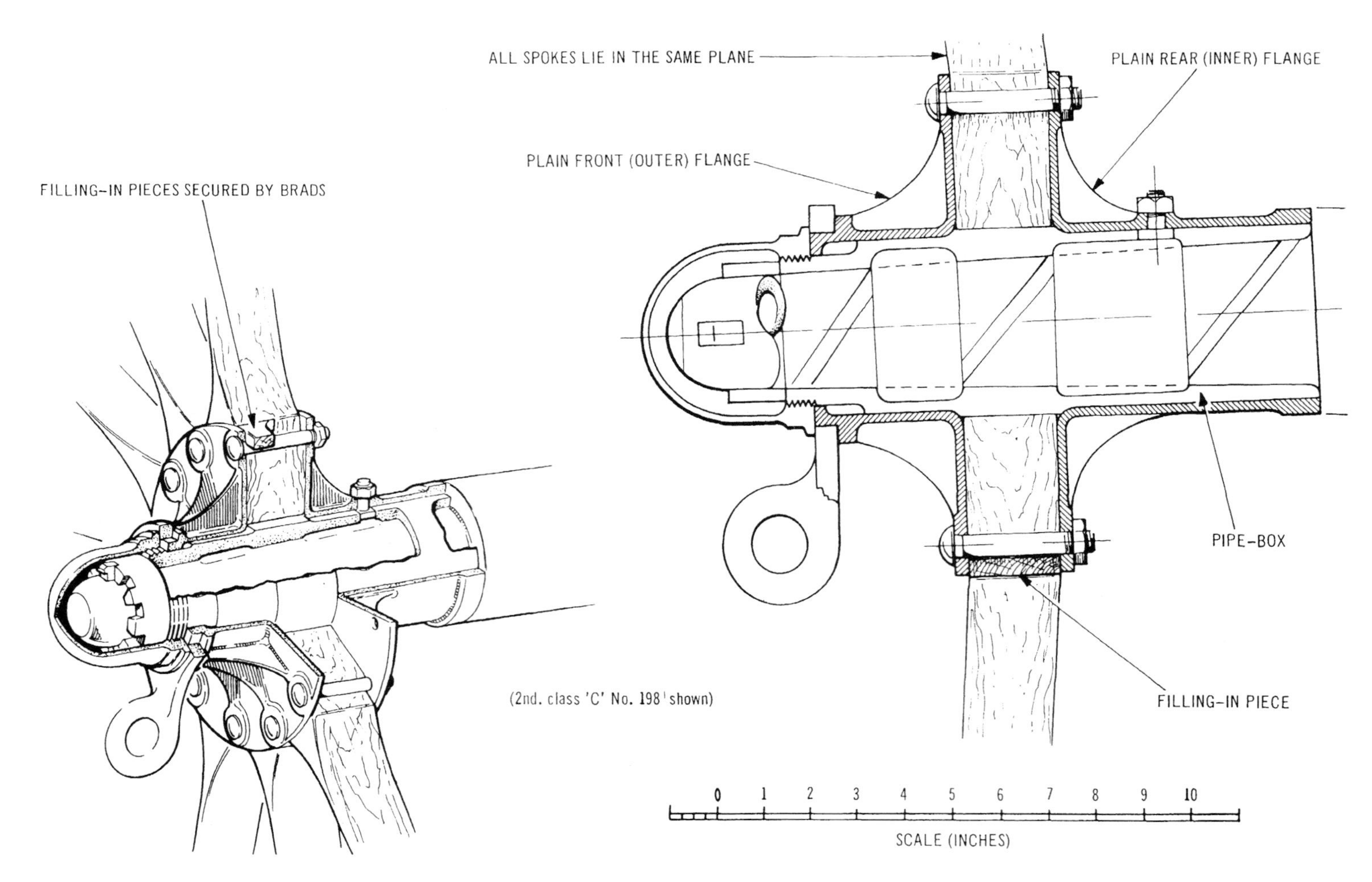

TYPICAL SINGLE SPOKED WHEEL

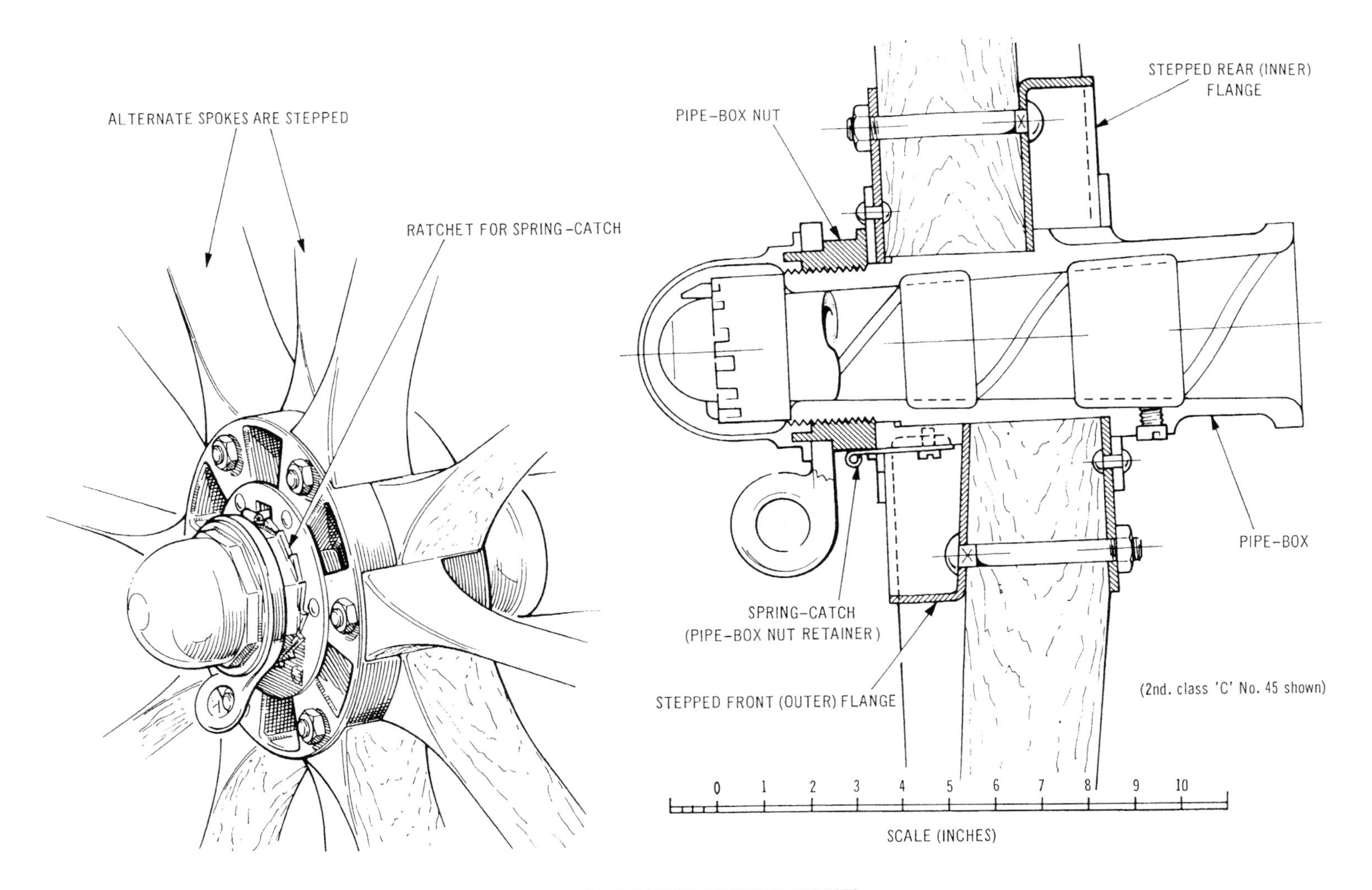

TYPICAL DOUBLE SPOKED WHEEL

SPOKE TO FELLOE JOINTS

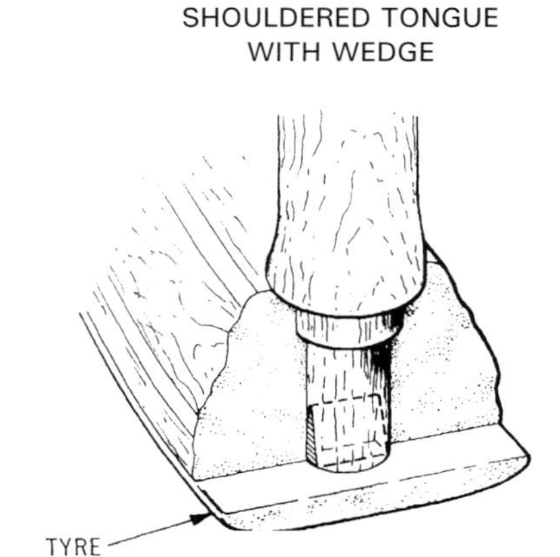

SHOULDERED TONGUE WITH WEDGE

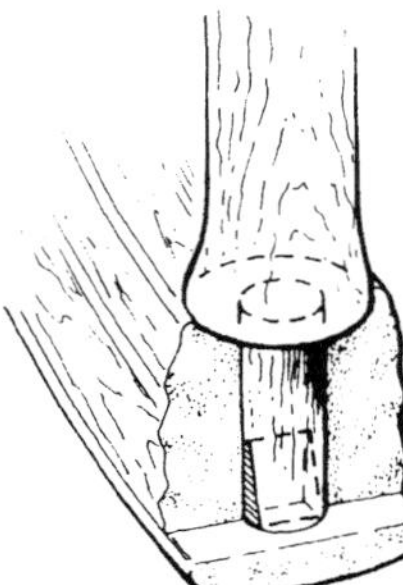

PLAIN TONGUE WITH WEDGE

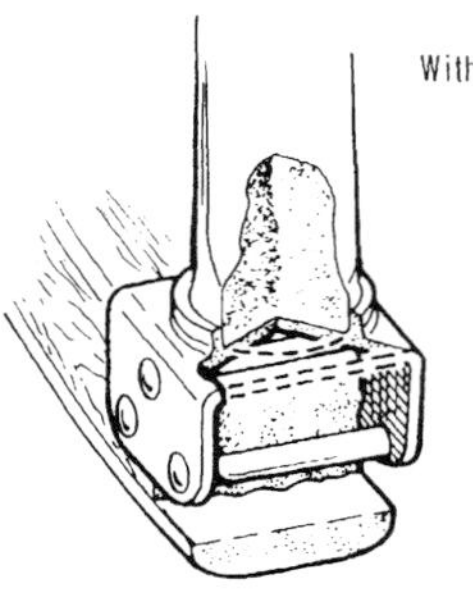

STEEL SOCKET

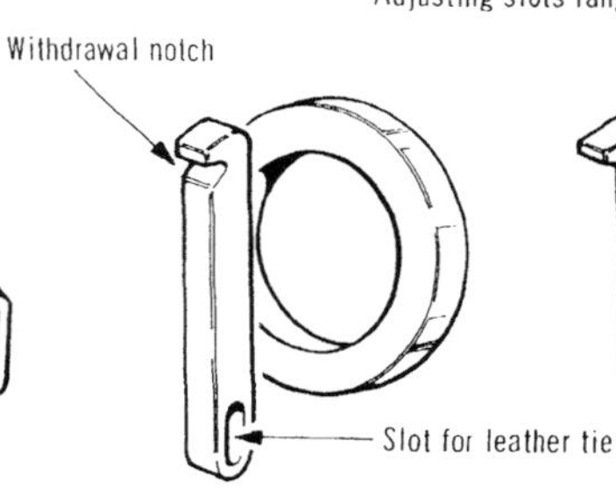

LONG LINCH-PIN AND PLAIN WASHER

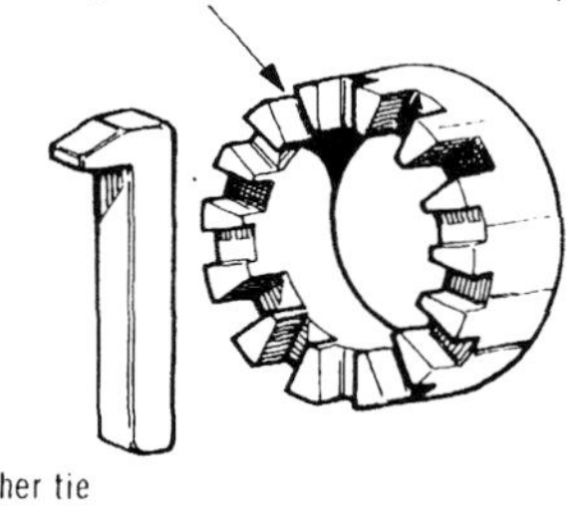

SHORT LINCH-PIN AND ADJUSTABLE WASHER (OR COLLAR)

Linch-pins and washers had the same class and number as the axletree on which they were used

FELLOE TO FELLOE JOINTS

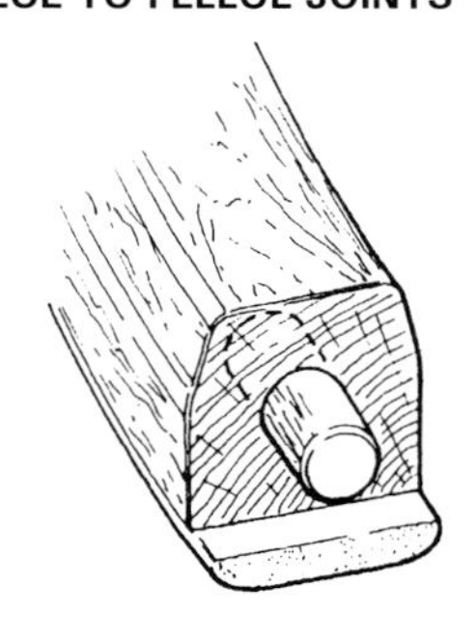

OAK DOWEL

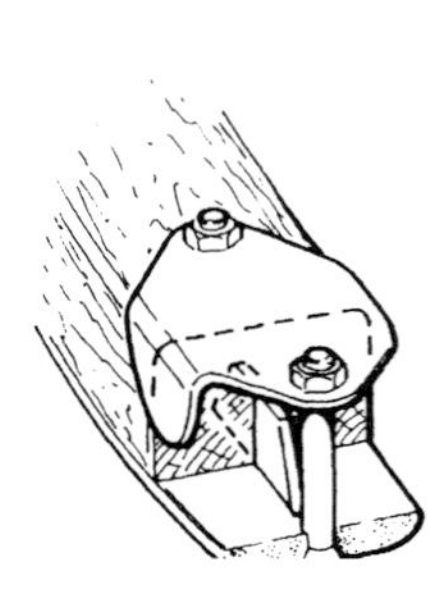

TRAPEZOIDAL STEEL DOWEL WITH STEEL CLIP PLATE

SPIKED STEEL CLUTCH PLATE

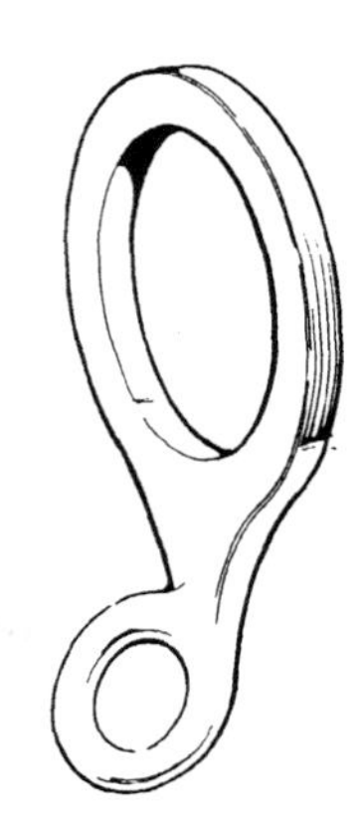

DRAG WASHER
(with eye for drag rope hook)

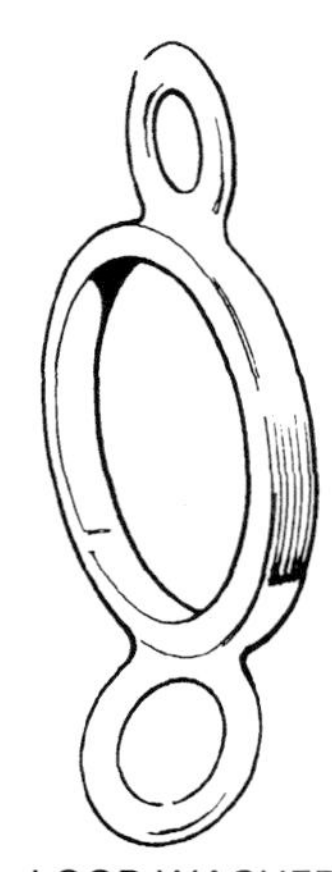

LOOP WASHER
(used with heavy field limbers and siege carriages; received the hook of an outrigger stay)

WHEEL CONSTRUCTION – DETAILS AND FITTINGS

dismounting the wheel from the axletree arm and removal of all old lubricant from both the arm and interior of the pipebox. Any burrs caused by grit would be removed with a half-round file. The pipebox and axletree arm would then be coated with fresh, clean grease and the wheel remounted.

A worn pipebox would give excess play on the axletree arm. In the event of a wheel fitted with an adjustable washer the slot giving the correct amount of play was selected for locking with the linch pin. Wheels fitted with plain washers would be adjusted by the addition of steel or leather washers between the pipebox and linch pin washer.

Bolts

To restore a bolt on which the thread had stripped, the bolt end was cut longitudinally and a piece welded in. Then the bolt was filed round and the thread re-cut. In the event of a bolt head breaking off, the bolt was replaced with a new one.

Woodwork

A vehicle left unused for any length of time would have the wheels rotated periodically, especially in wet conditions.

Shrinkage in the feet of the spokes on single spoked wheels could be taken up by tightening the flange nuts. On double spoked wheels, the pipebox nut would be tightened also.

The spring catch would be examined to ensure it had retained its spring temper and engaged the ratchet effectively.

The spokes and felloes would be inspected for deterioration. This usually showed itself by swelling and could be tested by tapping with a hammer – decaying wood giving a dull thud-like sound instead of the sharper noise heard from sound timber. Suspect material would have a sample removed with a thin blade or pricker from below any paint coating and the fibres examined.

Filling-in pieces

These would be inspected for security, and any loose or missing ones replaced.

Spokes

The life of a spoke, used in normal conditions, would be up to eight years. Intrusion of moisture, at either the foot or the tongue, was the most obvious cause of deterioration. In order to detect this it would be necessary to remove the tyre and flanges.

It was possible to replace a damaged spoke with a 'slip' spoke, as a temporary measure, until permanent repairs could be effected. This procedure is shown on page 32 as employed on a single spoked wheel. It will be seen from the main view that the rear (inner) flange, the pipebox and the two bolts adjacent to the spoke to be replaced, were removed, also the two filling-in pieces adjacent to the spoke.

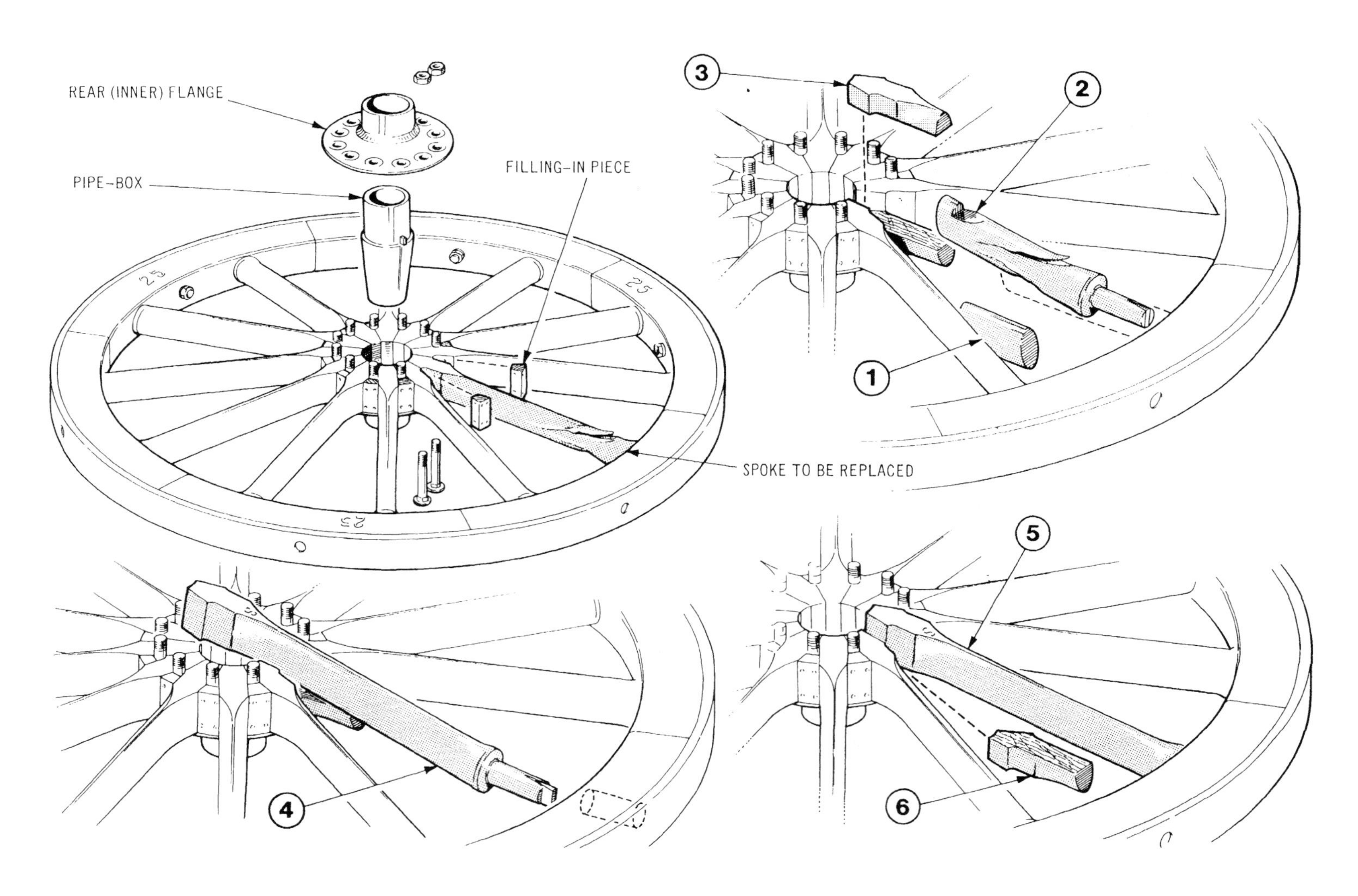

WHEEL REPAIR – "SLIP" SPOKES

A piece of the spoke three or four inches long was cut out close to the foot (**1**). The upper part of the spoke was notched and driven out of the felloe (**2**). The spoke foot was split down into two and the rear half knocked out (**3**). The replacement slip spoke was split at the tongue and a wedge loosely inserted. The tongue was then offered up to the hole in the felloe (**4**) and driven into place. The remaining half of the old foot was knocked out and the new spoke driven fully home (**5** and **6**). The new foot was trimmed to sit flush with the other spokes and painted. The pipebox and rear (inner) flange were replaced, together with the bolts and secured with the nuts. The filling-in pieces were replaced and secured, with new brads, to the adjacent spokes.

The above procedure was similar for a double spoked wheel, except that replacement of a front spoke entailed removal of the front (outer) flange and replacement of a rear spoke entailed removal of the rear (inner) flange. Also, on replacement of the flange, a hole would be bored through the foot of the new spoke for the flange bolt.

Slip spokes would be stamped with a letter 'S' and the year of fitting at a position just above the nave.

There would be not more than three slip spokes inserted into a wheel and not more than two of these would be adjacent to each other.

Felloes

These would usually begin to deteriorate at their joints with each other, by moisture penetration into the end grain, just below the tyre.

The joints could droop and open slightly at the bosom. This was remedied by removal of the tyre and the cutting of a small, wedge-shaped piece of wood from the end of the felloe at the sole. This repair entailed shortening the tyre before replacement on the wheel.

Minor splitting of the felloe could be contained by the insertion of screws.

It was possible to replace a damaged felloe with a 'slip' felloe, without removal of the tyre. This procedure is shown on page 34. A new felloe, already bored for spokes, dowels and tyre bolt, was measured against the felloe to be replaced and trimmed accurately to length. Four holes, to accommodate rivets, were bored through the felloe, equally spaced from each other, two between (and at right angles to) the spokes and one outside of each spoke (**1**).

The damaged felloe was removed, with sufficient care not to disturb the dowels or spoke tongues (**2**).

The slip felloe was slit through the centre, along the line of the spoke holes, with a hand saw. The spoke, dowel and tyre bolt holes were then enlarged slightly with a gouge to compensate for the saw cut thickness (**3**).

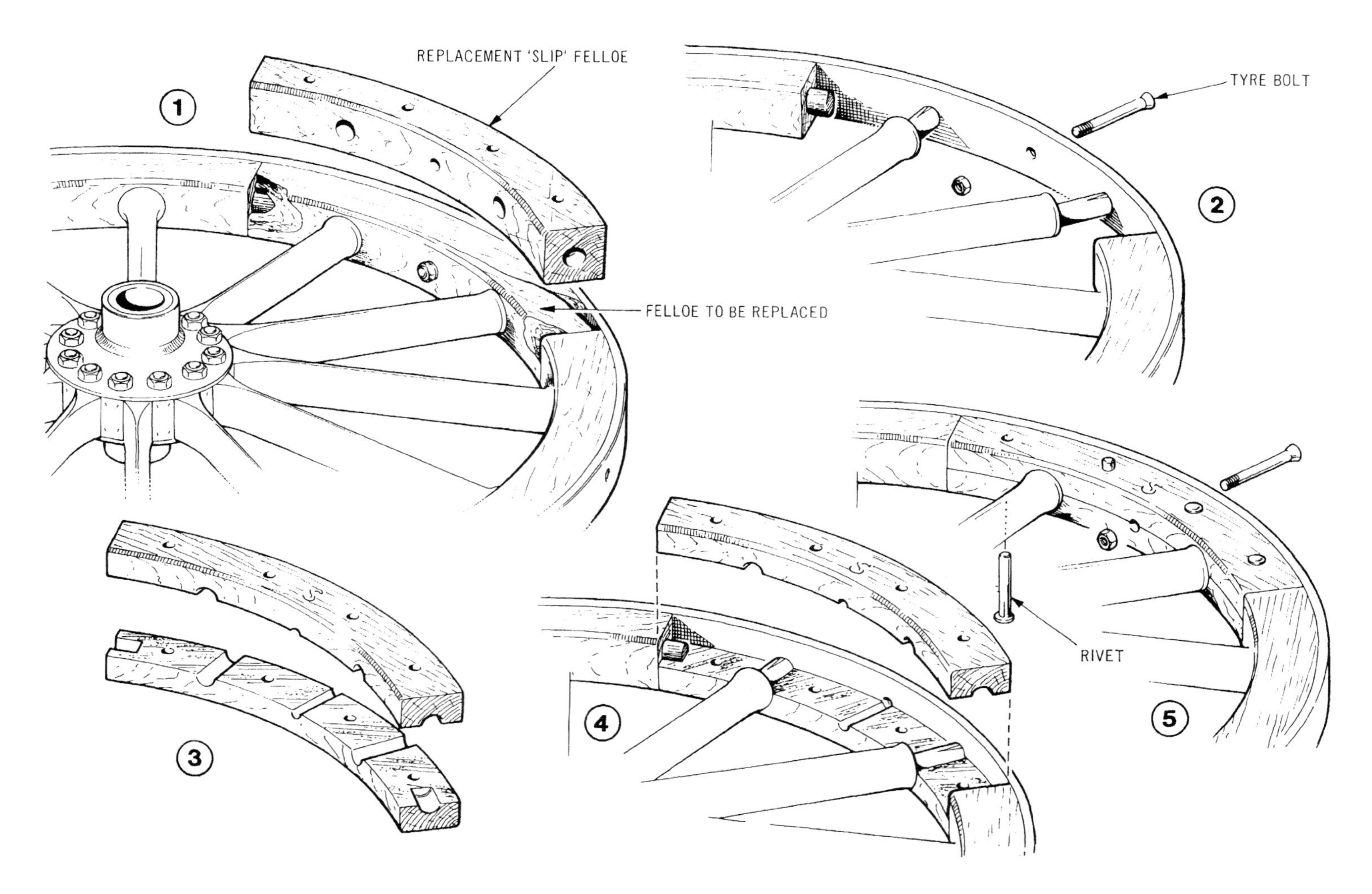

WHEEL REPAIR – "SLIP" FELLOES

The inner surfaces of the slip felloe halves were coated with white lead or paint. The halves were then placed in position and secured together with four rivets (**4** and **5**).

The tyre bolt was fitted through the tyre and felloe, the nut being tightened up on the bosom.

The slip felloe was stamped with the letter 'S' and year of fitting.

Only two slip felloes could be inserted into a wheel, and then not adjacent to each other.

Tyres – making and fitting

A length of mild, forged steel strip, of the correct width and thickness, was laid on the ground and the unshod wheel run along it to accurately mark off the dimension of one complete revolution (**1**). From this was subtracted an allowance for shrinkage – as a general rule one quarter of an inch was deducted per one foot of wheel diameter. To the resultant measurement was added one and a half inches for welding the joint.

Each end of the strip was prepared for an alternate lap welded joint by cutting along the centre for one and a quarter inches, then bending the half-widths in opposite directions, the bends to be such as to result in a final joint as shown in (**2**).

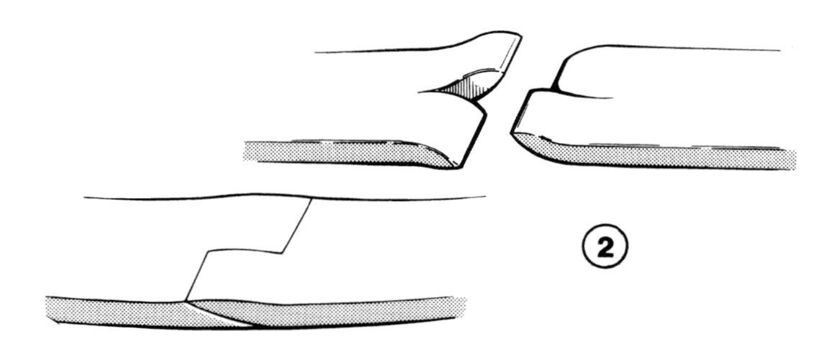

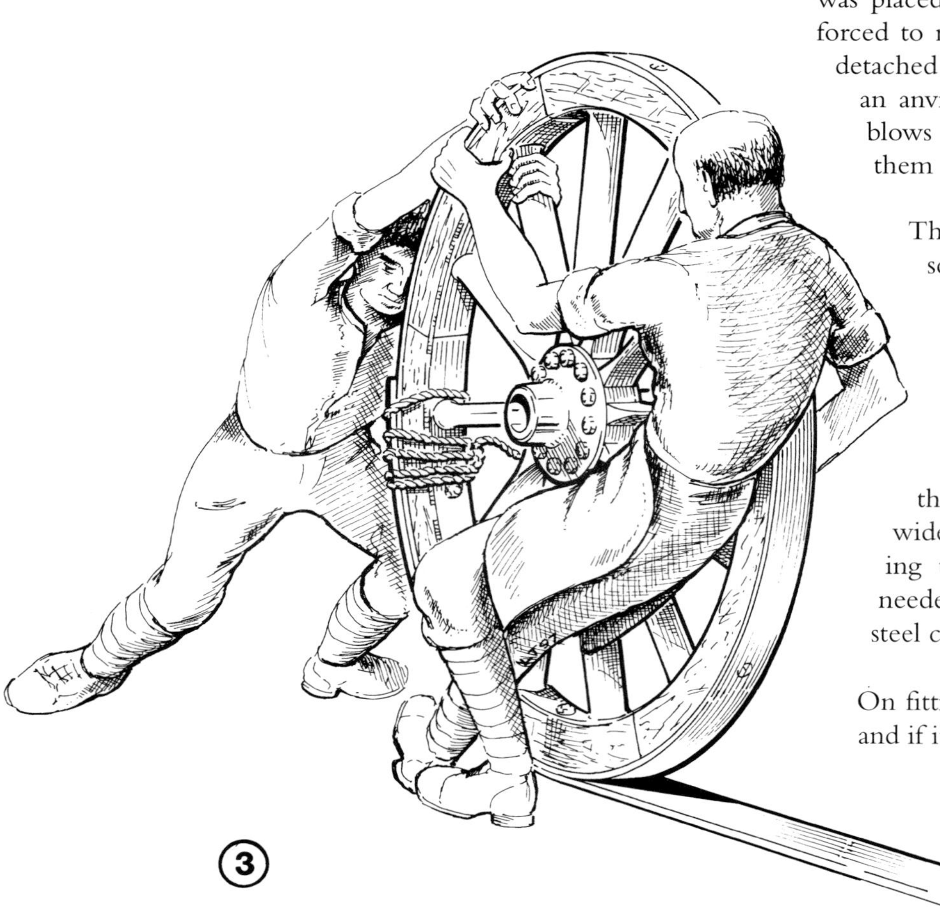

The strip was laid on the ground and a wheel, complete with tyre, was placed on the strip and lashed to it. The wheel was then forced to roll along the strip creating a hoop (**3**) which, when detached from the wheel, was bent finally to size and shape on an anvil. The ends were brought together and given a few blows on the inside of the tyre to clamp the laps and hold them together for the welding operation.

The joint was heated to a dull red, the surface cleaned of scale and hammered closed. The weld proper was done in two welding heats, one for each lap half, using a borax and sand flux.

The procedure above was used for mild steel tyres. If iron was used the alternate lap was not employed, instead the strip ends were 'upset' and 'scarfed' before the joint weld was made. Iron tyres up to three inches wide were welded at one heating if possible to avoid burning the metal. The variation in welding methods was needed due to the poorer forge welding properties of mild steel compared to iron.

On fitting, if the tyre was too short it could be 'drawn' out, and if it was too large it would be cut and rewelded.

The tyre would next be bevelled in order to fit closely onto the sole of the felloes. This was achieved by hammering it along one inside edge, evenly all around the tyre, using moderate blows with a sledgehammer every three inches or so giving about the correct bevel.

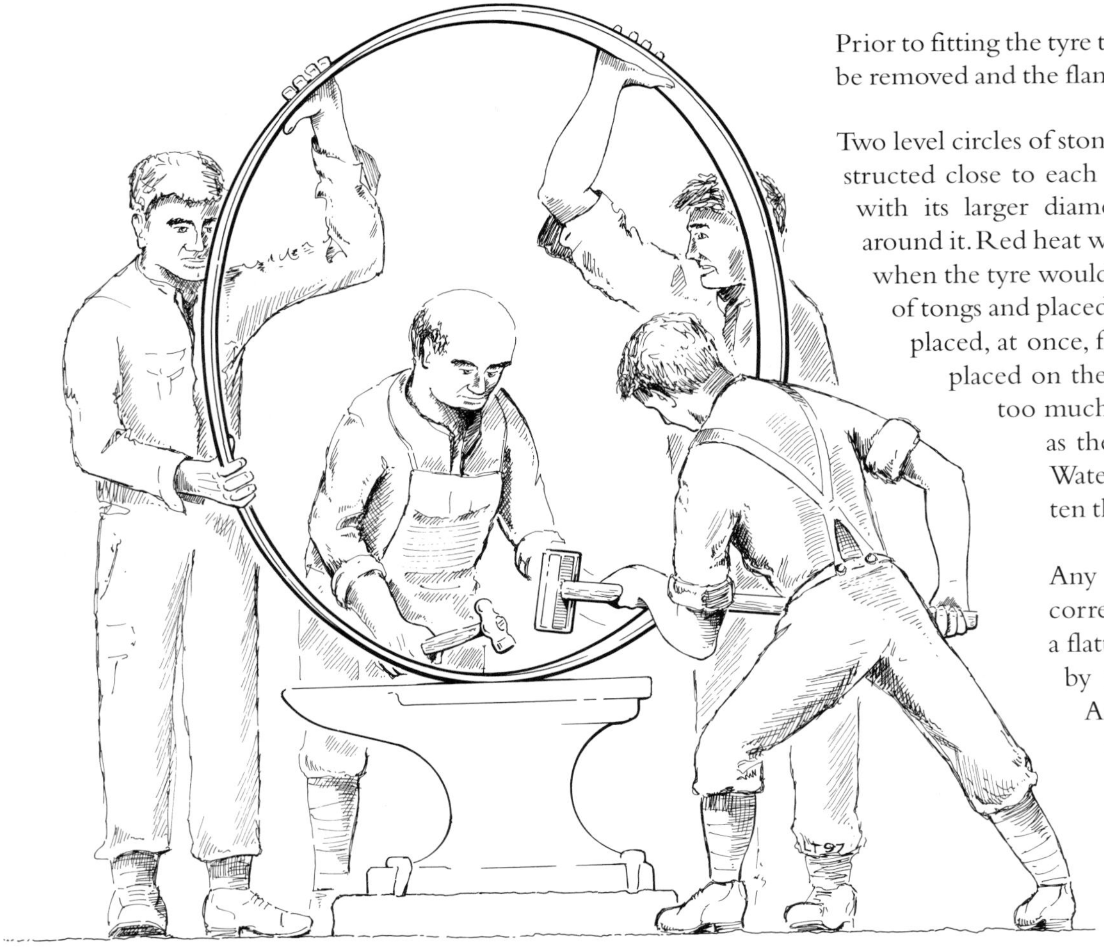

Tyre fitting

Prior to fitting the tyre to a metal-naved wheel, the pipebox would be removed and the flanges bolted up tight with the nave bolts.

Two level circles of stones, the diameter of the tyre, would be constructed close to each other. The tyre would be placed on one, with its larger diameter uppermost, and a wood fire made around it. Red heat would be obtained in about twenty minutes when the tyre would be lifted carefully, with three or four pairs of tongs and placed on the second circle. The wheel would be placed, at once, face downwards into the tyre and weights placed on the nave. These prevented the wheel dishing too much and ensured that the joints closed tightly as the tyre shrunk and compressed the wheel. Water was then poured around the tyre to hasten the cooling and prevent the felloes burning.

Any adjustment needed to seat the tyre correctly was made by striking the felloes with a flatter (used to avoid damage to the wood), or by striking the tyre with a mallet or maul. After complete cooling, should any further adjustment be needed, it would be done on an anvil, using a flatter and sledge hammer.

In the event of a tyre twisting in service, due to the felloes shifting, it could be adjusted on an anvil in the same way.

The tyre was drilled for the tyre bolts, one positioned through the centre of each felloe. The holes were then countersunk, the bolts inserted and nutted up on the bosom.

Finally, the pipebox was refitted.

Tyre shrinking

On wheels fitted with tyres over three inches wide and over half an inch thick (particularly heavy siege tyres), if the tyre became loose due to shrinkage of the wood, it could be shortened without need for cutting and rewelding, by the following method.

With the wheel standing on its sole the tyre bolts were removed and the wheel driven out of the tyre, from the back, with a flatter and sledge hammer.

A circular trench was dug, to a diameter to suit the tyre, about six inches wide and the same deep. In the bottom of the trench were placed stones for the tyre to rest horizontally upon. To level the tyre, water was poured into the trench to a point halfway up the tyre and the stones adjusted to obtain this level all around. The tyre was removed from the trench and the water level marked on a stick to enable the water to be maintained at the required height.

The tyre was then heated, in a circular wood fire, to an even red heat all round. It was then lifted carefully (to avoid twisting it out of shape) and placed in the trench, ensuring that the water was at the correct height. The water would be maintained at the level until the tyre was cool enough for a man to keep his hand upon it.

This operation would cause the part of the tyre not immersed to contract. The procedure was then repeated with the tyre reversed. A tyre of five feet diameter was shortened by about two inches in circumference by this method.

After the tyre was shrunk it could be that it was too small for the wheel, in which case a small amount would be cut off one end of two opposite felloes to fit the wheel to the tyre, this being preferable to drawing out the tyre. Shortening the felloes would also let them down onto the spokes, which would be of benefit in a wheel which had shrunk. As a general guide, the tyre length

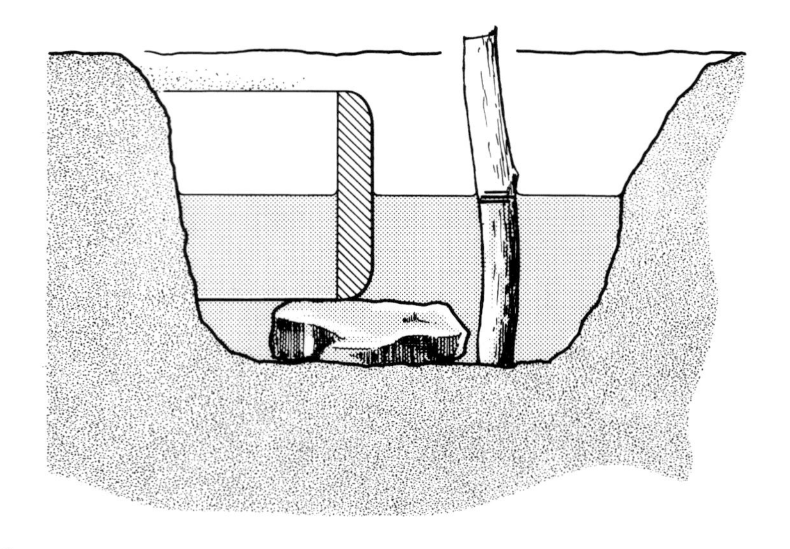

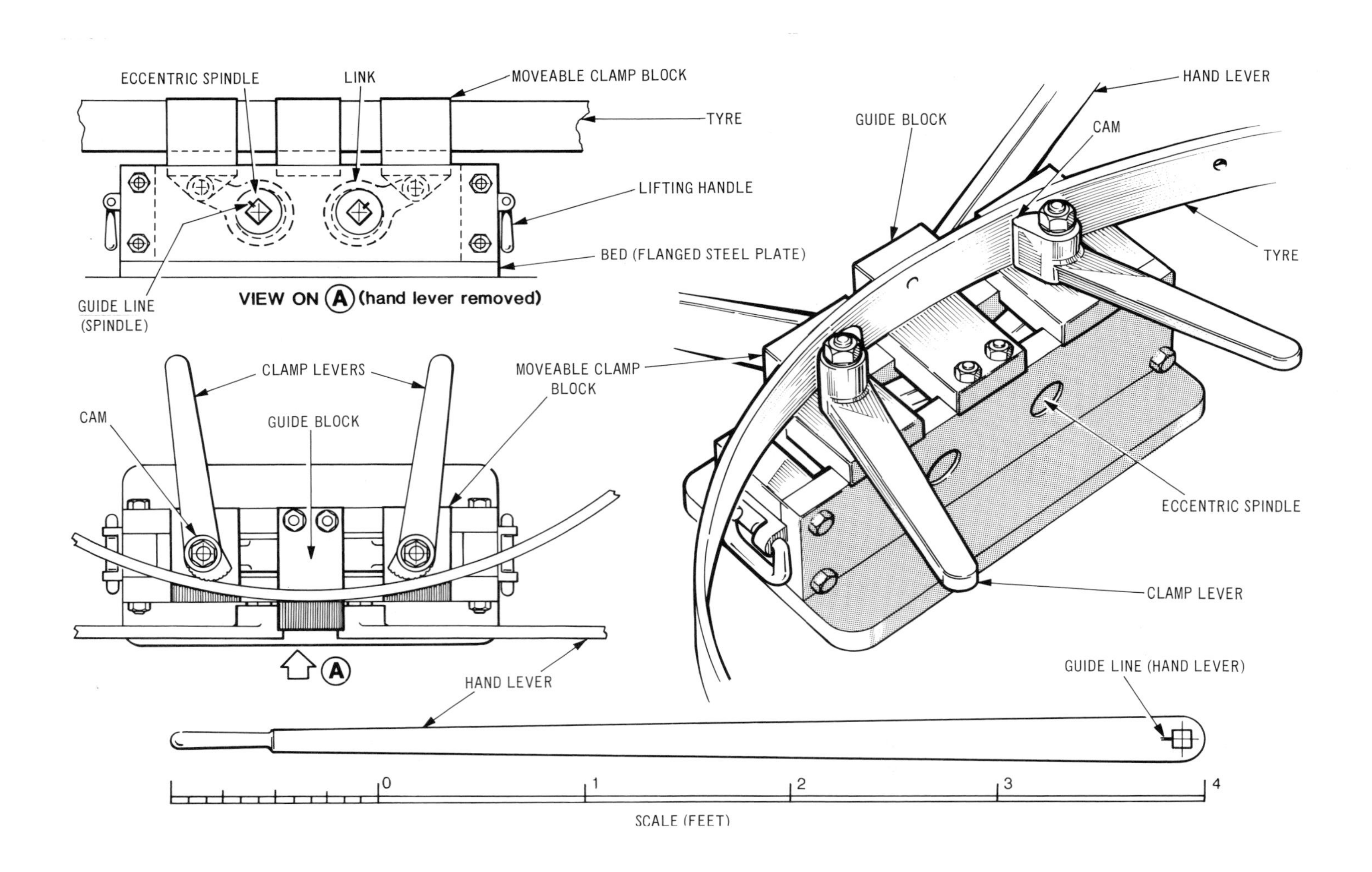

TYRE COMPRESSOR MK. 1

needed to be shorter than the wheel circumference by double the total measurement of the gaps in the felloe joints.

The pipebox would be removed from the nave and the tyre shrunk onto the wheel in the normal way.

Tyre Compressor Mk. I

For shortening tyres of three inches wide by half an inch thick, or less.

The diagram on page 40 shows the constructional details of the compressor. To prepare the compressor for use, the clamp levers were opened to their full extent. The eccentric spindles were turned so that the guidelines were vertical to separate the movable clamp blocks. The hand levers were then placed onto the square ends of the spindles to stand vertically upwards together.

The portion of the tyre to be shortened was brought to the necessary heat and placed into the compressor. The clamp levers were brought together causing the serrated cam faces to tightly grip the tyre against the clamp blocks. The hand levers were immediately forced away from each other, one man operating each lever, until the levers were horizontal. This turned the eccentric spindles, causing the links to draw the movable clamp blocks closer together and shorten the tyre by a distance of six-tenths of one inch. The grip of the cams on the tyre increased with the pressure, due to the geometric lock embodied in the design.

The clamp levers were then opened outwards to release their grip and the tyre lifted from the compressor.

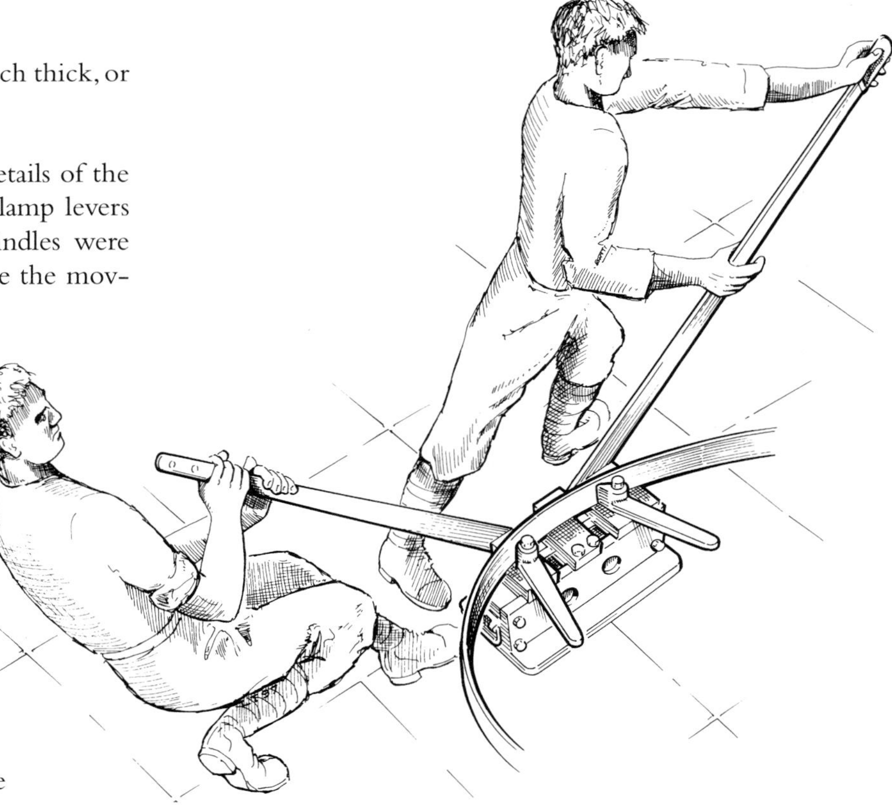

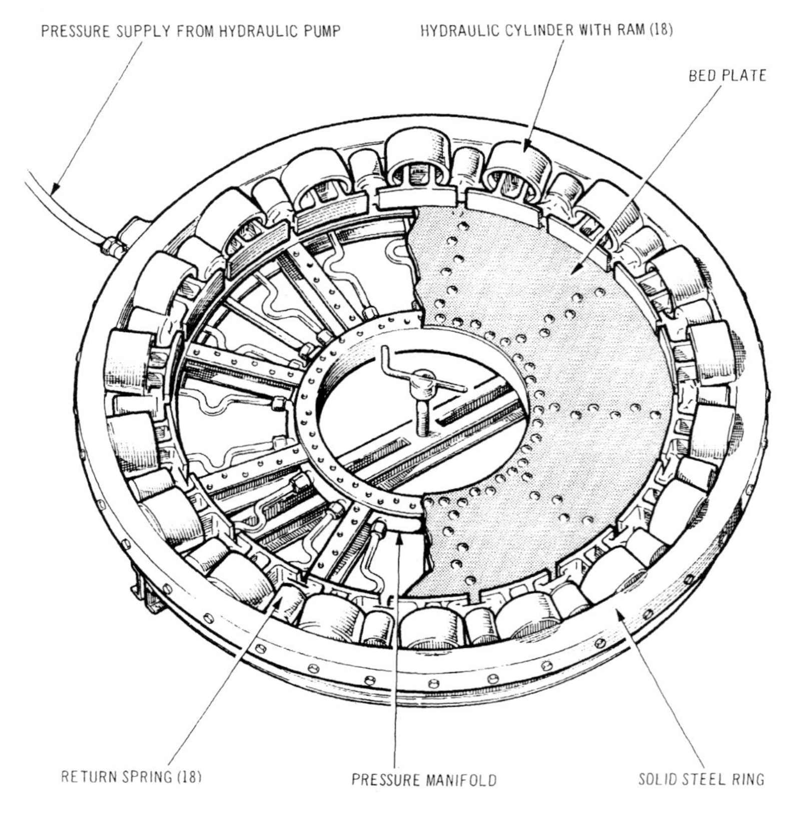

Tyre Setting Machine Mk. I

The machine was supplied with three sets of adaptors for packing the rams to fit wheels of differing diameters.

The wheel was placed face down onto the bedplate and secured with the central holding screw. The appropriate adaptors were placed between the tyre and rams.

The hydraulic pump required four men to operate the handwheels. When the necessary pressure had been obtained and released, the wheel was removed from the machine and sounded with a hammer to ensure that all the felloe joints were well tightened up. Should this not have been correct the wheel was again placed in the machine and more pressure applied.

The table shows the approximate pressures required to set tyres of various sizes.

WHEEL DIAMETER	TYRE SIZE	PUMP PRESSURE
3ft 4in.	3in. × ½in.	1,165lb
3ft 9in.	2½in. × ½in.	1,075lb
4ft 8in.	2½in. × ½in.	1,075lb
4ft 8in.	3in. × ½in.	1,255lb
5ft 0in.	3in. × ½in.	1,310lb

Rubber tyres

India rubber tyres were mounted in a specially grooved steel tyre which was shrunk and bolted to the wheel in the normal manner.

To remove an India rubber tyre, one end of the tyre was prised up at the join until clear of the groove and then peeled out all around the wheel.

Adjustments to the wheel could be made in the normal manner. Before fitting a new India rubber tyre the steel tyre groove would be thoroughly cleaned and coated with black Japan.

To fit an India rubber tyre, one side was pushed into the groove and the other side forced in with the special inserting tool, as shown. On finishing the joint, care was taken that the rubber was well compressed and not stretched.

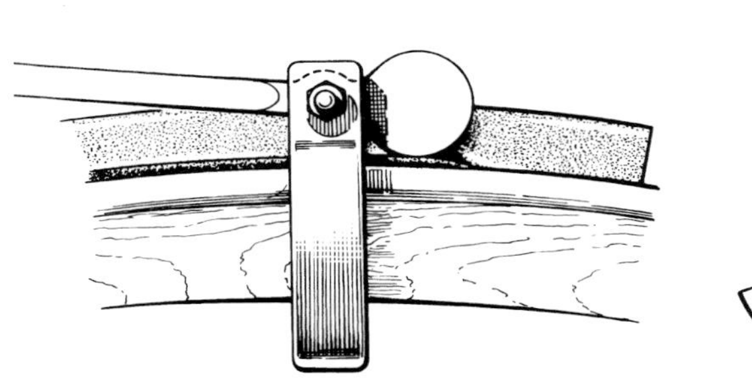

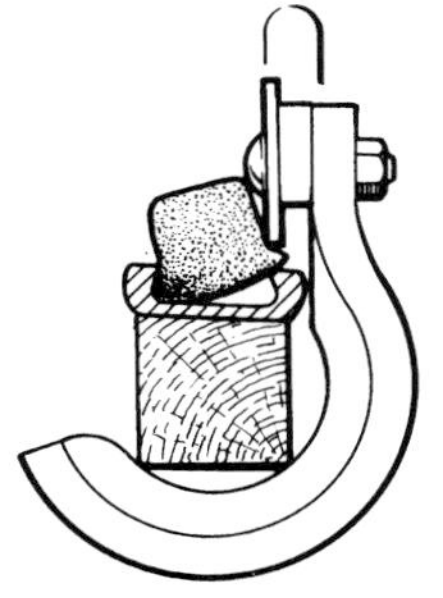

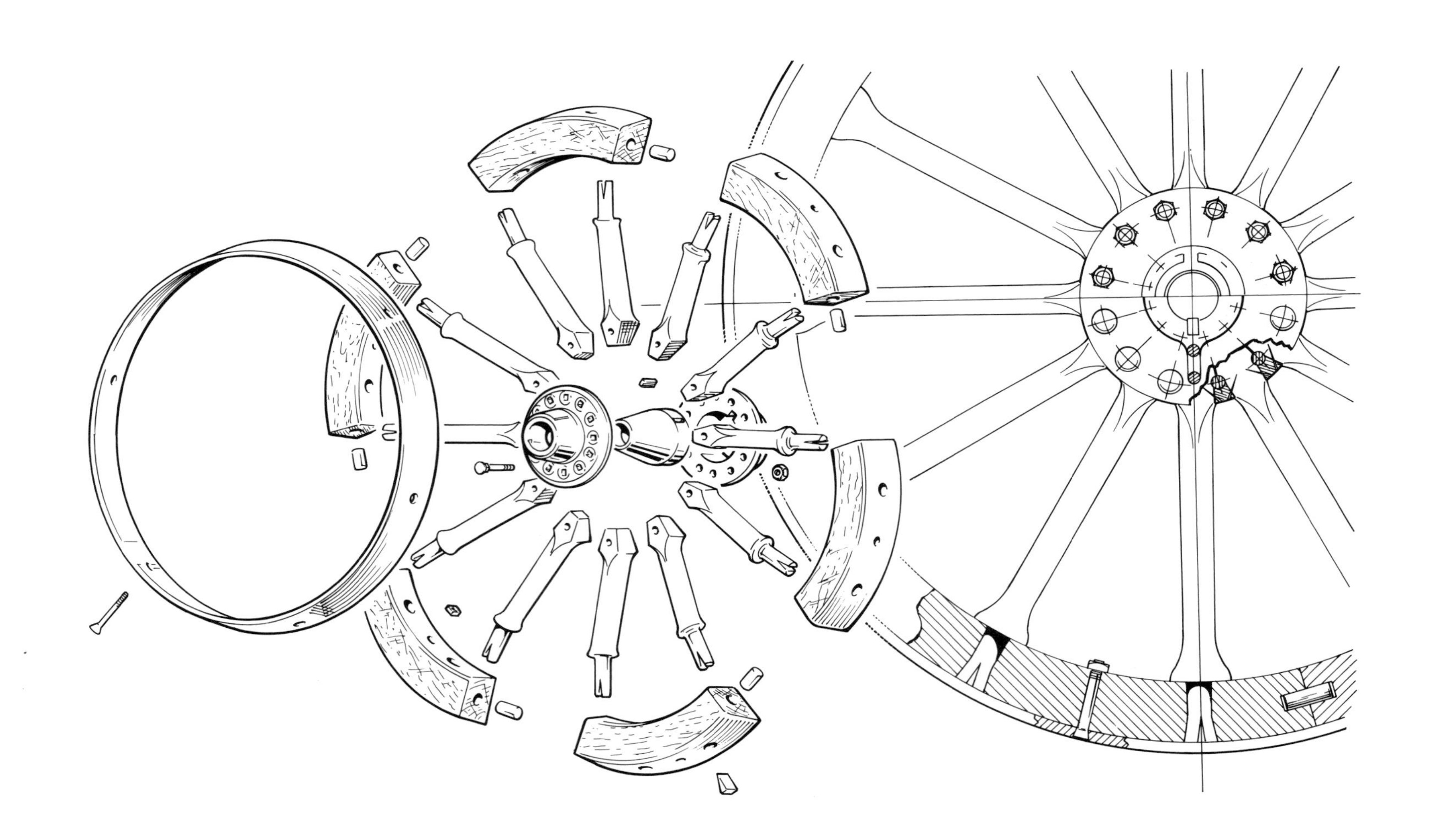

Wheel variations

The following pages detail sixteen of the wheel variations in common use during the period between the Boer and Great Wars. Where possible the carriages on which they were employed, the constructional materials and weights are quoted. Study of the foregoing pages, however, will make you realise that, once a wheel had left the manufacturer and was entrusted to craftsmen of widely varying abilities, strict adherence to the original specification was somewhat in doubt. The information contained in this section must therefore be regarded as a general departure point only, from which wheels in service varied to a degree governed by the whim of the artificer, or by the often difficult conditions under which maintenance and repair work was, of necessity, carried out.

1st class B No. 6 (see page 46)

QF 4.7 inch travelling carriage (converted from RML 40 pdr).

PIPEBOX Phosphor bronze.

FLANGES Gunmetal.

SPOKES Single type, twelve of oak, with oak wedges. Twelve nave bolts between the spoke feet, covered by elm filling-in pieces.

FELLOES Six of cut ash, with cylindrical oak dowels.

TYRE Wrought iron, six inches wide.

WEIGHT 588 pounds.

1st class B No. 8 (see page 47)

BL 6 inch howitzer carriage.

PIPEBOX Phosphor bronze.

FLANGES Cast steel.

SPOKES Double type, fourteen of oak, with oak wedges. Fourteen nave bolts through the spoke feet.

FELLOES Seven of cut ash, with cylindrical oak dowels.

TYRE Mild steel, four inches wide by three quarters of an inch thick.

WEIGHT 392 pounds.

1st class B No. 9 (shown)

QF 4.7 inch travelling carriage.

Details as for the No. 8 wheel except for the following:

FLANGES Cast manganese bronze.

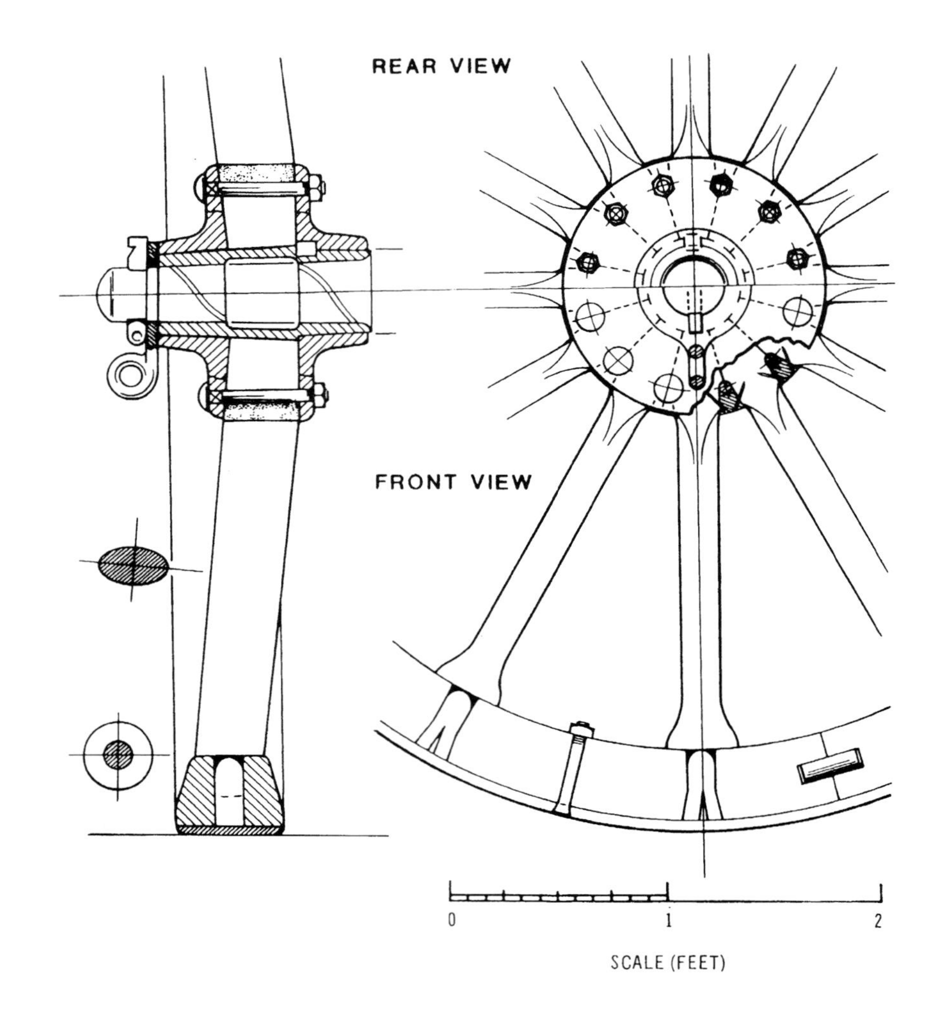

1st.class B No.6

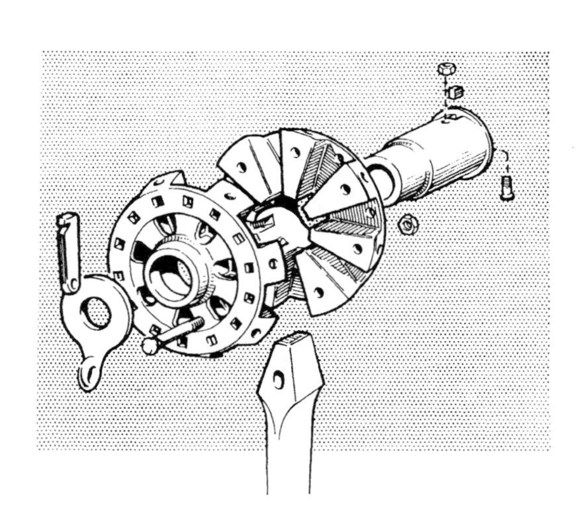

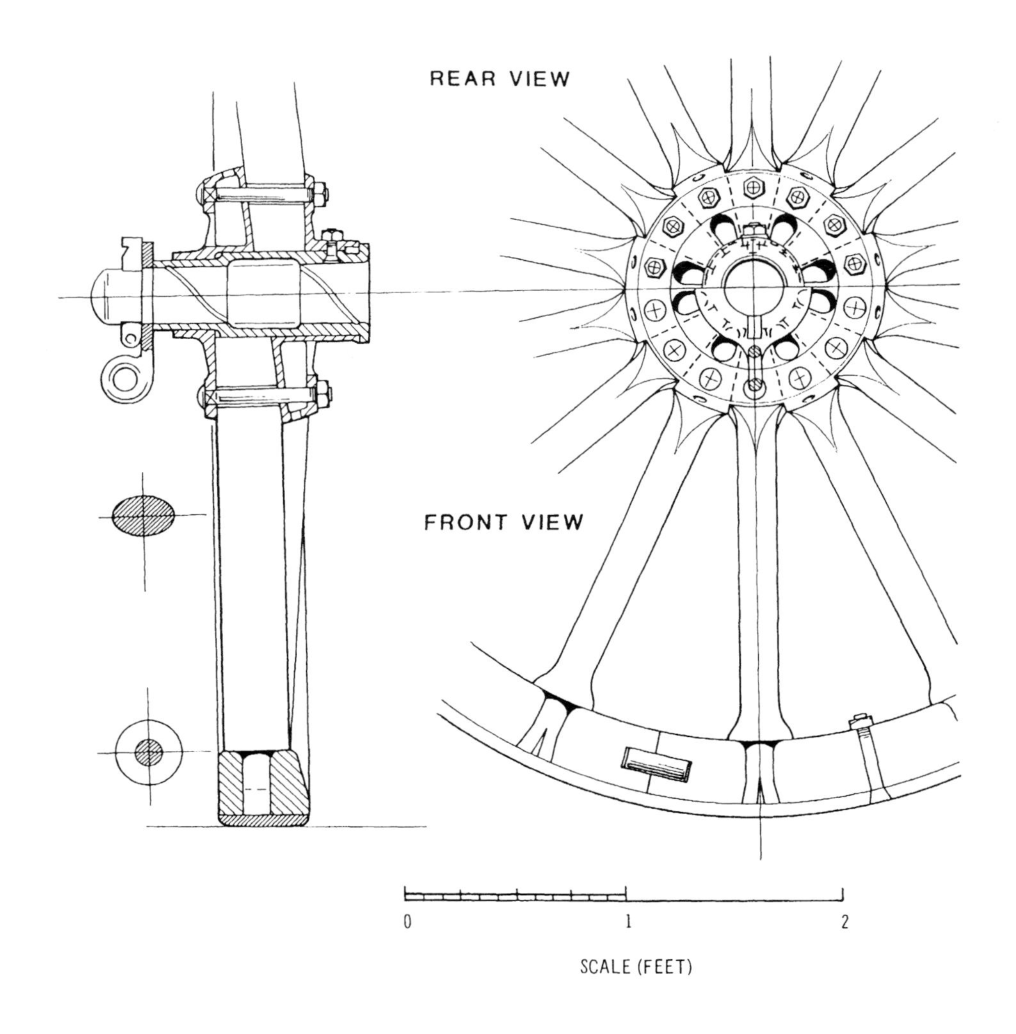

1st.class B No.8

1st.class B No.9 (shown)

TYRE Mild steel, five inches wide by five-eighths of an inch thick. Scantling is of increased thickness all over.

WEIGHT 420 pounds.

1st class B No. 10 (shown)

BL 60 pdr and 6 inch howitzer carriages.
QF 4.7 inch and 6 inch siege gun carriages and limbers.

PIPEBOX Phosphor bronze, runs in a dust excluder fitted to the axletree. The outer end was threaded to take a collar bearing for the loop washer and a gunmetal dust cap.

FLANGES Cast manganese bronze.

SPOKES Double type, fourteen of oak, with shouldered tongues and oak wedges. Fourteen nave bolts through the spoke feet.

FELLOES Seven of cut ash, with cylindrical oak dowels. The felloes have a greater radius than the wheel, ensuring that the joints are tight when the wheel is tyred.

TYRE Mild steel, six inches wide by half an inch thick. Secured by countersunk bolts, two to each felloe.

WEIGHT 349 pounds.

1st class B No. 11

BL 6 inch siege gun equipment cradle.

Details as for the No. 10 wheel, except that the diameter was six feet.

2nd class B No. 25 (see page 50)

QF 4.7 inch limber (converted RML 40 pdr).

PIPEBOX Phosphor bronze.

FLANGES Gunmetal.

SPOKES Single type, twelve of oak, with shouldered tongues split for oak wedges. Twelve nave bolts between the spoke feet, covered by elm filling-in pieces.

FELLOES Six of cut ash, with cylindrical oak dowels.

TYRE Wrought iron, three inches wide.

WEIGHT 242 pounds.

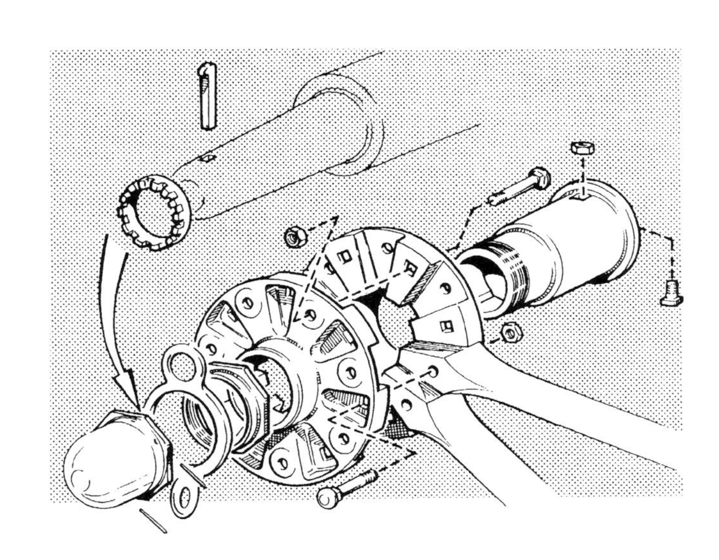

1st.class B No.10 (shown)

1st.class B No.11

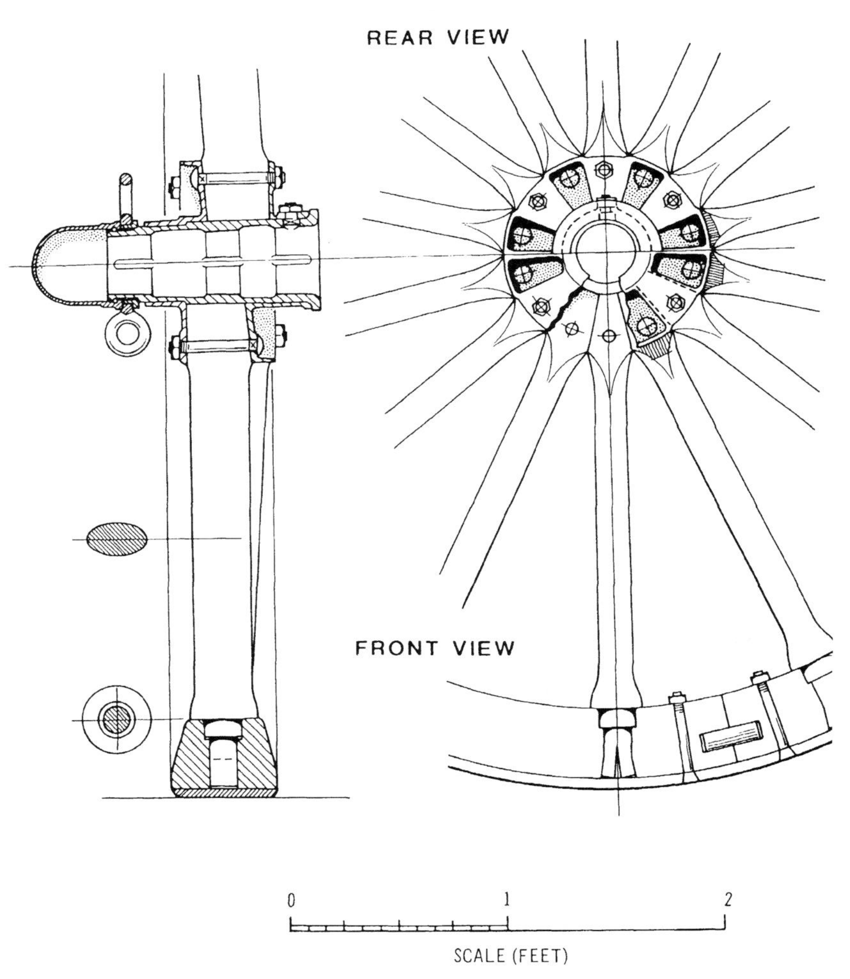

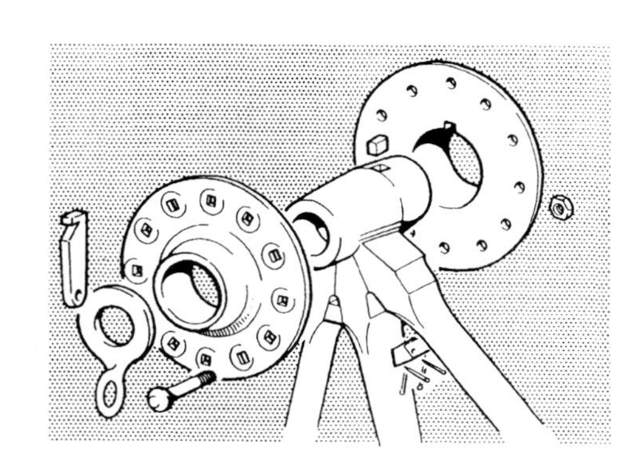

2nd.class B No.25

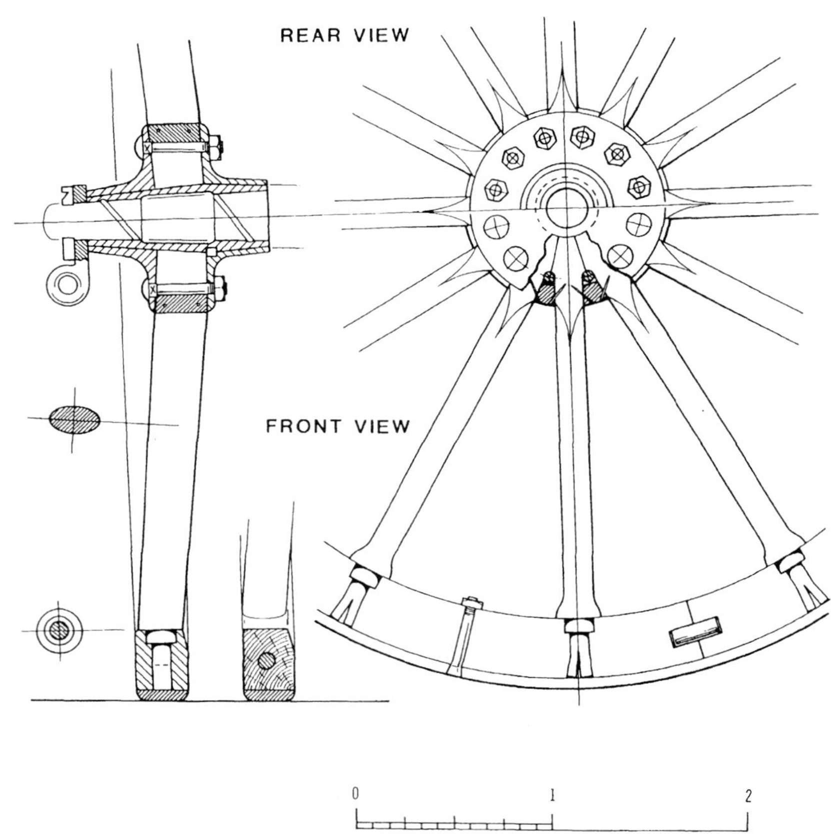

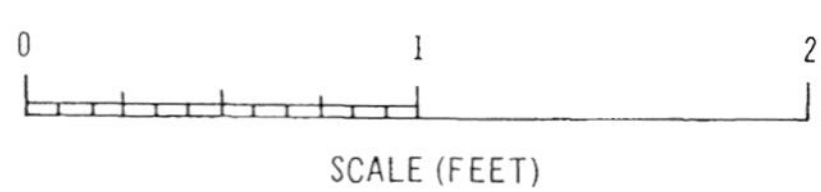

2nd class C No. 34 (see page 52)

QF 15 pdr equipment.

Fitted to the forge, store and spare wheel wagons. The No. 34A wheel design was based on this wheel.

2nd class C No. 34A (shown)

QF 15 pdr carriage and equipment.

This wheel was specially designed to replace the steel wheels originally supplied with the 15 pdr equipment.

PIPEBOX Two phosphor bronze, flanged, hollow cylinders, fitted inside a cylinder formed integrally with the front flange and secured with rivets.

FLANGES Steel. The front (outer) flange was formed on a cylinder over which fitted the rear (inner) flange.

SPOKES Single type, twelve of ash, their plain (no tongue) ends fitted into steel shoes riveted to the felloes. Twelve nave bolts through the spoke feet.

FELLOES Three of ash, steamed and bent to shape. Joints were by trapezoidal steel plate dowels inserted from the sole and steel clips secured by the tyre bolt nuts on the bosom.

TYRE Mild steel, three inches wide by half an inch thick. Secured by nine tyre bolts, one through each felloe centre and two at each felloe joint, also securing the steel joining clips.

2nd class C No. 35 (see page 53)

BL 12 pdr equipment.

The flanges of this wheel tended to deform and spread, so were modified by the addition of circumferential web pieces. This became the No. 35A wheel.

2nd class C No. 35A (shown)

BL 12pdr, BL 15 pdr, BLC 15 pdr, BL 5 inch howitzer equipment and some siege limbers.

PIPEBOX Cast phosphor bronze, threaded for a pipebox nut.

FLANGES Mild steel, stamped from plate. The rear (inner) flange was braced by a steel ring secured by rivets. The front (outer) flange was braced by a flanged gunmetal boss secured by rivets.

SPOKES Double type, fourteen of oak, with oak wedges. Fourteen nave bolts through the nave feet.

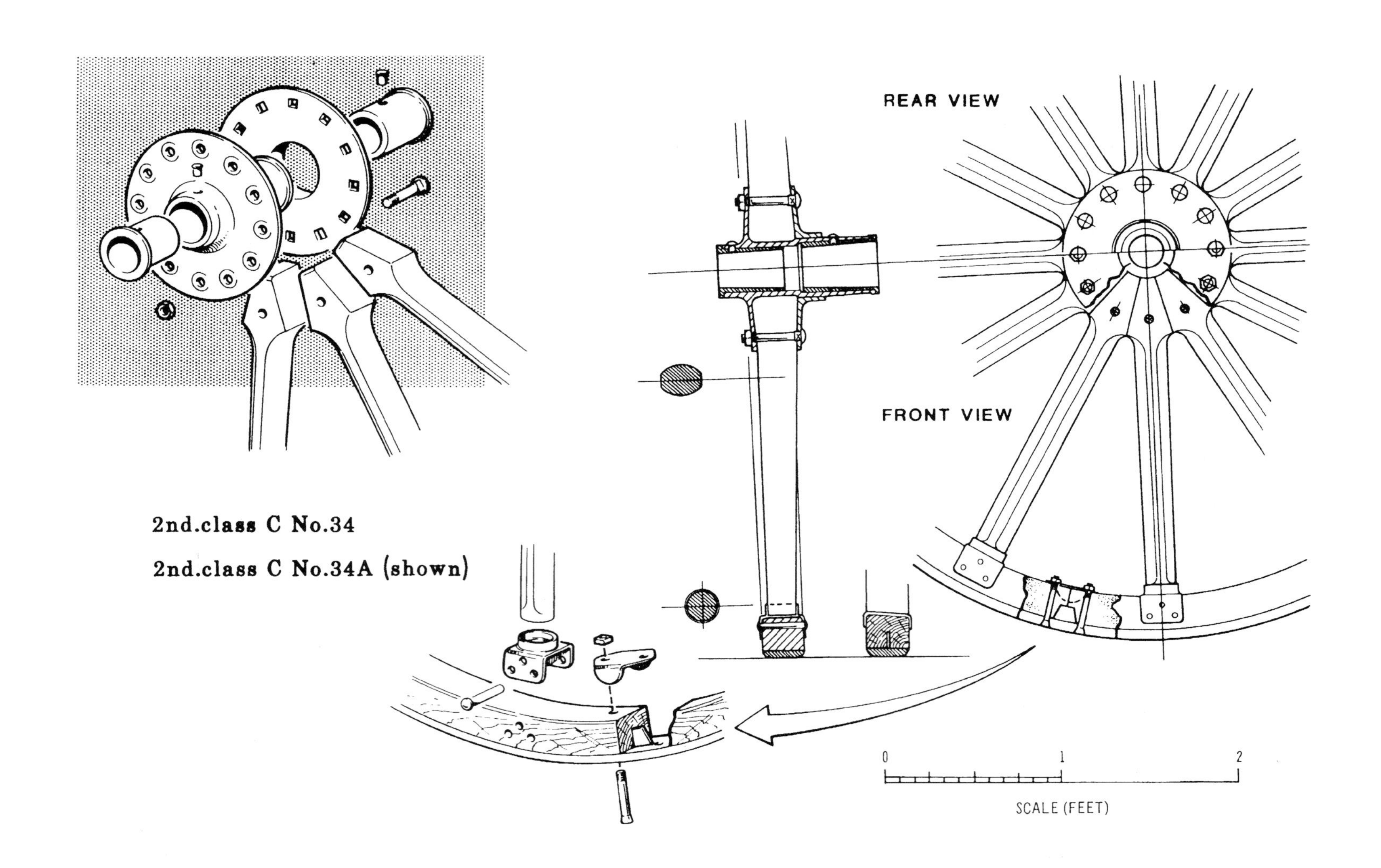

2nd.class C No.34

2nd.class C No.34A (shown)

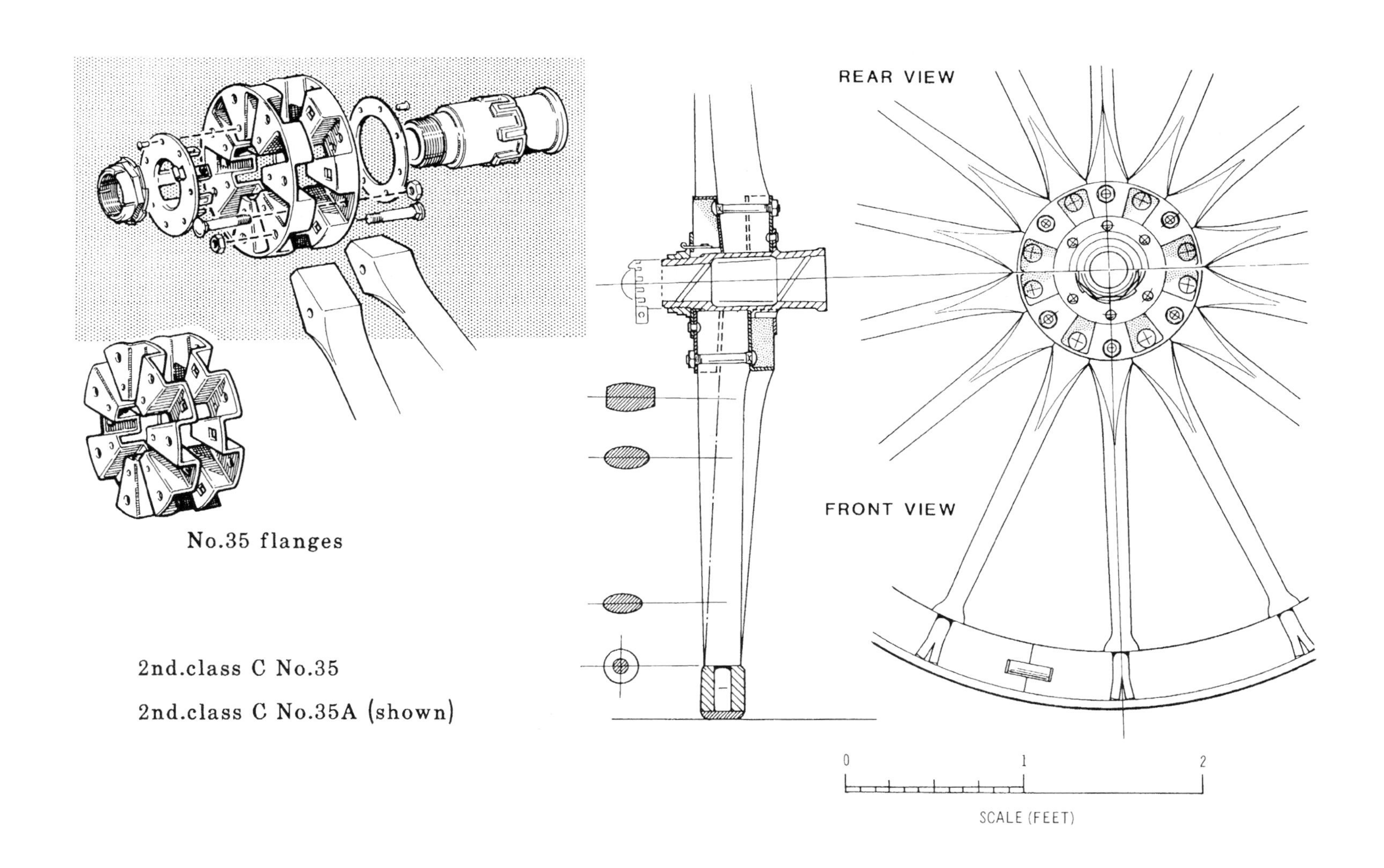

No.35 flanges

2nd.class C No.35

2nd.class C No.35A (shown)

FELLOES Seven of cut ash, with cylindrical oak dowels.

TYRE Mild steel, three inches wide by five-eighths of an inch thick.

WEIGHT 197 pounds.

2nd class C No. 36

BL 15 pdr travelling carriage and equipment.

PIPEBOX Phosphor bronze.

FLANGES Gunmetal.

SPOKES Single type, twelve of oak, with shouldered tongues split for oak wedges. Twelve nave bolts between the spoke feet, covered by elm filling-in pieces.

FELLOES Six of cut ash, with trapezoidal steel plate dowels.

TYRE Mild steel, three inches wide.

WEIGHT 234½ pounds.

2nd class C No. 41 *(see page 56)*

BL 5 inch howitzer equipment and some siege limbers.

PIPEBOX Phosphor bronze.

FLANGES Cast steel.

SPOKES Double type, fourteen of oak, with oak wedges. Fourteen nave bolts through the spoke feet.

FELLOES Seven of cut ash, with cylindrical oak dowels.

TYRE Mild steel, three inches wide.

WEIGHT 224 pounds.

2nd class C No. 42 *(see page 58)*

Early BL 15 pdr equipment.

PIPEBOX Phosphor bronze.

FLANGES Gunmetal. The rear (inner) flange was secured to the pipebox by two tapered pins with their small ends riveted over.

SPOKES Double type, fourteen of oak, with oak wedges. Fourteen nave bolts through the spoke feet.

2nd.class C No.36

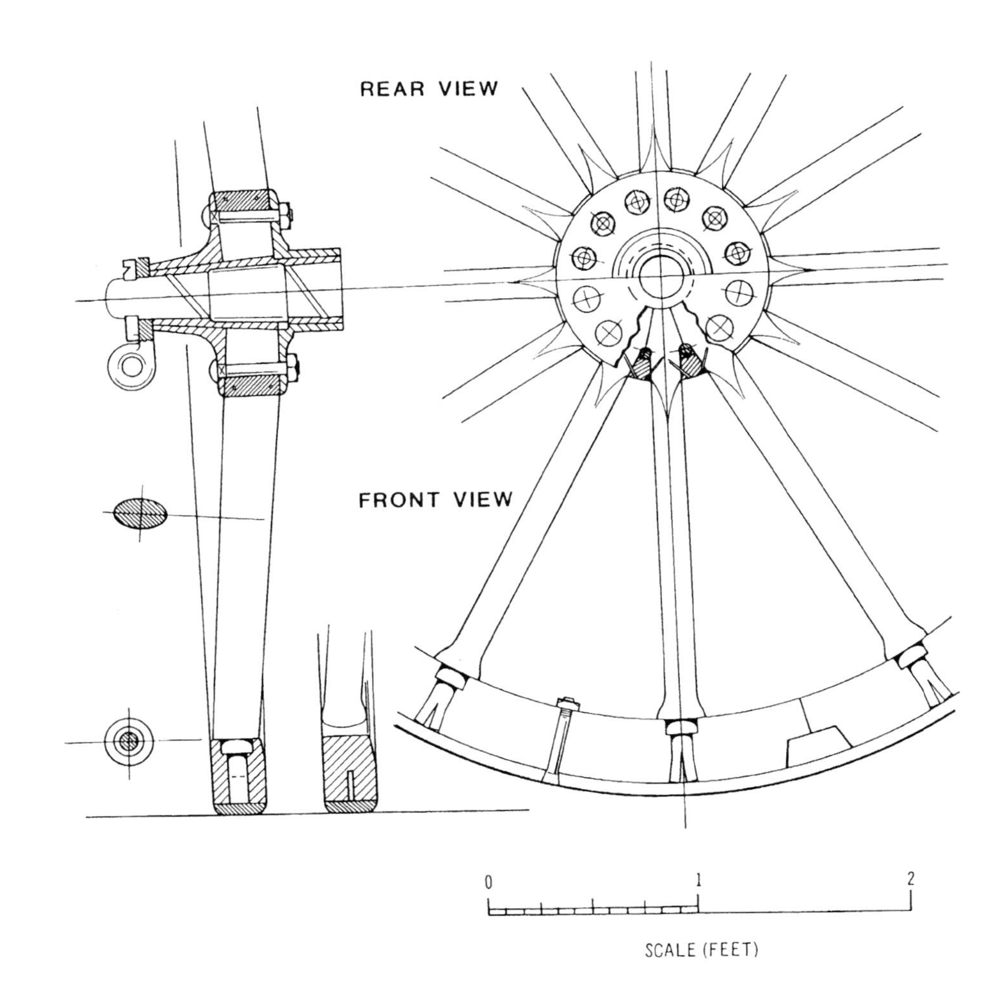

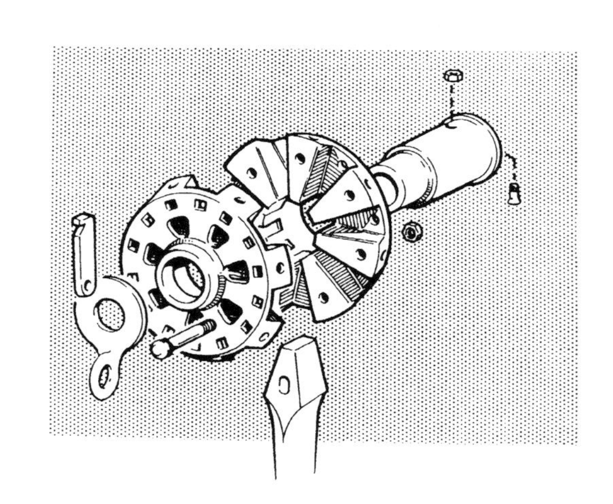

2nd.class C No.41

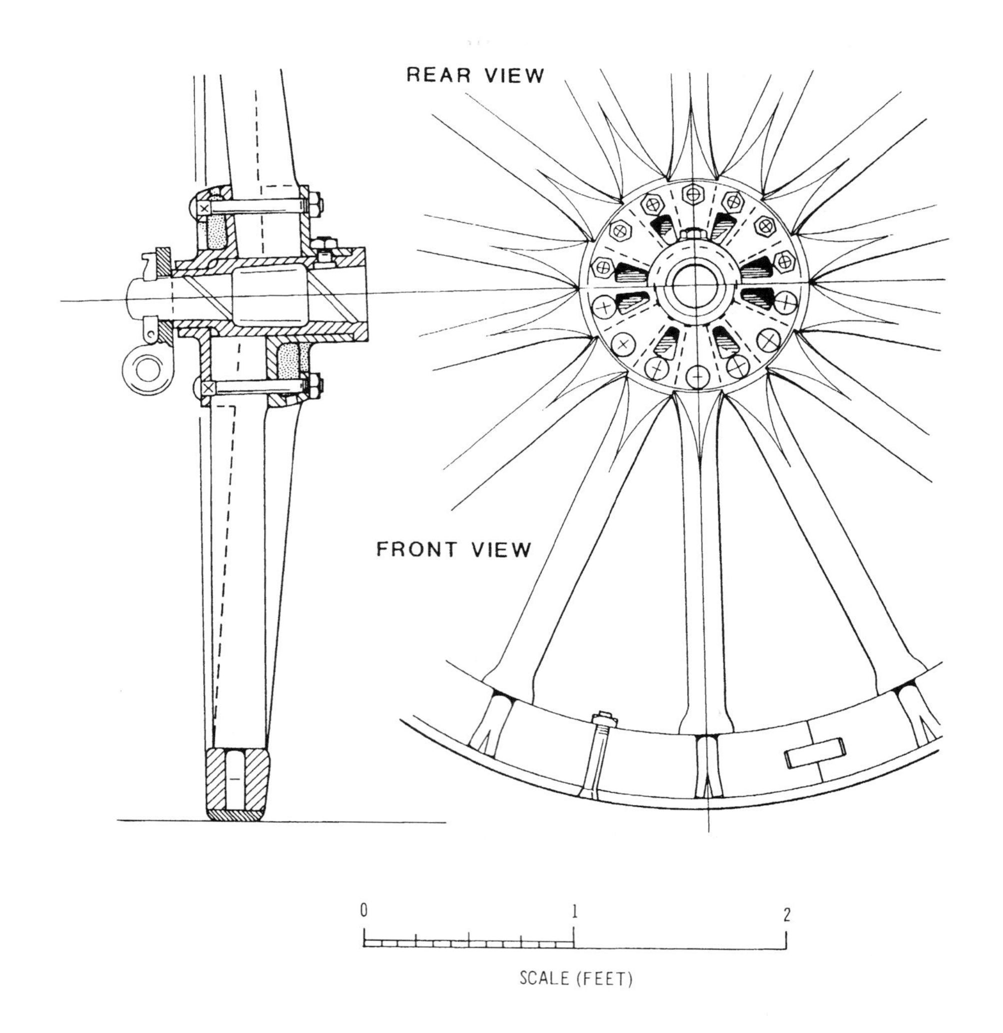

FELLOES Seven of cut ash, with trapezoidal steel plate dowels.

TYRE Mild steel, three inches wide.

WEIGHT 237 pounds.

2nd class C No. 43 (see page 59)

Early QF 13 pdr and 18 pdr equipment

PIPEBOX Phosphor bronze. The inner end fitted into a dust excluder on the axletree. The outer end was threaded for a pipebox nut and gunmetal dust cap. A threaded lubrication hole was plugged with a screw and leather washer.

FLANGES Mild steel plate stampings. The rear (inner) flange was braced by a steel ring secured by rivets. The front (outer) flange was braced by a flanged gunmetal boss secured by rivets. The boss carried a spring catch to lock the pipebox nut.

SPOKES Double type, twelve of oak with oak wedges. Twelve nave bolts through the spoke feet.

FELLOES Three of ash, steamed and bent to shape. Joints had trapezoidal steel plate dowels inserted from the sole and steel clips secured by the tyre bolt nuts on the bosom.

TYRE Mild steel, three inches wide by five-eighths of an inch thick. Secured by nine tyre bolts, one through each felloe centre and two at each felloe joint, also securing the steel joining clips.

WEIGHT 185 pounds.

No. 43 Mk. I (IP) For India service. Differed by having six cut ash felloes with twelve tyre bolts and of slightly heavier scantling.

No. 43 Mk. 2 (IP) For India service. Superseded the Mk. I. Differed by having six steamed and bent ash felloes and heavier scantling.

No. 43 wheels were converted to 2nd class C No. 45 wheels.

2nd class C No. 45 (see page 60)

QF 13 pdr, 18 pdr and 4.5 inch howitzer equipment.

PIPEBOX Phosphor bronze. The inner end fitted into a dust excluder on the axletree. The outer end was threaded for a pipebox nut and gunmetal dust cap. A threaded lubrication hole was plugged with a screw and leather washer.

FLANGES Mild steel plate stampings. The rear (inner) flange was braced by a steel ring secured by rivets. The front (outer) flange was braced by a flanged gunmetal boss secured by rivets. The boss

2nd.class C No.42

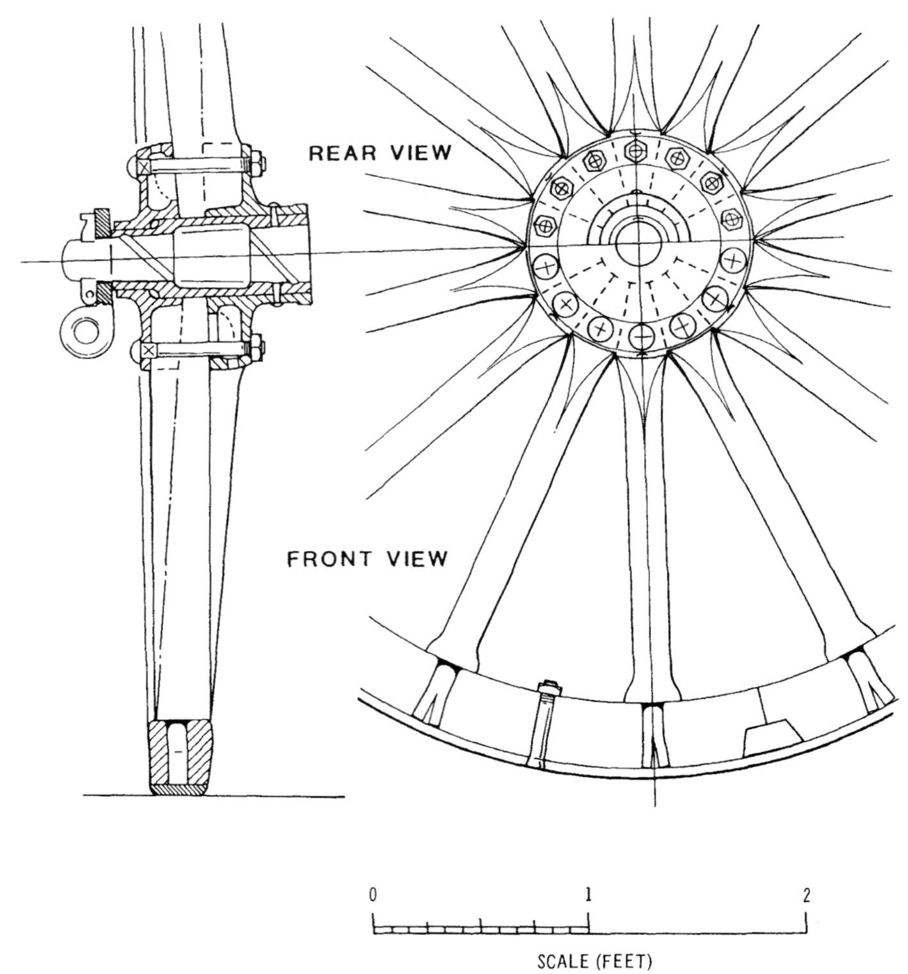

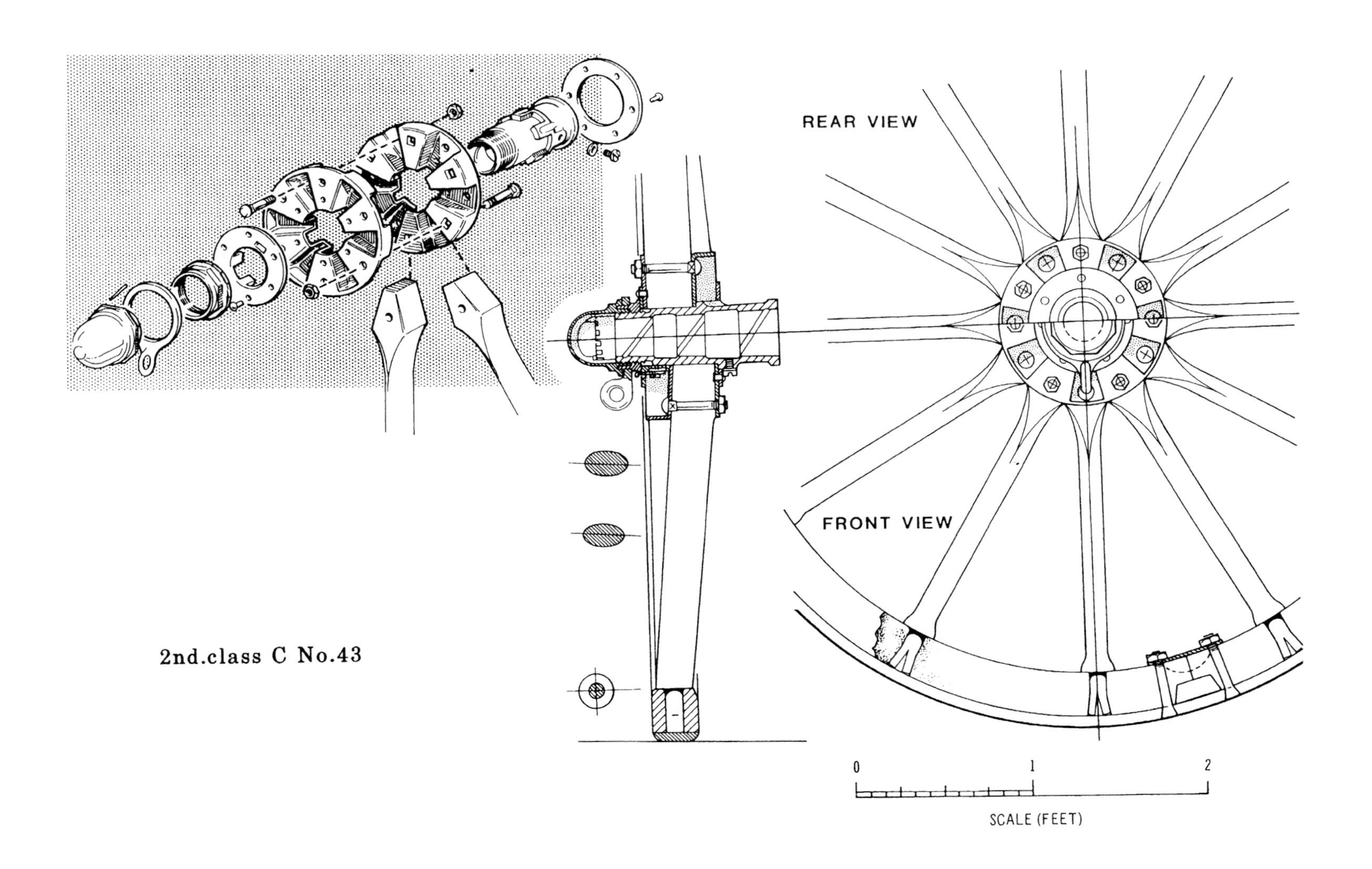

2nd.class C No.43

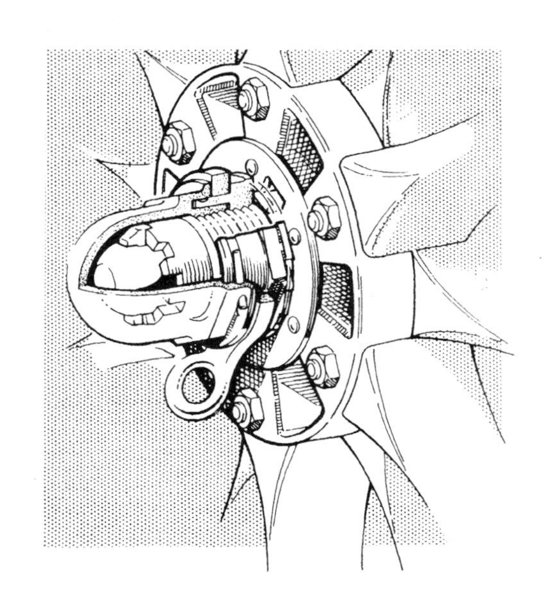

2nd.class C No.45

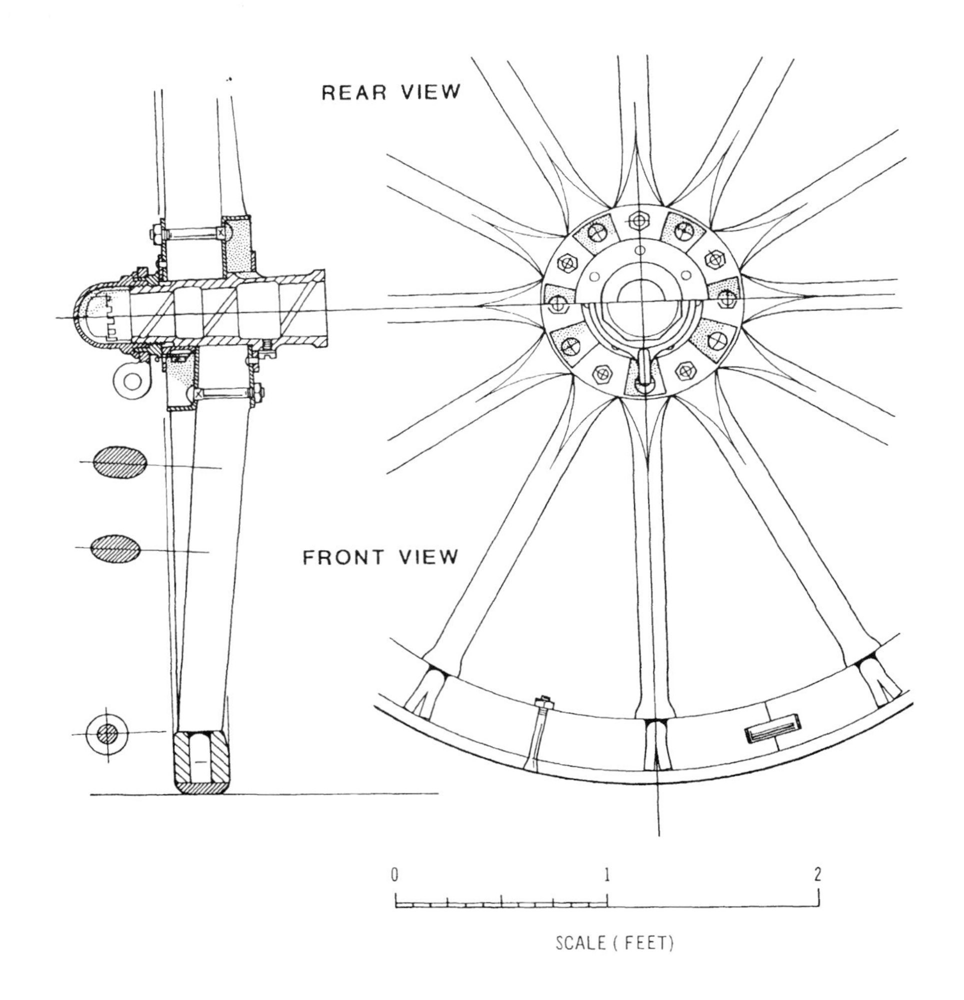

carried a spring catch to lock the pipebox nut.

SPOKES Double type, twelve of oak, with oak wedges. Twelve nave bolts through the spoke feet.

FELLOES Six of cut ash, with cylindrical oak dowels.

TYRE Mild steel, three inches wide by five-eighths of an inch thick.

WEIGHT 206 pounds.

Early pipebox nuts were of gunmetal, later ones were of steel.

No. 45 Mk. 2 The spokes were made stronger and the wheel weight increased to 216 pounds.

No. 45 Mk. 3 The spoke tongues entered the felloes but stopped half an inch short of the sole.

2nd class C No. 198 (see page 62)

General service limbered wagon and some RE vehicles.

PIPEBOX Phosphor bronze, the outer end threaded to take a gunmetal dust cap.

FLANGES Manganese bronze, the front (outer) flange machined to carry a drag washer.

SPOKES Single type, twelve of oak (of very light scantling) with oak wedges. The spokes were braced with steel sockets at their junction with the felloes, the sockets being riveted to the felloes. Twelve nave bolts between the spoke feet, covered by elm filling-in pieces.

FELLOES Six of cut ash, joined by spiked steel clutch plates. The joints were strengthened by steel clips secured by tyre bolt nuts on the bosom.

TYRE Mild steel, two and a half inches wide by three-eighths of an inch thick.

WEIGHT 124½ pounds.

2nd class C No. 200 (see page 63)

General service wagon (rear), trench cart Mk. 2 and various RE vehicles. Also used as an emergency replacement for the 2nd class C No. 45 wheel.

PIPEBOX Phosphor bronze, secured by the old-type drag washer and long linch pin.

FLANGES Steel.

SPOKES Single type, twelve of oak, with shouldered tongues split for oak wedges. Twelve nave bolts

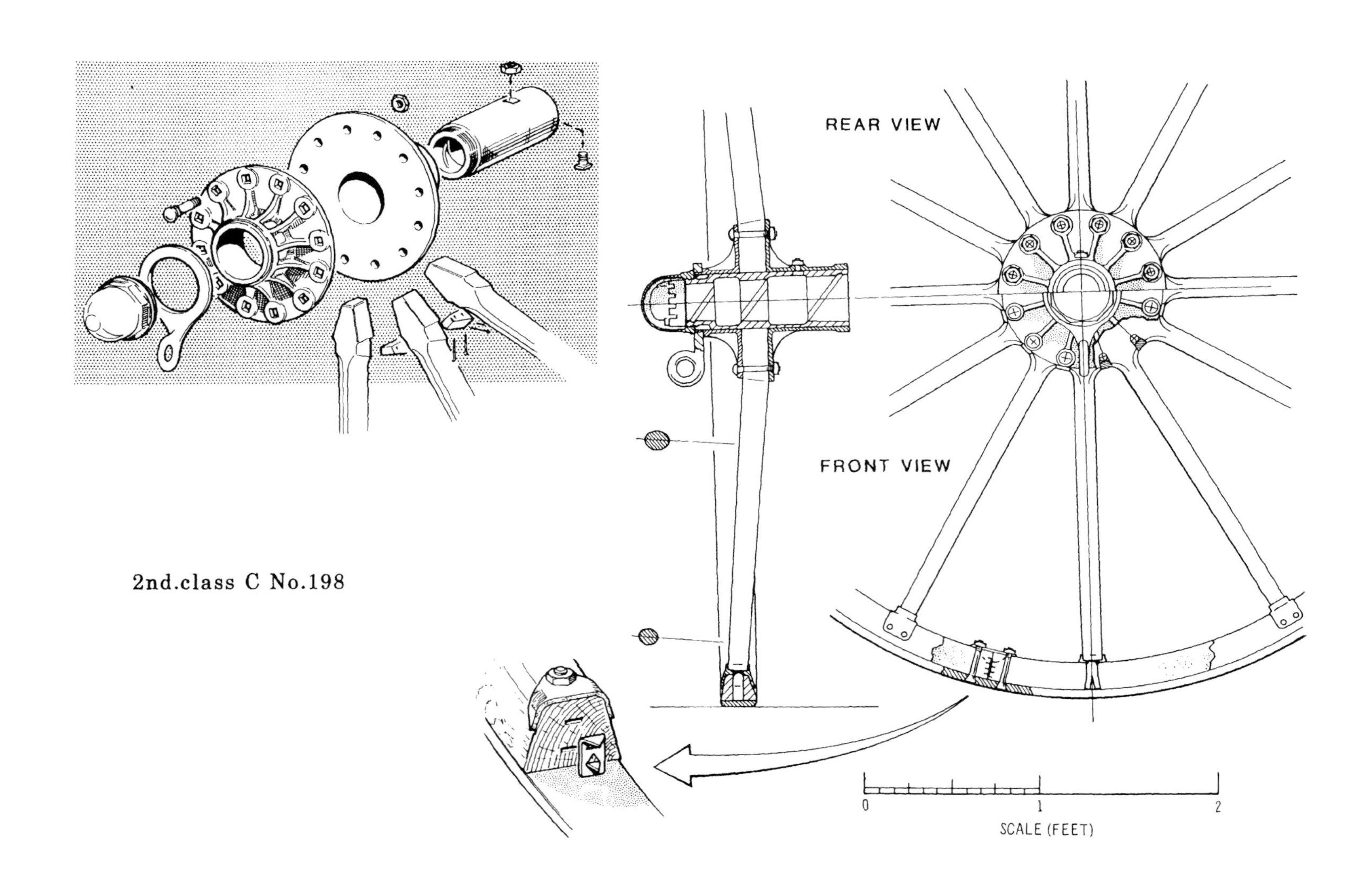

2nd.class C No.198

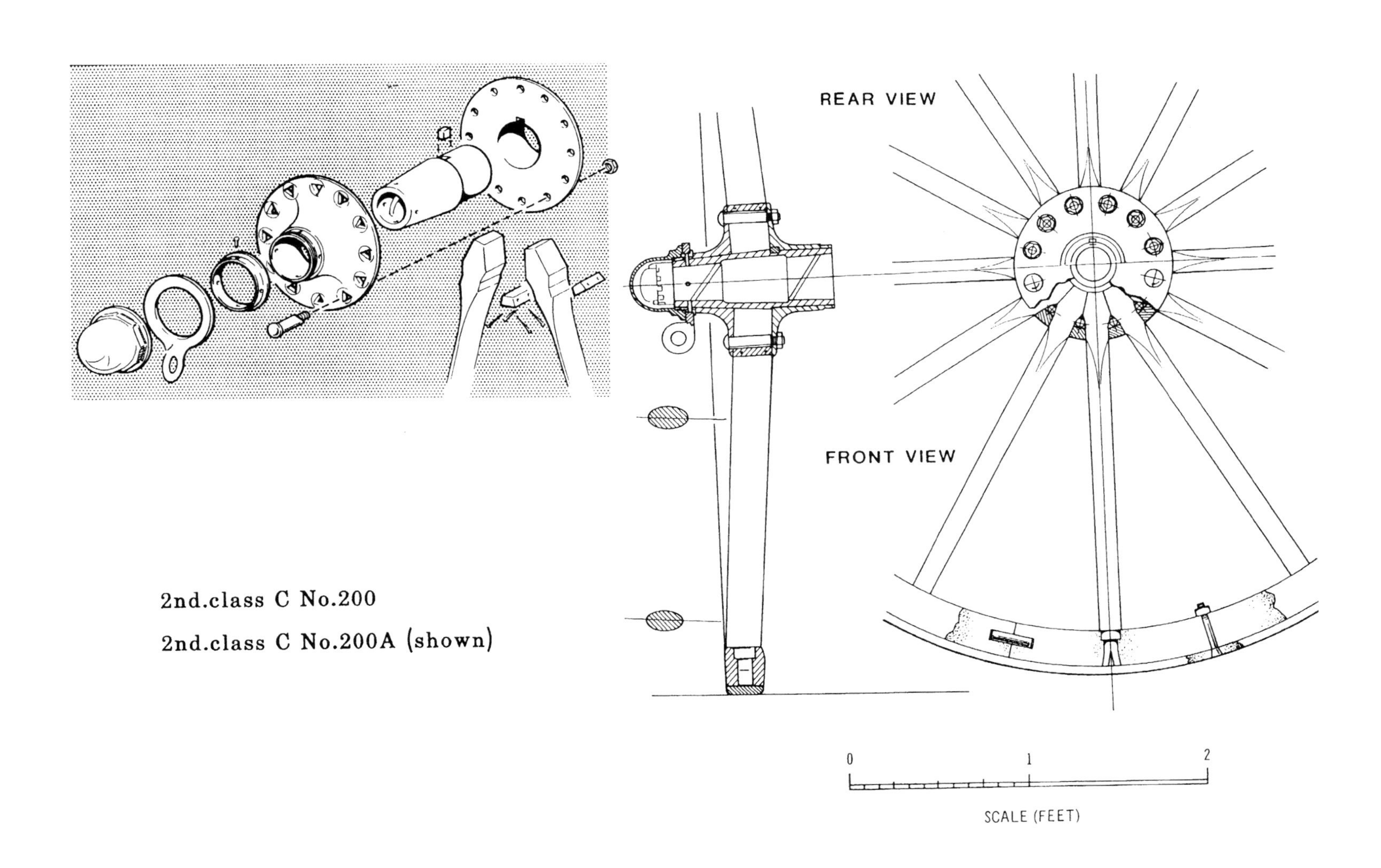

2nd.class C No.200

2nd.class C No.200A (shown)

of triangular section, between the spoke feet, covered by elm filling-in pieces.

FELLOES Six of cut ash, with cylindrical oak dowels.

TYRE Mild steel, two and a half inches wide by three-eighths of an inch thick.

2nd class C No. 200A (shown)

Differing from the No. 200 wheel in having an adjustable washer with short linch pin and gunmetal dust cap.

2nd class C No. 204 (see opposite page)

Ambulance wagon (rear).

PIPEBOX Phosphor bronze.

FLANGES Steel. The front (outer) flange was threaded to take a gunmetal dust cap.

SPOKES Single type, twelve of oak, with shouldered tongues split for oak wedges. Twelve nave bolts between the spoke feet, covered by elm filling-in pieces.

FELLOES Six of cut ash, with cylindrical oak dowels.

TYRE Mild steel rim, secured to the wheel by six bolts. The steel rim was undercut to take an India rubber tyre.

WEIGHT 178 pounds.

3rd class B No. 48 (see page 66)

Ambulance wagon (front).

PIPEBOX Phosphor bronze.

FLANGES Steel. The front (outer) flange was threaded to take a gunmetal dust cap.

SPOKES Single type, twelve of oak, with shouldered tongues split for oak wedges. Twelve nave bolts between the spoke feet, covered by elm filling-in pieces.

FELLOES Six of cut ash, with cylindrical oak dowels.

TYRE Mild steel rim, secured to the wheel by six bolts. The steel rim was undercut to take an India rubber tyre.

WEIGHT 150 pounds.

2nd.class C No.204

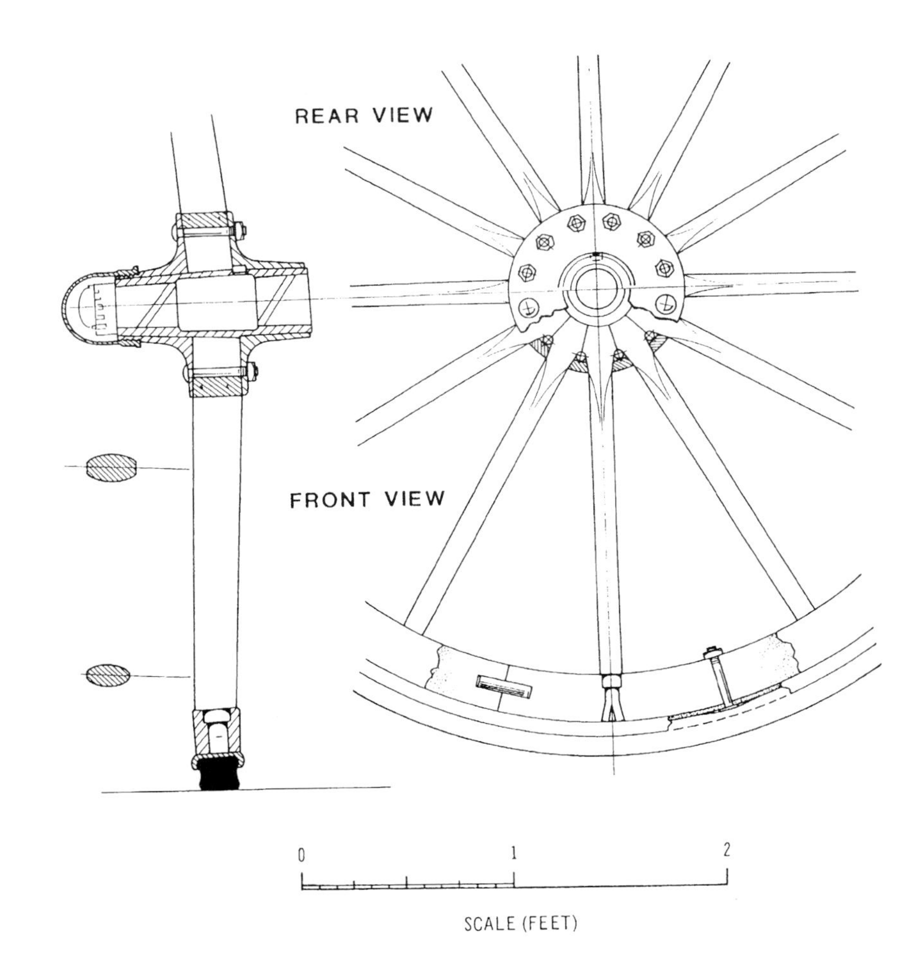

3rd.class B No.48

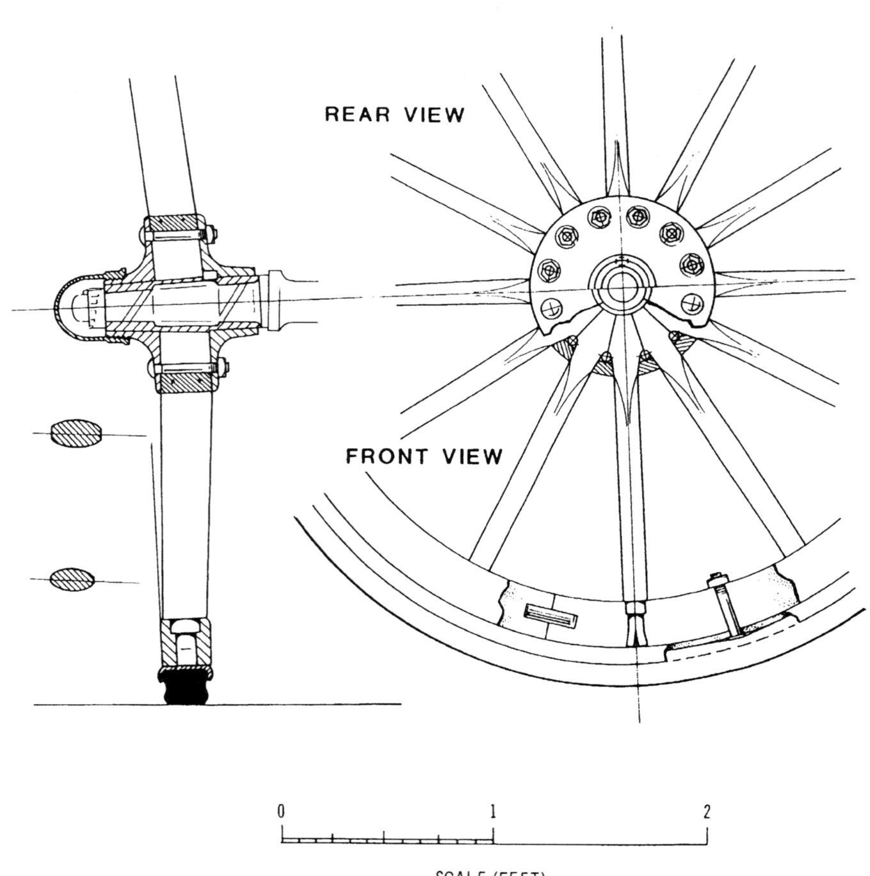

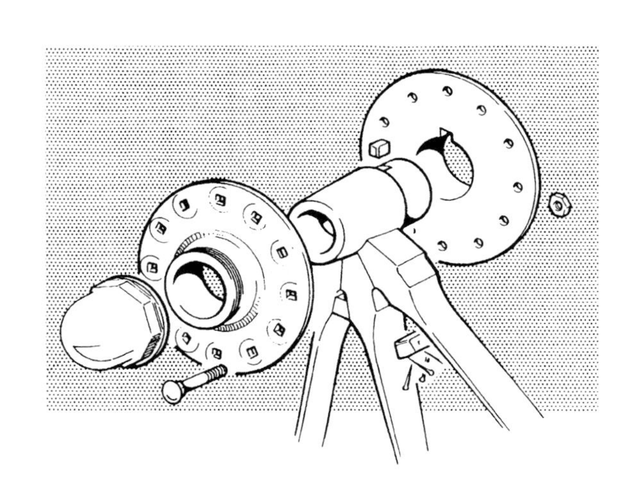

3rd.class B No.159A

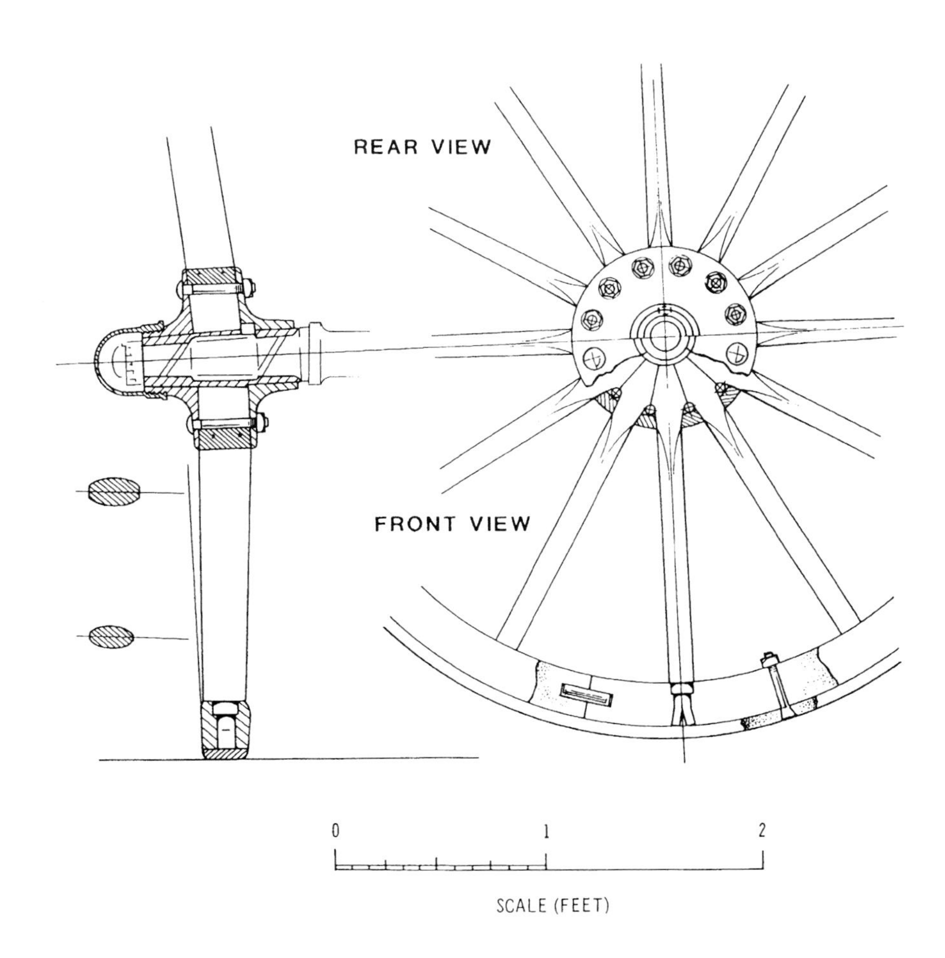

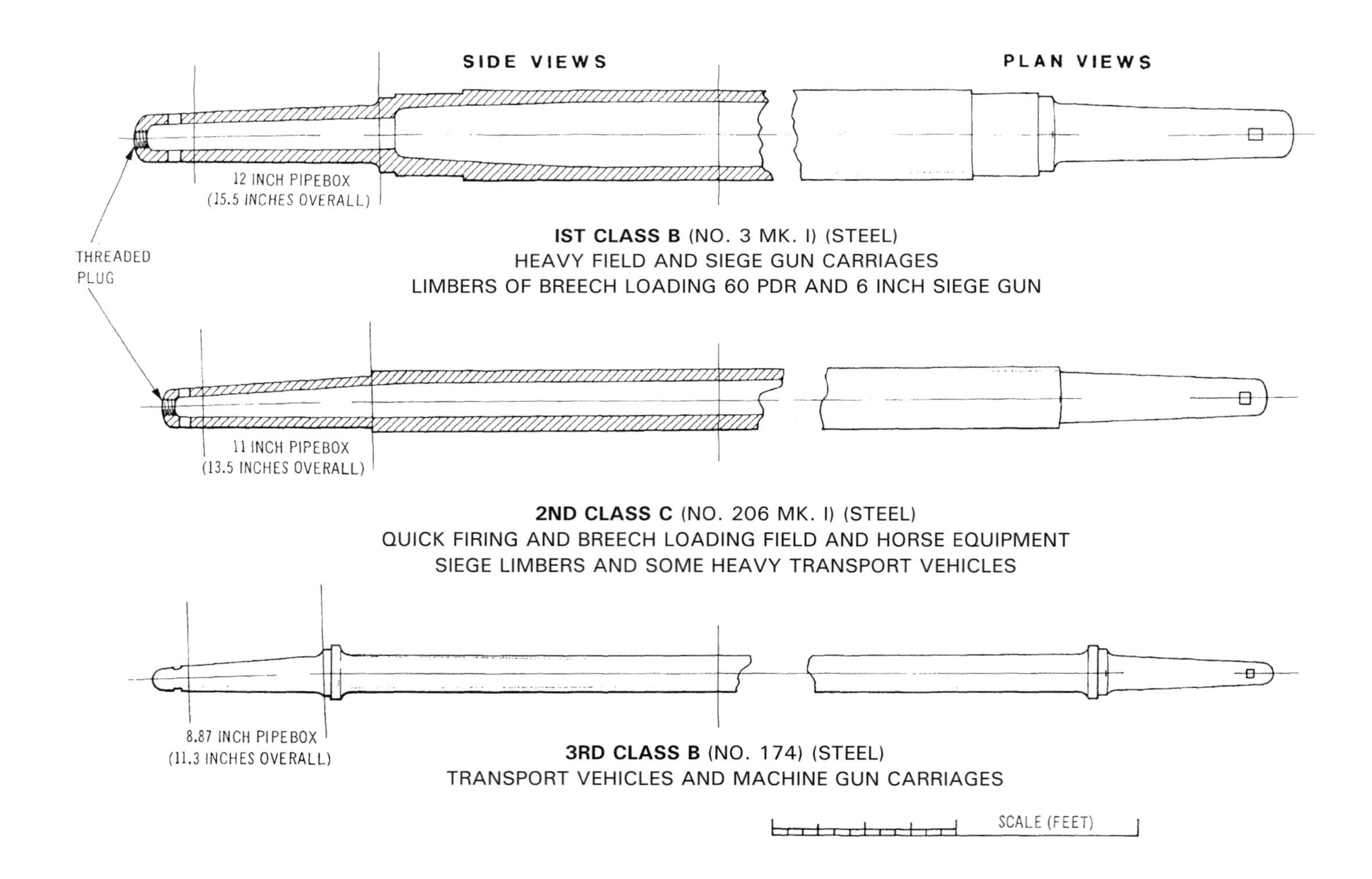
SIDE VIEWS
PLAN VIEWS
12 INCH PIPEBOX
(15.5 INCHES OVERALL)
THREADED
PLUG
IST CLASS B (NO. 3 MK. I) (STEEL)
HEAVY FIELD AND SIEGE GUN CARRIAGES
LIMBERS OF BREECH LOADING 60 PDR AND 6 INCH SIEGE GUN
11 INCH PIPEBOX
(13.5 INCHES OVERALL)
2ND CLASS C (NO. 206 MK. I) (STEEL)
QUICK FIRING AND BREECH LOADING FIELD AND HORSE EQUIPMENT
SIEGE LIMBERS AND SOME HEAVY TRANSPORT VEHICLES
8.87 INCH PIPEBOX
(11.3 INCHES OVERALL)
3RD CLASS B (NO. 174) (STEEL)
TRANSPORT VEHICLES AND MACHINE GUN CARRIAGES
SCALE (FEET)

AXLETREES

3rd class B No. 159A (see page 67)

General service wagon (front).

PIPEBOX Phosphor bronze.

FLANGES Steel. The front (outer) flange was threaded to take a gunmetal dust cap.

SPOKES Single type, twelve of oak, with shouldered tongues split to take oak wedges. Twelve nave bolts between the spoke feet, covered by elm filling-in pieces.

FELLOES Six of cut ash, with cylindrical oak dowels.

TYRE Mild steel, two and a half inches wide.

Axletrees

Axletrees were divided into lst, 2nd, 3rd and Special classes, and subdivided into patterns, according to the dimensions of their arms. In the 1st and 3rd classes were patterns A and B. In the 2nd class were patterns A, B and C.

Dimensions of axletree arms most commonly in use during the first decade of the 1900s are shown here. All arms of the same class and pattern were similar in dimensions and were suitable for all wheels of a corresponding class and pattern.

Some 2nd class, C pattern axletrees were strengthened with a radius formed at the root of each arm and fitted with a plastic metal ring (see the chapter on Materials). These axletrees were stamped, on the ends of the arm, with the letters 'PW' to indicate the use of a plastic washer.

In addition to the above, some special axletrees were in use on mountain artillery and miscellaneous carriages.

Axletrees in heavy service could possibly bend, usually near the centre. Also the arms were prone to wear at the bearings and shoulders. The instructions to remedy wear were as follows.

The arm was to be thoroughly cleansed, then heated and lightly rubbed over with a smooth file to obtain a pure metallic surface. The arm temperature should be just sufficient to enable a sal-ammoniac flux to melt and be well rubbed over the surface with a heated, worn, smooth file. The surface was then tinned by applying plastic metal and flux, well worked in with the file. Surplus flux was then brushed off in order to avoid blow-holes and the temperature allowed to reduce. Molten plastic metal was then applied from a ladle and shaped with two hardwood spatulas to the desired dimensions. After gradual cooling the arm was filed or turned to final size using a straight-edge and serviceable pipebox as gauges.

BREECH LOADING 15 PDR MK. IV

Although not truly quick firing guns, the Breech Loading 15 pdr. Mk. IV and Breech Loading (Converted) 15 pdr Mk. I are included in this section of the book in order to show the development from a recoiling carriage into a stable carriage with long recoiling barrel. The so-named 'quick firing' 15 pdr Mk. I was not a true quick firing gun, as the cartridge and projectile were loaded separately and not as a fixed round.

WEIGHTS (as packed)

Carriage with gun	19cwt 1qtr 12lb
Carriage limber	16cwt 3qtr
Ammunition wagon	20cwt 3qtr 23lb
Wagon limber	16cwt 2qtr

Trail and tensile stay plate (see page 74)

Tensile stay plate

The tensile stay plate, of flanged steel, was riveted to the bottom plate forward of the elevating gear. It projected out and forward of the trail, each end terminating in a bracket, formed with an eye riveted to the stay plate. These brackets were secured by a bolt to the axletree outer seat and step brackets. A circular aperture in the stay plate centre panel allowed the front spring case to engage with a catch on a cross-shaft for travelling. The cross-shaft was supported in two manganese bronze bearings bolted, one each side, into the side plates, forward of the elevating gear location. To the right-hand end of the shaft was keyed a handle lever.

Trail

The trail comprised a frame, two side plates, two transoms, a top plate, bottom plate and trail eye, all secured together by rivets. The frame was angle steel, the plates of nickel steel. The bottom plate was cut away between the axletree and elevating gear locations in order to reduce weight. The transoms formed a box near the trail eye, fitted with a hinged lid secured by hasp and turnbuckle, in which was carried an oil can. The trail eye was of remanufactured iron (see the chapter on Materials) with a steel insert welded in.

Axletree and swinging arm brake (see page 79)

Axletree

The axletree was a hollow steel forging, the ends having 2nd class, C pattern arms, to carry 2nd class, C pattern, No. 35A wheels.

BREECH LOADING 15PDR. MK. IV

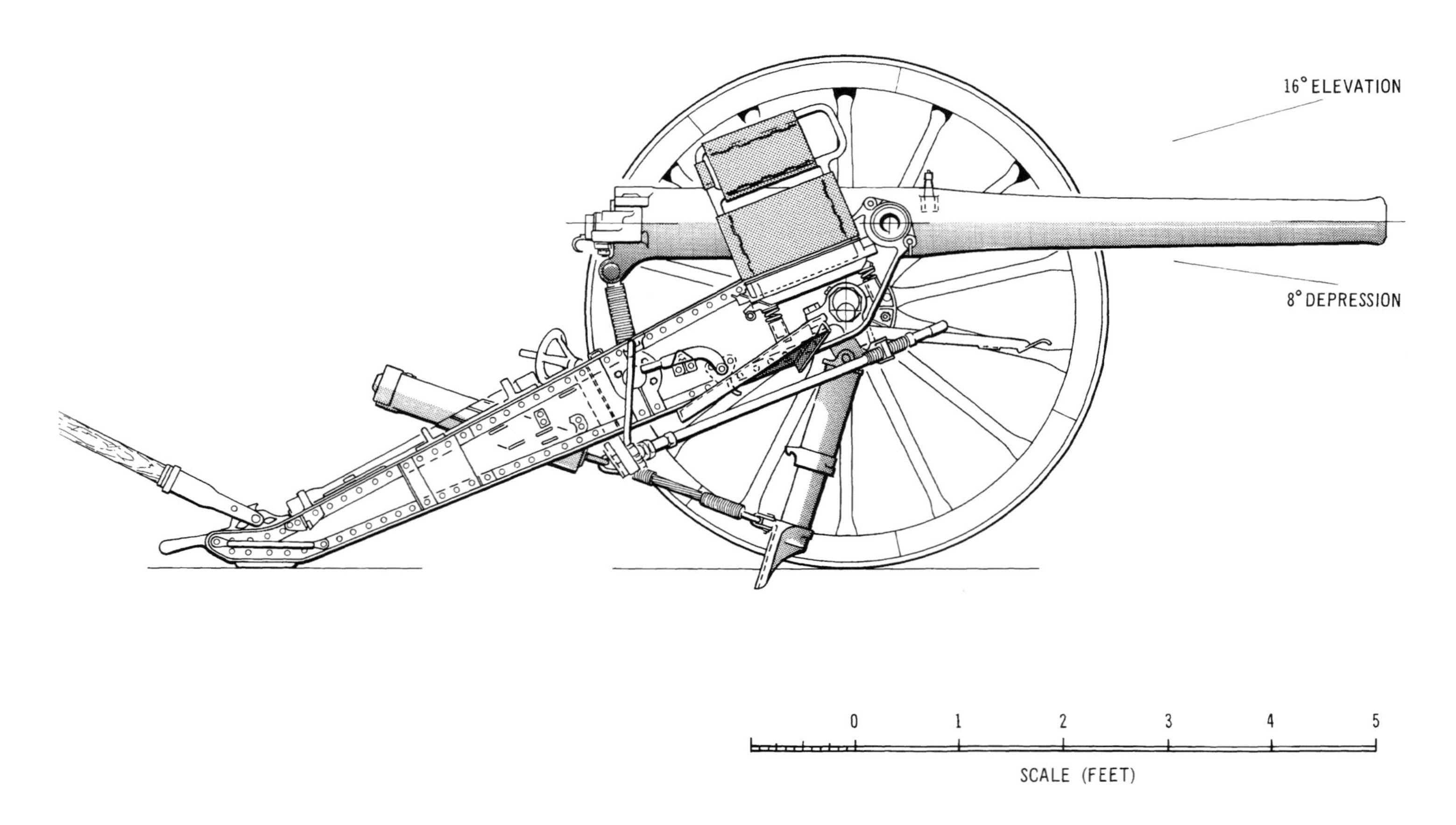

CARRIAGE – BREECH LOADING 15PDR. MK. IV

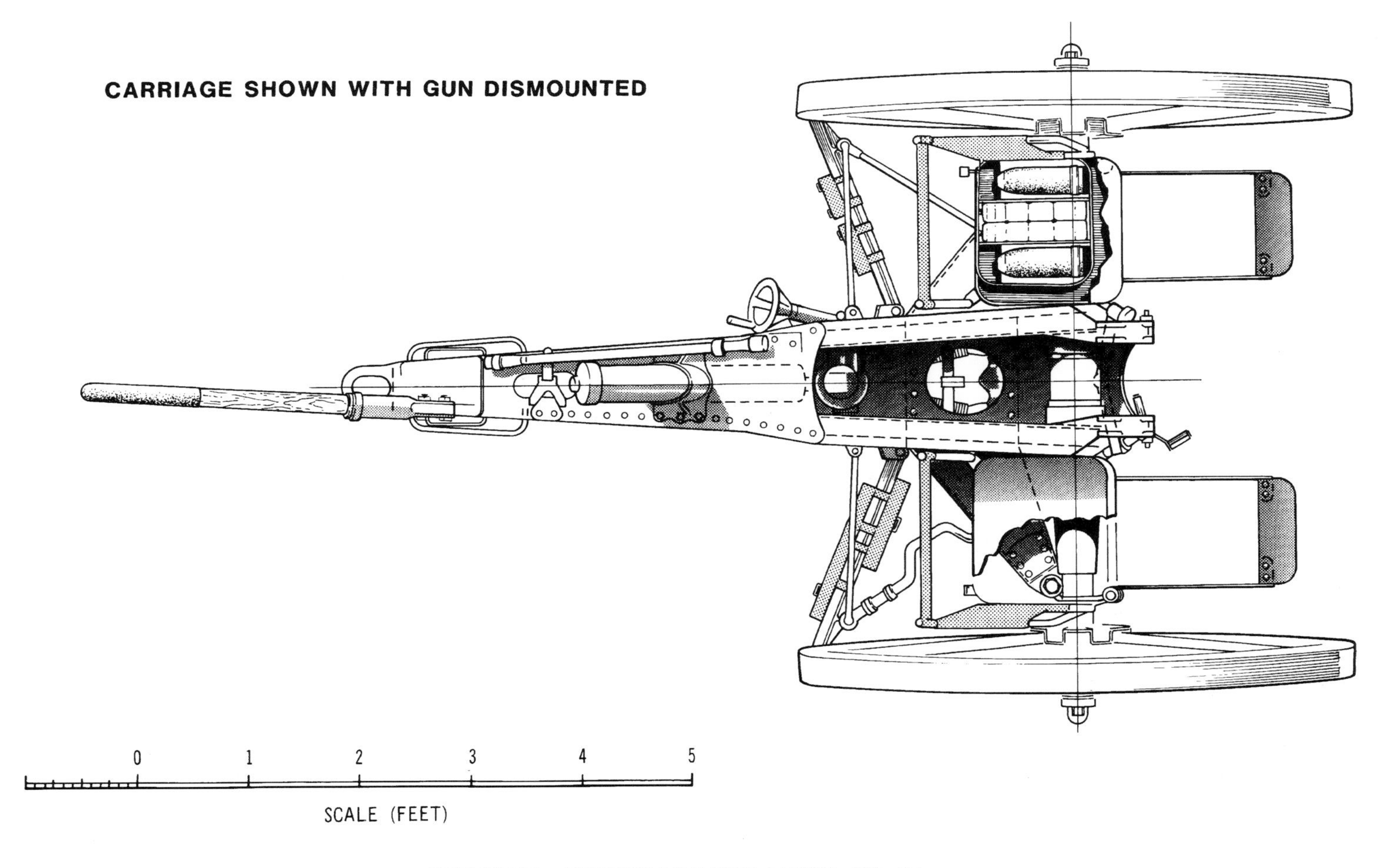

CARRIAGE – BREECH LOADING 15PDR. MK. IV

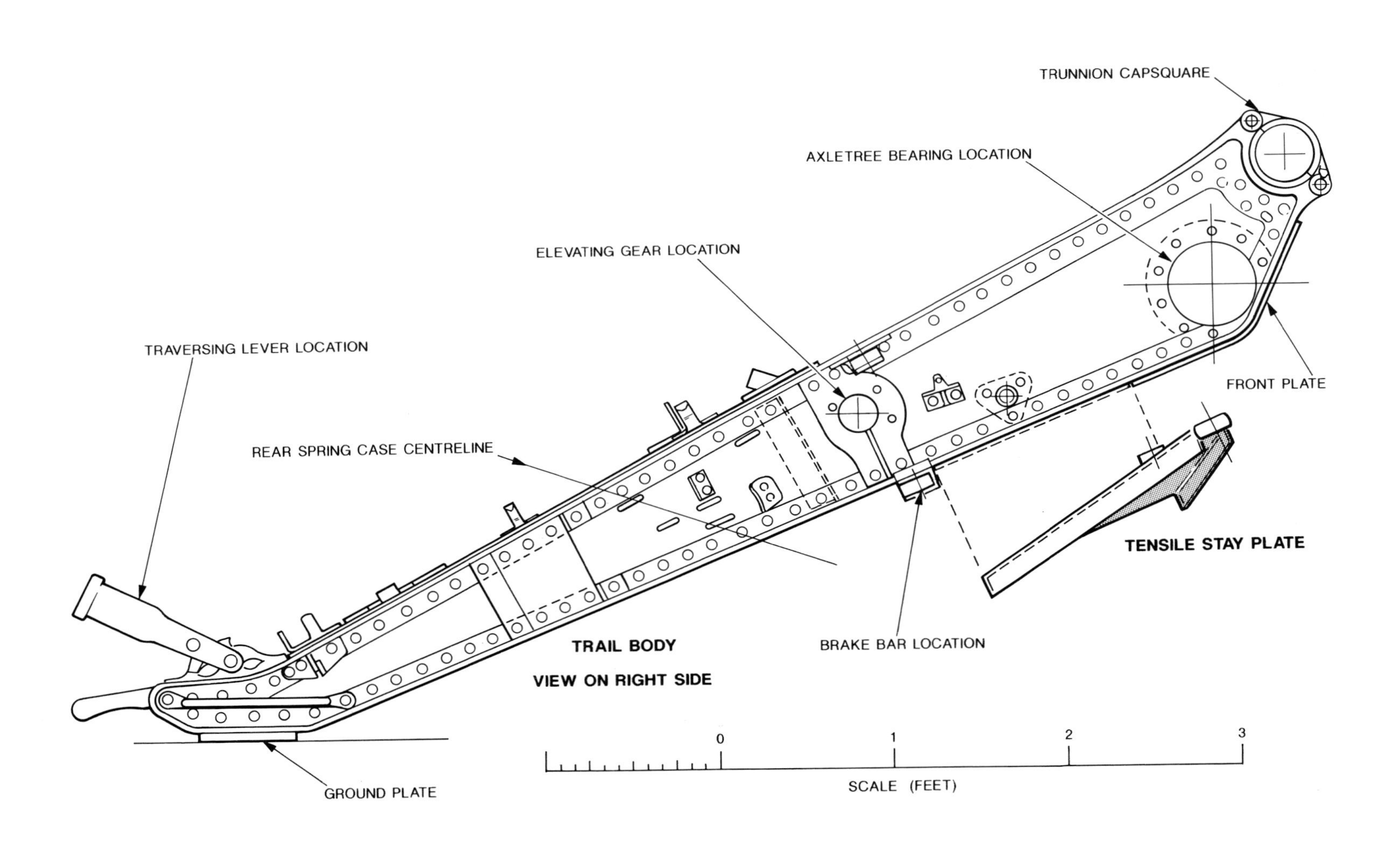

TRAIL AND TENSILE STAY PLATE

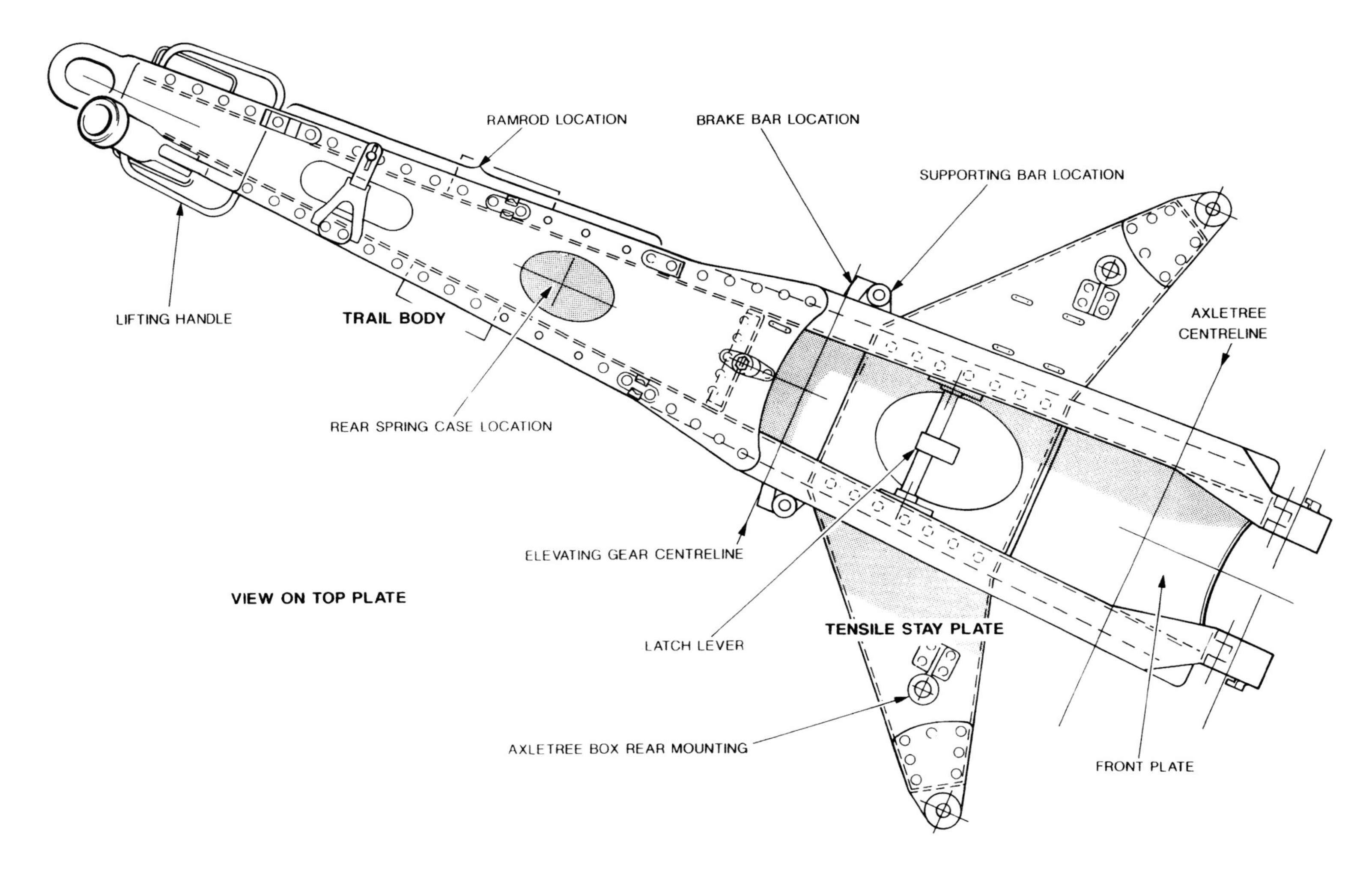

TRAIL AND TENSILE STAY PLATE

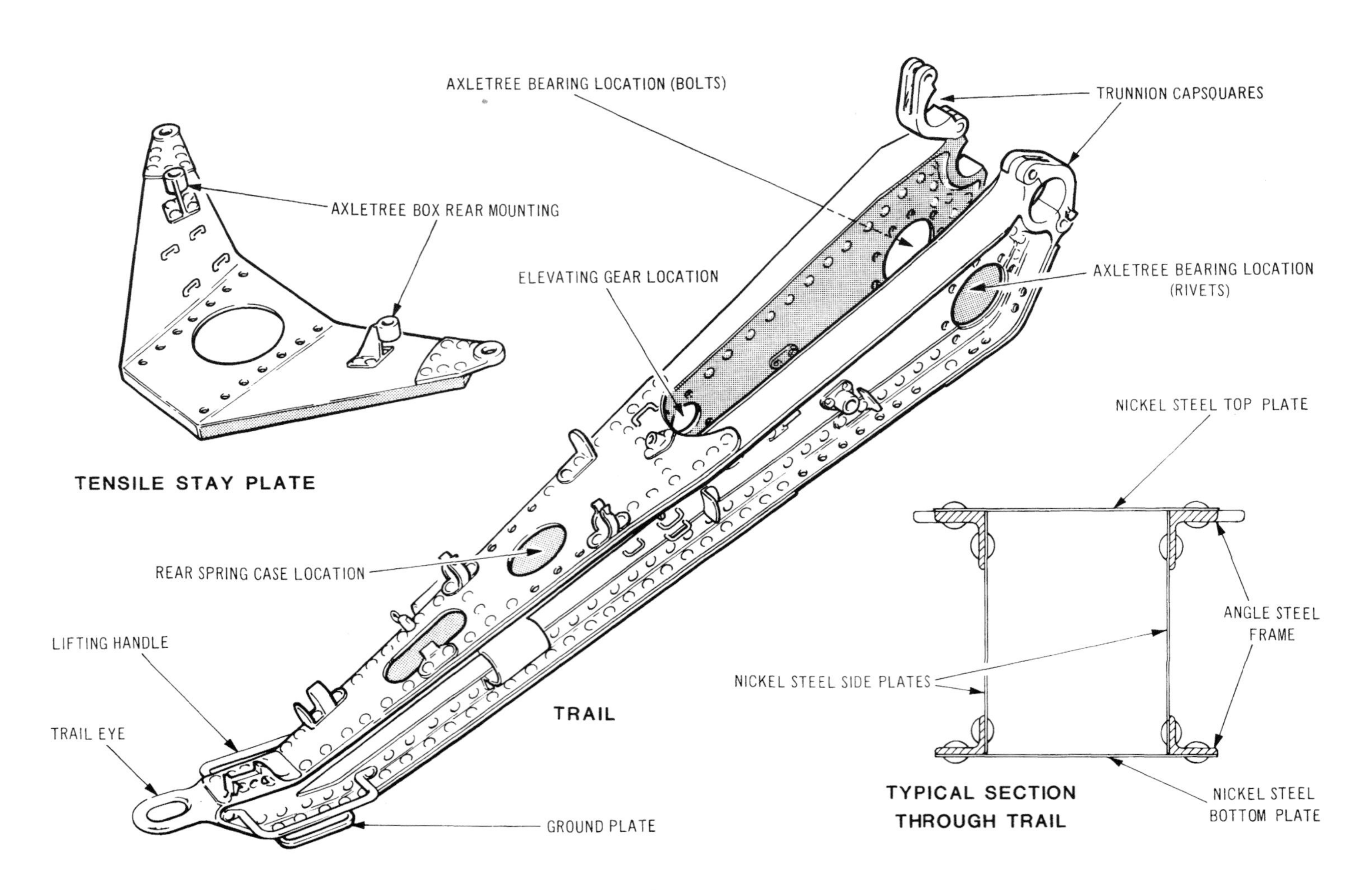

TRAIL AND TENSILE STAY PLATE

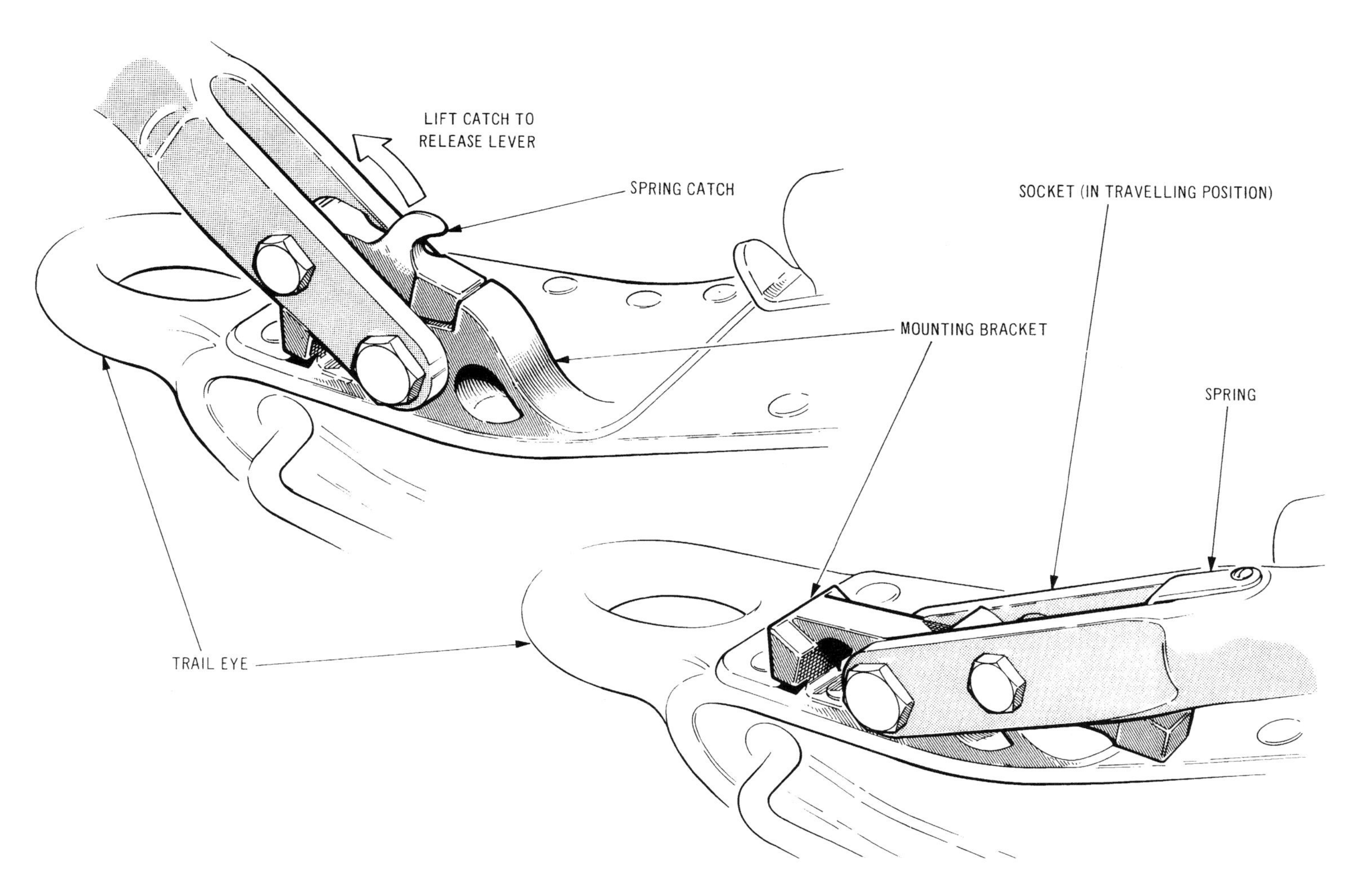

TRAVERSING LEVER

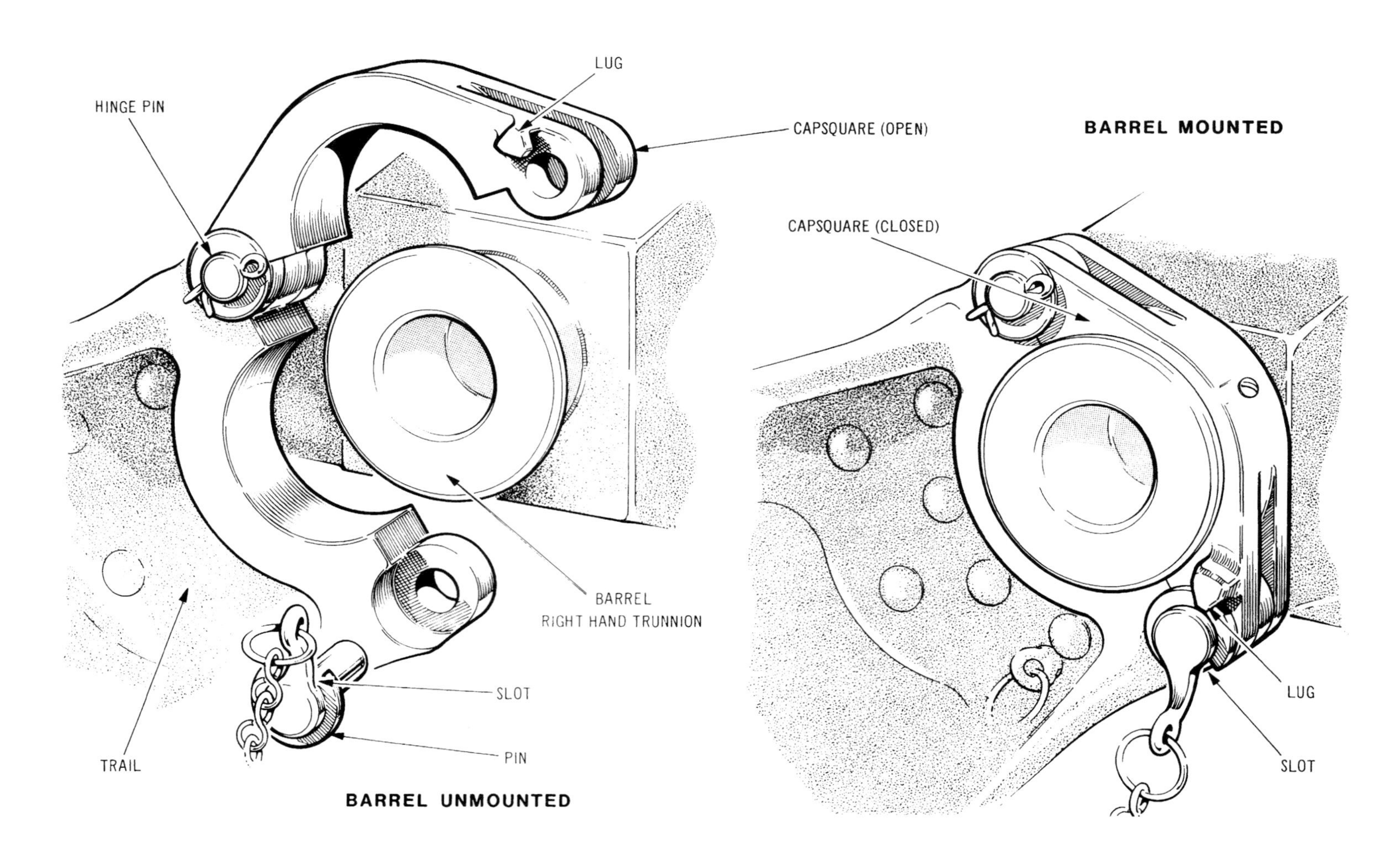

TRUNNION MOUNTINGS

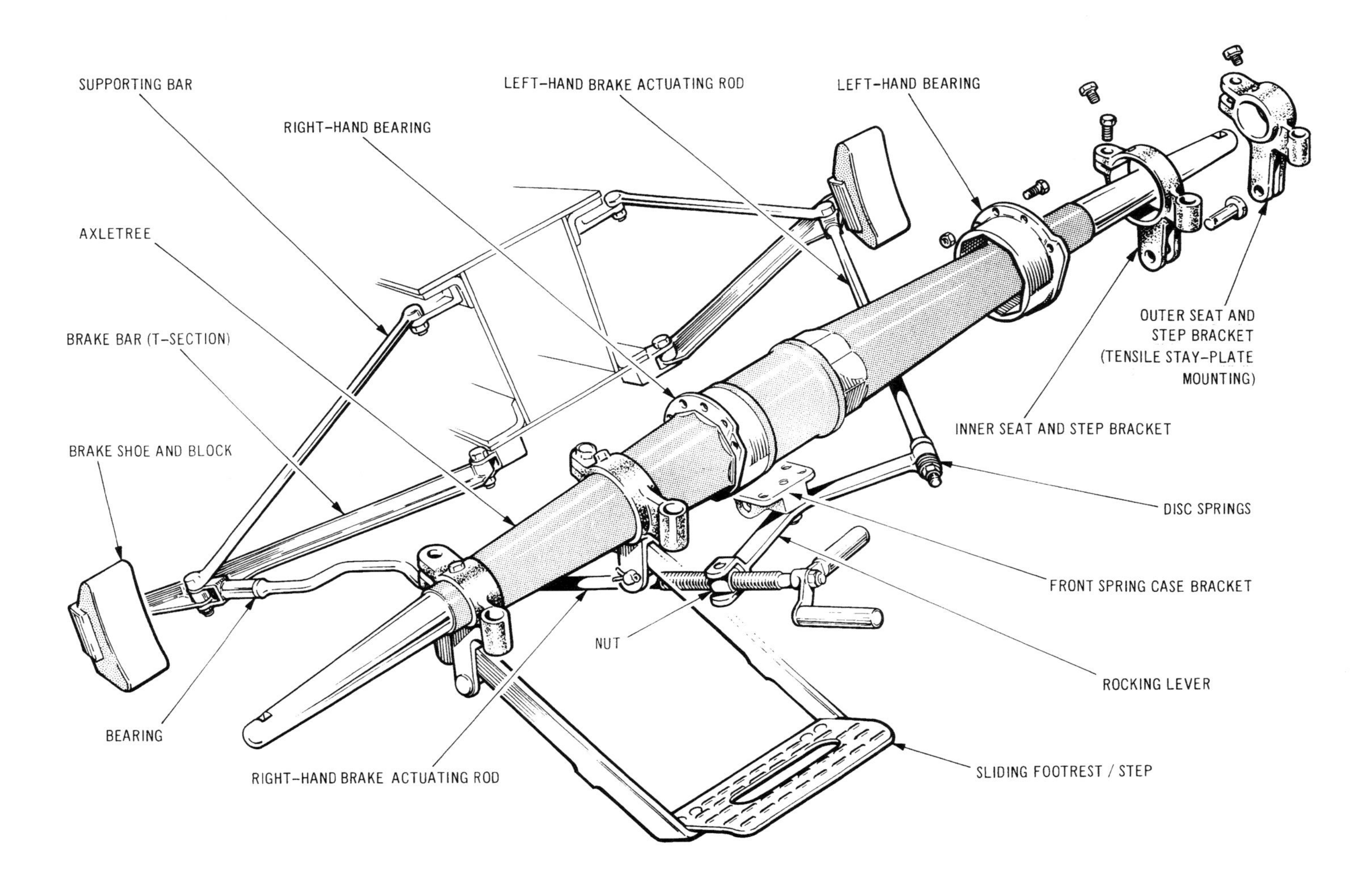

AXLETREE AND SWINGING ARM BRAKE

At the two bearing locations it was octagonal in section. The bearings were secured into circular holes in the side plates, the left-hand bolted and the right-hand riveted. Removal of the left-hand, bolted bearing enabled the axletree to be withdrawn from the trail, through the left-hand side plate.

Outboard of each bearing were clamped two brackets, each located by a bolt fitted through the bracket and threaded into the axletree wall. These brackets supported the forward feet of the axletree boxes and were the bearings for sliding footrests.

The outer brackets were also locations for the tensile stay plate ends.

Swinging arm brake

The brake right-hand actuating rod carried a handle at the forward end and was cranked at the rear, to enable brake operation from either end. Turning the handle caused the threaded rod to travel forward through a nut – formed with trunnions and mounted on one end of a rocking lever – until the right brake block contacted the wheel. Subsequent turning of the handle caused the rocking lever to draw the left-hand rod forward until the left brake block contacted the wheel.

Disc springs were located at the forward end of the left-hand rod to cushion the brake action.

Axletree boxes

The axletree boxes were of plate and angle steel. Each was mounted on three feet, riveted to the box bottom. Two feet at the front located in the axletree seat and step brackets, the third – at the rear – located in a socket on the tensile stay plate. All were secured by nuts and locking pins. Spiral springs were coiled around the feet to cushion the boxes.

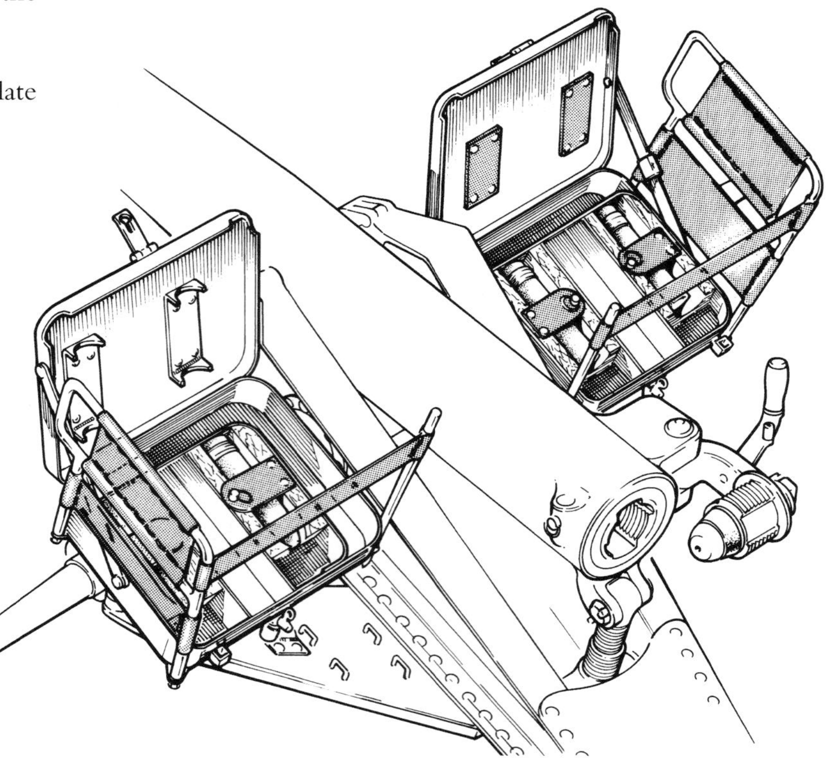

The lids, hinged at the front, were secured by a hasp and turnbuckle.

The boxes were internally divided into three sections, the two outer ones in each box were fitted with beech blocks to carry projectiles. The right-hand box carried two rounds of case shot and the left-hand two rounds of shrapnel, all secured by leather straps retained by pins. The central sections each contained two cartridges in tin boxes. The case shot were held steady by leather pads and the shrapnel by steel brackets riveted inside the lid.

The lids were fitted with blanket straps to form seats and guard irons were riveted to the box sides. The lids were of hardened steel plate and, when open, were supported by folding stays to serve as shields.

Front and rear springs

Front springs and spade (see page 83)

The front spring case was telescopic and consisted of two cases.

The upper case was closed at the top by a screwed plug, formed with an eye, which hinged to the mounting bracket by means of a hinge pin. The other end was threaded internally.

The lower case had a guide ring riveted to the top, a loose-sliding external collar and was threaded at the bottom end to screw into the spade bracket.

The spade, of nickel steel, was riveted to the bracket. The lower case slid into the upper case and the loose collar screwed into the upper case until flush. It was then secured by a set screw.

Two spiral springs were inserted into the upper case and put into initial compression by the screw plug. When screwed fully home the plug was retained by a keep screw and pin.

Two blocks, secured by nuts to the spade and spade bracket, were drilled for shackle pins, the shackles holding steel wire ropes connecting to the rear spring shackle.

In preparation for firing, the latch lever handle pin was removed and the latch lever handle lifted to allow the spade to drop to the ground, just to the rear of the axletree. Recoil caused the spade teeth to dig in as the carriage moved over the spade. If the gun was fired on hard ground, the springs cushioned the shock to the carriage, the spring coils being fully compressed with the spade vertical below the axletree.

To stow the spade for travelling, one man each side would lift it smartly until the latch engaged. The handle pin would then be inserted through the lever handle.

Rear springs (see page 84)

The rear spring case was of steel, riveted to a manganese bronze bracket which bolted to the trail top plate.

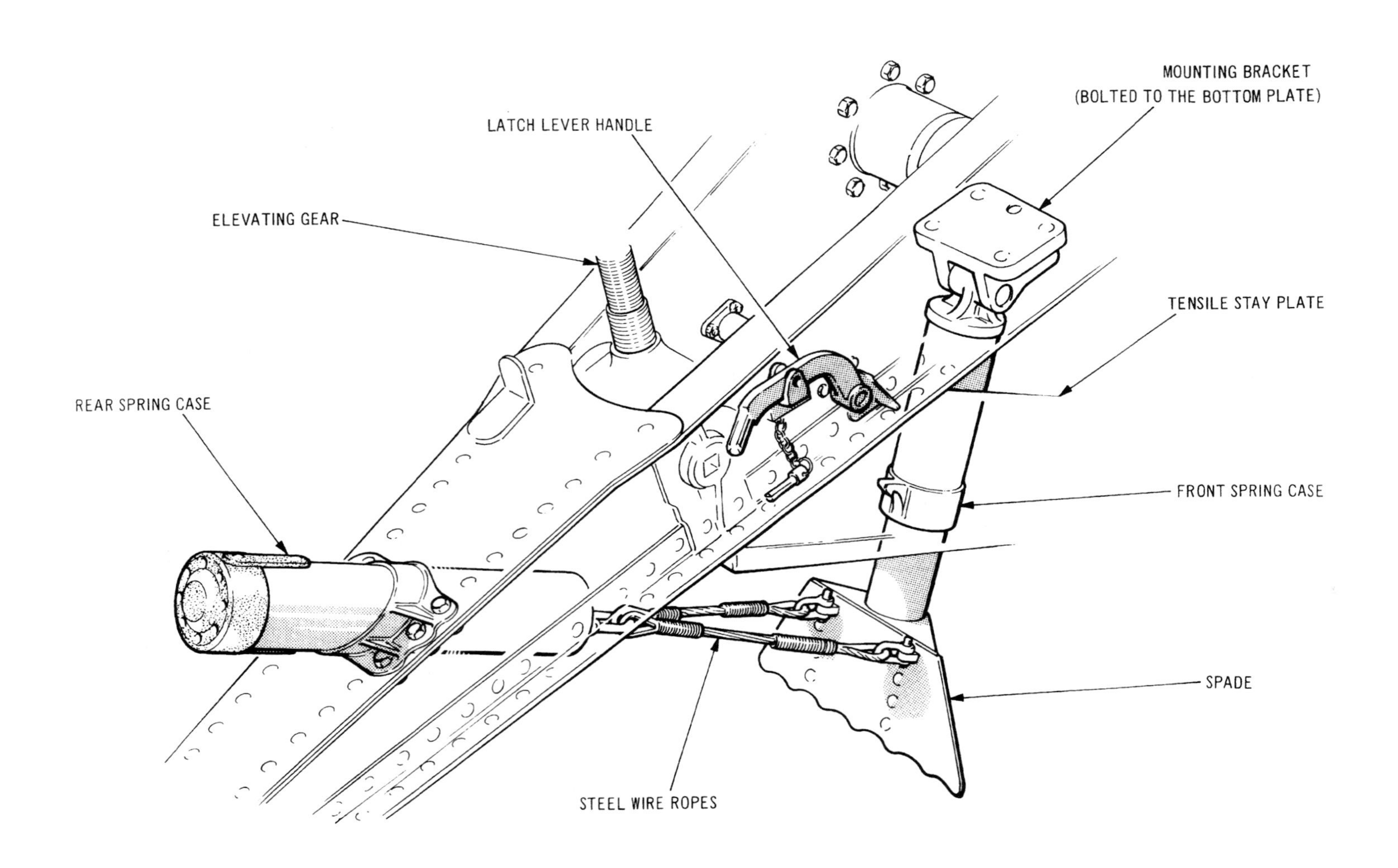

FRONT AND REAR SPRINGS

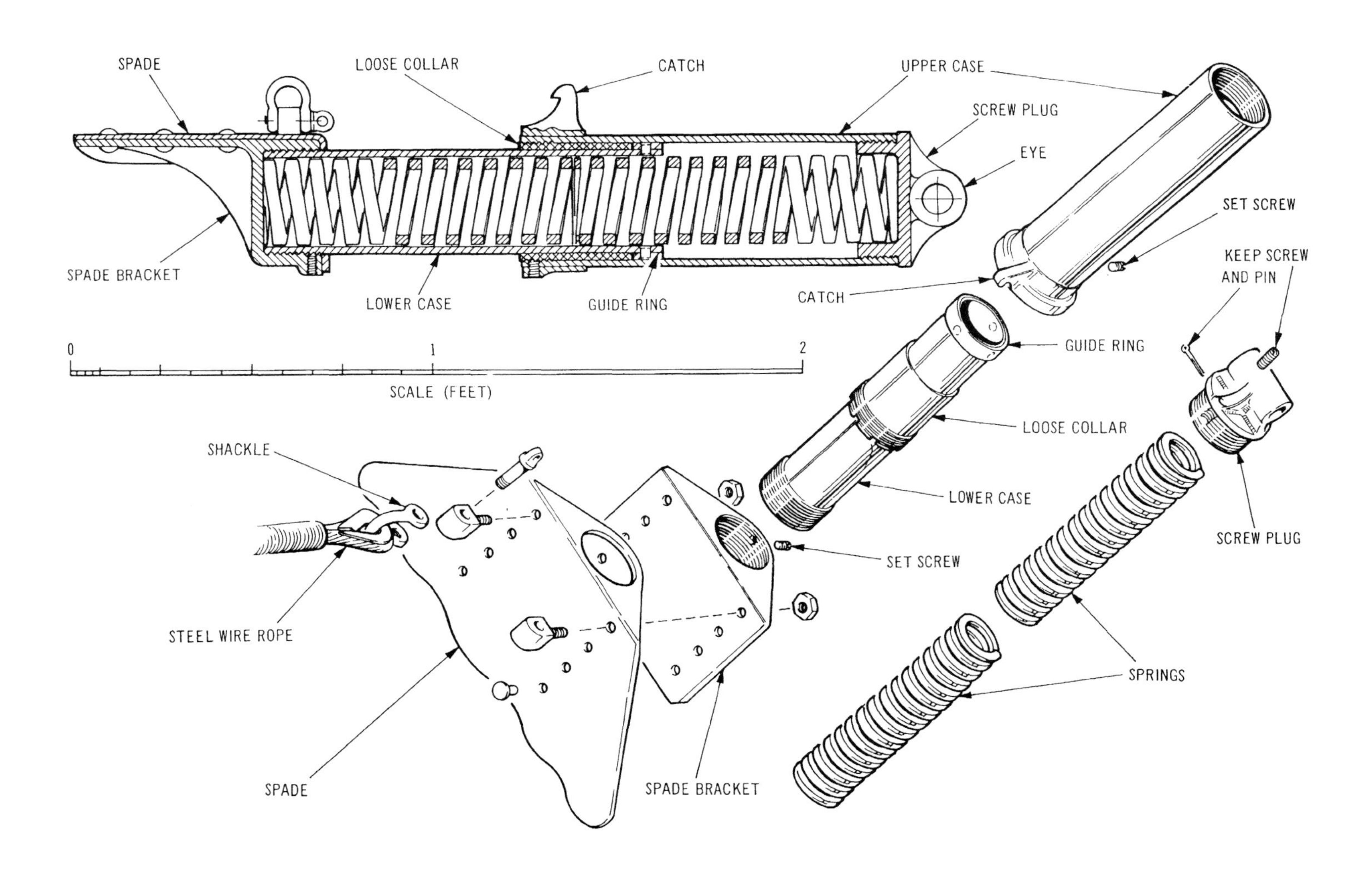

FRONT SPRINGS AND SPADE

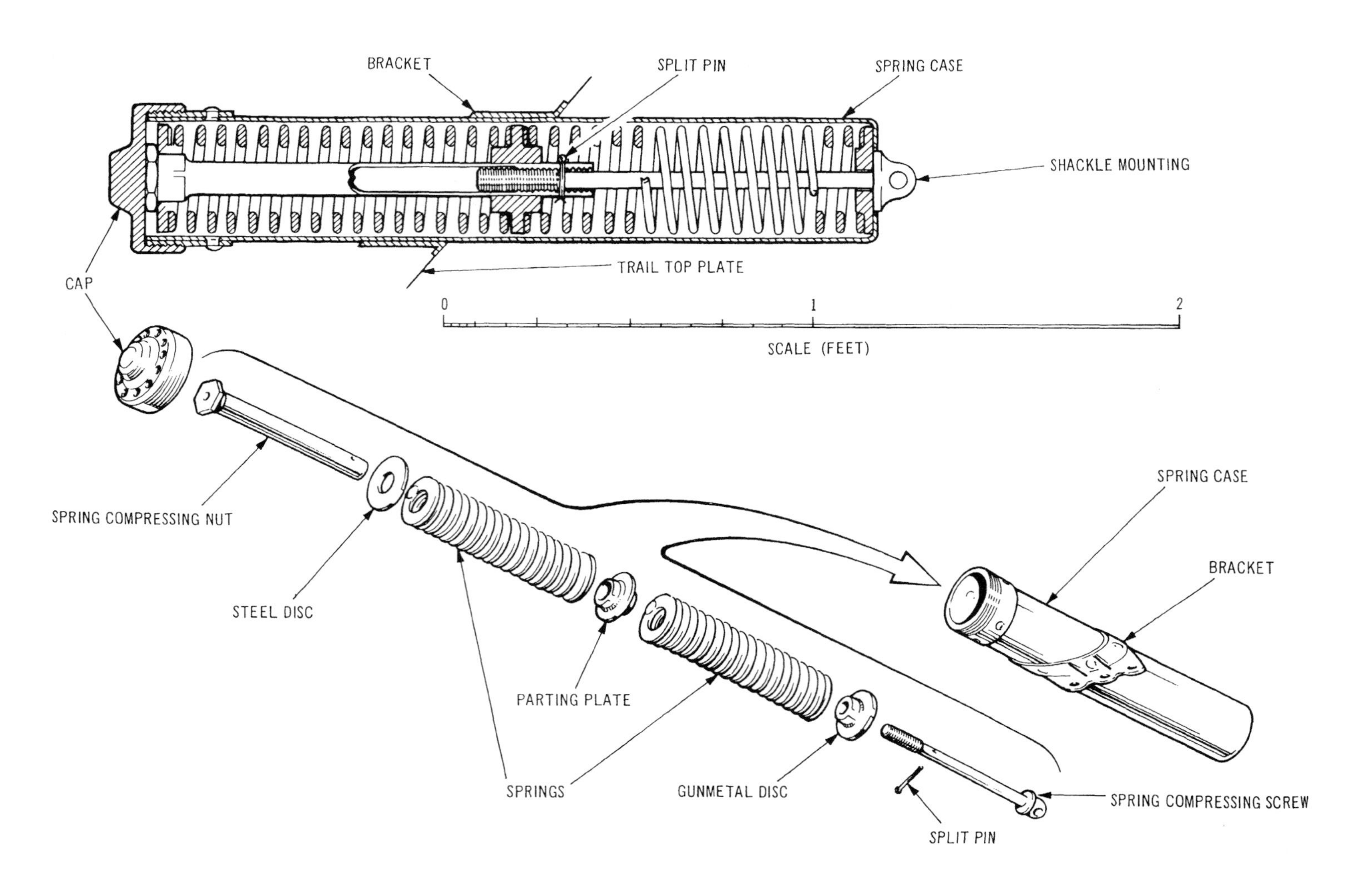

REAR SPRINGS

The springs were put into initial compression with the compressing nut and screw, the assembly being locked with a split pin. The springs were inserted into the spring case and the cap screwed on.

When installed in the trail, a shackle, hinged to the end of the compressing screw, connected the two steel wire ropes to the spade shackles.

Recoil of the carriage, on firing, caused the steel wire ropes attached to the spade to draw the compressing screw forward, compressing the rear springs and absorbing the energy. The springs then returned the carriage to the firing position.

Elevating gear (see page 86)

The elevating gear was of double screw pattern.

The inner elevating screw was threaded right-hand and ran in threads cut in the bore of the outer elevating screw. The top of the inner screw was formed into a short crosshead for attachment to the barrel lugs.

The outer elevating screw was threaded left-hand externally and ran in a nut, pressed into the oscillating bracket and secured by set screws. Two longitudinal keyways, cut in the external threads, were engaged by keys in the driving bush bore.

The driving bush, which was externally keyed into the bevel gear wheel bore. The driving bush was threaded at the lower end for a nut which secured and supported the bevel gear wheel.

The bevel gear wheel was fitted with a hinged cap at the lower end to protect the elevating screw. The cap contained a retaining spring to lock the driving bush nut.

The two-piece oscillating bracket was formed with trunnions, which ran in two manganese bronze bearings, bolted into the carriage side plates. The left-hand bearing also supported the handwheel shaft.

Turning the handwheel caused the intermediate shaft to rotate and turn the bevel gear wheel. The drive continued through the keyed driving bush and turned the outer elevating screw, causing it to travel up or down through the nut, dependent on the direction of rotation. As the outer elevating screw turned, the inner elevating screw – being prevented from rotating by attachment to the barrel lugs – travelled up or down through the internal thread in the outer elevating screw bore.

This compact arrangement made the barrel movement much more rapid than was possible with a single screw.

Barrel and breech (see page 87)

Barrel construction

The steel A tube had successive layers of steel wire wound around it surrounding the chamber and a portion of the bore.

An outer steel jacket fitted over the wire and A tube and held the A tube captive against internal shoulders with a threaded steel

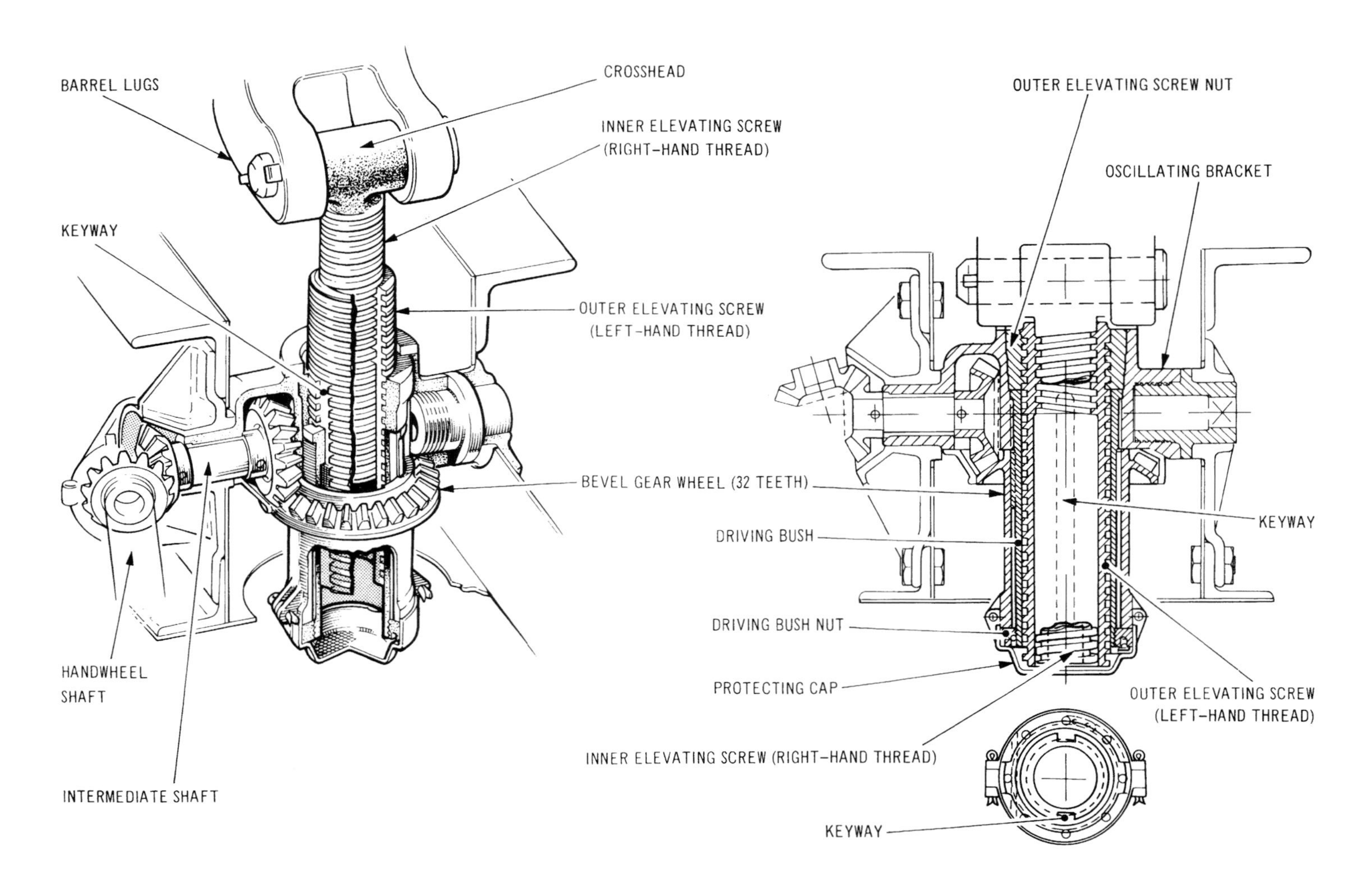

ELEVATING GEAR

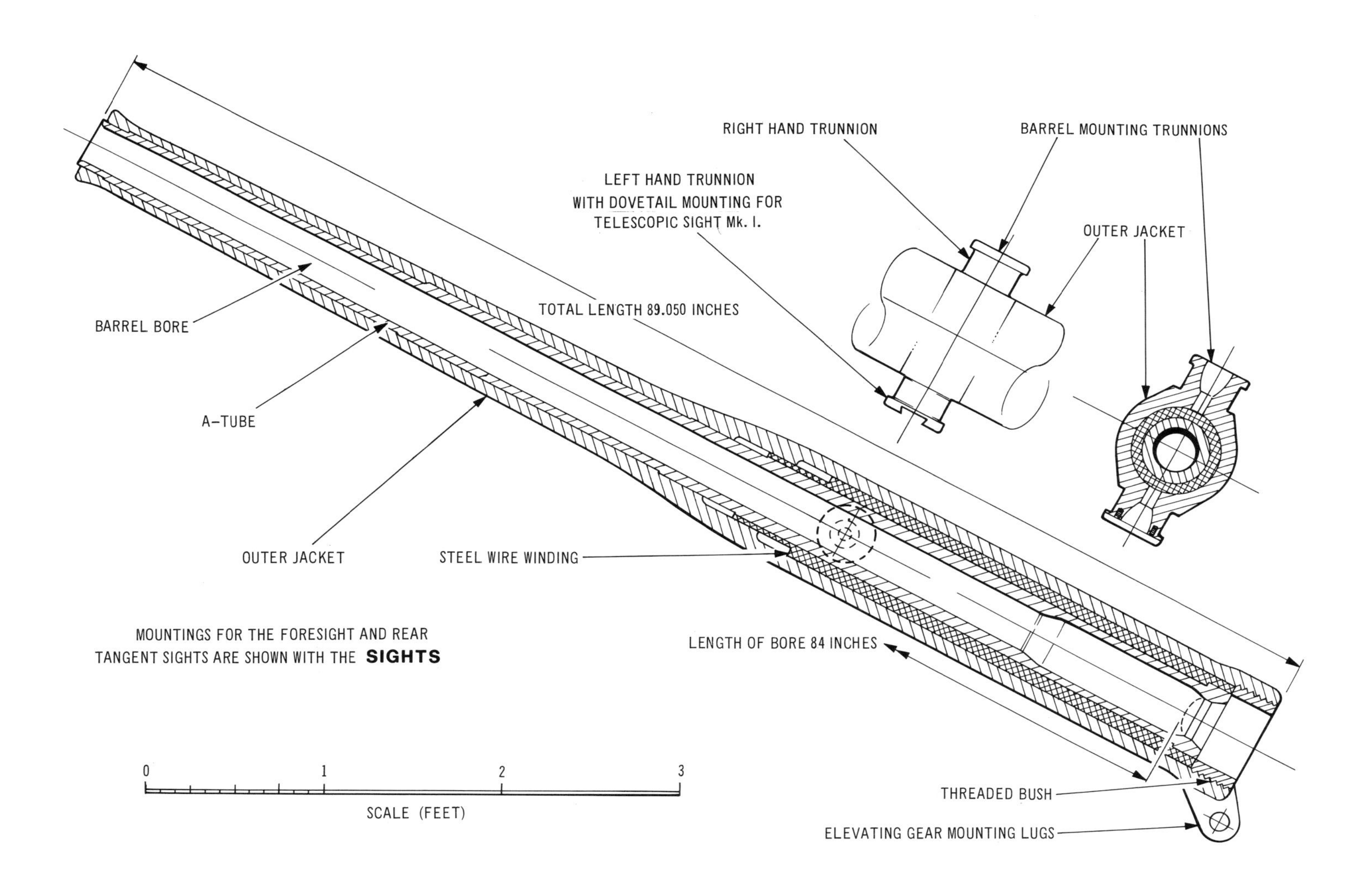
RIGHT HAND TRUNNION
BARREL MOUNTING TRUNNIONS
LEFT HAND TRUNNION
WITH DOVETAIL MOUNTING FOR
TELESCOPIC SIGHT Mk. I.
OUTER JACKET
TOTAL LENGTH 89.050 INCHES
BARREL BORE
A–TUBE
OUTER JACKET
STEEL WIRE WINDING
MOUNTINGS FOR THE FORESIGHT AND REAR
TANGENT SIGHTS ARE SHOWN WITH THE SIGHTS
LENGTH OF BORE 84 INCHES
0
1
2
3
SCALE (FEET)
THREADED BUSH
ELEVATING GEAR MOUNTING LUGS

bush, screwed in at the breech. The outer jacket carried barrel mounting trunnions at the sides and lugs, at the breech end, to receive the elevating gear.

The chamber was cylindrical, 11 inches long and 3.6 inches in diameter, the diameter reduced at front and rear. Chamber capacity was 117 cubic inches.

The barrel bore of 3 inches diameter had polygroove rifling, 18 hook section grooves of 0.04 inch deep, 0.40inch wide, for a length of 71.6 inches. The rifling, of gain twist, started at 1 turn in 120 calibres at the breech, increasing to 1 turn in 28 calibres at 35.8 inches from the muzzle and was constant thereafter.

A face for a clinometer was machined on the jacket upper side, rear of the trunnions. Vertical and horizontal lines were cut into the muzzle face. Barrel weight was 7cwt (784 pounds).

Breech

The breech was of the Welin interrupted parallel screw system. It departed from the interrupted screw systems in general use by having threaded segments of varying diameters, instead of the usual constant diameter. This resulted in the engagement of four sections of thread instead of the usual three. As the screw circumference was divided into six equal parts, the resultant portion in engagement was two-thirds instead of the customary one half. The relationship of breech screw segments to the barrel segments can be seen in the illustrations.

One obvious disadvantage of this system would have been the complexity of manufacture involved in producing the thread.

The breech screw was located onto the carrier by interrupted screw threads and secured by an axial steel vent, which passed through the breech screw from the front and was retained in position by a sleeve, spring and ring nut within the carrier bore.

The axial vent carried the De Bange obturator at the breech screw front. The obturator is described in detail separately (see page 97).

The carrier was hinged, by a bolt, to mounting lugs on the rear, right side of the barrel jacket. In addition to mounting the breech screw, the carrier also provided mountings and housings for the breech operating and firing assemblies.

The breech operating lever was hinged, together with a pinion, onto a stud housed within the right side of the carrier. With the breech closed, the lever was held by a spring catch, which engaged with a recess in the left-hand elevating screw lug top face.

The lever pinion engaged with the link pinion, also housed within the carrier body. The link pinion attached to one end of the link, the other end of the link being secured, by a pivot, to the breech screw rear face. Into the rear face of the link was machined a cam groove, in which ran the tube retaining block guide bolt.

The tube retaining block operated vertically within a slide box body. The slide box mounted into the carrier rear face, onto interrupted collars machined into the axial vent shaft. A safety shutter,

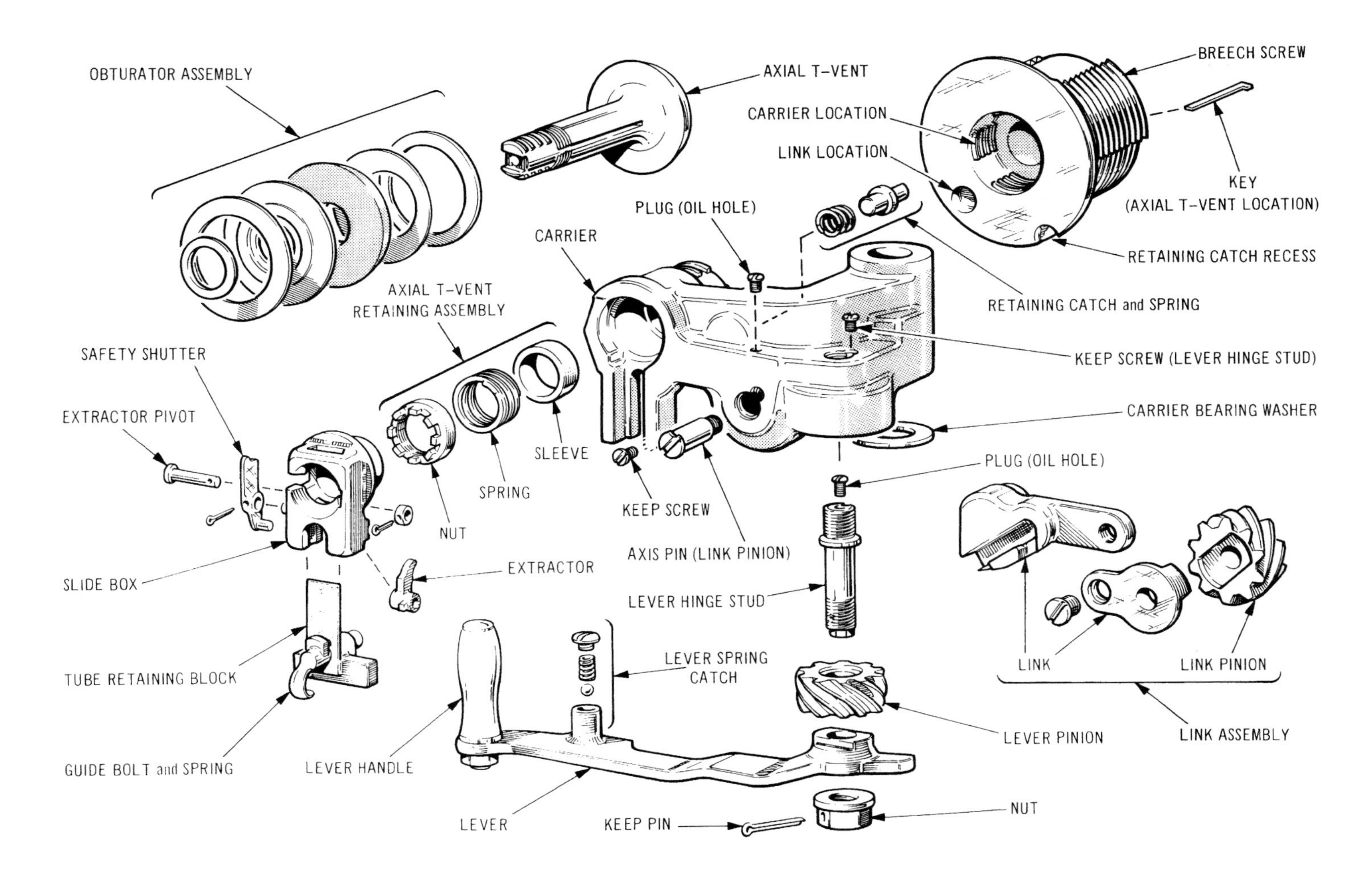

BREECH COMPONENTS

1 TUBE RETAINING BLOCK
2 BARREL JACKET
3 BREECH SCREW
4 SLIDE BOX
5 CARRIER
6 CARRIER HINGE BOLT
7 BREECH MECHANISM LEVER
8 ELEVATING GEAR ATTACHMENT LUG
9 LEVER SPRING CATCH
10 LINK
11 LEVER HANDLE
12 GUIDE BOLT
13 BREECH BUSH
14 STEEL WIRE WINDING
15 AXIAL T-VENT
16 OBTURATOR PAD AND DISCS
17 BARREL LUG (CARRIER HINGE)
18 SAFETY SHUTTER

BREECH

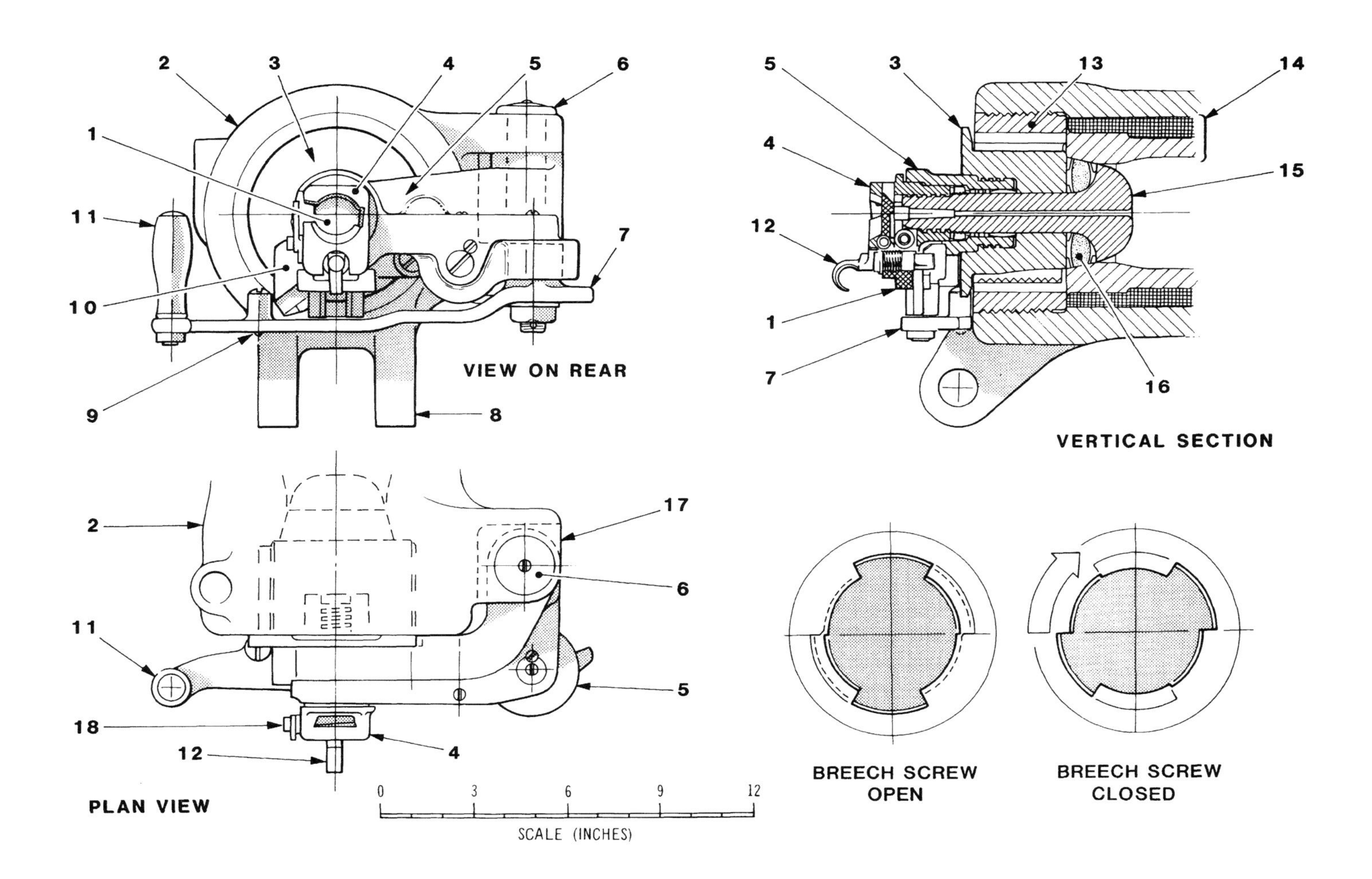
2
3
4
5
6
1
11
7
10
9
8
VIEW ON REAR
5
3
13
14
4
15
12
1
7
16
VERTICAL SECTION
2
17
6
11
5
18
4
12
PLAN VIEW
0
3
6
9
12
SCALE (INCHES)
BREECH SCREW
OPEN
BREECH SCREW
CLOSED

BREECH

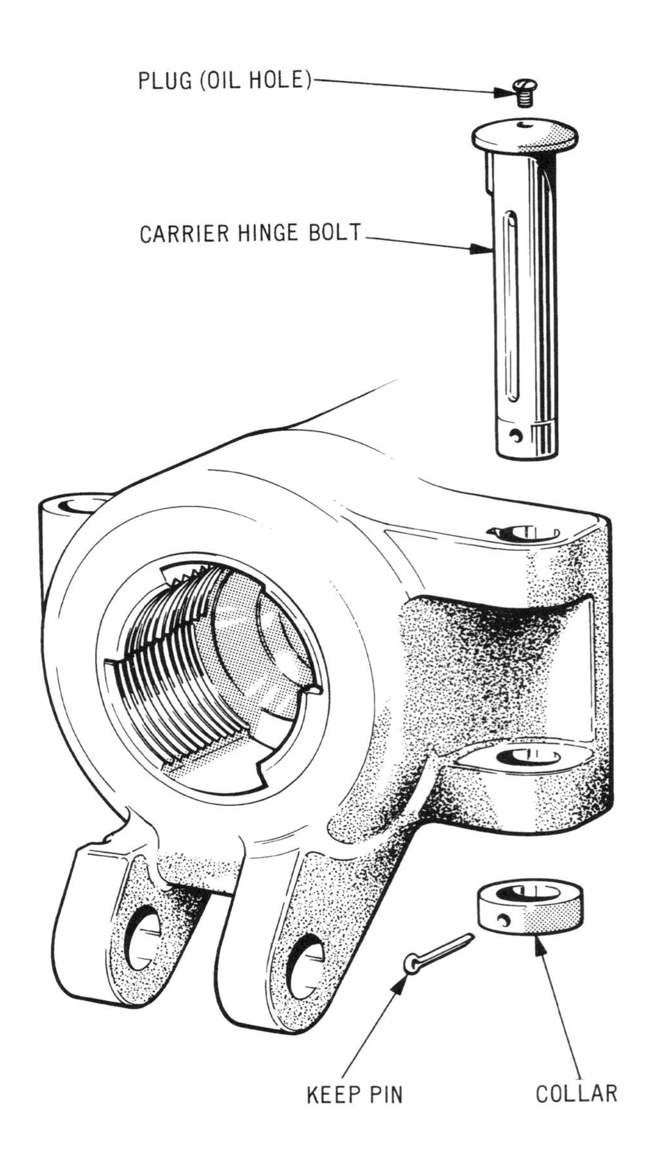

mounted on a pivot at the left side of the slide box, prevented the attachment of a firing lanyard to the T-friction tube at any time other than when the breech block was being closed and locked.

Pivoted within the slide box body and operated by the tube retaining block was the extractor. Upon lowering the tube retaining block, the extractor would pivot to the rear and expel the T-friction tube from its housing recess in the rear face of the axial vent shaft.

To illustrate the breech operation clearly, it has been considered advantageous to separate the various component simultaneous functions pictorially and link them in the text where appropriate.

Views A, D and F show the breech as closed and locked.

To open the breech, the lever handle would be firmly pulled to the rear, freeing the spring catch from the left-hand elevating screw lug. Continued movement rotated the lever and link pinions, the link pinion drawing the link to the right, rotating the breech screw through sixty degrees in an anti-clockwise direction (view B). This transverse movement of the link caused the retaining block guide bolt to move downwards in the cam groove, together with the retaining block (view E). This movement pivoted the safety shutter forward to close the firing lanyard aperture. As the retaining block moved clear of the loading hole in the slide box rear, the extractor pivoted to expel any fired T-friction tube rearwards.

At the condition shown in views B and E, the link abutted the link pinion, preventing any further rotation of the breech screw

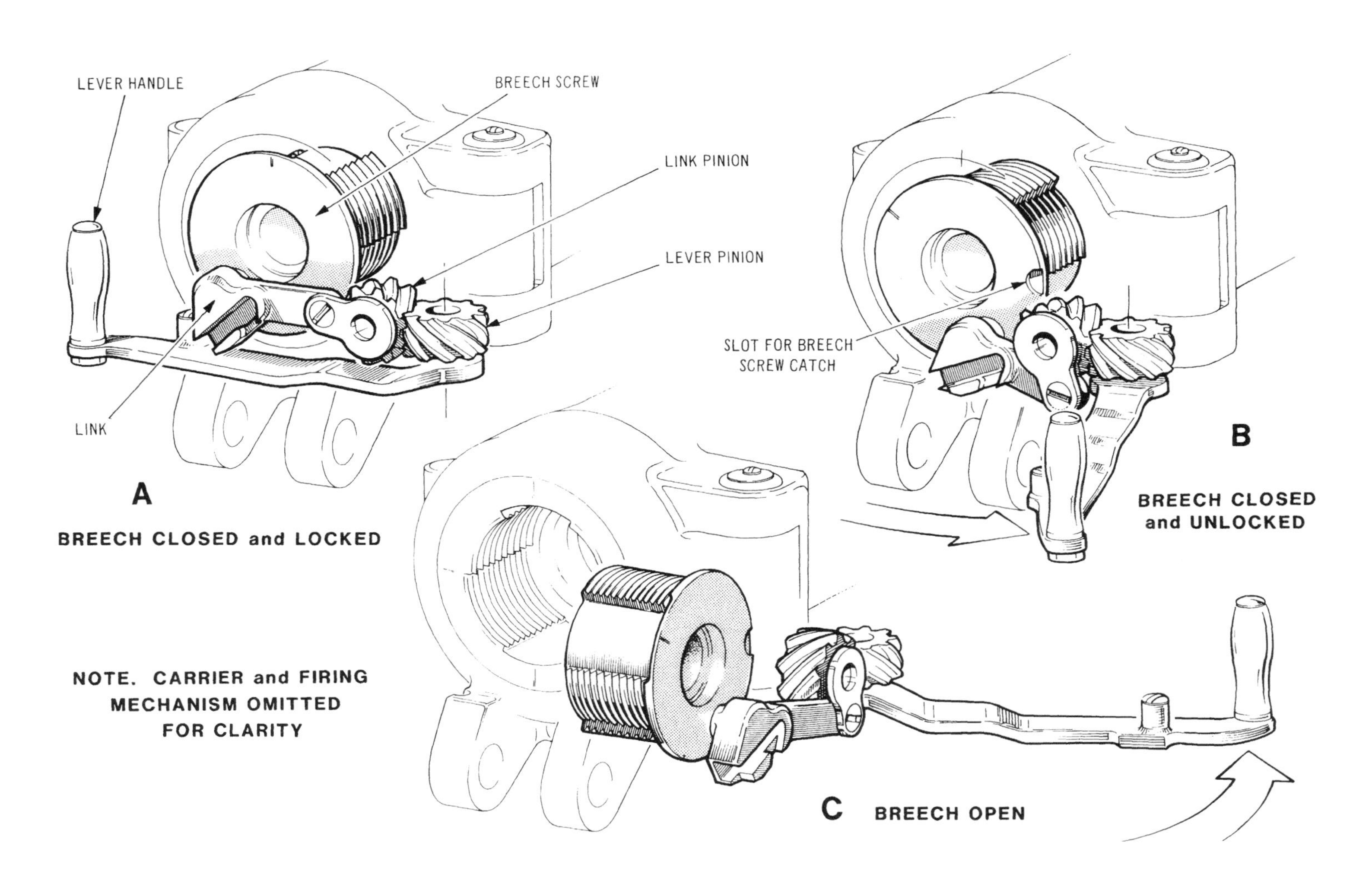

BREECH SCREW – OPERATION

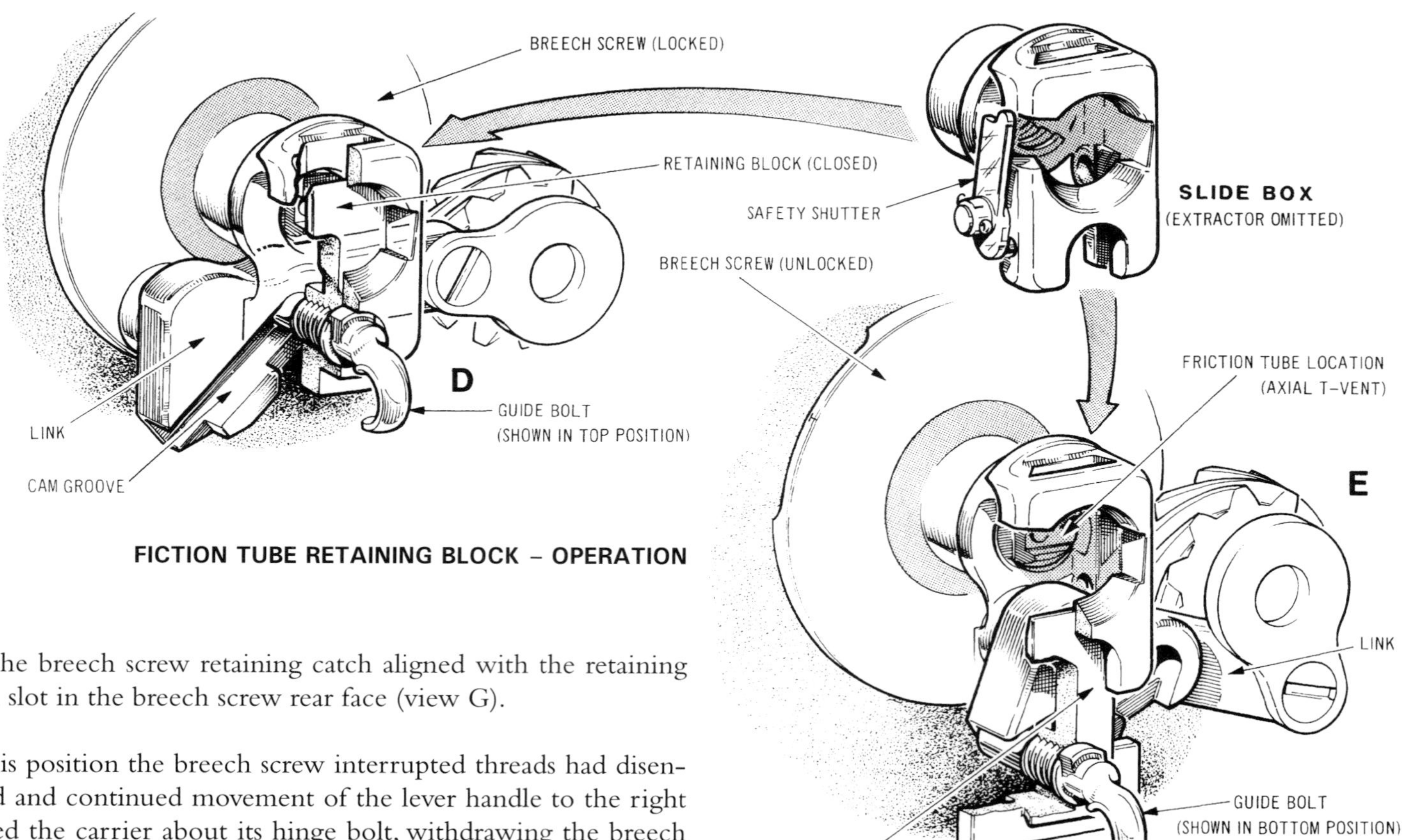

FICTION TUBE RETAINING BLOCK – OPERATION

and the breech screw retaining catch aligned with the retaining catch slot in the breech screw rear face (view G).

At this position the breech screw interrupted threads had disengaged and continued movement of the lever handle to the right rotated the carrier about its hinge bolt, withdrawing the breech screw from the breech opening (view C).

As the breech screw moved rearwards away from the barrel, the spring-loaded retaining catch located into the retaining catch slot

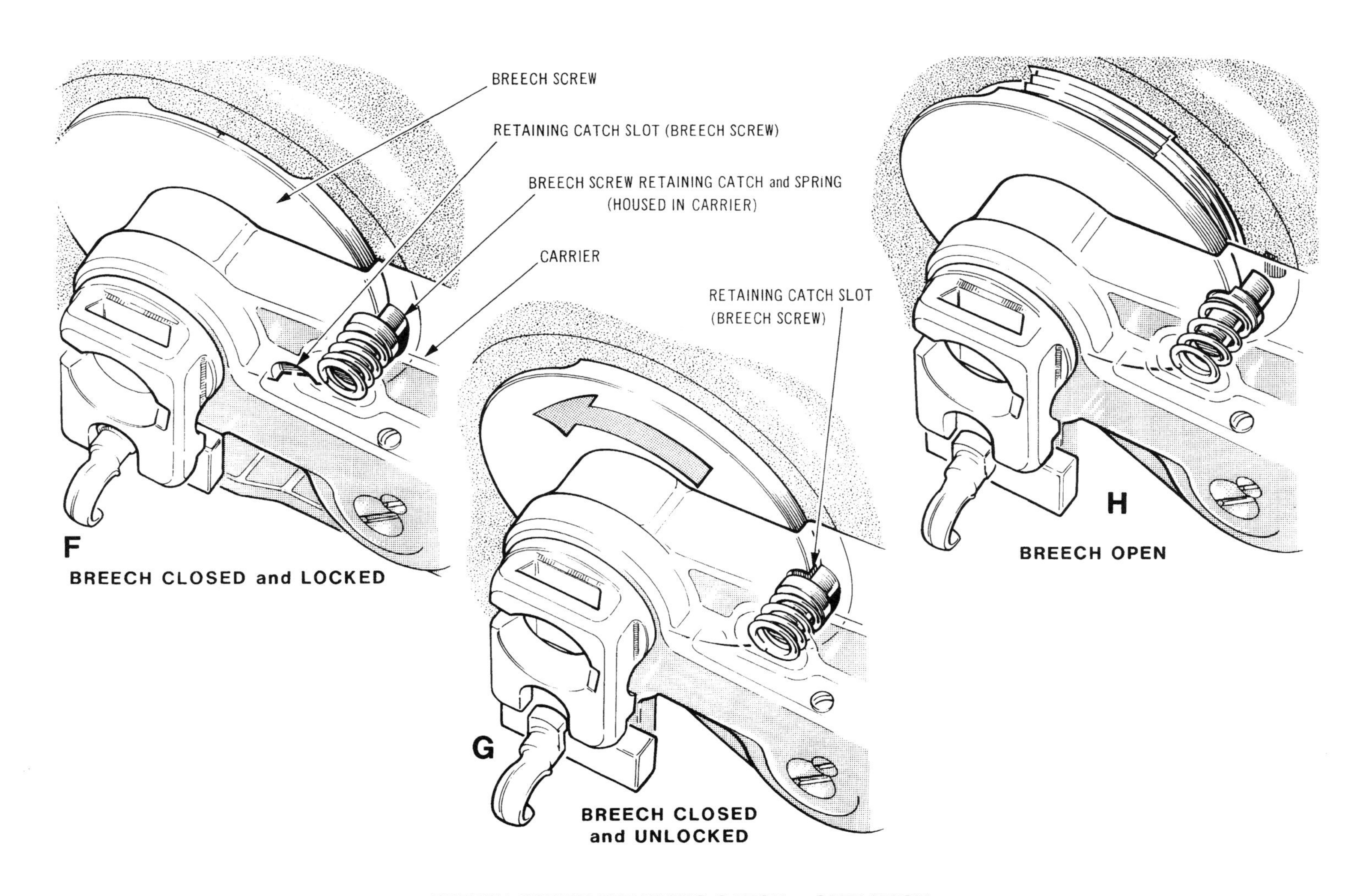

BREECH SCREW RETAINING CATCH – OPERATION

(view H) and locked the breech screw to the carrier. Continued movement of the lever handle to the right then moved the breech screw into the fully open position (view C).

In closing the breech, the lever handle would be swung to the left, inserting the breech screw into the barrel opening. As the breech screw abutted the barrel rear face, the protruding retaining catch would be pressed back into the carrier body, moving out of the retaining catch slot and freeing the breech screw to rotate clockwise and lock.

For drill purposes, or in the event of a misfire, the tube retaining block could be lowered by withdrawing the guide bolt sufficiently to clear the link cam groove and pressing it downwards.

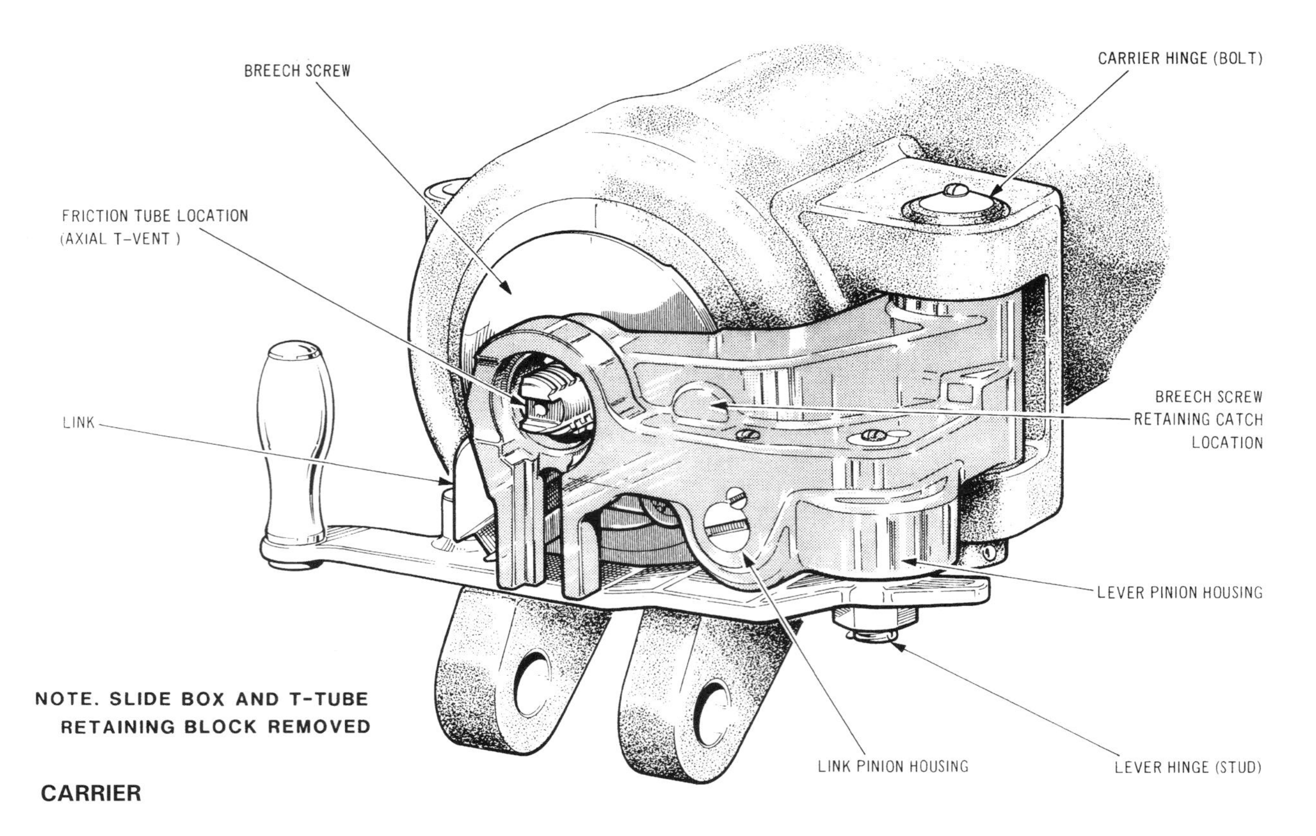

NOTE. SLIDE BOX AND T-TUBE RETAINING BLOCK REMOVED

CARRIER

To remove the retaining block, the guide bolt would be pulled fully back and pressed downwards. To remove the slide box, the retaining block would be removed and then the slide box rotated anti-clockwise through ninety degrees and withdrawn.

To remove the axial vent and obturator, the ring nut would be unscrewed through the carrier bore and withdrawn rearwards with the spring. The axial vent and obturator could then be withdrawn forward from the breech front face.

Obturator (see page 98)

The De Bange obturator was located between the flat, front face of the breech screw and the rear of the T-vent mushroom head.

The pad was a strong, sewn canvas cover, packed with asbestos which had been 'worked into a proper consistency with mutton suet'. The pad was shaped by pressing in a hydraulic press. When installed, the pad stitching would be at the rear. The pad was marked 'front' and 'rear' to ensure correct assembly.

The two tin discs were marked as being the front or rear disc on their inner (concave) face to ensure correct assembly. When assembled, the obturator would be a snug fit within the coned seat in the A-tube bore. Any excess play between the obturator and breech screw front face would be removed by the use of steel adjusting discs provided.

On closing the breech, the pad would enter the coned seat and be pressed home by the breech screw turning to lock.

On firing, gas pressure forced the T-vent rearwards to compress and expand the obturator and seal the breech. After firing, the natural elasticity of the pad material relaxed the seal sufficiently enough for the breech to be opened by a straight pull after the screw was unlocked.

During rapid firing, the pad would possibly soften with heat, whereupon it would be removed and thrown into a bucket of cold water to restore it to good condition.

Spare obturators and adjusting discs were carried, the obturators being kept complete on the T-vent in the gun or in a bronze box provided for the purpose. This was due to a tendency of the pad to swell in the direction of its axis, causing difficulty in adjusting it on the T-vent – the obturator needed to turn freely when fitted into the breech screw. Stiffness in breech operation could be caused by a pad in poor condition or the use of too many adjusting discs. To help maintain the pad in good condition it would occasionally be rubbed with a mixture of Russian tallow and oil.

Sights

The BL 15 pdr Mk. IV gun was fitted with the Grenfell pattern tangent rear sight. Both the Mk.V and MK.VI sights were fitted, the Mk.VI taking over as the Mk.V was used up (1911). Both sight Mk. numbers are described here, but only the Mk.VI is illustrated. Both rearsight Mk. numbers were retained in position in a socket, formed on the barrel rear left side, by a spring catch.

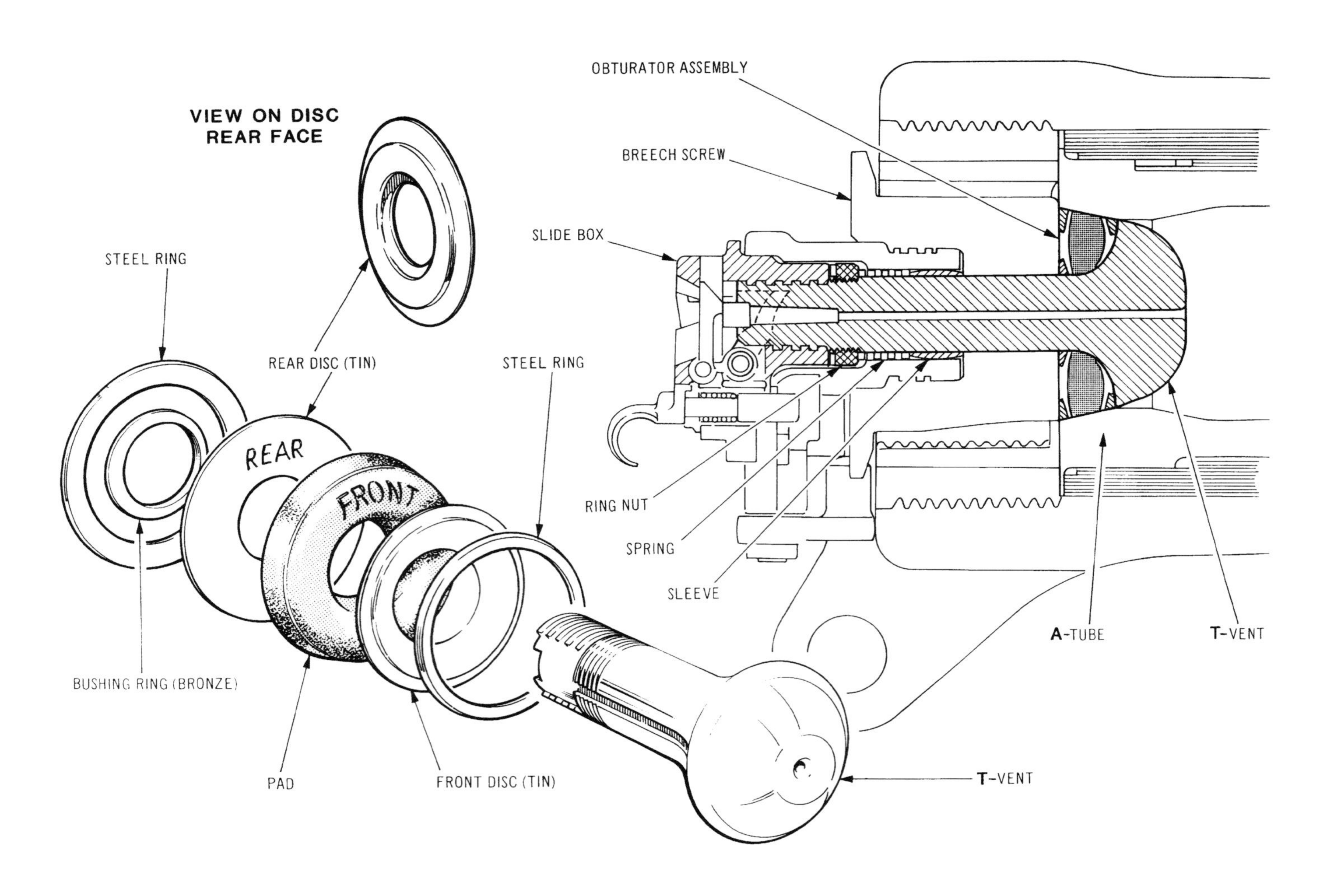
VIEW ON DISC
REAR FACE
OBTURATOR ASSEMBLY
BREECH SCREW
SLIDE BOX
STEEL RING
REAR DISC (TIN)
STEEL RING
REAR
FRONT
RING NUT
SPRING
SLEEVE
A-TUBE
T-VENT
BUSHING RING (BRONZE)
PAD
FRONT DISC (TIN)
T-VENT

OBTURATOR

Both sight Mk. numbers employed the same foresight. This consisted of a steel stem, fitted with a steel acorn point at the top and formed with a dovetail mounting at the bottom, to slide into a mounting boss on the side of the jacket, secured there by a spring catch.

Mk. V sight

The sight was of steel.

The rectangular section sight bar had, at the top, a crosshead provided with a notched deflection leaf and traversing screw giving one and a half degrees of deflection, left and right. The sight bar was graduated on the rear face to eleven degrees, reading to ten minutes.

The sight body had a socket, with milled head and a drum, the latter engraved with a yard scale from 100 to 4,600 yards, reading to 25 yards. The graduations between 1,000 and 1,200 yards were red lacquered to aid rapidity of fire at these ranges. The drum had a pinion, engaging with a rack on the sight bar front face.

Mk. VI sight (illustrated on page 100)

The Mk.VI tangent sight was of steel, the square section sight bar having, at the top, a half-crosshead provided with a notched deflection leaf and traversing screw giving two degrees of deflection, left and right.

The sight bar was graduated, on the rear face, with a yard scale to 5,500 yards (for a muzzle velocity of 1,581 feet per second). The sight bar left face had a scale to fifteen degrees, reading to five minutes. A rack on the sight bar front face was engaged by the pinion of the Mk. I automatic clamp.

The bronze automatic clamp had a milled head and pinion, also a cam plate and case to lock the sight at any required setting. It was fitted with a glass lens for use in reading the yard scale on the tangent sight bar.

Telescopic Sight Mk. 1

A steel bracket was attached to the left-hand trunnion by a dovetail and two fixing screws. The bracket had two V bearings in which rested the frame trunnions. Between the frame trunnions was a projection which located at the lower end of the levelling screw and served to level the sight when the gun was sited on uneven ground, a transverse level being provided on the frame for this purpose.

The sight consisted of a telescope, the front end being secured by a pivot at the centre of the vertical arc. The rear end was held to the arc circumference by a vernier piece, attached to the telescope and overlapping the arc inner edge.

The elevation angle was set by turning the micrometer head of the elevating worm spindle, this in turn moving the telescope along the vertical arc. The vernier of the vertical arc read to two

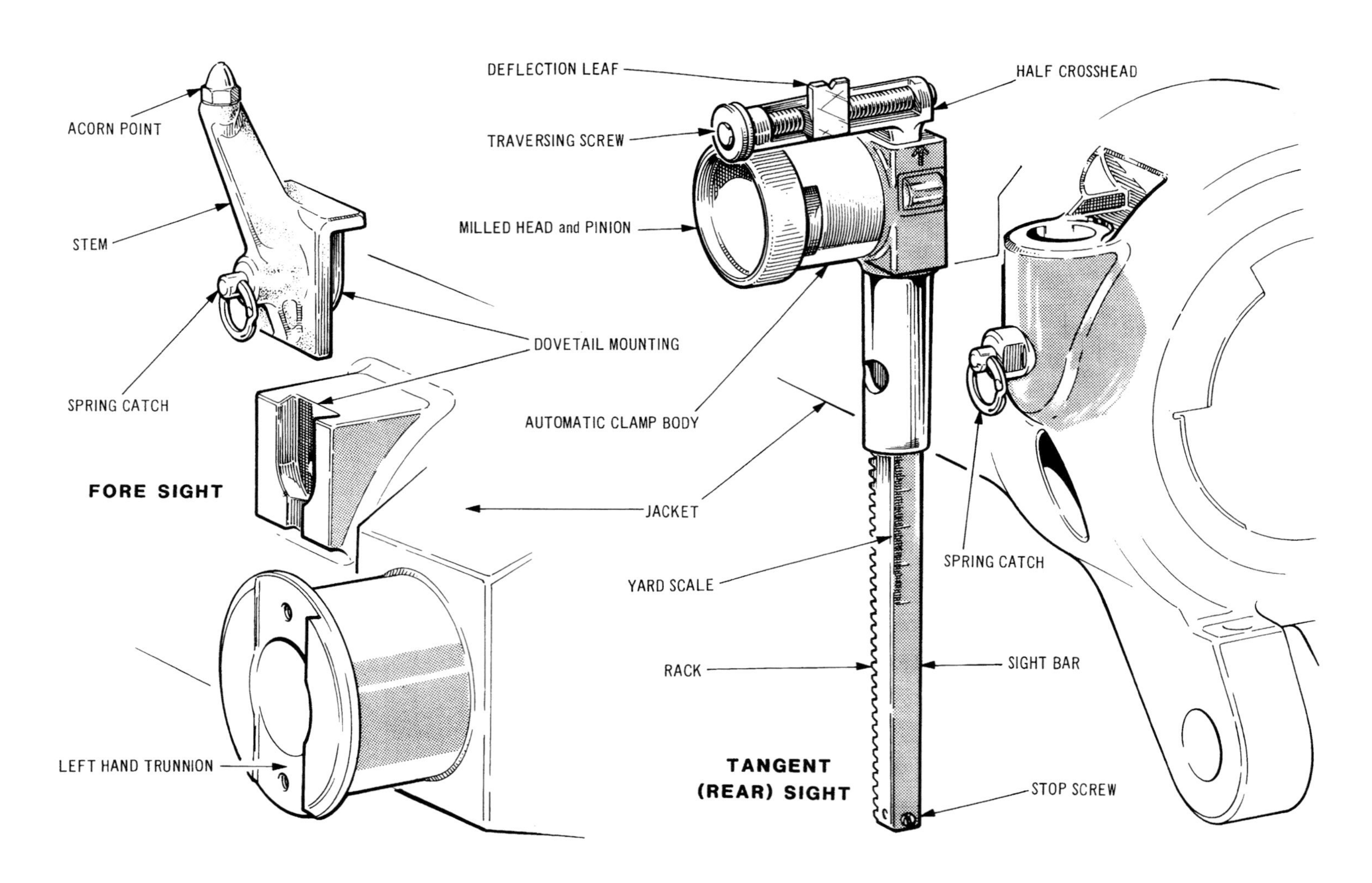

DEFLECTION LEAF
HALF CROSSHEAD
ACORN POINT
TRAVERSING SCREW
STEM
MILLED HEAD and PINION
DOVETAIL MOUNTING
SPRING CATCH
AUTOMATIC CLAMP BODY
FORE SIGHT
JACKET
SPRING CATCH
YARD SCALE
RACK
SIGHT BAR
LEFT HAND TRUNNION
TANGENT
(REAR) SIGHT
STOP SCREW

SIGHTS

minutes, as did the spindle micrometer head. One revolution of the spindle equalled one degree on the vertical arc.

Deflection was set with the deflection nut. Turning the nut moved a diaphragm, within the telescope, laterally along a graduated scale. There were two pointers within the telescope – a horizontal pointer used for laying and a vertical pointer, which registered on the graduated scale the amount of deflection given to the horizontal pointer. Both pointers moved together. The smallest division on the deflection scale read three minutes. The maximum deflection, required for a hurricane across the range, was thirty minutes – this was graduated on the sight together with a drift scale.

The field of the telescope was 1 in 20, at 1,000 yards the view circle diameter being 50 yards.

The telescope was an ordinary inverting type with an achromatic object glass and astronomical eyepiece. This reduced the telescope length to a minimum, gave a large field and standardised the deflection method with that of the service sight.

In use, the horizontal pointer would be focused with the eyepiece, then the target object focused onto the horizontal pointer with the object glass.

The sight was provided with a strap for carrying purposes, fastened loosely around the vertical part of the frame away from the trunnions. The bracket was provided with a shaped leather cover secured by a strap.

Seven sights were issued to each battery, one being reserved for instructional purposes only. One other was fitted with a longitudinal level to be used as a clinometer.

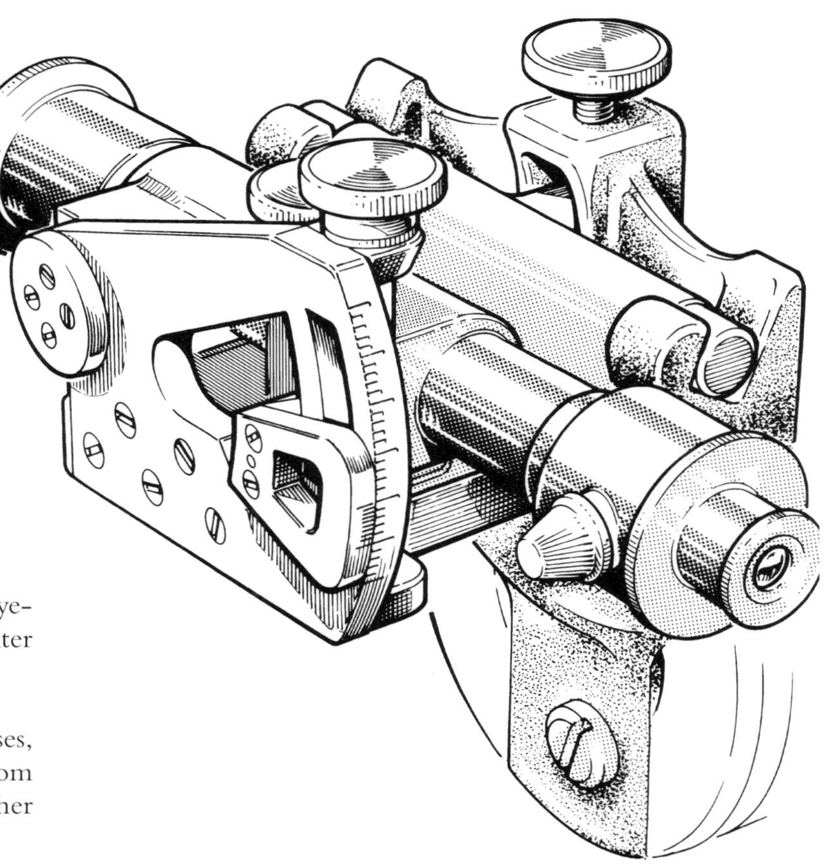

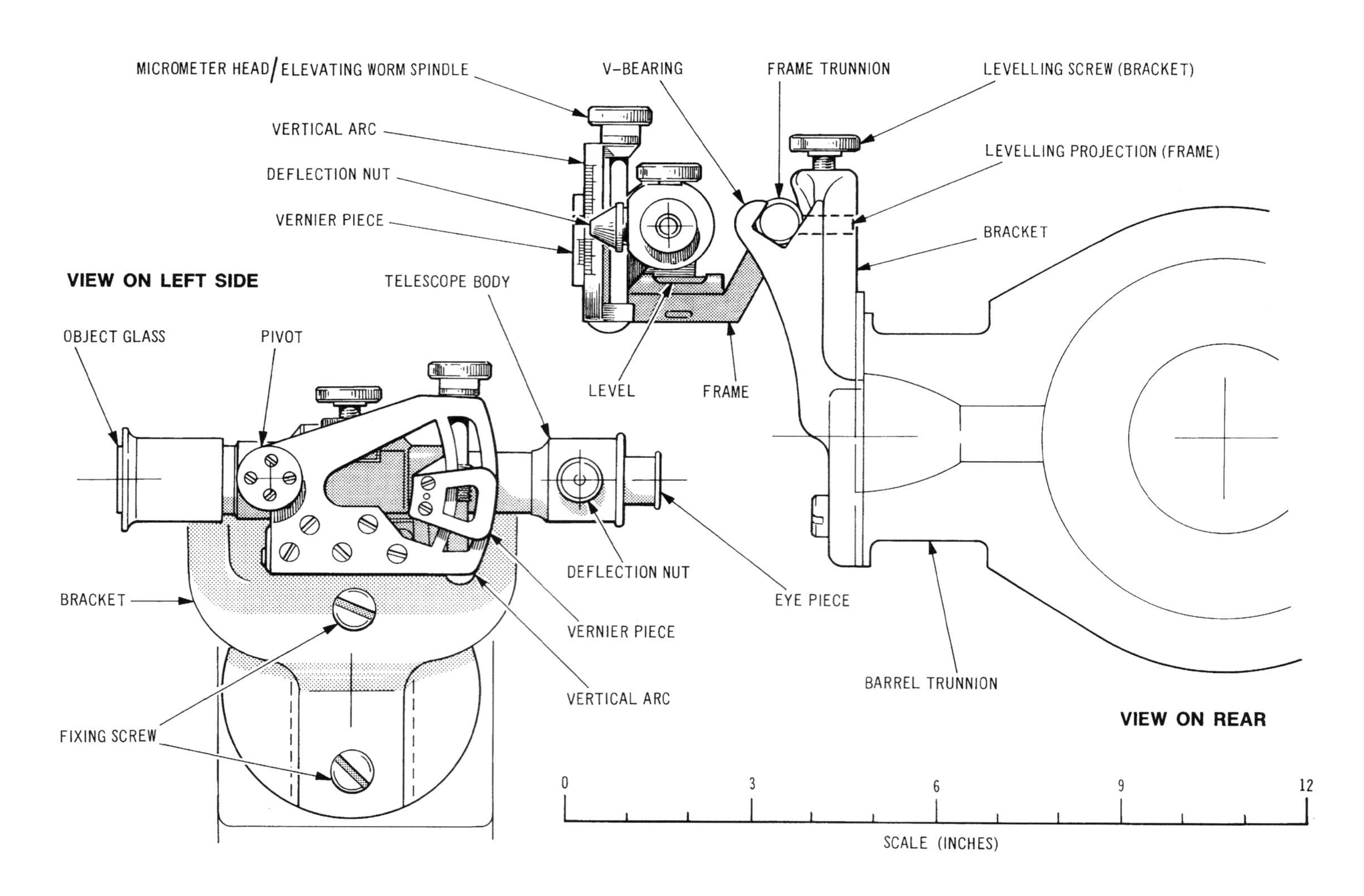

TELESCOPIC SIGHT MK. 1

T-friction tubes (see page 104)

The friction bar was of half-round copper wire, twisted into a round bar, with one end formed into a loop. The other end was roughened.

With the friction bar installed, the hole in the side of the head was filled with two grains of detonating composition paste, applied over the roughened portion of the friction bar. The hole was then sealed with a gut skin disc, a shellacked cork plug and filled flush with shellac cement.

The body was filled with eight grains of pistol powder and sealed with a shellacked cork plug covered with shellac cement and a paper disc. A brass locking pin prevented the body unscrewing from the head. The plug retaining the soft copper ball was drilled through with three flash holes.

Sudden withdrawal of the friction bar ignited the detonating composition and the flame flashed around the ball, through the plug flash holes and ignited the pistol powder charge in the body.

Pressure drove the soft copper ball back into the tapered hole to seal the tube and prevent gas leakage to the rear.

Fired tubes would be immersed in mineral oil within 24 hours of use, then returned to Woolwich for repair and refilling.

T-friction tubes were issued in square tin boxes, ten to a box. Both top and bottom of the box were removable, being secured by soldered strips. This allowed five tubes to be withdrawn from the top and five from the bottom.

The drill tube was of hardened steel, to the same dimensions as the service tube. The lanyard hooked into the curved spring end and required a pull of about 50 pounds to withdraw it.

Cartridges, projectiles and fuzes

Cartridges (see page 105)

Service cartridges were made from red shalloon, between 14.75 and 15.25 inches long, sewn longitudinally with one row of silk into a cylinder 1.90 inches in diameter. One end was closed with a circular piece of red shalloon, sewn with two rows of silk.

The charge consisted of 15.75 ounces of size 5 cordite, made up in a bundle and tied in five places with two turns of silk. At each end of the bundle was wound two drams of guncotton yarn, the centre of each yarn winding being one inch from the end of the cordite. The open end of the cartridge was closed and choked with silk.

The blank charge, for saluting, was in a cartridge of No. 1 silk cloth, the length was 5.5 inches maximum and the diameter 3 inches maximum. The end was choked with silk twist and the cartridge hooped with three silk braids.

The charge consisted of 1 pound 4 ounces of black LG powder.

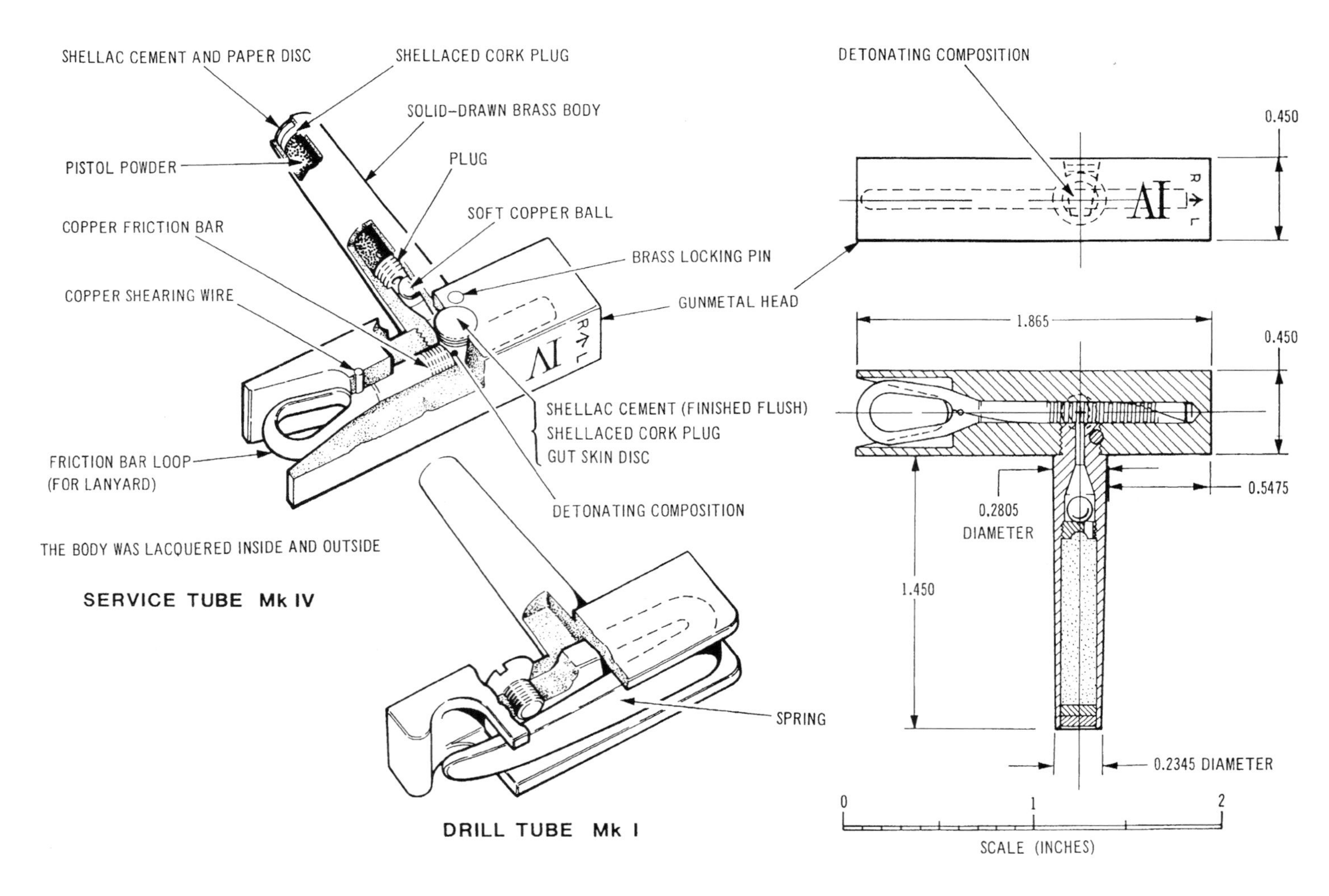

T-FRICTION TUBES

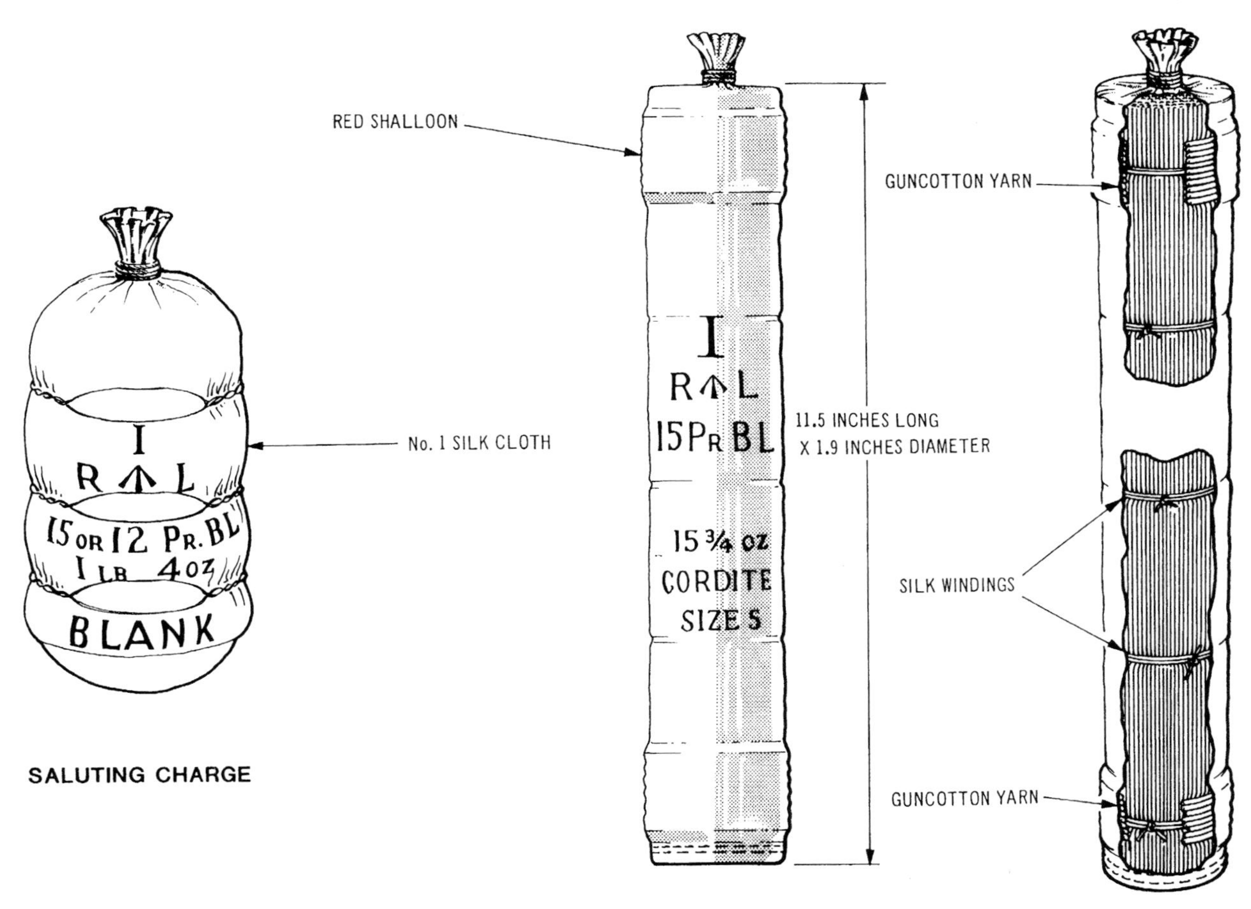

SALUTING CHARGE

SERVICE CHARGE

CARTRIDGES

Case Shot Mk.V

The body was of sheet tin – grade XXS-lap jointed and soldered into a cylinder 2.97 inches in diameter.

The base of forged steel had the end of the body cylinder pressed into a channel and machined around it for a copper driving band. The bottom of the channel was milled to prevent turning of the driving band on discharge. The driving band held the body captive.

A recess in the base end was fitted with a straight handle and had a hole bored through into the body, the hole being counterbored on the body side and closed by an iron disc, soldered in.

The body had an inner steel lining, in two segments, resting against the base. Within this lining and resting against the base was a loose steel disc.

The body was filled with 290 steel balls (weighing 34 to the pound), the interstices being filled with a mixture of clay and sand in equal parts.

The top of the body was covered by an iron or steel disc, the sides of the body being spun over it and soldered.

On firing, the gun bore was sealed by the copper driving band and gas pressure, through the base recess hole, tore the soldered disc free and forced the loose disc and balls forward, breaking the body away from the base, ensuring the release of the balls before the shot left the bore of the gun.

The Mk. IV case shot had the body screwed and soldered to the base. There was no hole in the base recess and the handle was of bent pattern. On firing, the base unscrewed itself from the body as the shot passed through the barrel rifling.

Shrapnel shell (see page 108)

The forged steel body had a circumferential groove machined 0.45 inch from the base. Three ridges were left projecting on the groove base. These were cut across axially with six equally spaced chisel marks to prevent the copper driving band, which was pressed into the groove, turning on the shell body.

The shell was filled with 192 mixed metal balls (weighing 35 to the pound), contained in a perforated tin cylinder. A tin cap covered the balls, held by seven tabs on the tin cylinder being turned over it and soldered. The interstices were filled with resin. Any deficiency in the final weight of the shell was made up by adding buckshot to the filling.

The driving bands for both Mk. IV and Mk.V shells fitted into identical grooves. The fillings were the same.

The Mk. VI shell had a different driving band groove, being narrower with two ridges 'waved', not chiselled. It was filled with 230 balls at a weight of 41 to the pound.

Shells would only be fuzed on active service, when their use was considered to be imminent. The only other occasion would be at practice camps. The shells would not be fuzed unless necessary due to the deterioration of fuzes once removed from their storage cylinders.

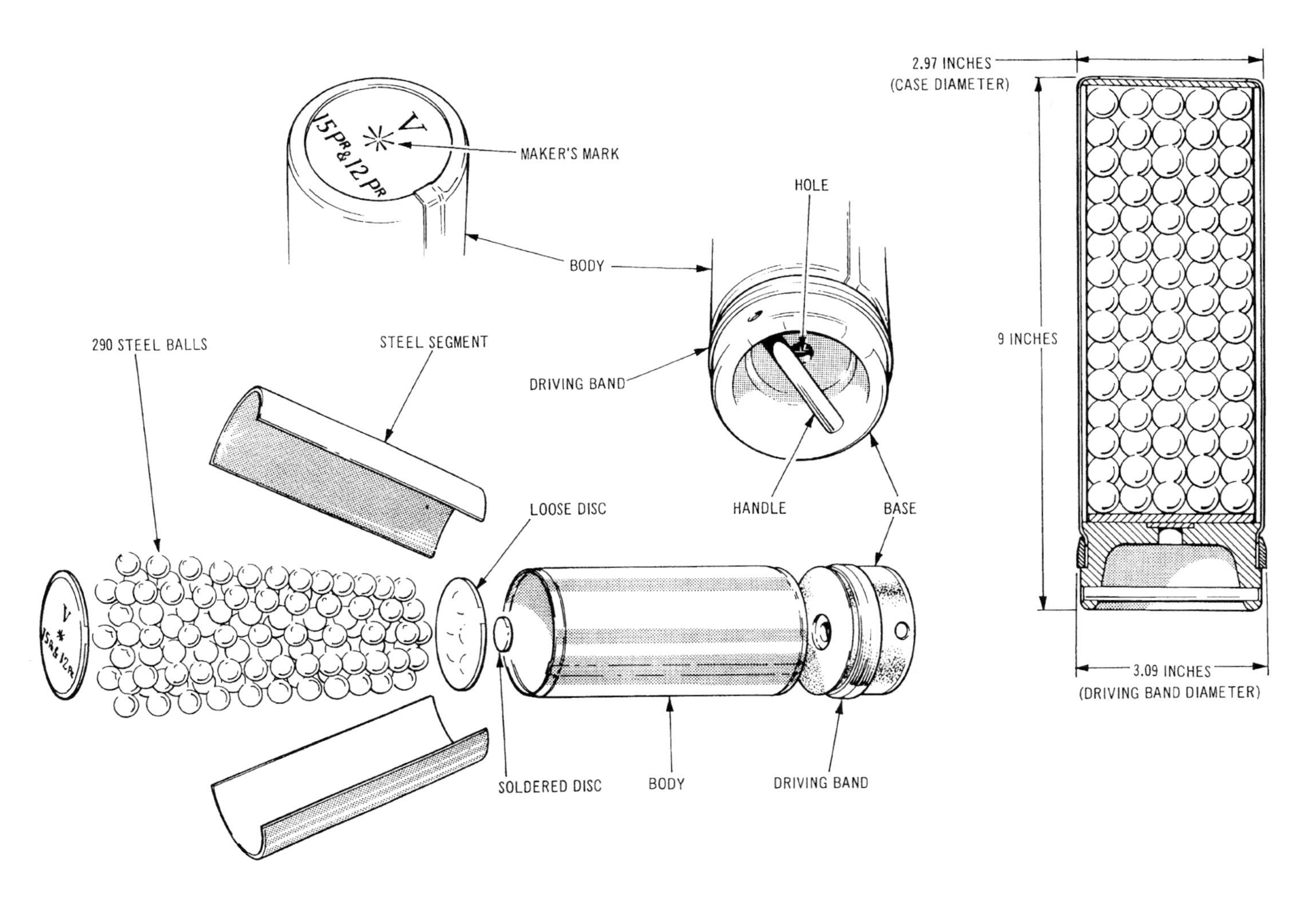

CASE SHOT MK. V

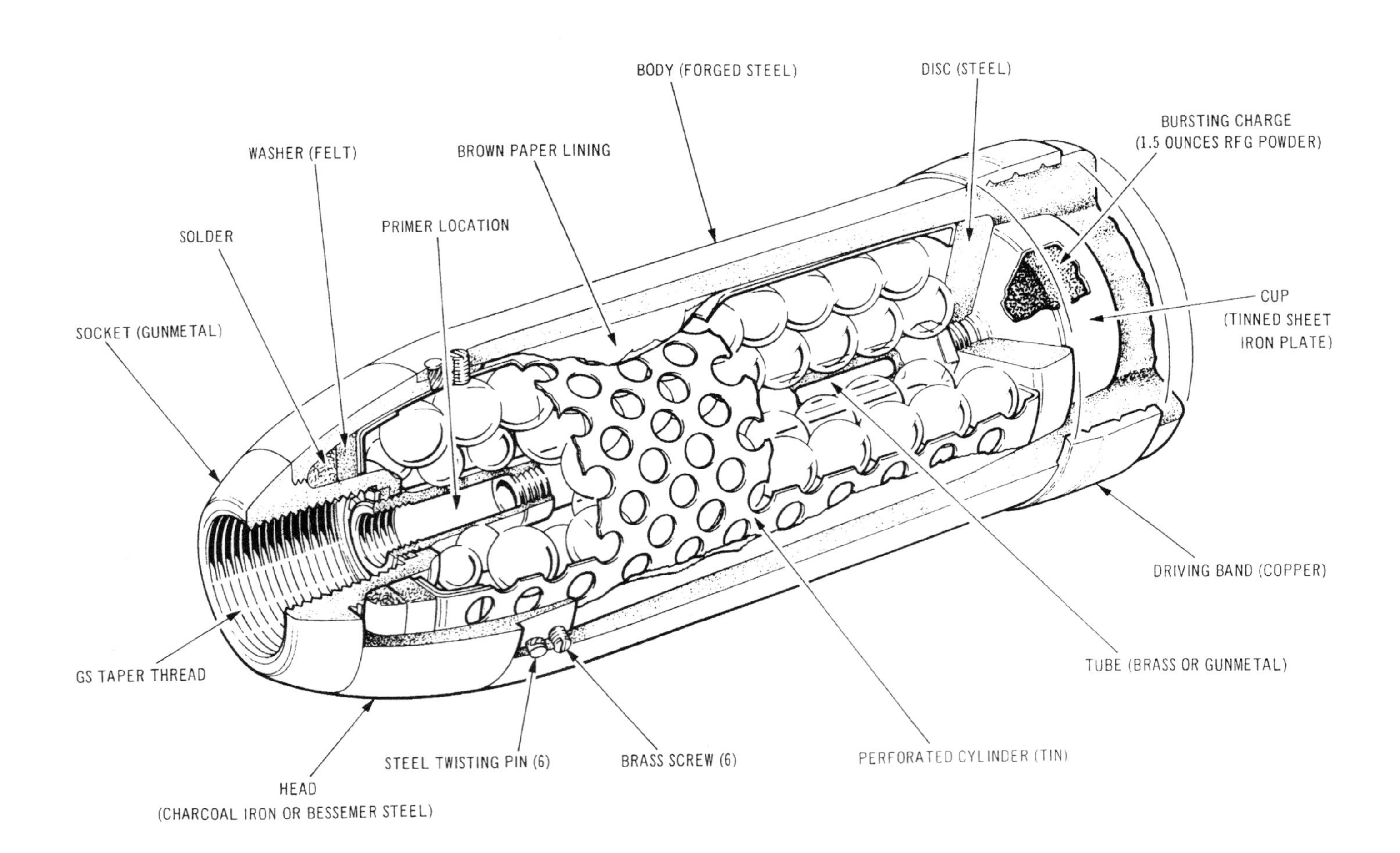

SHRAPNEL SHELL

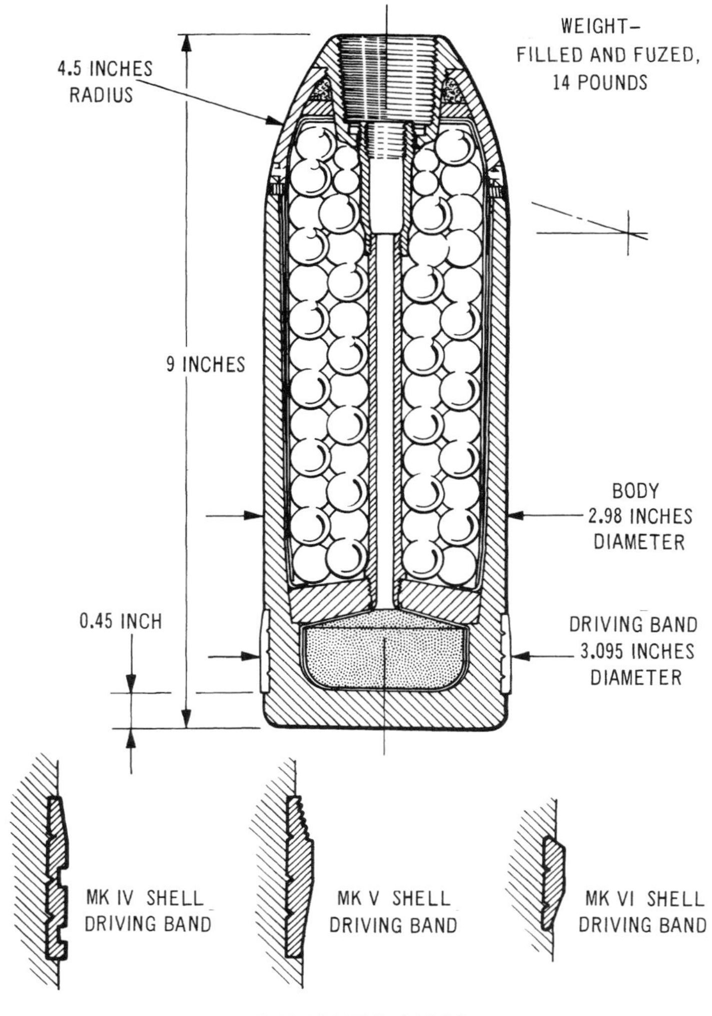

SHRAPNELL SHELL

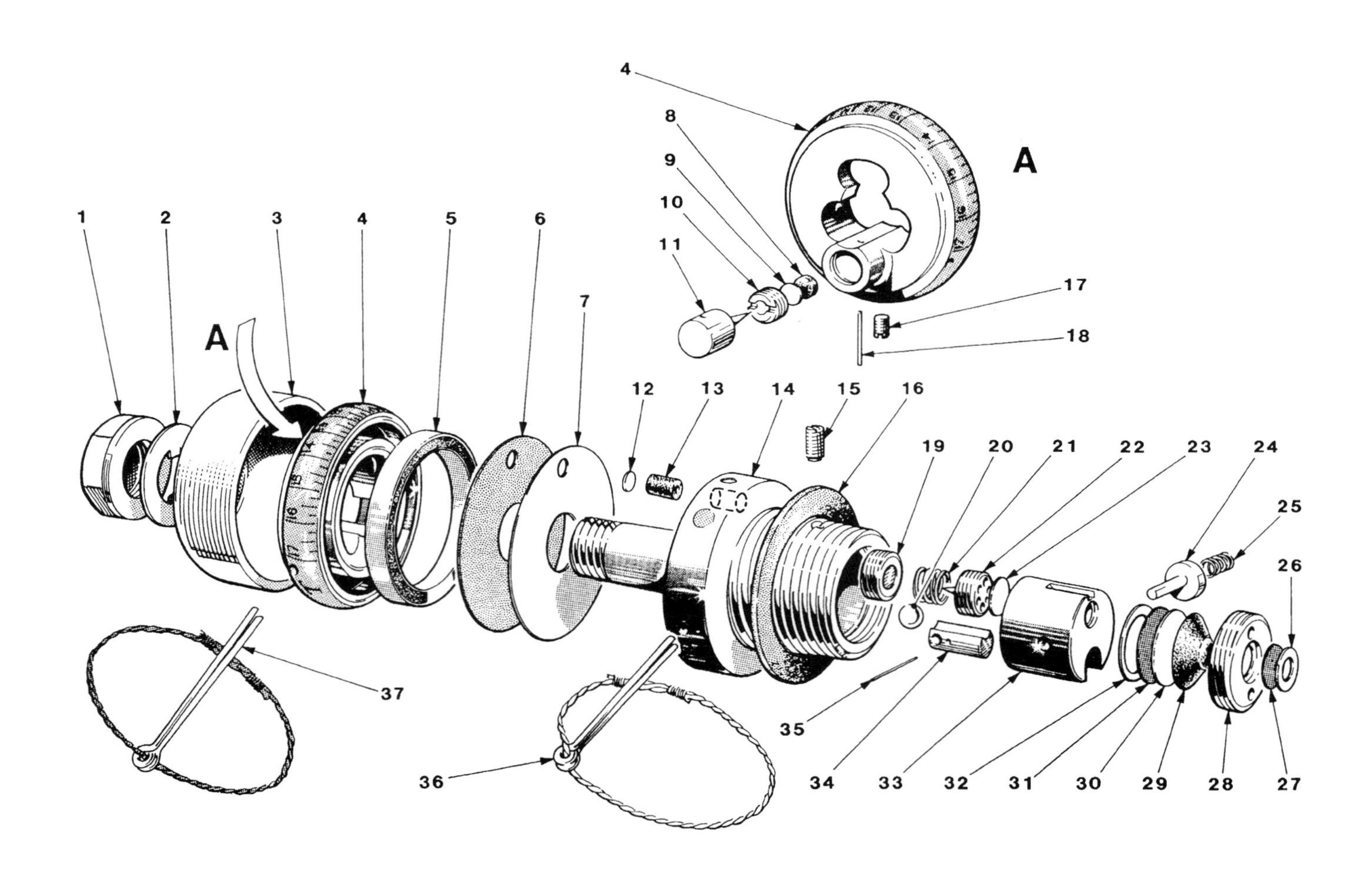

PERCUSSION AND TIME FUZE NO. 56 MK. IV

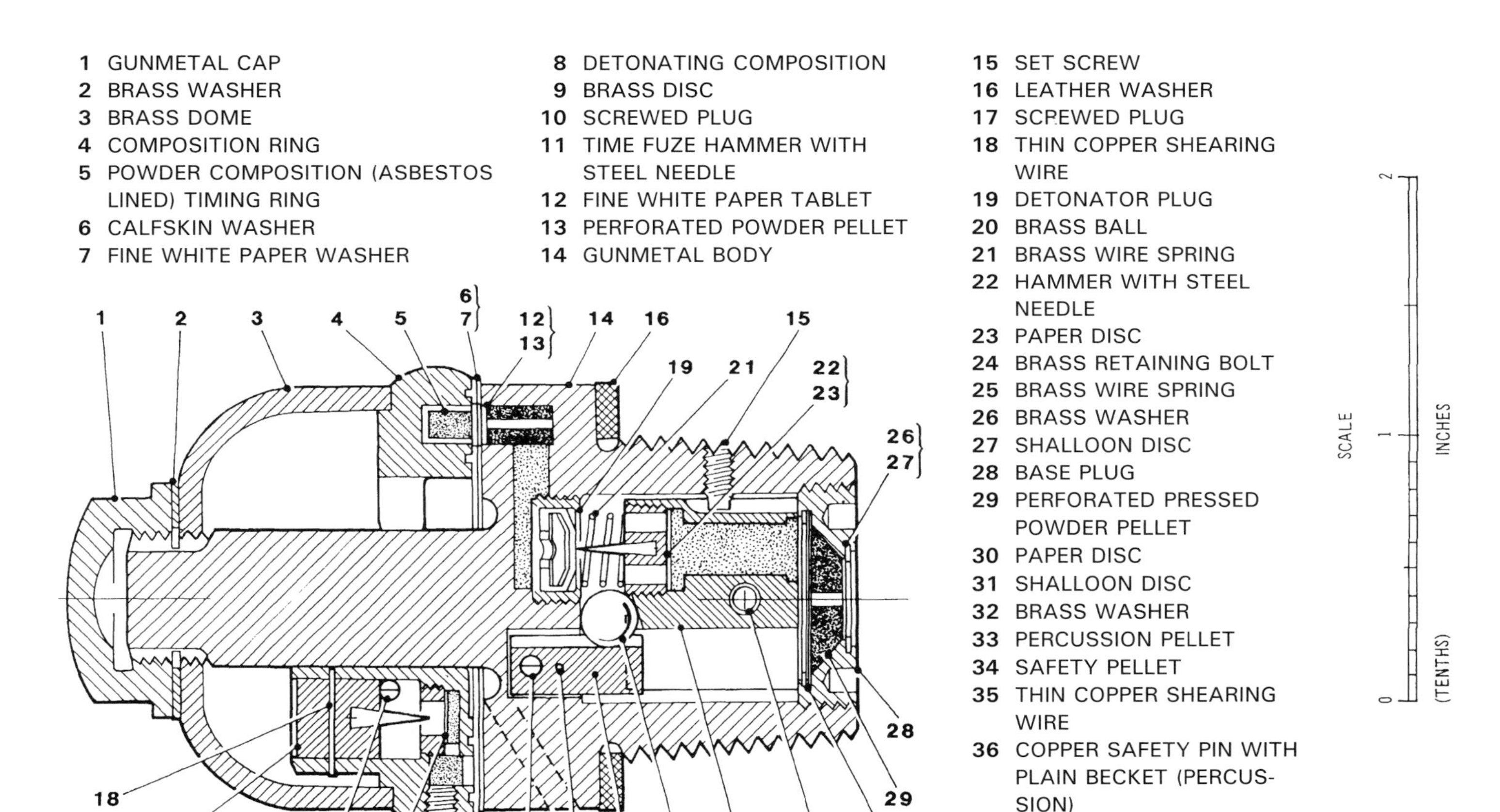

PERCUSSION AND TIME FUZE NO. 56 MK. IV

Percussion and Time Fuze No. 56 Mk. IV

Time fuze operation

The timing ring was numbered from 0 to 18 around the outside, each division being subdivided into halves and quarters. A broad arrow marked the position at which the internal groove (**D**), which contained the powder composition, was interrupted by a bridge, soldered in.

To set the time fuze, the cap was loosened with the universal fuze key and the numbered ring moved around until the range number ordered was in line with the mark on the body. The cap was then screwed down tightly.

At the moment of loading both safety pins were withdrawn. On discharge, the hammer (**A**) set back shearing the copper wire (**B**) and the needle penetrated the detonator (**C**). The detonator ignited the time ring (**D**) which burned around the distance selected to the access hole into the perforated powder pellet (**E**). Flame then flashed through the radial magazine (**F**), the percussion detonator (**G**), the powder contained in the percussion pellet (**I**) and the base plug (**J**), the last jet of flame being directed into the shell, igniting the bursting charge.

Should the time fuze fail to operate, the shell would detonate on impact, due to removal of the percussion safety pin on loading. At rest the fuze would burn for 13 seconds.

Fuzes were issued one in a tin cylinder.

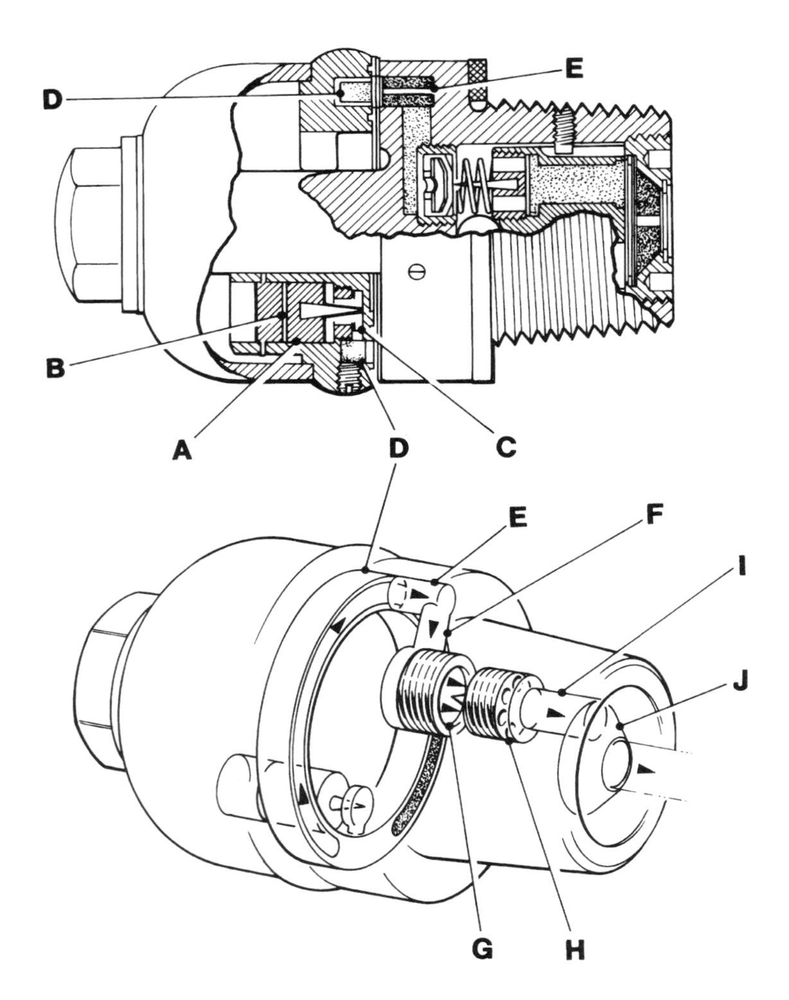

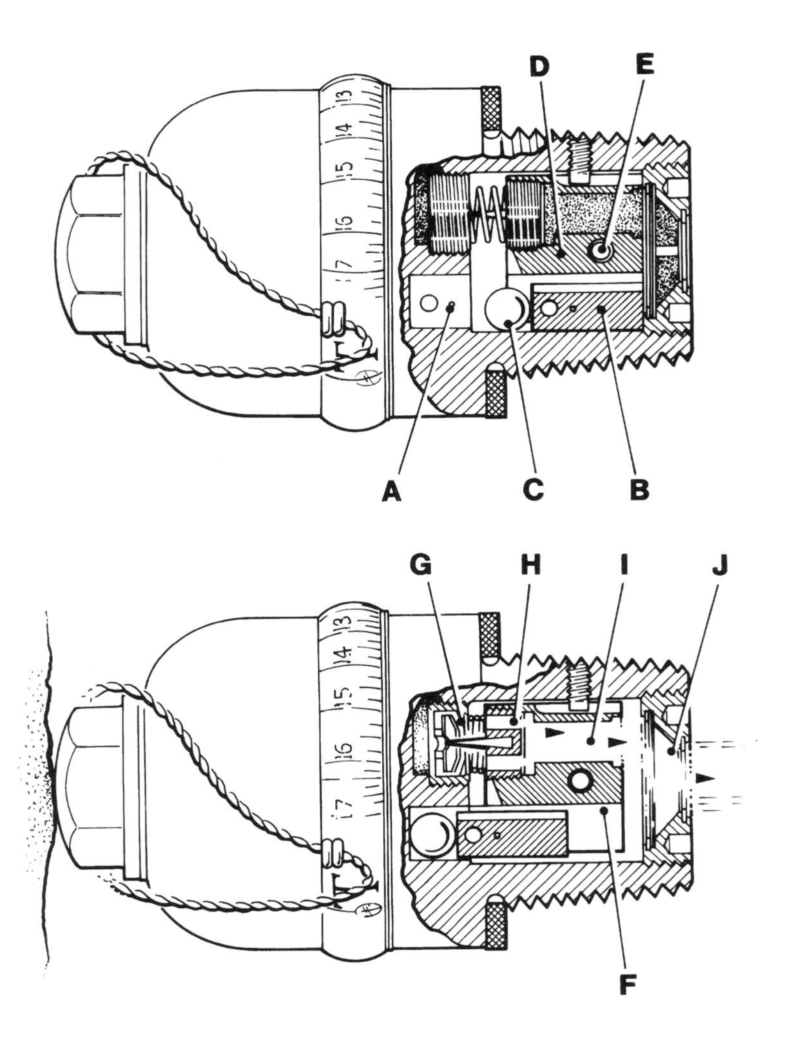

Percussion fuze operation

If the fuze was required to act as a percussion fuze only, the safety pin marked 'P' was withdrawn at the moment of loading. The pin marked 'T' was left in position with the becket looped over the cap. On discharge, the copper wire (**A**) sheared, allowing the safety pellet (**B**) to move back and allow the brass ball (**C**) to fall into the space vacated by the safety pellet. The spinning of the shell caused the retaining bolt (**E**) to move outwards, clear of the percussion pellet (**D**).

On impact, the percussion pellet moved forward (**F**) and the needle penetrated the detonator (**G**), which flashed through the six flame holes (**H**) and ignited the powder in the percussion pellet (**I**) and base plug (**J**), the last jet of flame being directed into the shell, igniting the bursting charge.

Fuze indicator

The bar, or base plate, of Delta metal was suspended, in use, on two steel hooks riveted to the rear face (**A**).

The front face upper scale was graduated in yards and the lower face carried a corrector scale.

The centre portion was grooved to carry a slide, also made of Delta metal. The slide was reversible, scribed on one side with a scale for use with Time and Percussion Fuze No. 56, on the reverse was scribed a scale for use with Time and Percussion Fuze No. 60. An index arrow on each scale indicated the normal

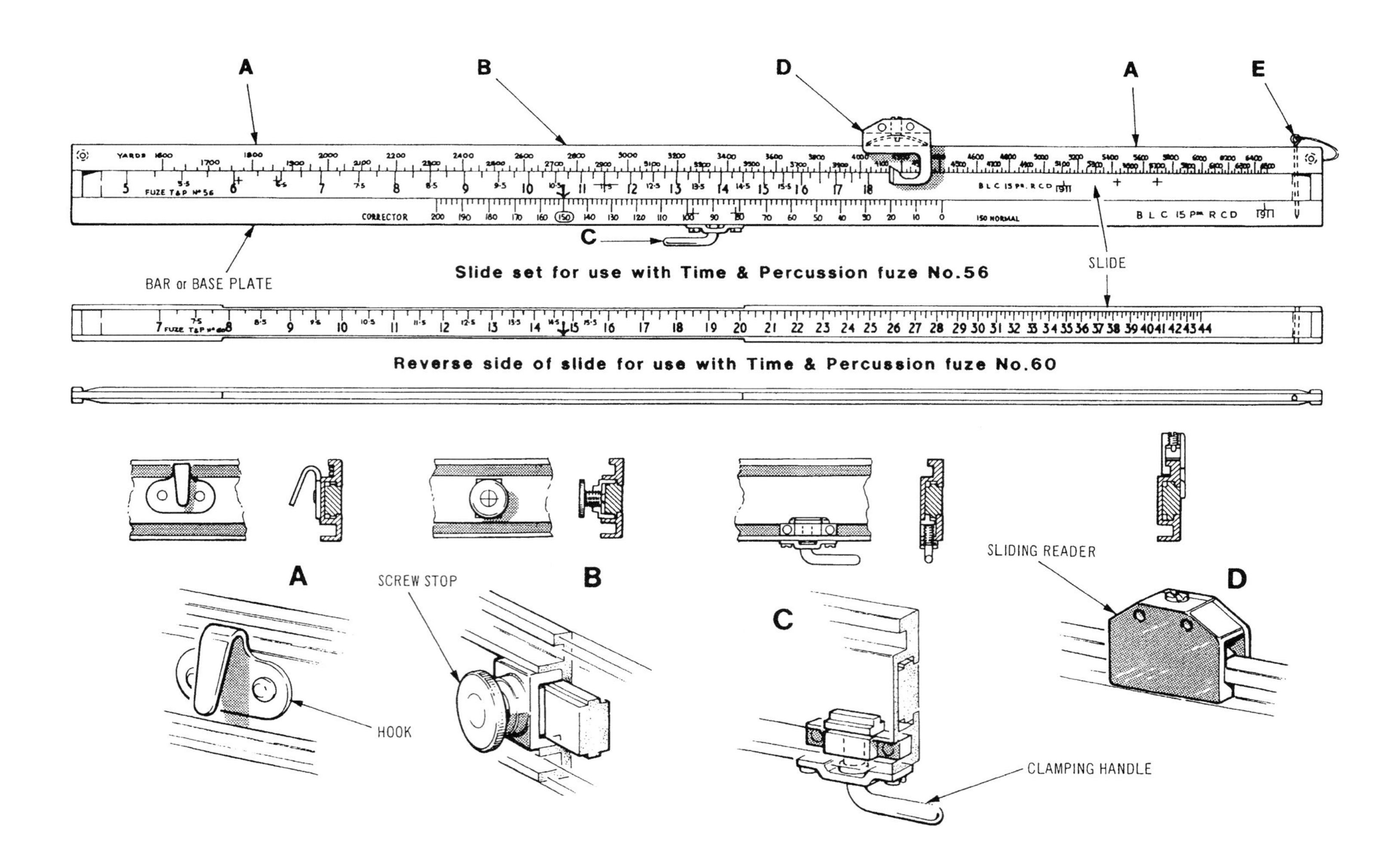

FUZE INDICATOR

position when placed in coincidence with the 150 division mark on the corrector scale. These index arrows and the 150 division mark were coloured red, all other markings were black.

Fitted to the base plate rear face was a screw stop (**B**). This prevented the slide being totally withdrawn by accident but enabled it to be reversed when required.

The slide was clamped in the required position by the clamping handle fitted to the base plate bottom (**C**).

The yard scale graduations were indicated by a sliding steel reader on the base plate top (**D**). Movement was regulated by an adjustable spring. A stop pin secured the slide in place when not in use (**E**).

Limber

The limber frame consisted of four nickel steel plate futchells (**1**), flanged top and bottom. The outer futchells were also formed with a vertical flange to prevent lateral movement of the ammunition box (**9**). The futchells (**1**) were connected at the front by an angle section nickel steel plate (**3**) riveted across the ends. A hook for a swingletree was riveted to the front end of each outer futchell (**1**). The futchells were connected at the rear by a channel section nickel steel plate (**4**) riveted across the ends. Two channel section nickel steel cross stays (**5**) joined the outer and inner futchells (**1**) near the centre. The inner futchells (**1**) were reinforced at the rear by a nickel steel plate, riveted to the lower flanges. A staple for the draught pole was riveted between the inner futchells (**1**) near the front and a draught pole socket near the rear.

The forged nickel steel limber hook (**6**) had three arms, the lower two were riveted to the bottom plate and inner futchells (**1**). The upper arm was riveted to the inner futchell's top flanges. The

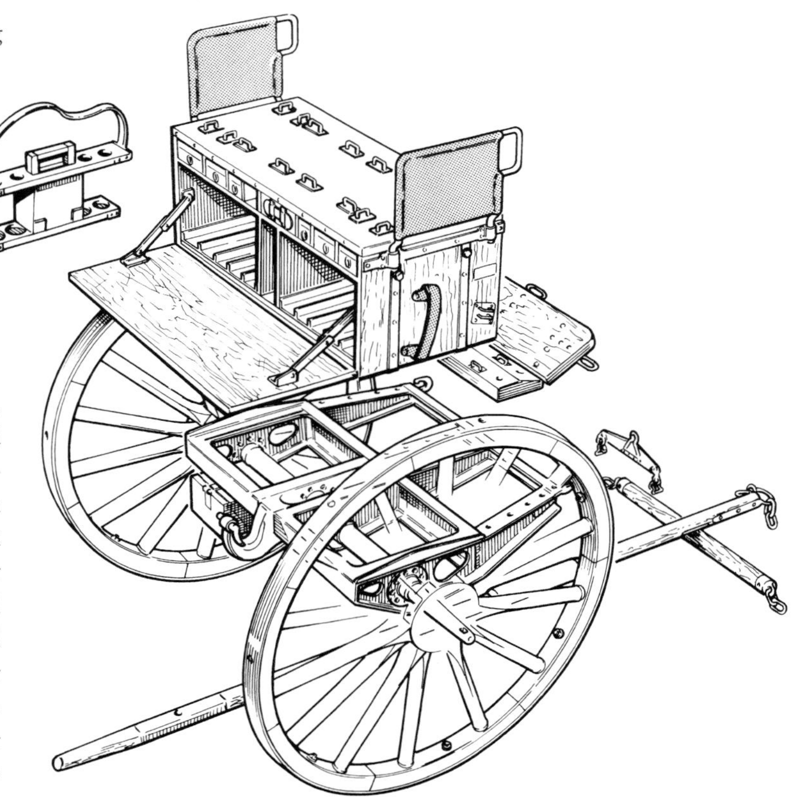

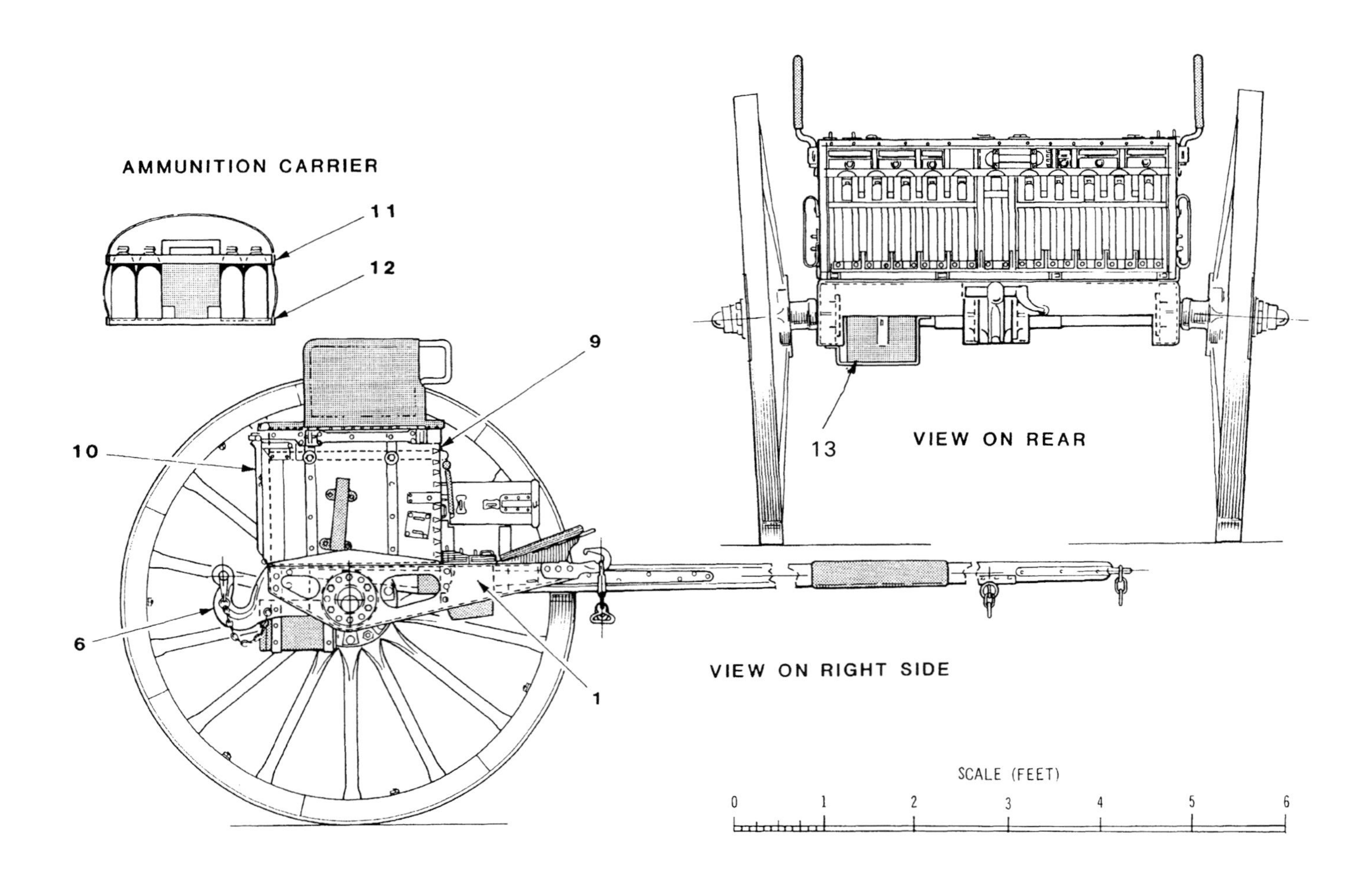
AMMUNITION CARRIER
11
12
9
10
6
1
13
VIEW ON REAR
VIEW ON RIGHT SIDE
SCALE (FEET)
0
1
2
3
4
5
6

LIMBER

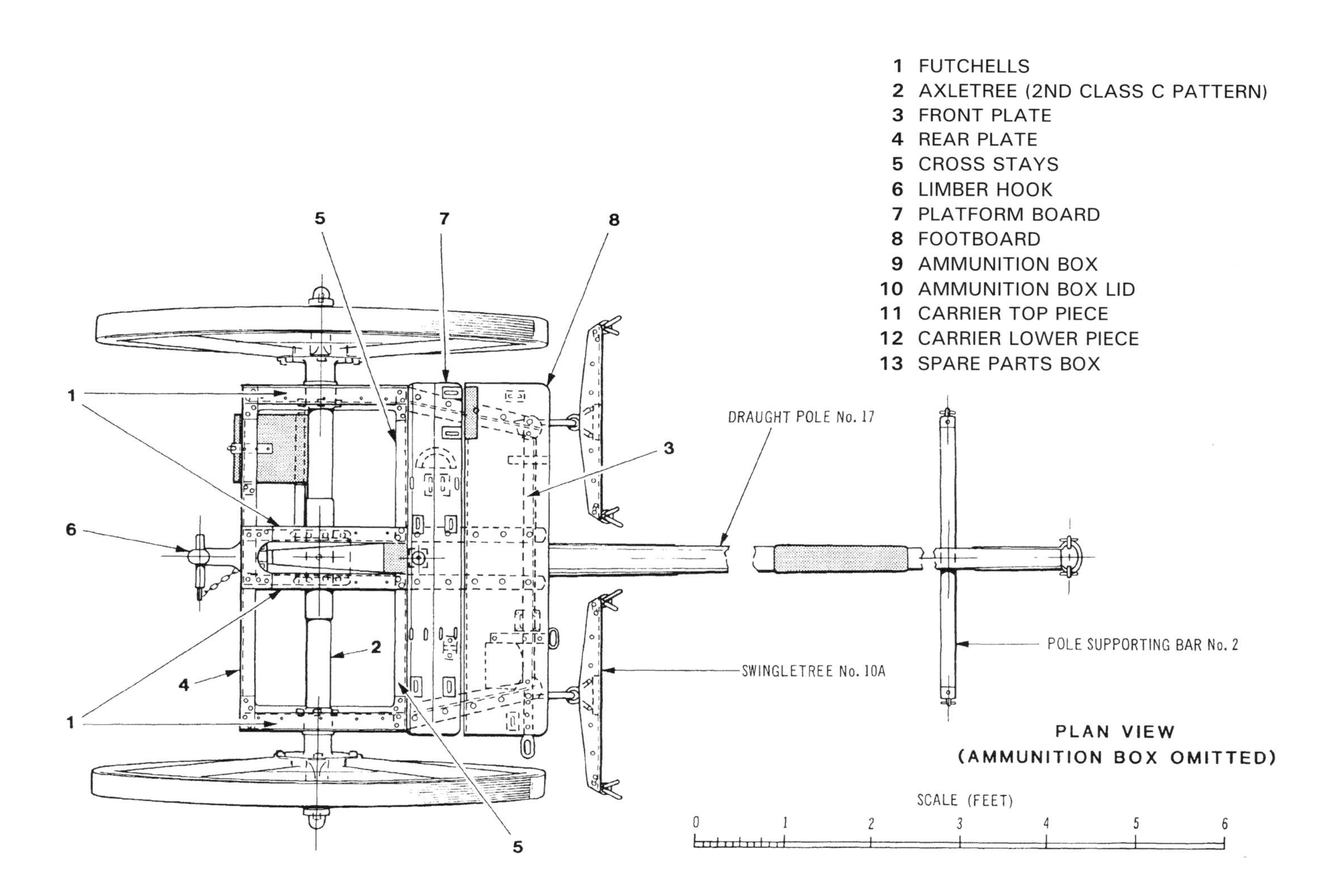
1 FUTCHELLS
2 AXLETREE (2ND CLASS C PATTERN)
3 FRONT PLATE
4 REAR PLATE
5 CROSS STAYS
6 LIMBER HOOK
7 PLATFORM BOARD
8 FOOTBOARD
9 AMMUNITION BOX
10 AMMUNITION BOX LID
11 CARRIER TOP PIECE
12 CARRIER LOWER PIECE
13 SPARE PARTS BOX
DRAUGHT POLE No. 17
SWINGLETREE No. 10A
POLE SUPPORTING BAR No. 2
PLAN VIEW
(AMMUNITION BOX OMITTED)
SCALE (FEET)
0
1
2
3
4
5
6

LIMBER

hook (**6**) had a hardened steel bearing plate welded in to prevent wear and was fitted with a steel keyed pin with chain.

The tubular steel axletree (**2**) fitted into bearings attached to the futchells (**1**), the inner bearings being riveted and the outer bearings bolted. The outer bearings had keys formed on them which fitted into keyways machined on the axletree shoulders. A locating pin passed through each outer bearing and the axletree (**2**) and was secured by a split pin.

The wheels were pattern No. 35A.

A platform board (**7**) of ash and a footboard (**8**) of elm were bolted across the front of the futchells (**1**), the footboard (**8**) being raised to a sloping position on elm brackets. The draught pole was secured in the pole staple by a pin passed down through the platform board (**7**) and held underneath by a key.

The ammunition box (**9**) was constructed of deal, with ends of elm. It was bolted to the limber frame.

The interior was divided horizontally into two compartments, the upper one partioned to carry fuzes, friction tubes and a small stores tray. The lower compartment held eleven ammunition carriers in angle section brass runners, screwed to the box bottom. The carriers were steadied at the top by beech battens secured to the underside of the horizontal partition board.

An ammunition carrier consisted of two rectangular pieces of beech, the lower one being recessed for the projectile bases and cartridge box, the top piece having cutouts to fit over the noses of the shells. Each carrier had a canvas lifting/carrying strap and held four rounds of shrapnel plus four cartridges, an exception being the centre carrier which held two rounds of case shot and four cartridges.

The box top was canvas covered, bound with iron and fitted with staples for straps to secure greatcoats and blankets. The upper corners were formed with sockets for the standards of the guard.

Ammunition wagon

The perch (**5**) was formed from steel plate into a box section tapering from the rear to the front. At the front was riveted a perch eye (**6**) having a hardened steel bearing piece welded in.

The frame consisted of two sides (**2**) of nickel steel plate, shaped to receive the axletree bearings (**14**). The sides (**2**) were bent upwards at the front to give the elm footboard (**3**) the required slope. A vertical flange was formed on each side (**2**) to prevent lateral movement of the ammunition box.

At the rear, the perch (**5**) and frame sides (**2**) were connected by a rear plate (**15**) formed to channel section and riveted in place.

Centrally, the perch (**5**) and frame sides (**2**) were joined by three cross stays (**13**) of channel section, one cross stay (**13**) each side joining a frame side (**2**) and the perch (**5**), the third stay being riveted inside the perch body.

The axletree (**16**) was of 2nd class, C pattern, the bearings (**14**)

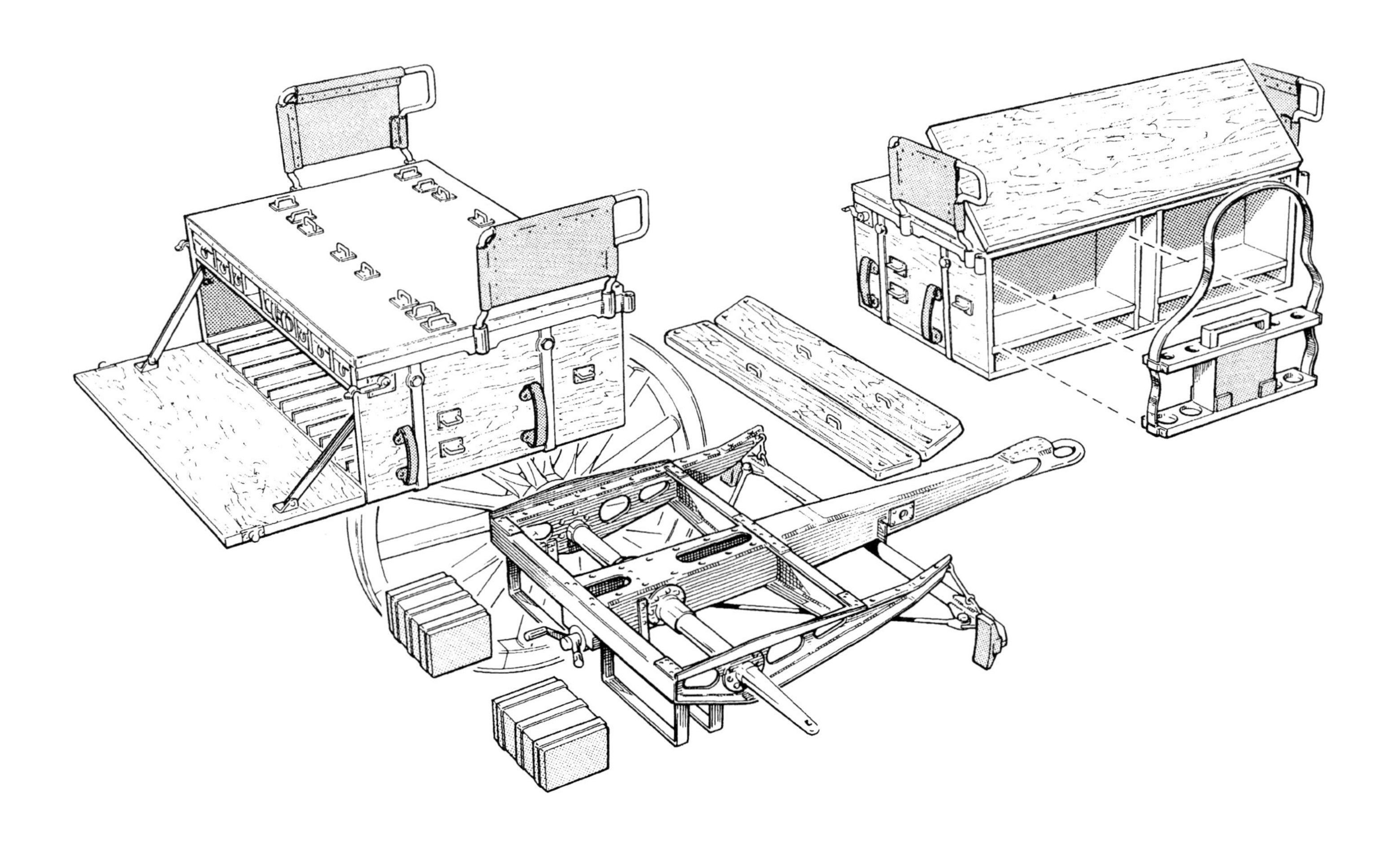

AMMUNITION WAGON

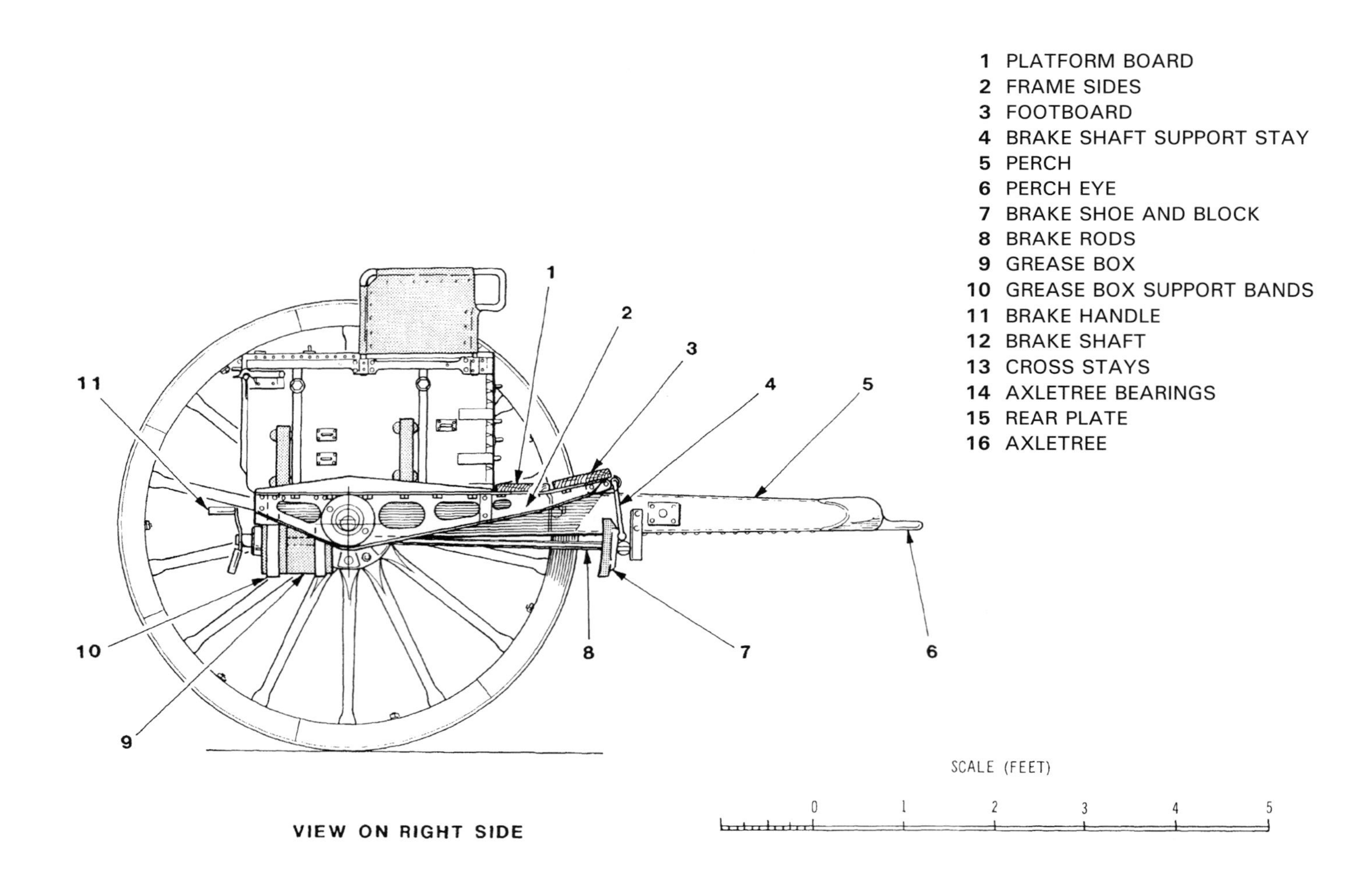

AMMUNITION WAGON

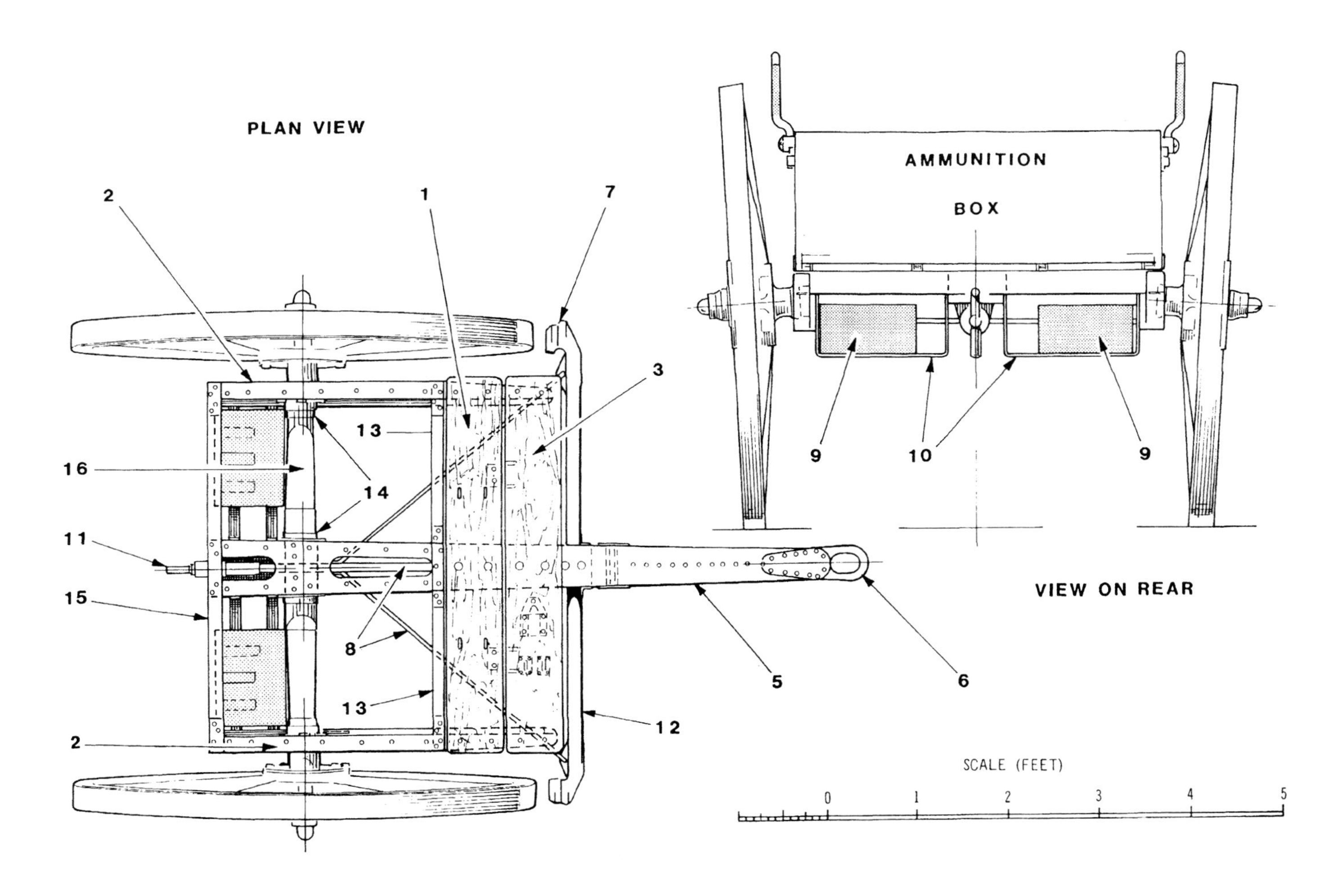

AMMUNITION WAGON

being riveted to the perch (**5**) and bolted to the frame sides (**2**).

The wheels were 2nd class, C pattern, No. 35A.

Two wood boxes (**9**) to hold grease tins were supported on steel bands (**10**) riveted to the perch (**5**) and frame sides (**2**). The frame sides (**2**) were joined at the front by an ash platform board (**1**) and elm footboard (**3**).

The brake consisted of a tubular steel shaft (**12**), fitted with a brake shoe and cast iron brake block (**7**) at either end. The transverse shaft (**12**) was hung below the perch (**5**) from the frame sides (**2**) front ends by support stays (**4**).

The shaft (**12**) was connected by three brake rods (**8**), the central one being threaded at the rear and working in a gunmetal nut fitted with a handle (**11**). The screw and nut were supported in gunmetal bearings bolted to the perch underside (**5**). A bracket, fitted below the perch, limited the brake shaft movement.

Ammunition box

Construction materials of the ammunition box were similar to that carried on the limber, the ammunition wagon box being larger. It was internally divided by a transverse vertical partition. The rear compartment was subdivided to contain twelve ammunition carriers in the lower part and fuzes, friction tubes plus a small stores tray in the upper part. The rear compartment lid was hinged at the bottom and supported, when open, on sliding stays. The front compartment was subdivided into three parts, the two outer ones containing two carriers each, the central part containing stores. The front compartment lid was hinged at the top and opened upwards. The lids were secured, when closed, by spring locks.

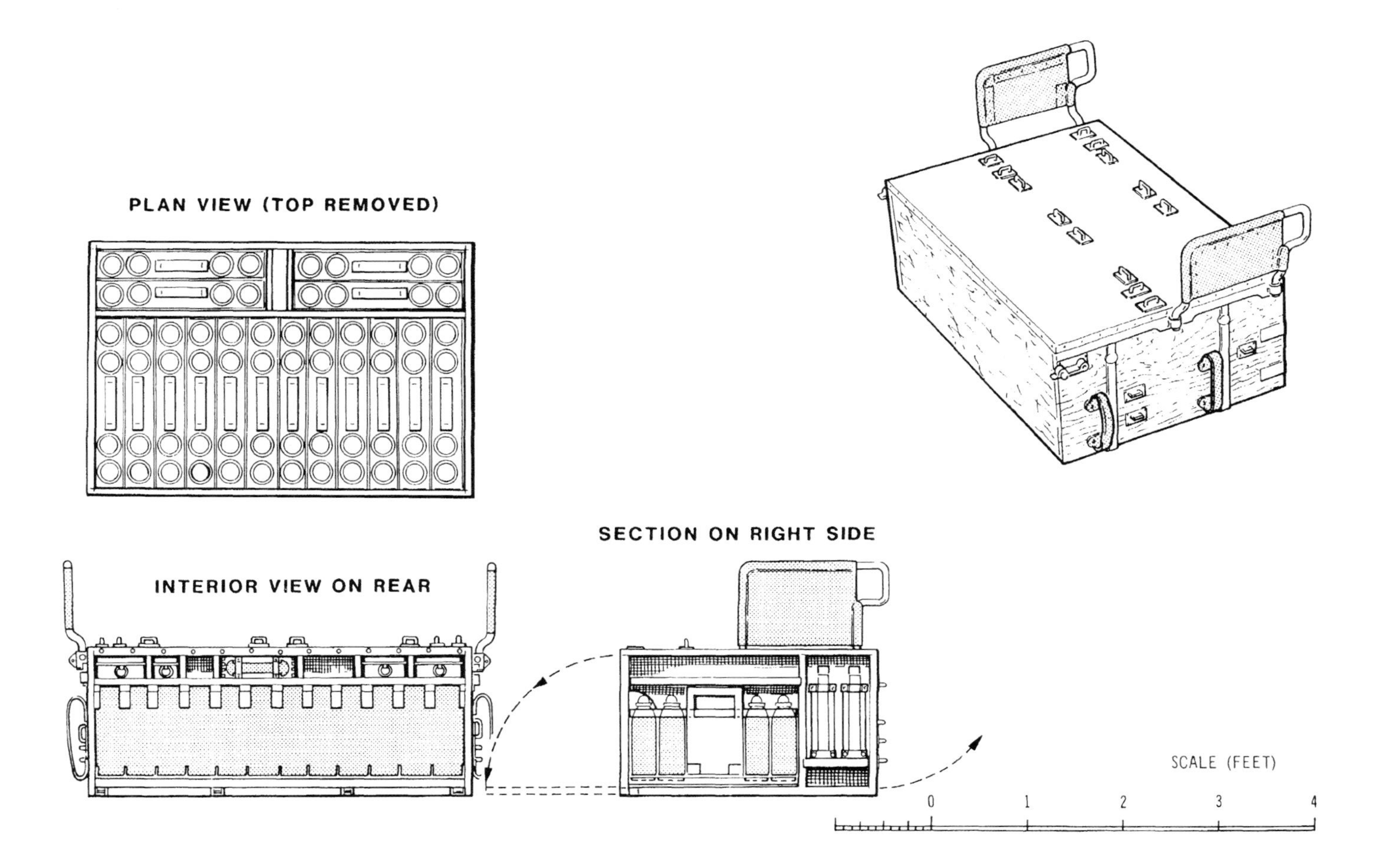

AMMUNITION BOX

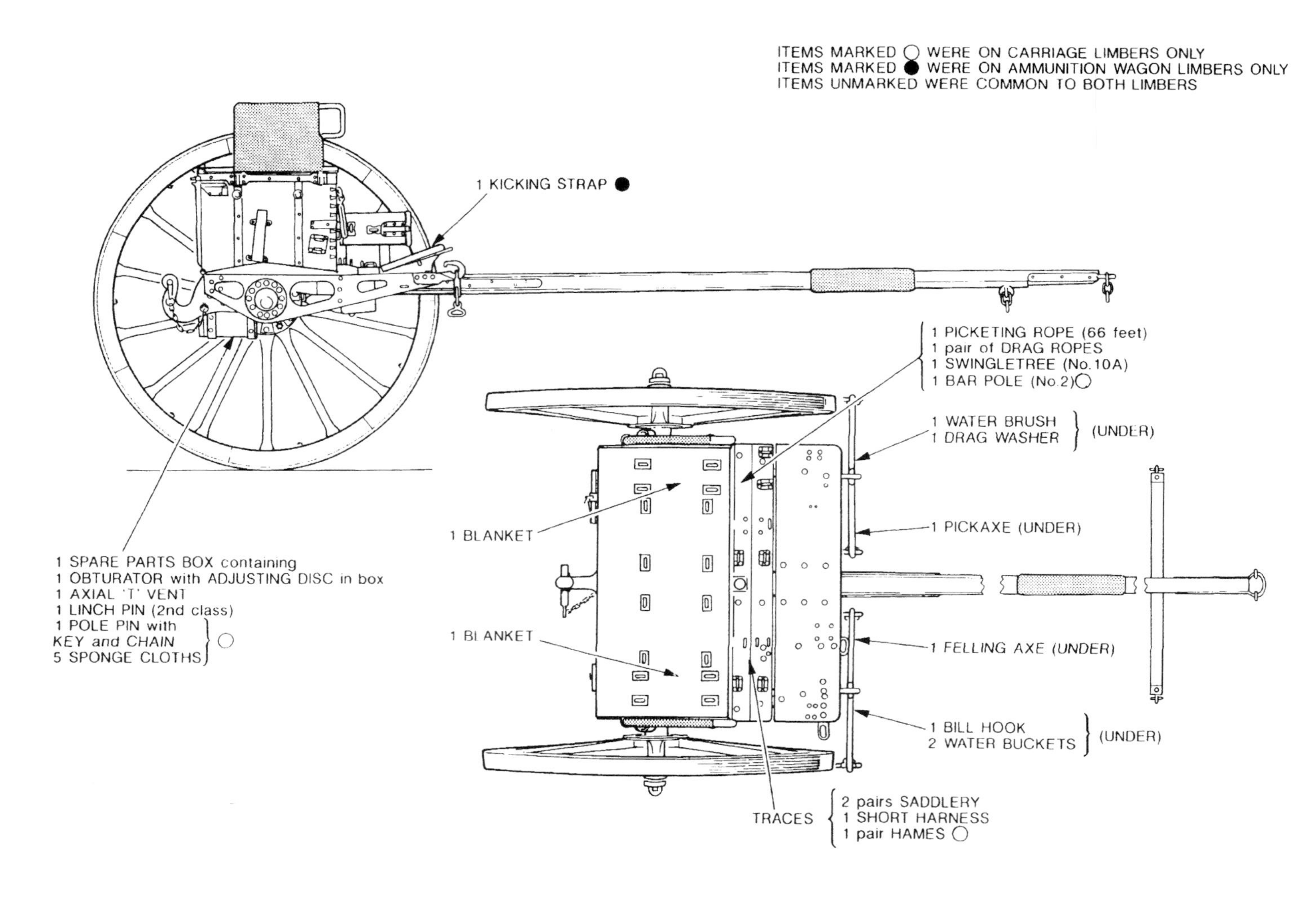

LIMBER STORES AND EQUIPMENT

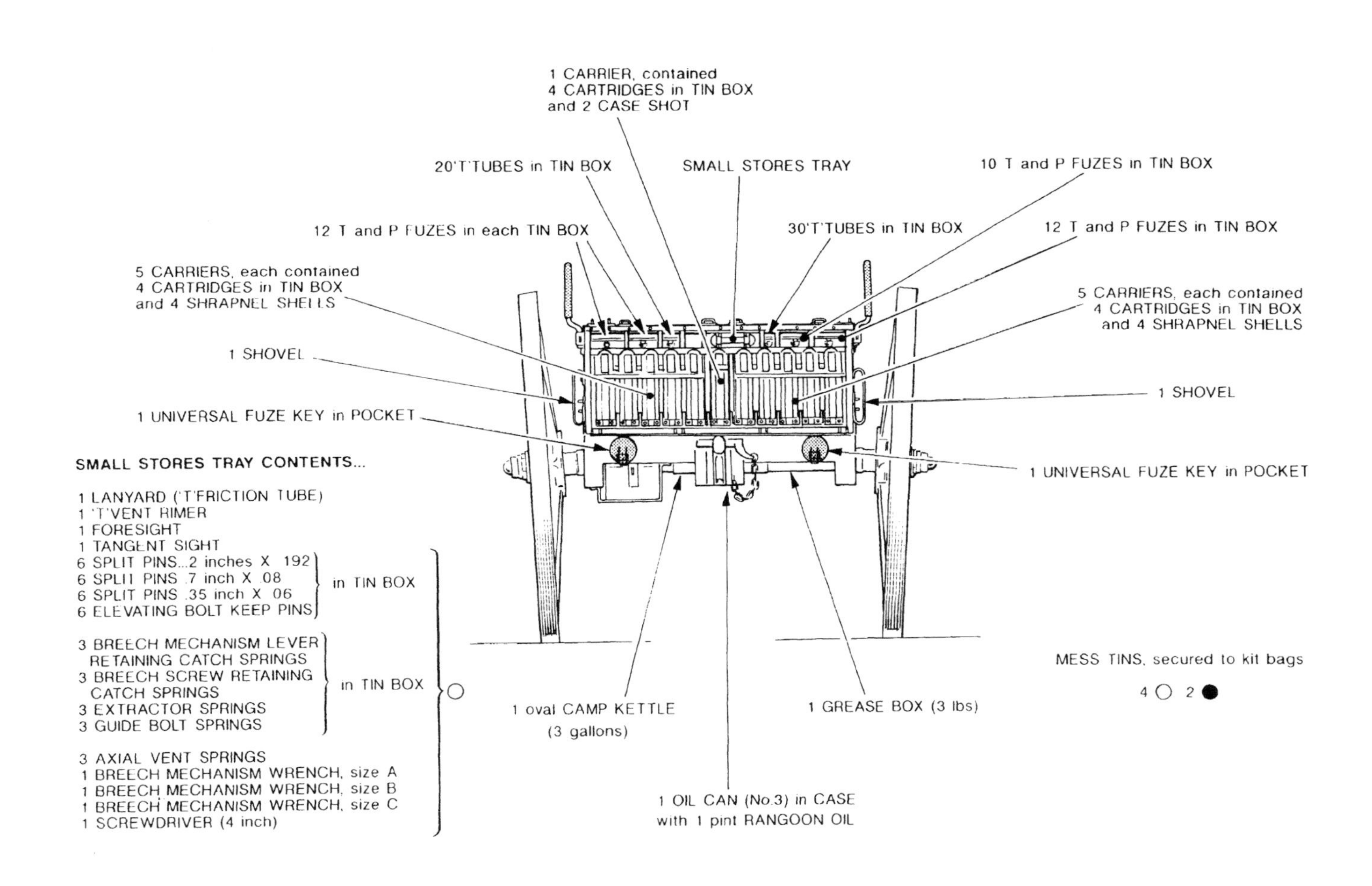

LIMBER STORES AND EQUIPMENT

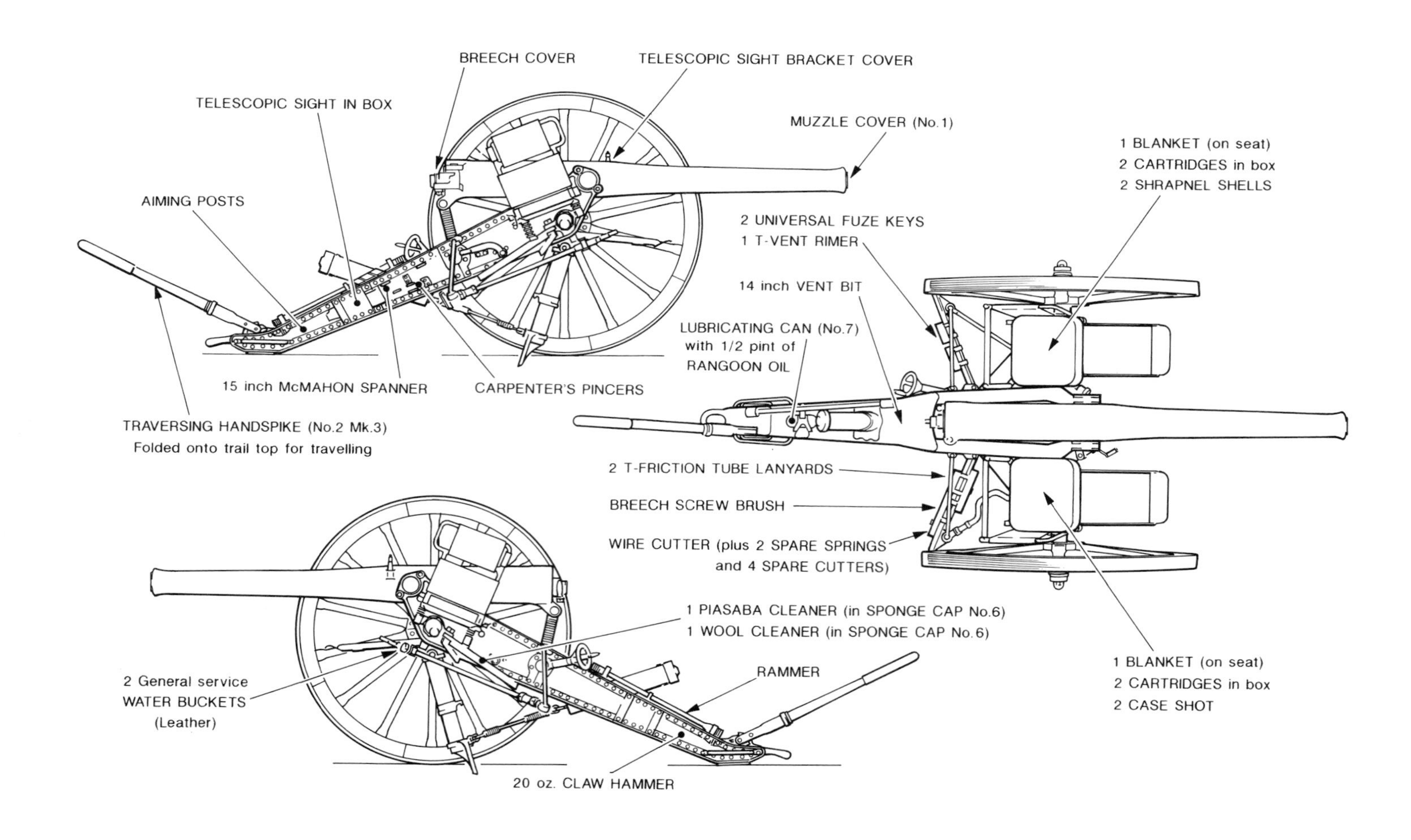

CARRIAGE STORES AND EQUIPMENT

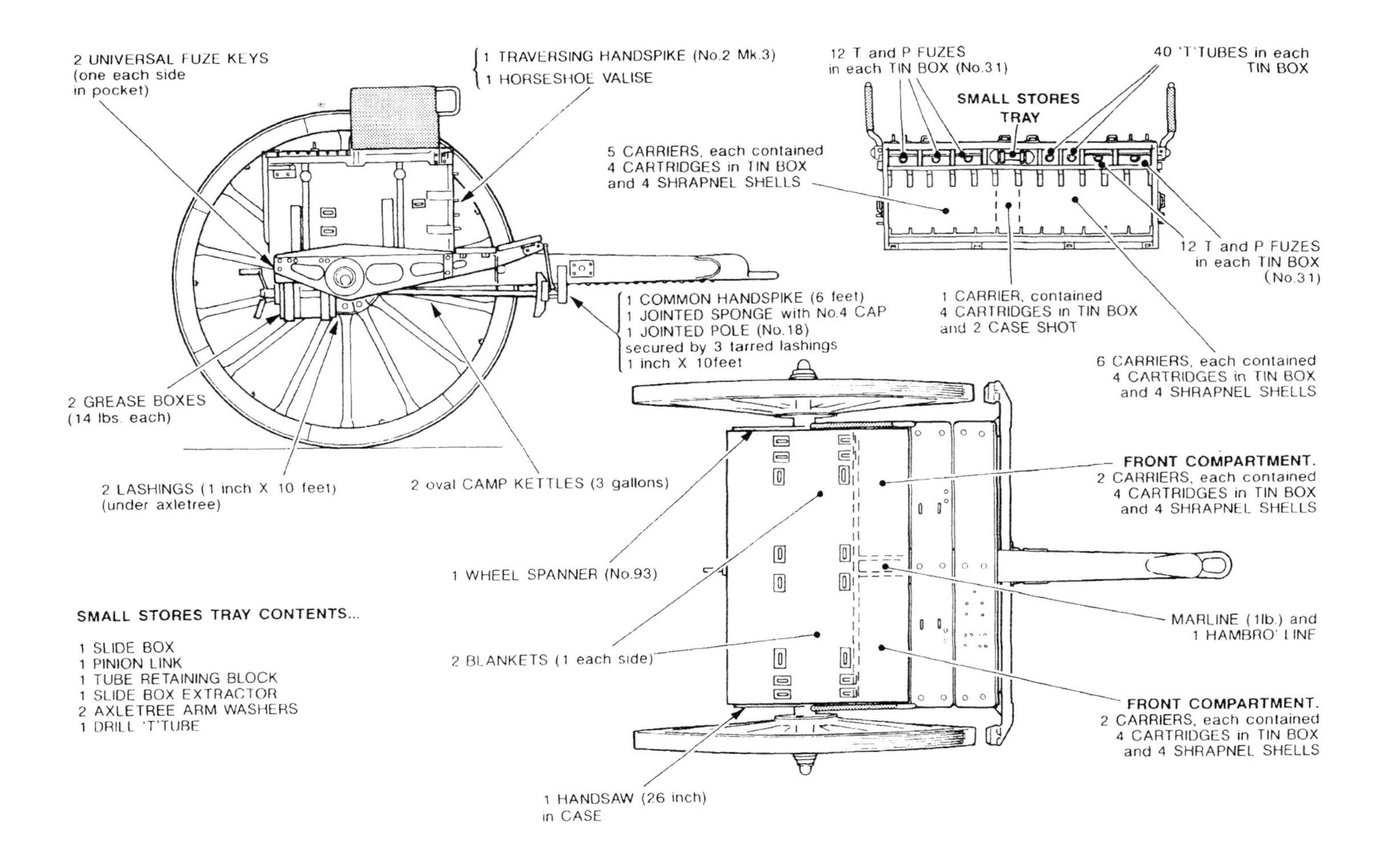

AMMUNITION WAGON STORES AND EQUIPMENT

BREECH LOADING (CONVERTED) 15 PDR MK. I

As a result of harsh lessons learned during the Boer War, guns were developed to improve the rate of fire, ammunition wagon numbers were increased and bulletproof shields fitted to afford the gun's crew some degree of protection from enemy fire. Many measures were adopted due to the Army Reforms of 1905. Among these was the merging of the former Yeomanry and Volunteers into the Territorial Force. Part of their artillery consisted of 15 pounder guns converted to so-called 'quick firing'. The gun illustrated and described in the following section is a converted Breech Loading 15 pdr Mk. I, this Mk. number being selected to avoid repetition of details in the previous section.

Weights (as packed)

Carriage with gun (without stores, shield and toolbox)	24cwt 2qtr 16 lb
Carriage limber	16 cwt 3 qtr
Ammunition wagon	20cwt 1 qtr 23 lb
Wagon limber	16 cwt 2 qtr

Trail (converted)(see page 132)

The trail extension consisted of angle steel side brackets, closed by steel side plates and connected by top and bottom plates with a transom.

The trail eye was riveted to the rear end and a hardened steel sole plate was riveted to the extension underside. A steel guide plate, to bear against the front of the spade, was riveted to the trail underside.

The trail extension rested upon the spade assembly and could be traversed through two degrees of movement, left or right, by sliding on the spade.

Trail spade with traversing and locking arrangement (see page 133)

The trail spade assembly comprised the following parts: a steel spade frame (**8**), a nickel steel spade blade (**7**), a steel trough (**9**) and steel stays (**6**). All other components combined to form the traversing and locking assembly.

The spade frame consisted of a curved blade (**7**), stiffened by toe plates at the sides and centre. The upper portion had an aperture cut in it and was braced at the top by an angle frame (**8**) in which were cut five notches, engaged by a pawl catch (**11**). When travelling, the catch locked the trail to the spade. The trail passed through and worked across the spade aperture, being clipped to the spade by a steel pivot block (**10**) bolted to the top of the trail eye. A trough (**9**) was riveted to the spade rear. Tapered stays (**6**) were riveted to the spade front equipped with lifting handles.

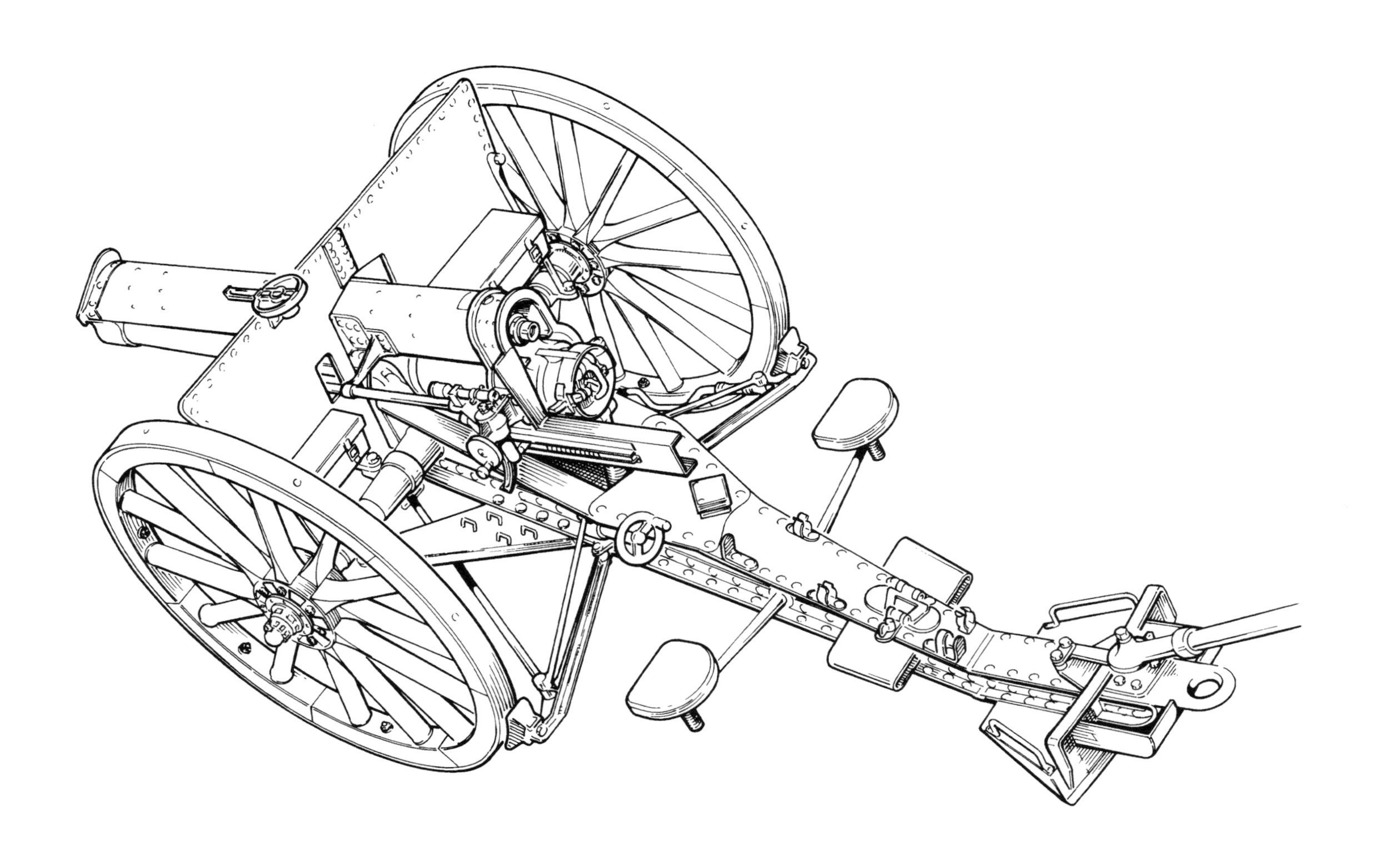

BREECH LOADING (CONVERTED) 15 PDR. MK. I

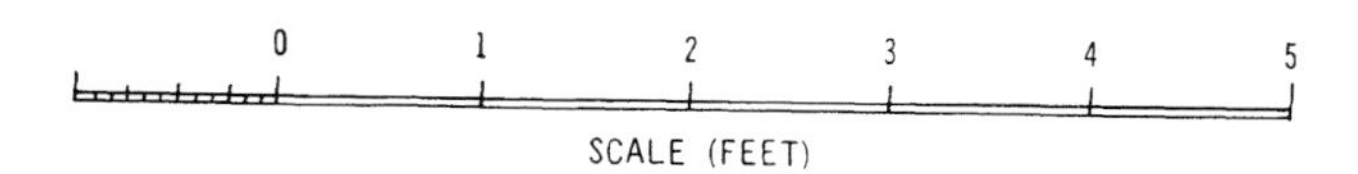

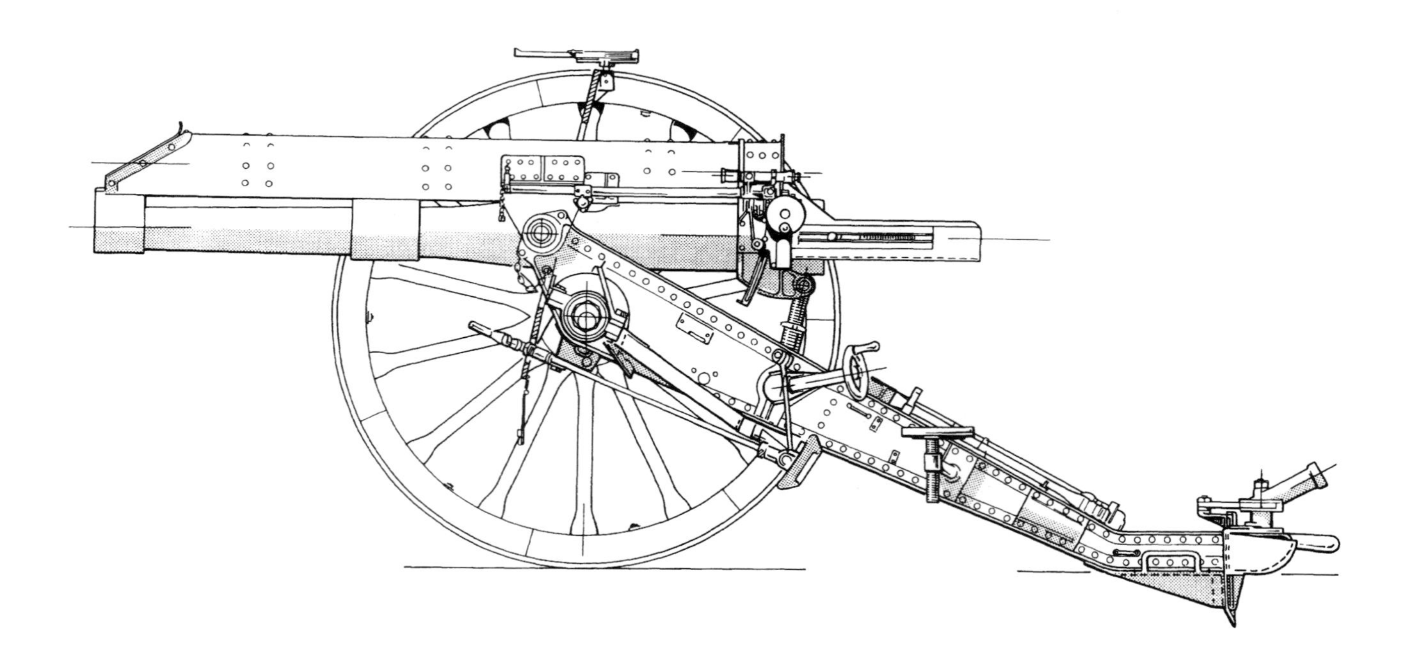

CARRIAGE – BREECH LOADING (CONVERTED) 15 PDR. MK. I

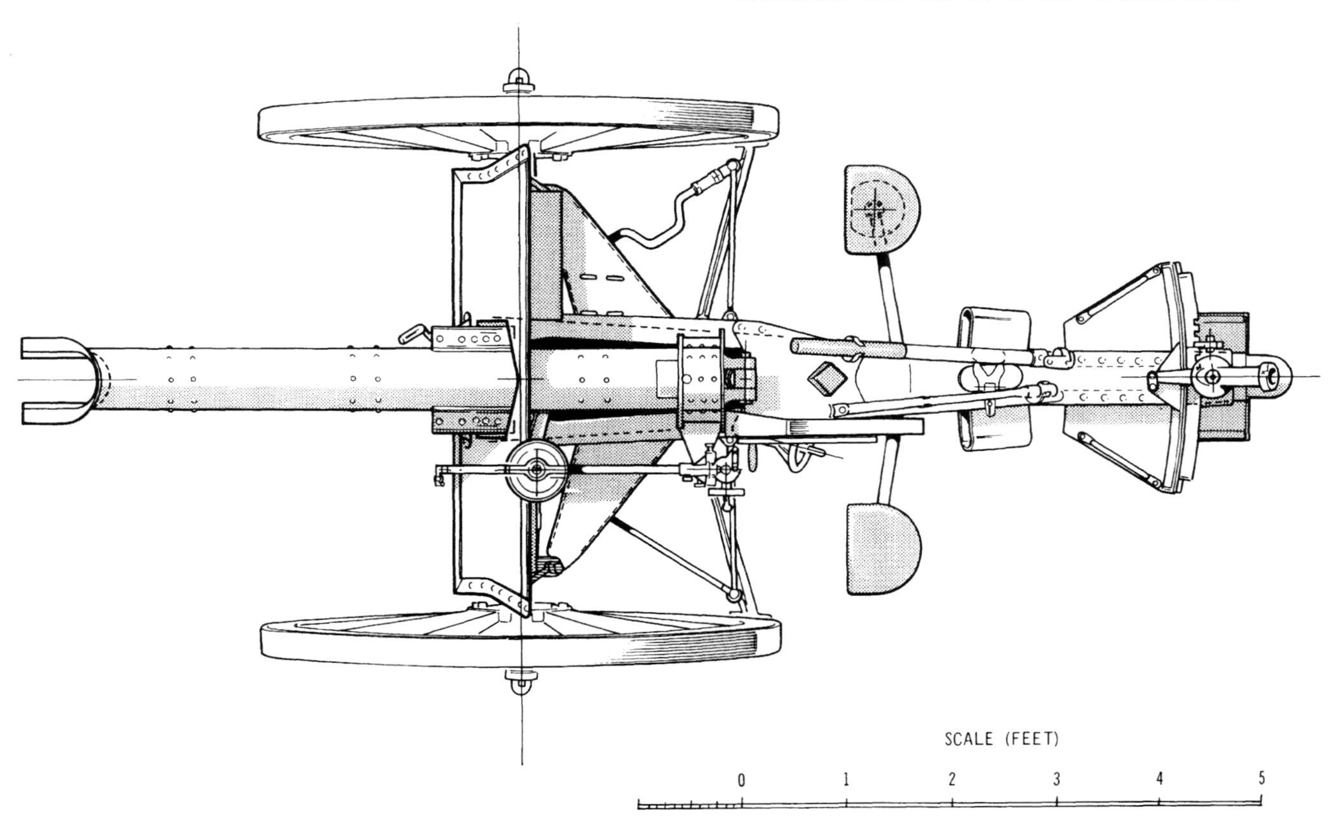

CARRIAGE – BREECH LOADING (CONVERTED) 15 PDR. MK. I

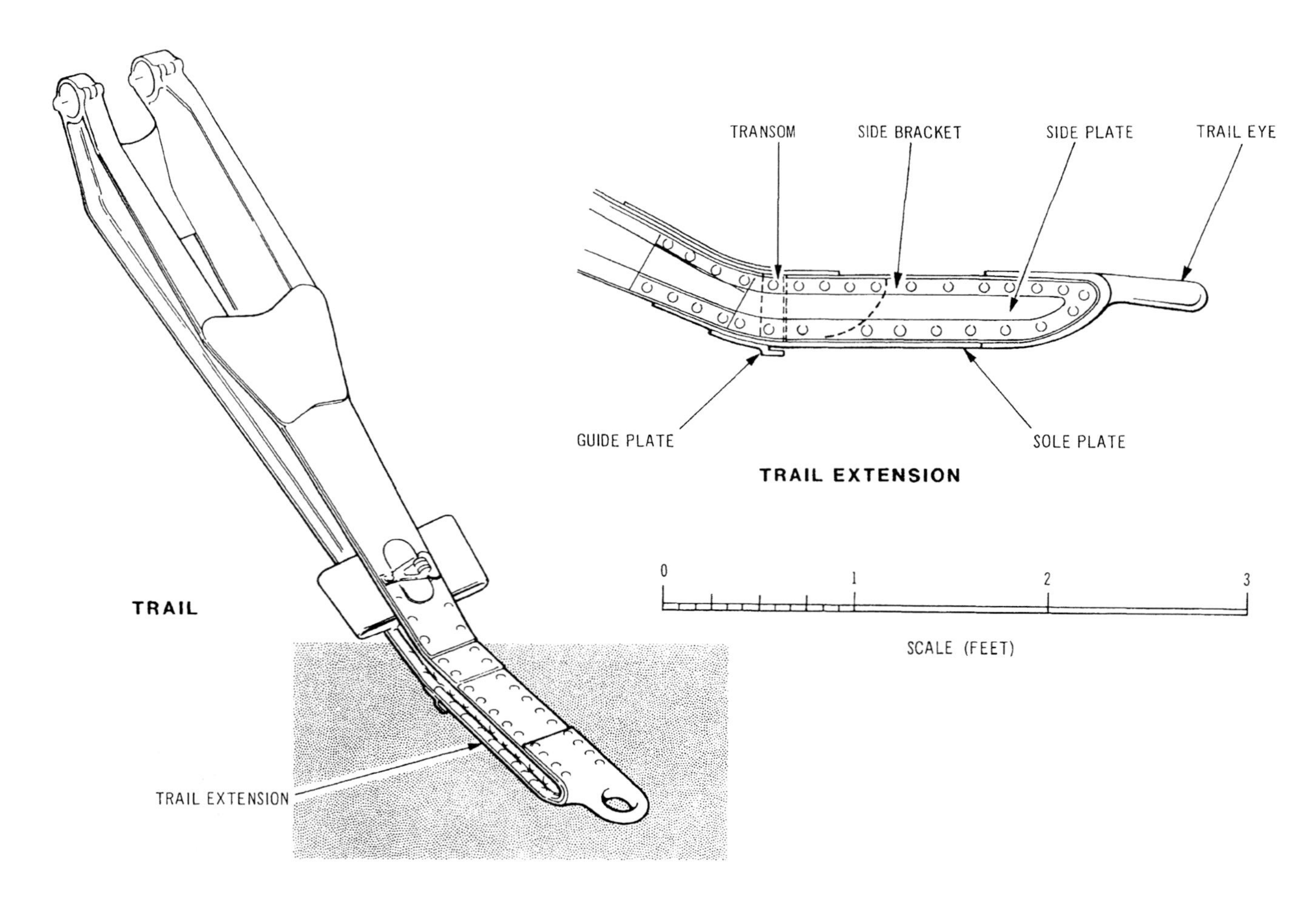

TRAIL (CONVERTED)

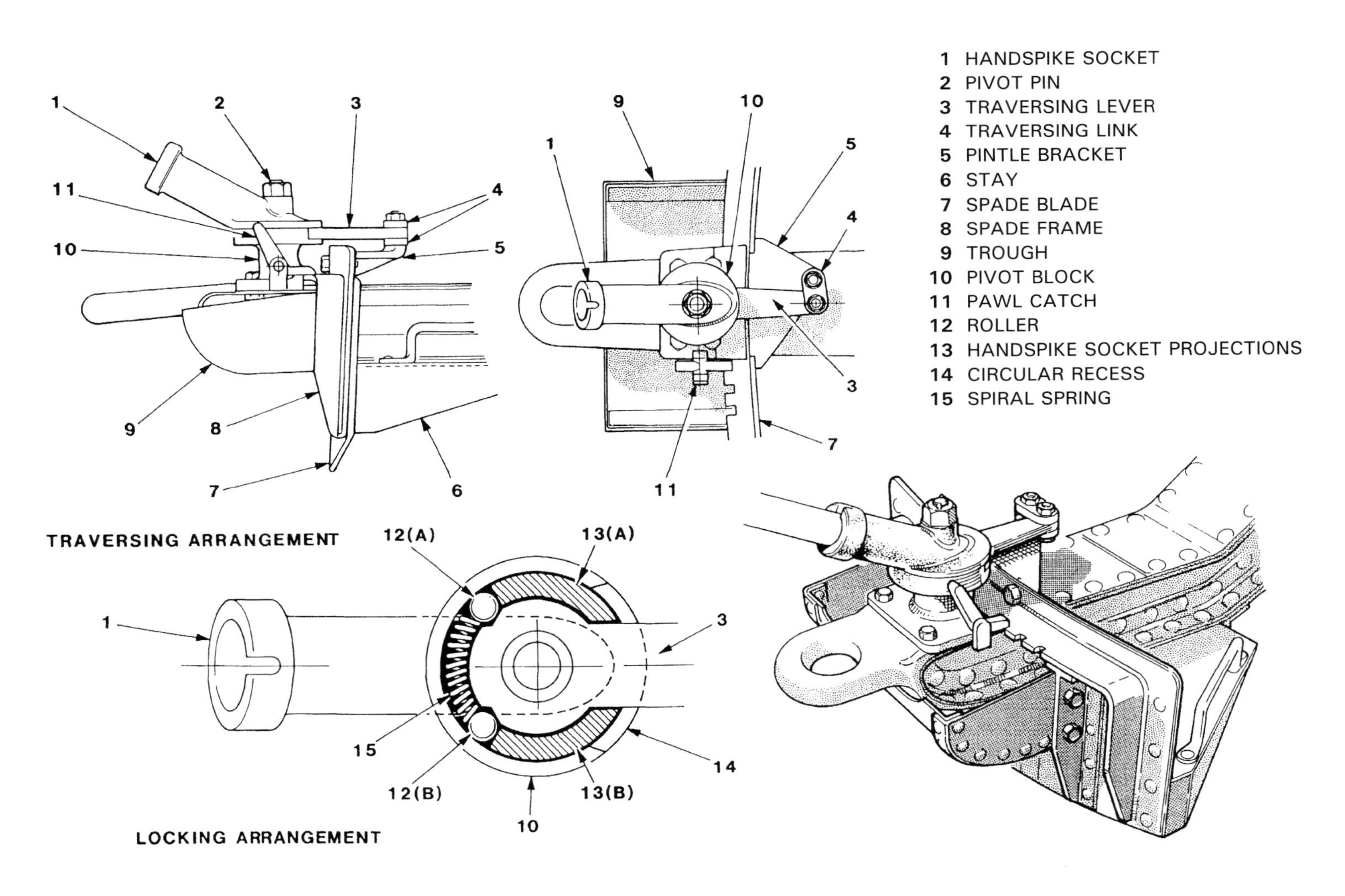

TRAVERSING AND LOCKING ARRANGEMENT

To traverse, the handspike (**1**) was moved in the required direction (say to the left), causing the socket projection (**13B**) to free the roller (**12B**) from the wedging action of the flat cut into the traversing lever (**3**). At the same time the socket projection (**13A**) butted against the traversing lever (**3**); continued movement of the handspike (**1**) traversed the trail across the spade.

With the handspike socket (**1**) at rest, the assembly locked itself against any tendency of the trail to move the traversing lever (**3**), by means of the flats cut into the traversing lever (**3**) jamming the rollers (**12**).

Cradle

The cradle was a steel forging, forming, when in position, an inverted trough. The lower edges were flanged towards the inside and were the ribs, or rails, on which the barrel bearing rings moved longitudinally on firing.

The front, upper portion of the cradle was tapered and strengthened by angle steel. At the rear, a forged steel band was riveted to the cradle. This band had formed on it the lugs for attachment of the elevating gear.

The body of the cradle was braced by three semi-circular transoms, riveted to the interior. These had circular bores forming bearings to locate the outer spring case, the two rear transom bores being screw-threaded, the thread being continuous from one bearing to the other.

Trunnion assemblies were riveted to the cradle, each formed of three manganese bronze brackets. The two lower brackets had circular bosses fitted one inside the other and retained by a large rivet. These bosses formed the trunnions proper.

Holes were provided on the left-hand side for the two mounting brackets of a rocking bar sight and at the rear for a steel guard, to protect the gun layer.

On the outside face of the layer's guard were riveted steel guides, in which ran a rectangular steel bar, fitted with the firing handle. On the inside of the bar and protruding towards the barrel, was a projection which engaged the firing lever pivoted to the breech. The firing handle was held in the forward position by a spiral spring.

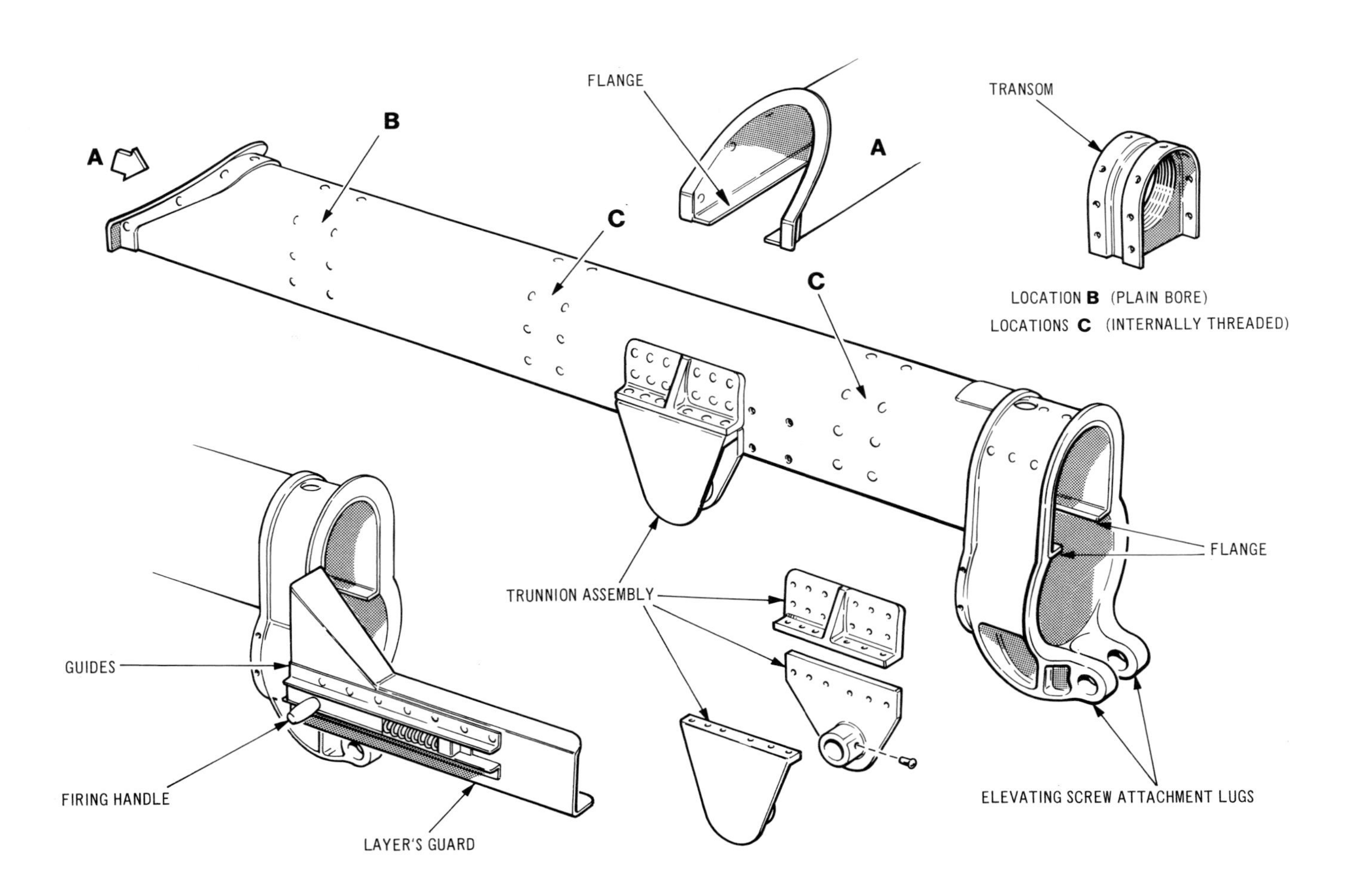
FLANGE
TRANSOM
B
A
A
C
C
LOCATION B (PLAIN BORE)
LOCATIONS C (INTERNALLY THREADED)
FLANGE
TRUNNION ASSEMBLY
GUIDES
FIRING HANDLE
LAYER'S GUARD
ELEVATING SCREW ATTACHMENT LUGS

CRADLE

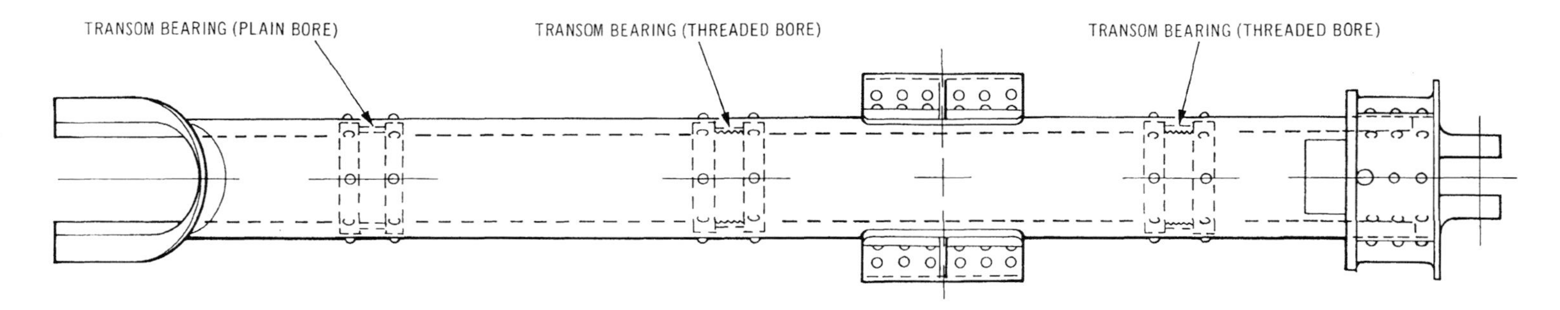

PLAN VIEW

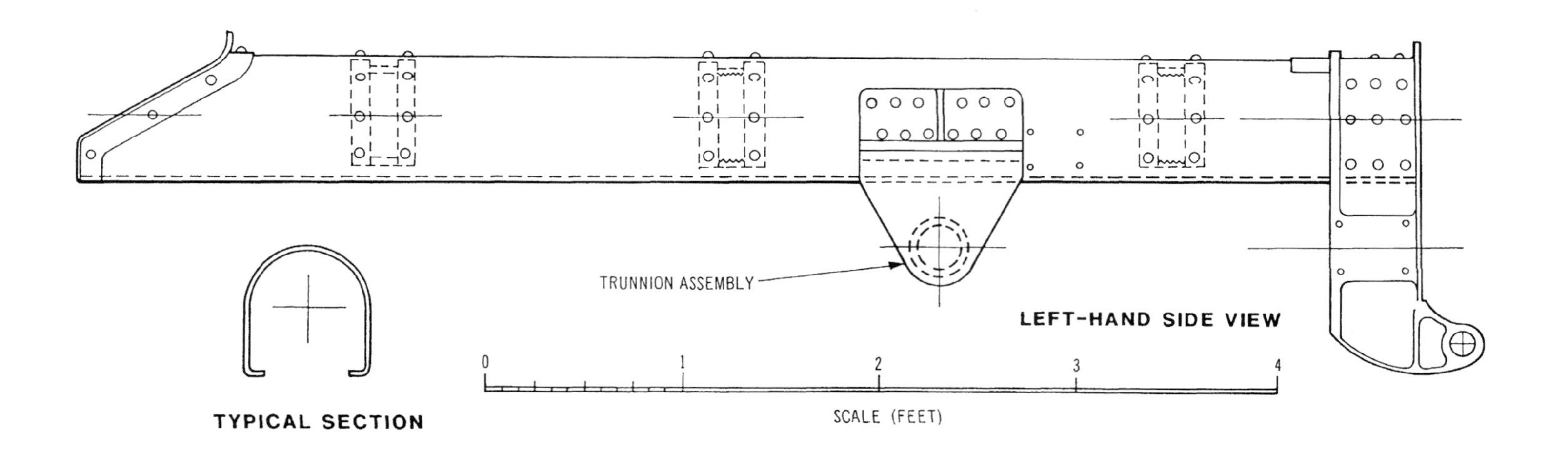

LEFT-HAND SIDE VIEW

TYPICAL SECTION

CRADLE

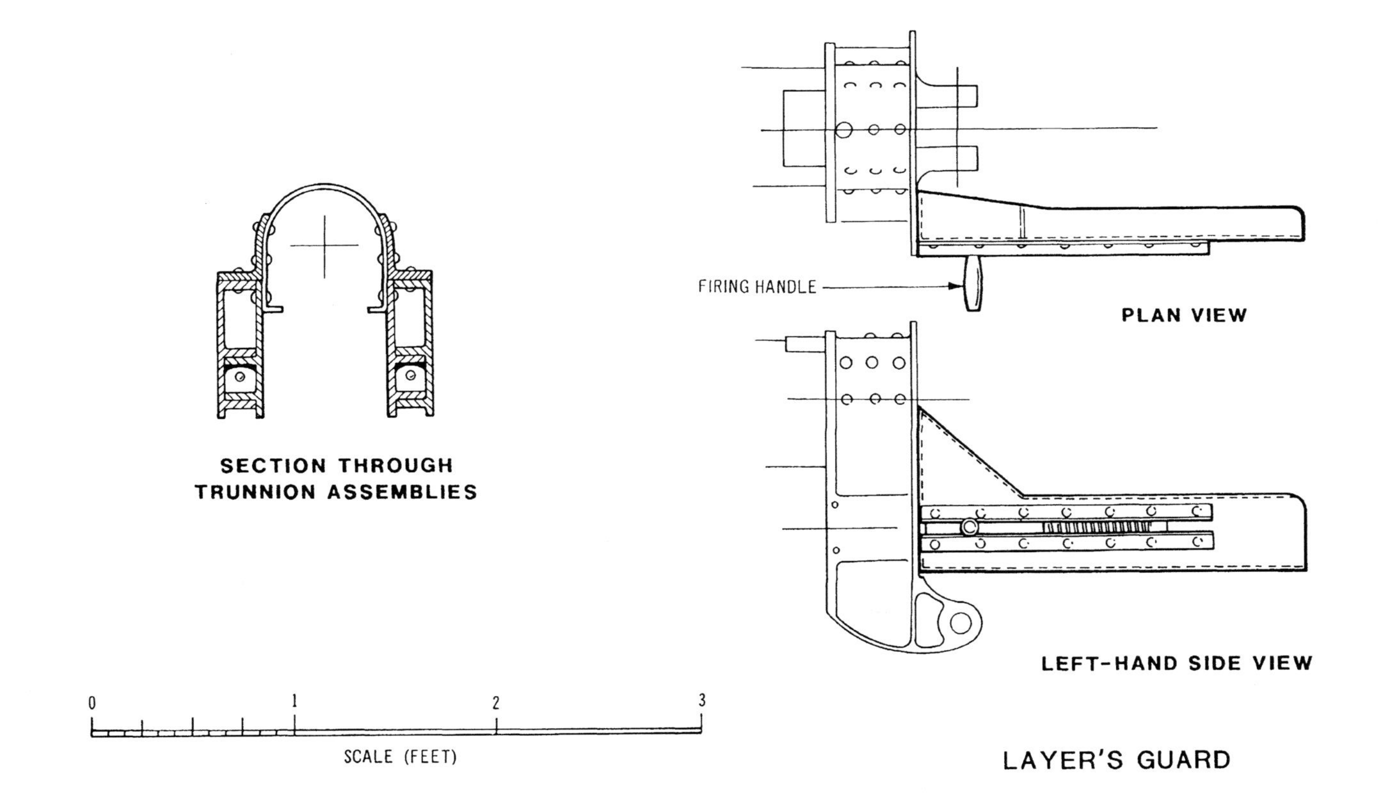
FIRING HANDLE
PLAN VIEW
SECTION THROUGH
TRUNNION ASSEMBLIES
LEFT-HAND SIDE VIEW
0
1
2
3
SCALE (FEET)
LAYER'S GUARD

CRADLE

Hydraulic buffer and springs

The hydraulic buffer (**25**) was a forged steel tube, the rear end closed by a steel connecting bracket (**24**) screwed and soldered in place. The bracket (**24**) connected to the barrel lug (**21**) by flanged front (**19**) and rear (**22**) connecting nuts, the front nut (**19**) being drilled through the top to admit a filler hole plug (**20**) to close the filler hole in the connecting bracket (**24**).

The connecting bracket bore was threaded to take a steel controlling plunger (**17**) screwed up against a copper washer (**23**), the thread being grooved to enable air to vent during filling of the buffer with the plunger unscrewed through two turns.

Screwed into the front of the buffer cylinder (**25**) was a manganese bronze stuffing box (**29**), butted against a sealing washer of anhydrous leather. The stuffing box (**29**) held two manganese bronze, coned supporting rings (**27**) trapping a packing ring of asbestos (**28**) protected by canvas, all held against the piston rod (**15**) by a manganese bronze gland (**3**). The stuffing box (**29**) was locked on assembly by a small spring stud with keep pin (**4**) housed in a recess in the front end of the buffer cylinder (**25**).

Tapered grooves were cut into the bore of the buffer cylinder (**25**) to graduate hydraulic pressure during recoil. The tubular steel piston rod (**15**) was secured to the outer spring case cap (**2**) at the forward end and keyed to prevent rotation. The rear end carried a manganese bronze piston (**18**) screwed and soldered on.

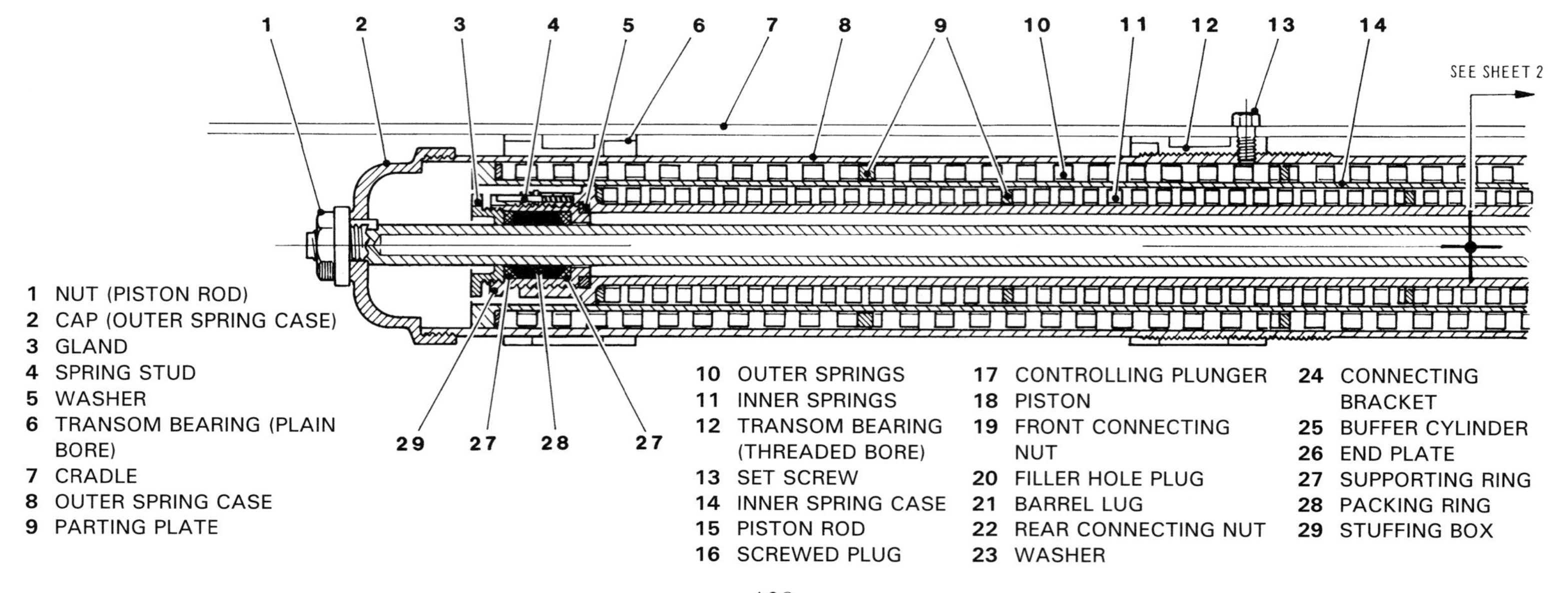

1 NUT (PISTON ROD)
2 CAP (OUTER SPRING CASE)
3 GLAND
4 SPRING STUD
5 WASHER
6 TRANSOM BEARING (PLAIN BORE)
7 CRADLE
8 OUTER SPRING CASE
9 PARTING PLATE
10 OUTER SPRINGS
11 INNER SPRINGS
12 TRANSOM BEARING (THREADED BORE)
13 SET SCREW
14 INNER SPRING CASE
15 PISTON ROD
16 SCREWED PLUG
17 CONTROLLING PLUNGER
18 PISTON
19 FRONT CONNECTING NUT
20 FILLER HOLE PLUG
21 BARREL LUG
22 REAR CONNECTING NUT
23 WASHER
24 CONNECTING BRACKET
25 BUFFER CYLINDER
26 END PLATE
27 SUPPORTING RING
28 PACKING RING
29 STUFFING BOX

A chamber, formed by plugging the piston rod (**16**) had, operating within it, the controlling plunger (**17**), which was tapered at its front and two flats, deepened at their rear, to control the hydraulic oil during running out. A threaded recess in the rear of the controlling plunger (**17**) was used during operation of the spring compressing apparatus.

Two banks of springs, an outer bank (**10**) and inner bank (**11**), surrounded the buffer cylinder (**25**) contained within steel cases. The outer spring case (**8**) was screwed into the two rear transom bearings (**12**) and secured by a set screw (**13**). The outer spring case (**8**) had a rear inner flange, bearing against the outer springs (**10**). The inner spring case (**14**) was a loose fit between the buffer cylinder (**25**) and outer spring case (**8**). It had a front outer flange and rear inner flange bearing against the outer springs (**10**) and inner springs (**11**) respectively.

The buffer cylinder (**25**) had a front external flange bearing against the inner springs (**11**). There were four springs in each bank, separated by manganese bronze parting plates (**9**). Steel end plates (**26**) were placed at the front and rear of each bank. The outer springs (**10**) had a right-hand pitch and the inner springs (**11**) a left-hand pitch.

On firing, the gun barrel recoiled towards the rear, drawing the buffer cylinder (**25**) over the piston (**18**) and forcing the hydraulic

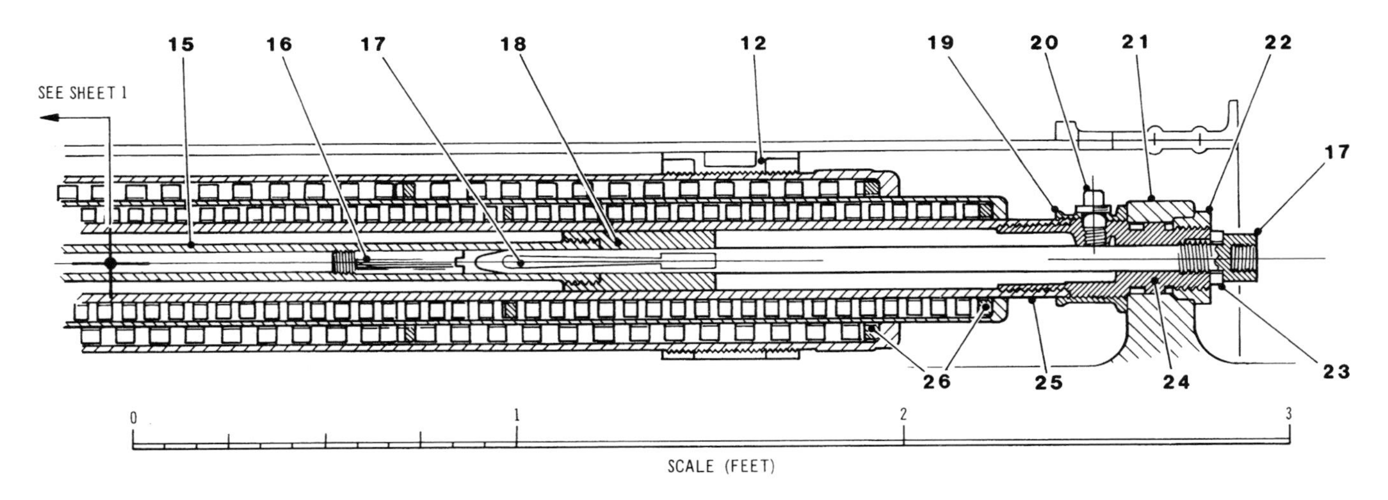

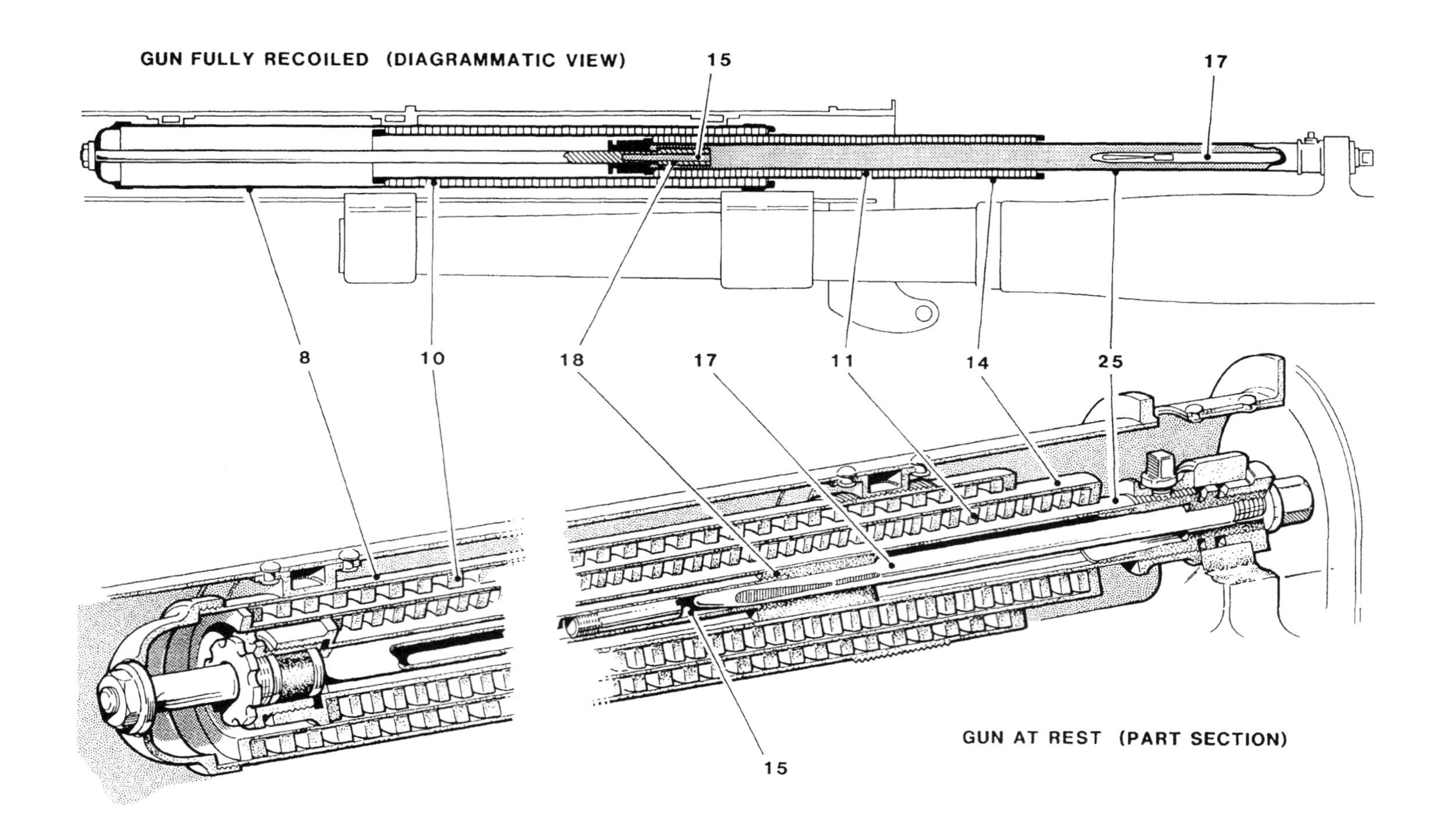

HYDRAULIC BUFFER AND SPRINGS (OPERATION)

oil rearwards through the clearance between the two. The tapering grooves graduated the flow in such a manner as to give the required hydraulic resistance without allowing the carriage to lift about the point of the trail.

With recoil energy absorbed, the springs (**10** and **11**) returned the barrel to the firing position. The controlling plunger (**17**) displaced the oil in the piston rod recess (**15**) and cushioned the final movement, bringing the barrel gradually to rest.

Recoil travel was 42 inches.

Shield

The shield was of sheet steel, strengthened by wooden slats, secured to the axletree by brackets and stays. It was in two parts, upper and lower, these being hinged together. The lower part would be raised and strapped for travelling.

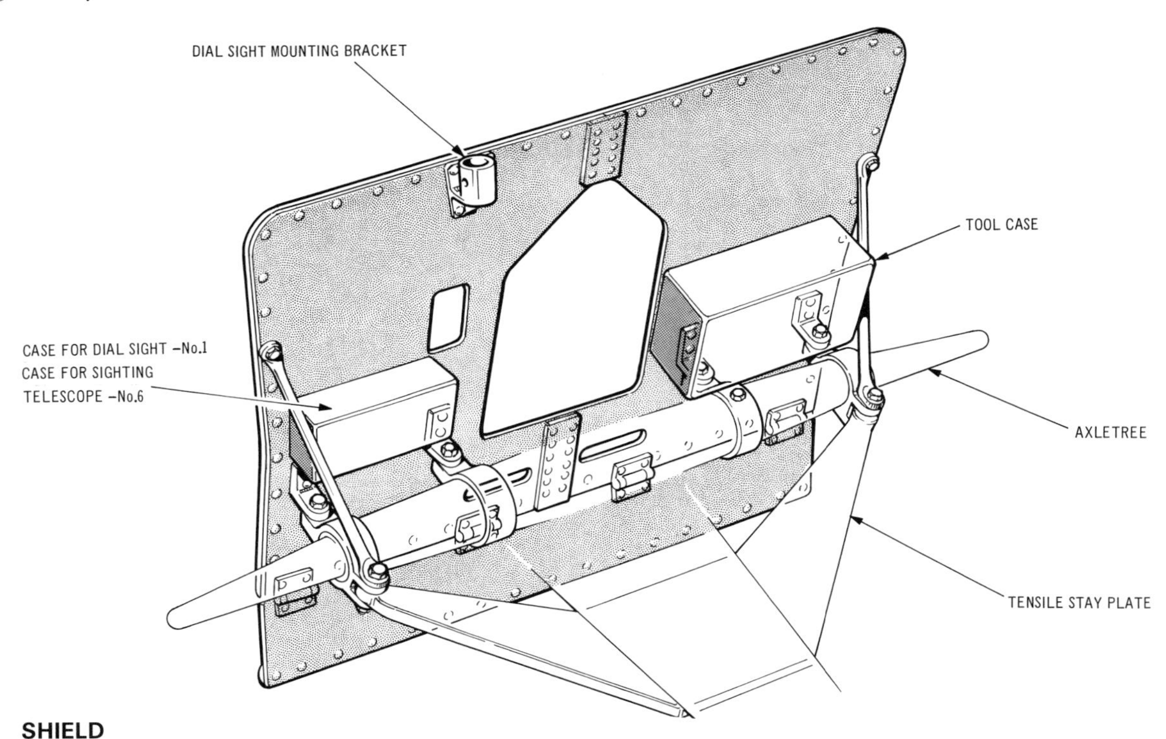

SHIELD

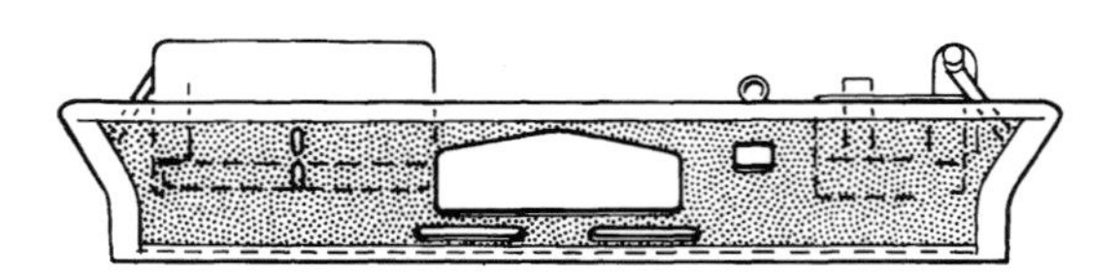

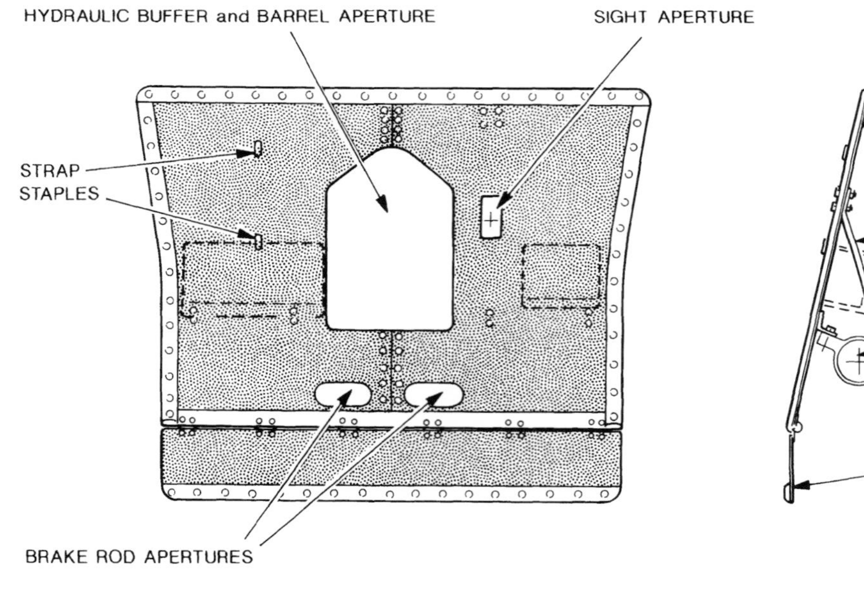

VIEW ON SHIELD FRONT FACE

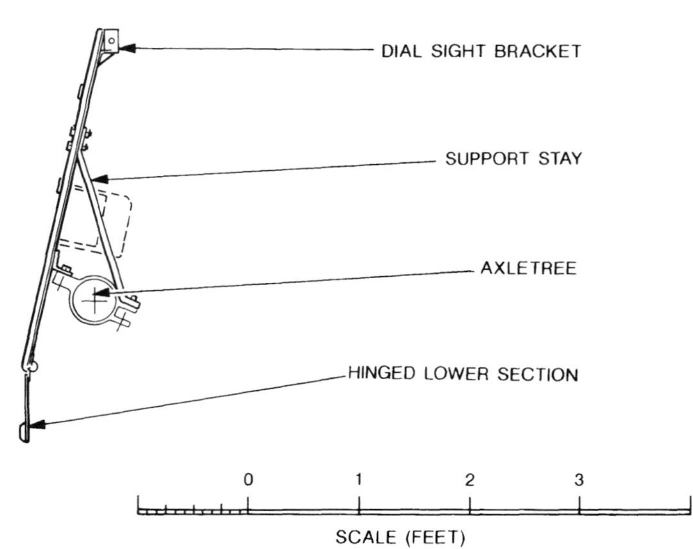

SHIELD

Barrel and breech

The Breech Loading Mk. I barrel was converted by removing the trunnions, sight brackets and elevating gear attachment lugs. The radial T-vent hole was plugged. The holes in the jacket which passed through the trunnion centres were sealed with screwed steel plugs. Holes in the hood for fitting tangent sights were plugged with white metal alloy.

The converted barrel consisted of a steel A tube, partially reinforced by a jacket shrunk on and secured by interlocking rings. The jacket was extended at the rear and machined internally for the breech screw. Bearing against the front of the jacket and shrunk onto the A tube was the C hoop, locked to the A tube by a set screw.

A steel bearing ring was shrunk around the chase and another around the muzzle. These supported the barrel in the cradle. Towards the rear end of the jacket was a steel breech ring, shrunk on and secured by interlocking rings, formed with a lug for the attachment of a hydraulic buffer.

Onto the rear end of the jacket was screwed a steel hood, for the attachment and protection of the breech fittings, secured by an inset steel plate and screws.

The chamber was cylindrical, 11 inches long and 3.625 inches in diameter, slightly coned at the entrance and reducing at the front with a curved slope. Chamber capacity was 117 cubic inches.

These barrels were rifled to one of three patterns, listed in the table.

A face for a clinometer was machined on the hood upper side at the rear.

The barrel Mk. number, registered number, manufacturer's initials, year of conversion and weight were engraved on the upper side of the breech ring at the rear.

Barrel weight was 8cwt (896 pounds).

Rifling	Grooves				
Mk. No.	Number	Depth	Width	Type	Twist
1	12	.04	.60	Polygroove-hook section	Increasing from 1 turn in 120 calibres at breech to 1 turn in 28 calibres at 35.8 inches from muzzle then constant
2	18	.04	.40		
3	18	.04	.265	Poygroove-plain section	Straight from breech to 53.6 inches from muzzle, then gain twist to 1 turn in 30 calibres at muzzle

After 1912 Mk. 2 rifling replaced Mk. 3 in manufacture and repair.

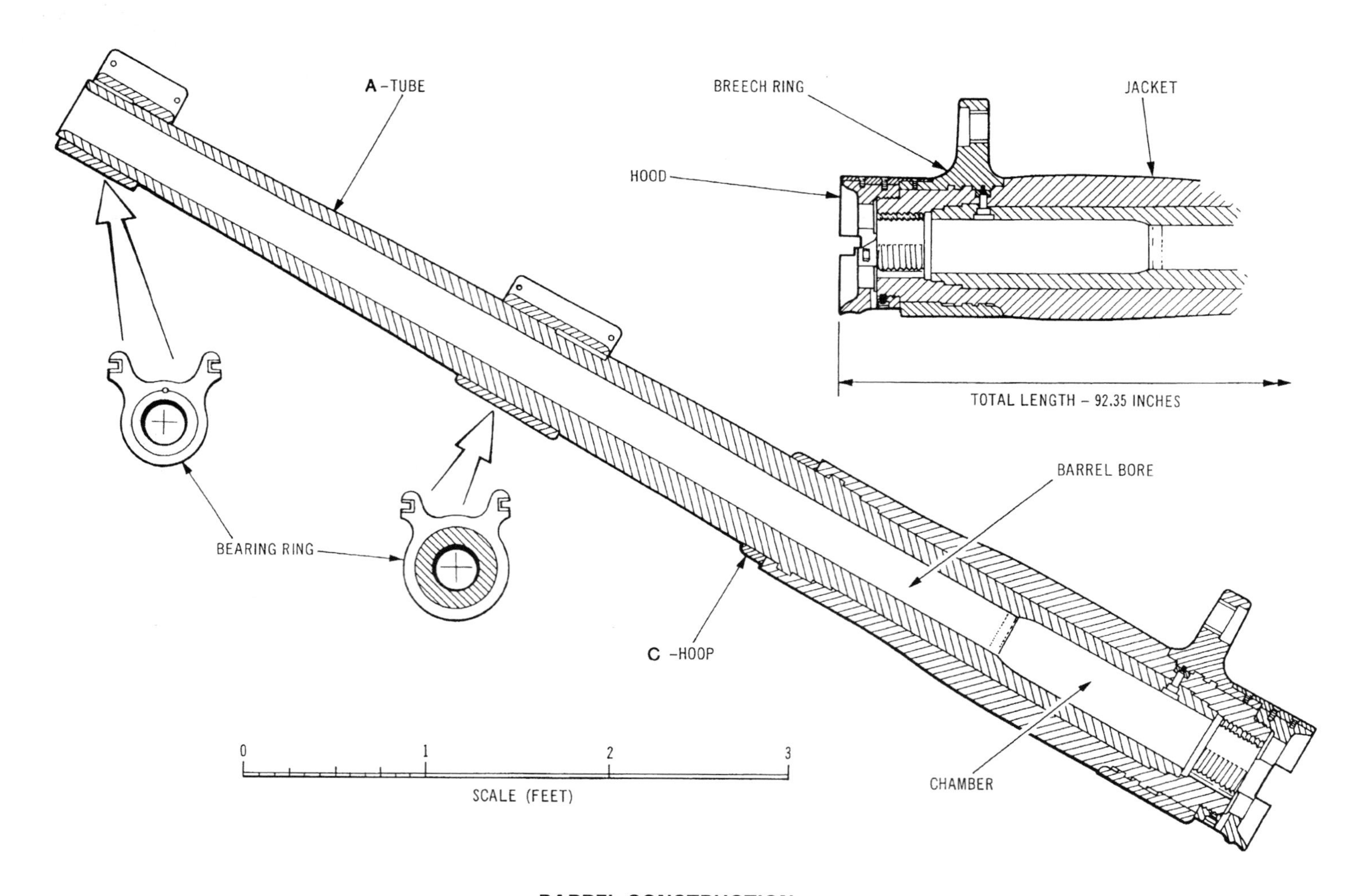

BARREL CONSTRUCTION

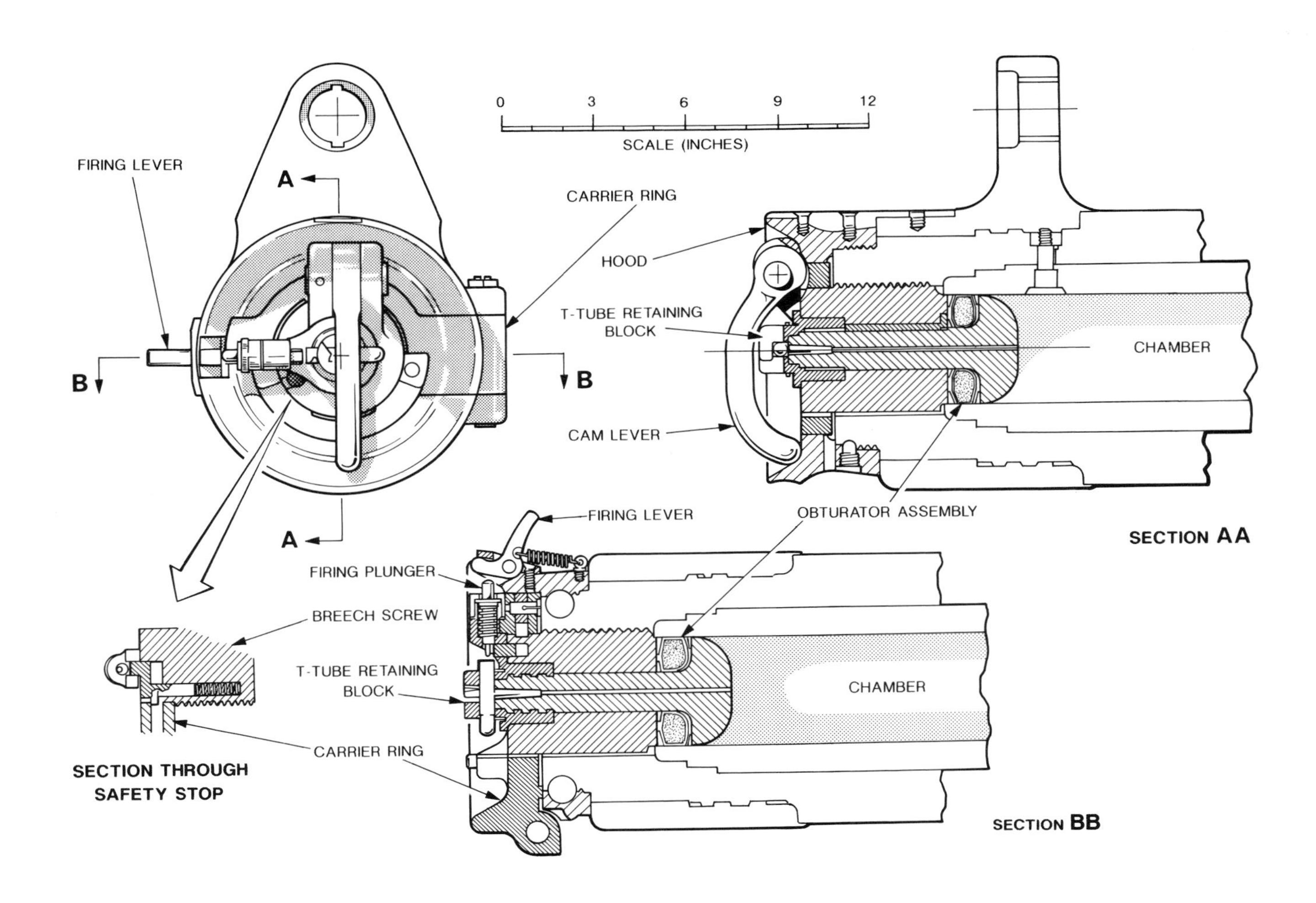

BREECH MECHANISM

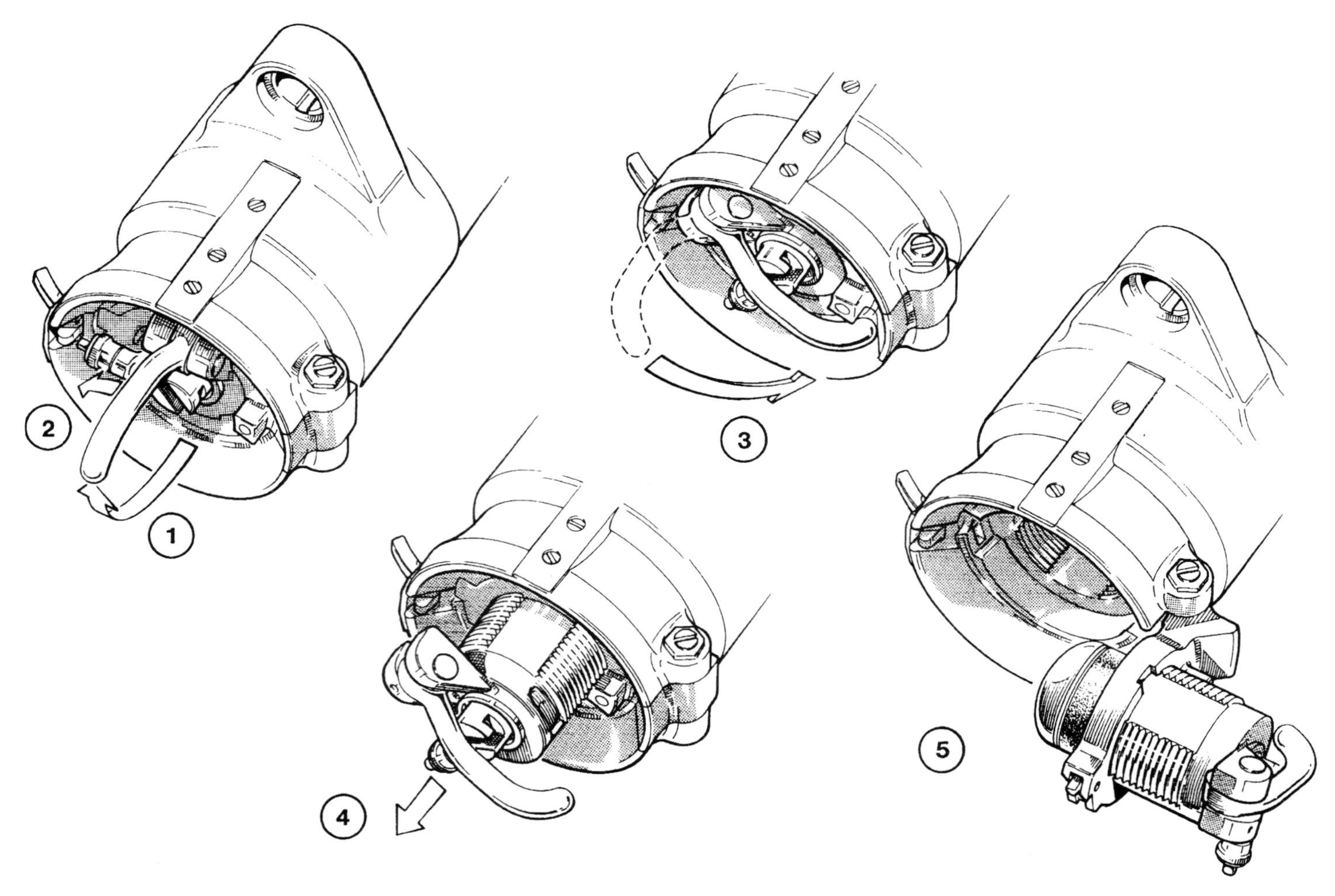

BREECH OPERATION

Breech operation

(**1**) Raising the cam lever moved the cam eccentric clear of the locking slots in the carrier ring and hood.

(**2**) Rotation of the cam lever, anti-clockwise through one-sixth of a turn, aligned the breech screw interrupted threads with cutouts in the carrier ring bore. The movement also caused the spring-loaded safety stop to block any operation of the firing plunger.

(**3**) Pushing the cam lever down caused the cam eccentric to contact the carrier ring face. This forced the breech screw and obturator assembly to move rearwards, partially disengaging the obturator assembly from the breech chamber.

(**4**) The cam lever was pulled rearwards, withdrawing the breech screw through the carrier ring, until the spring-loaded carrier retaining clip engaged a slot in the breech screw body. The retaining clip, together with the stop bolt, prevented any further withdrawal of the breech screw through the carrier ring.

(**5**) The carrier ring retaining clip, by engaging the breech screw slot, had withdrawn from the hood slot, so the carrier ring, complete with breech screw and obturator, could be swung clear of the breech entrance.

To close the breech, the cam lever was raised and the carrier ring, with breech screw, was swung against the breech face. This forced the retaining clip to pivot free of the breech screw slot and engage the hood slot, locking the carrier ring to the hood. The breech screw was then pushed home and turned to the locked position. This rotation caused the safety stop to engage a groove in the carrier ring bore and be moved clear of the firing plunger. The cam lever was lowered to lock the cam eccentric into the locking slots cut in the carrier ring and hood.

A small hole, through the left side of the breech into the hood slot, enabled a vent bit to be inserted, to push back the carrier ring retaining clip in the event of it jamming.

To remove the T-tube retaining block, safety stop, axial T-vent and obturator, the breech would be fully opened and the safety stop pressed inwards, far enough to allow the retaining block to be turned through one-quarter of a revolution. The retaining block could then be withdrawn, also the safety stop and spring. The axial T-vent could then be withdrawn, complete with the obturator assembly, from the front of the breech screw.

To remove the breech screw, the carrier ring retaining clip would be pressed upwards and the breech screw pushed forwards through the carrier ring. The stop bolt could then be pushed out from the rear and, with the retaining clip still pressed upwards, the breech screw withdrawn from the carrier ring.

T-tube retaining block

This component held the T-friction tube during the firing cycle and, in addition, acted as a retaining nut for the axial T-vent with obturator assembly. Part of the retaining block housed the firing plunger assembly.

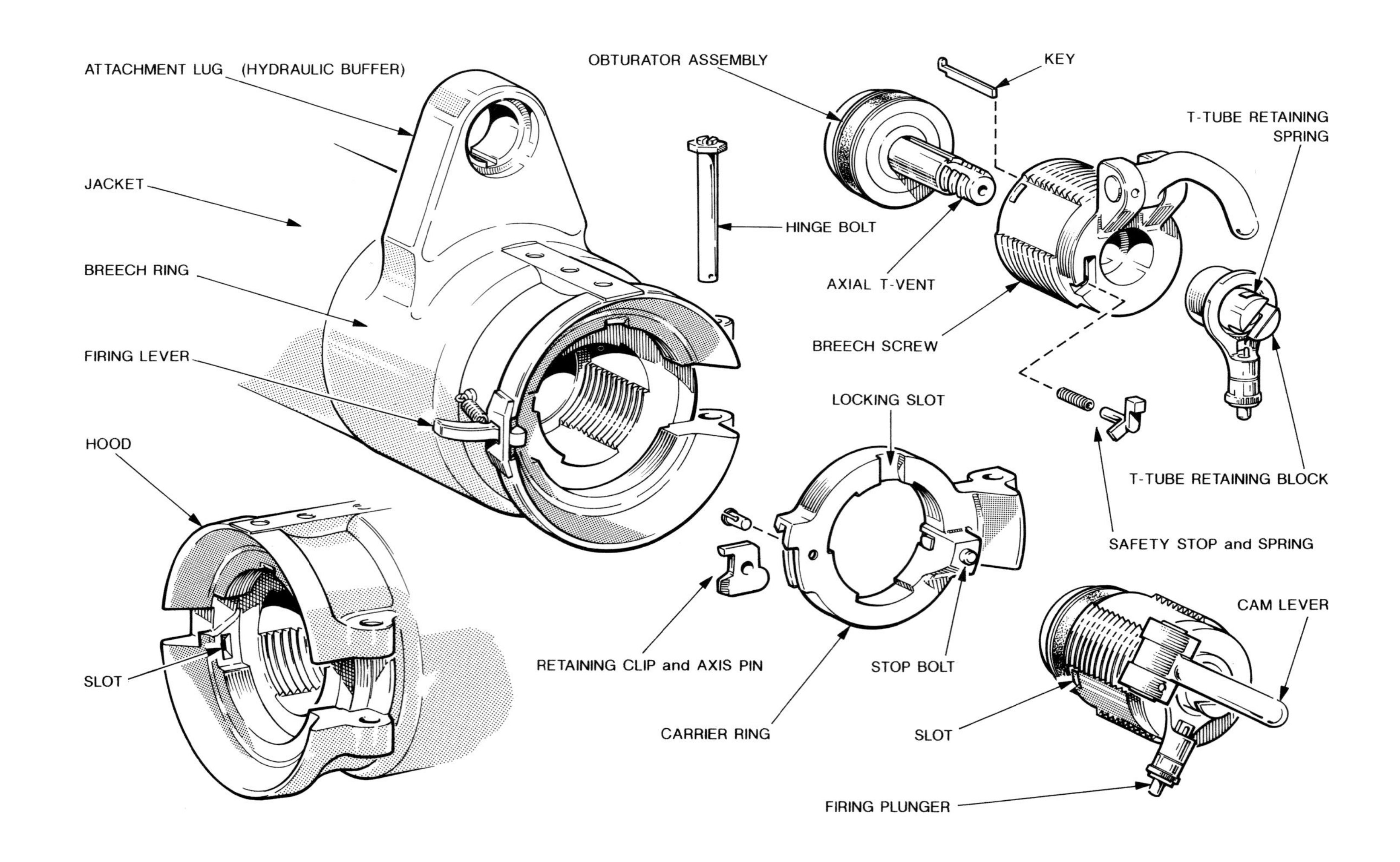

BREECH COMPONENTS

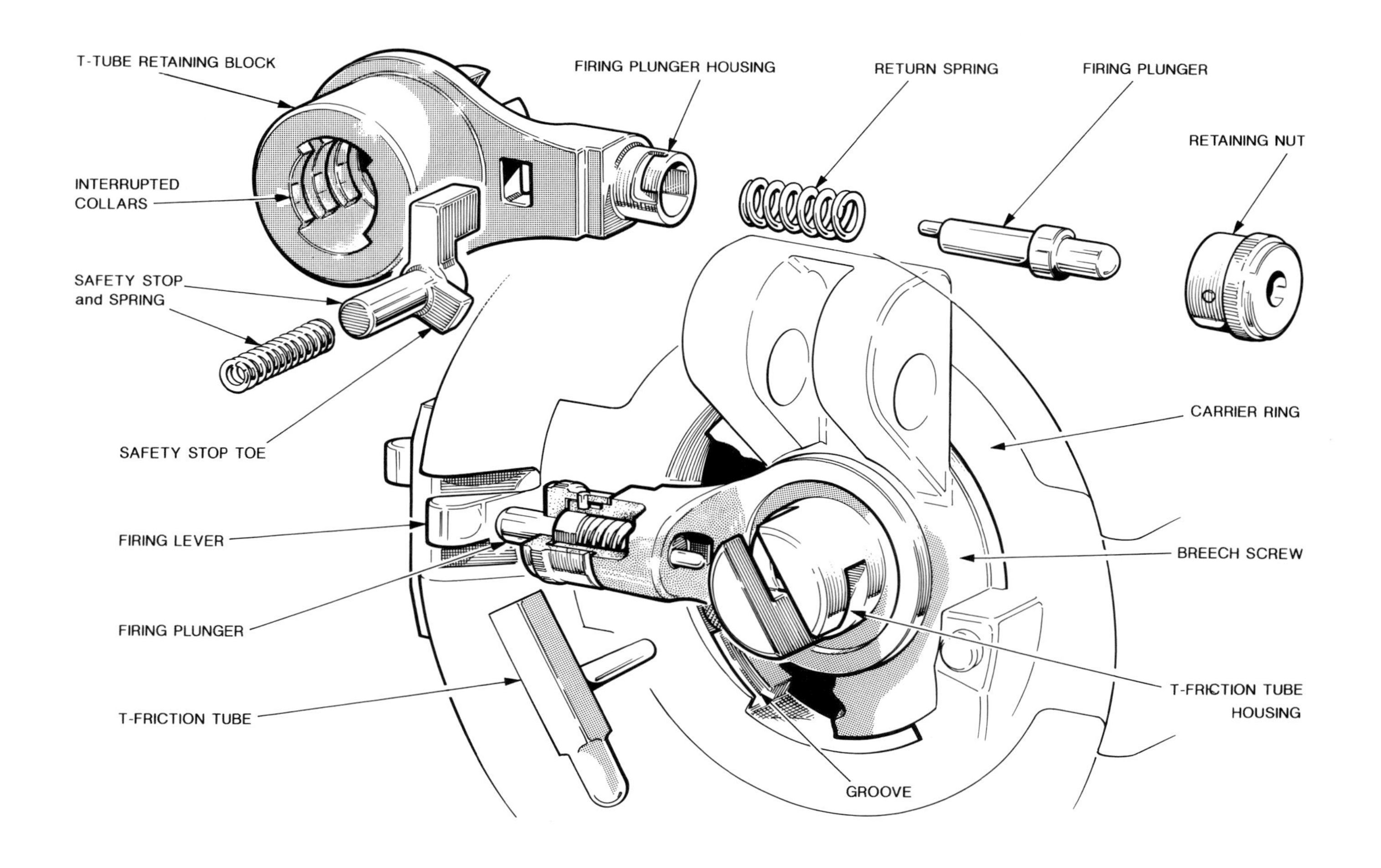

T-TUBE RETAINING BLOCK

The block bore was machined with interrupted collars which engaged corresponding interrupted collars on the axial T-vent shaft.

The firing plunger assembly consisted of a plunger return spring, plunger and retaining nut. The plunger had a flat machined on the surface to ensure correct assembly in the housing; plunger and spring being retained by a nut with a bayonet-type catch.

A spring-loaded safety stop, housed in the breech screw rear face, prevented any firing plunger operation while the breech screw was unlocked. Rotation of the breech screw, to open the breech, caused the safety stop toe to travel in a groove cut in the carrier ring bore and the safety stop to move in front of the firing plunger. Closing the breech caused the stop to move clear of the firing plunger.

The safety stop also acted as a lock to hold the retaining block in position. To remove the T-tube retaining block from the breech screw, the safety stop was pressed in fully, the retaining block turned through ninety degrees and then withdrawn. The axial T-vent could then be removed from the breech screw front face.

T-friction push tube Mk. 1

The head was of brass, square in section, with one end rounded to ensure correct loading of the tube in the breech vent and also to facilitate extraction.

Housed within the head were the detonator and friction push bar. The detonator had explosive composition contained between perforated brass discs, held together in a copper shell.

On tubes manufactured after December 1908, a pressure relief hole, 0.08 inch in diameter, was bored longitudinally through the head. This was closed at the end with shellac putty and coated with Pettman's cement. The body, screwed into the head and secured with a brass pin, contained eight grains of fine grain powder, sealed at the outer end with a shellacked cork plug, shellac cement and a paper disc. A soft copper ball was retained in the body inner end by a screwed plug drilled with three flash holes.

Pushing the friction bar into the body sheared the shearing wire and forced the conical bar end through the detonator into the roughened recess, the roughened surfaces igniting the composition. The flame passed into the body, around the ball and through the three plug flash holes into the fine grain powder, which fired out through the body outer end. Pressure drove the soft copper ball back into the tapered hole to seal the tube and prevent gas leakage to the rear.

In the event of a misfire, the tube could be removed from the breech and a new one inserted with the breech closed. This would be carried out with extreme care – T-tubes or main charges (or both) could detonate during the operation.

Should the axial T-vent channel become choked with fouling from the main charge, the tapered T-tube seating would be cleared with a T-vent rimer, sufficient enough to permit the insertion of a T-friction tube. This, when fired, would clear the axial T-vent of fouling. Fired tubes would be immersed in mineral oil

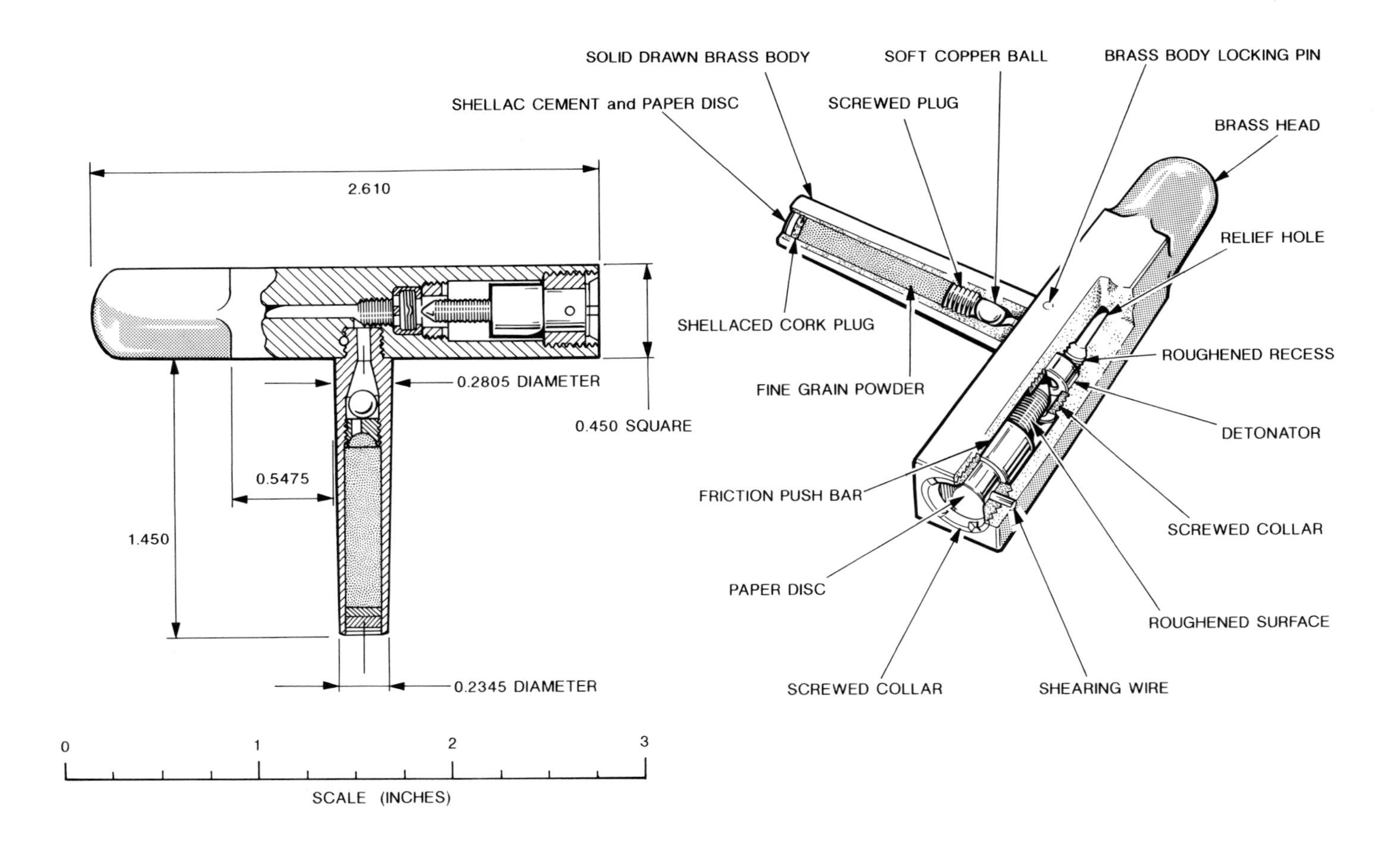

T-FRICTION PUSH TUBE MK. I

as soon as possible after firing, then returned to Woolwich for repair and refilling.

T-friction tubes were issued in square tin boxes, ten to a box. Both top and bottom of the box were removable, being secured by soldered bands. This allowed five tubes to be withdrawn from the top and five from the bottom.

T-tubes manufactured before December 1908, lacking a relief hole, were converted into drill tubes after firing, by boring out the head recess to house a brass spiral spring, bearing on a flat ended push bar. The body was plugged with wood.

The drill tube was bronzed all over and stamped DRILL CONVERTED.

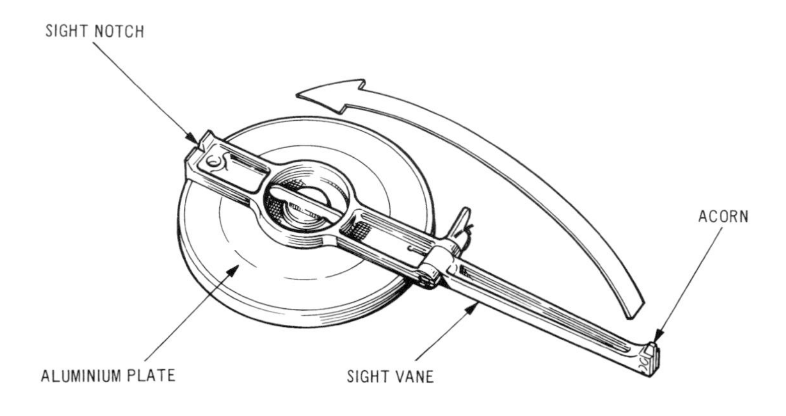

Sights

Dial Sight No. 1

The sight consisted of a horizontal aluminium plate with a degree scale ring secured to the periphery by screws. The ring graduations read 0 to 180 degrees, left and right.

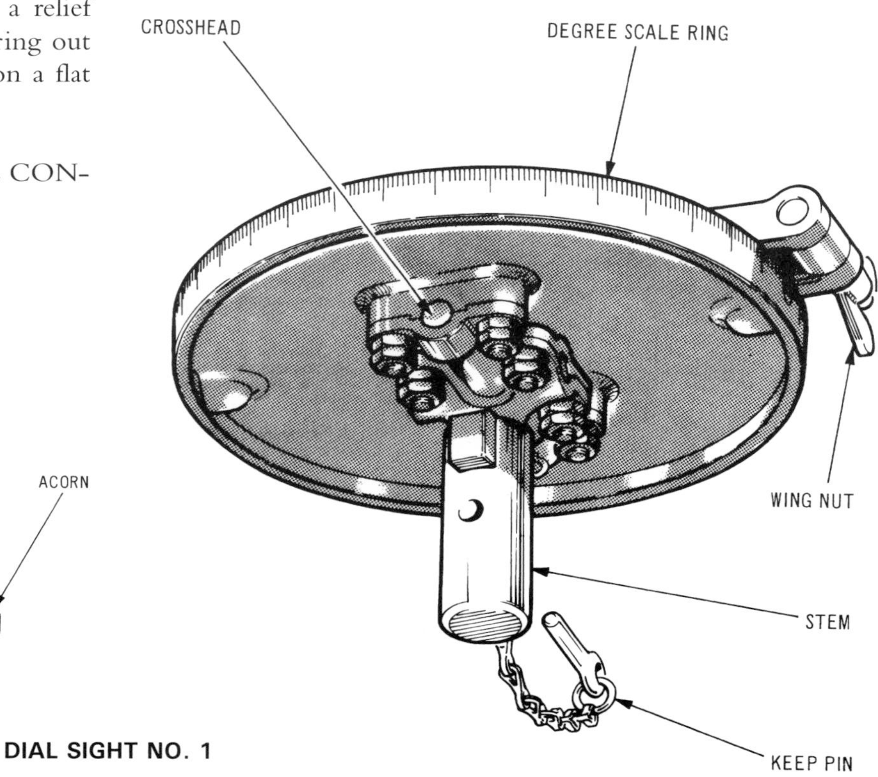

DIAL SIGHT NO. 1

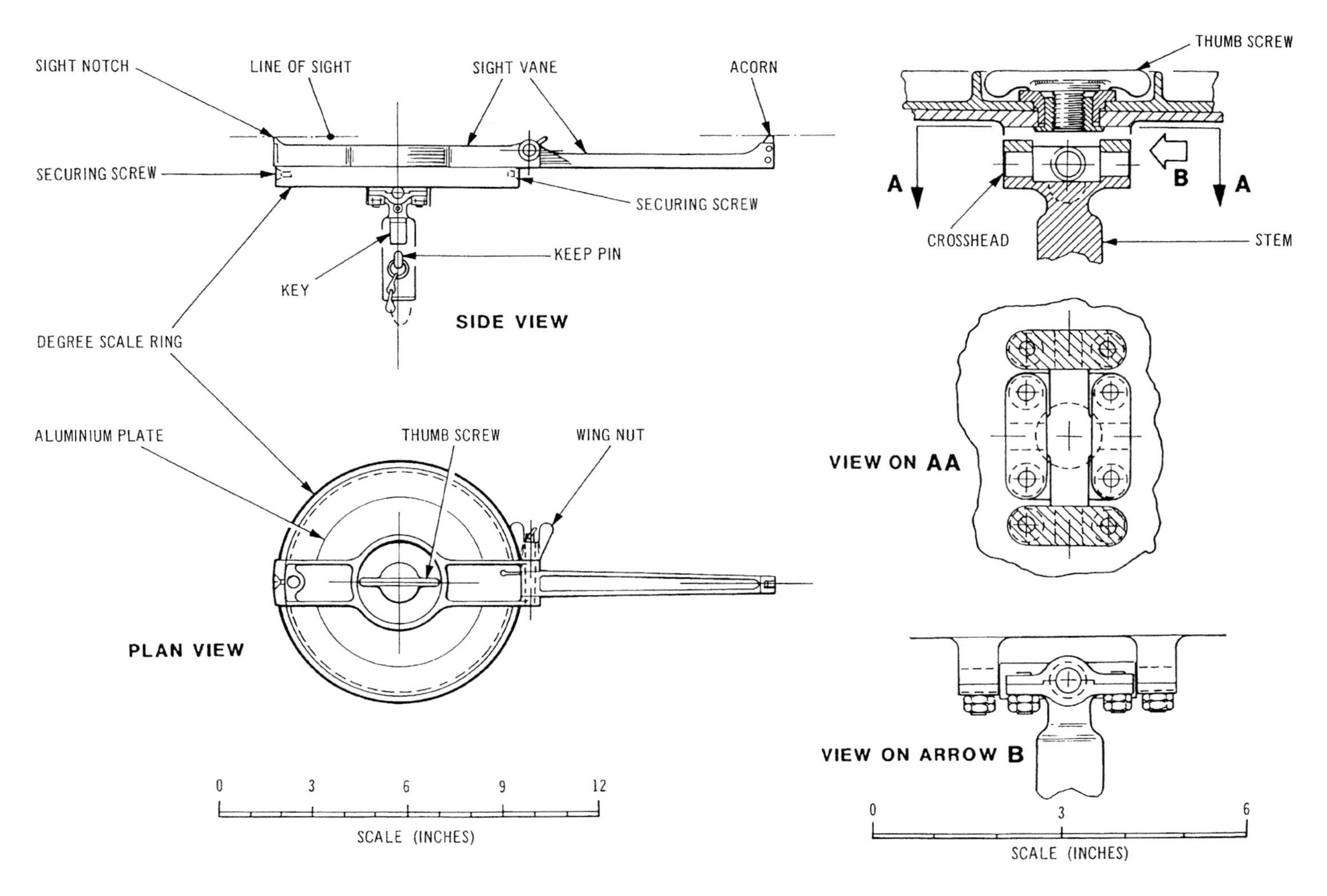

DIAL SIGHT NO. 1

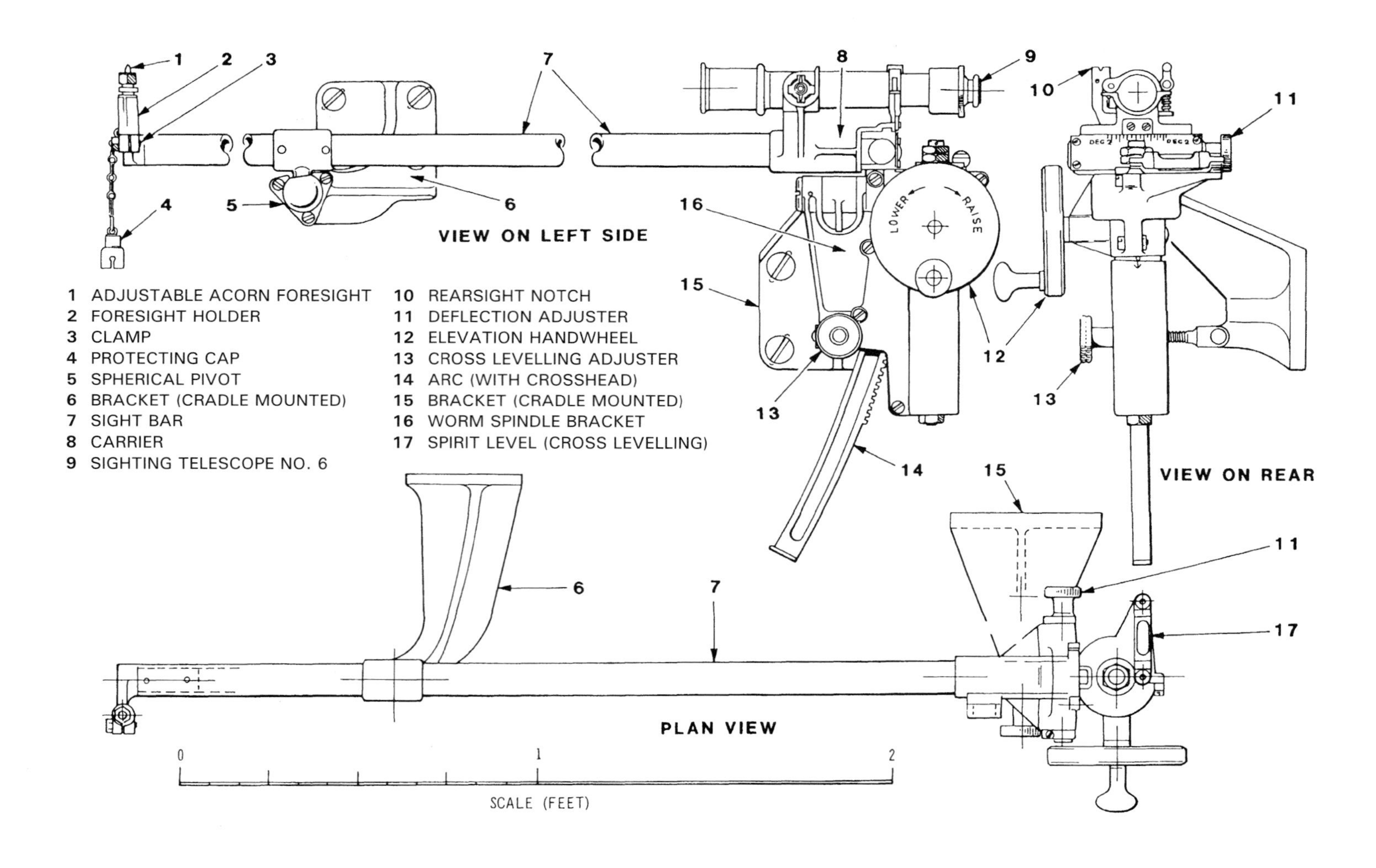

ROCKING BAR SIGHT

Secured by a thumb screw to the plate top surface was a two-part sight vane, joined by a bolt and wing nut. The vane was provided with a notch and acorn for sight laying, and a pointer for reading the degree scale.

The plate pivoted to a crosshead and could be set through 8 degrees, front or rear. The crosshead pivoted to a stem and could be set through 32 degrees of tilt, left or right.

In use, the sight stem fitted into a bracket on the shield and was secured by a key and steel keep pin.

Rocking bar sight

A bracket (**15**), mounted on the cradle (left side, rear) had, hinged to it, a two-piece manganese bronze worm spindle bracket (**16**). This bracket was tilted at an angle of 1½ degrees to the left for drift compensation.

A steel tube sight bar (**7**) carried the foresight holder (**2**), riveted to the front end. The sight bar (**7**) could pivot about a spherical mounting (**5**) attached to a cradle mounted bracket (**6**). To the sight bar rear end was attached a gun metal carrier (**8**) onto which was mounted a No. 6 sighting telescope (**9**). The front telescope mount had a steel plate, formed with a notch, for use as a rearsight (**10**). The carrier (**8**) had worm teeth machined on it to engage the deflection adjuster worm gear (**11**). A groove machined into the carrier (**8**) was engaged by a guide on the crosshead top face (**18**). Secured to the carrier rear face (**8**) was an adjustable reader arrow, which read against a nickel alloy deflection scale plate secured to the crosshead rear face (**18**).

For cross-levelling adjustment, a cross spirit level (**17**) was attached to the worm spindle bracket (**16**). On the worm spindle bracket front underside was a bearing in which ran a milled head adjuster nut (**13**). This nut travelled along a screw with forked crosshead, pinned to the rear cradle mounted bracket (**15**).

The range sight gear consisted of a toothed steel arc (**14**) with crosshead (**18**), running in a curved, rectangular section groove in the worm spindle bracket (**16**). The arc had a stop at the lower end. The crosshead (**18**) was set at an angle of 1½ degrees on the arc (**14**) to offset the drift compensation angle of the worm spindle bracket.

The vertical worm spindle (**19**) had worm teeth engaging the arc teeth (**14**), bevel gear teeth engaging the gun metal handwheel bevel gear (**12**) and a nut (**20**) formed at the bottom in which ran a steel screw (**21**). To the screw (**21**) was secured a gun metal sleeve (**22**) fitted with a key engaging a keyway cut into the worm spindle bracket (**16**) to prevent the sleeve (**22**) rotating.

Held by screws to the worm spindle nut (**20**) was a nickel alloy yard scale drum (**23**) marked with spiral graduations. These were read against an arrow marked on the top edge of the sleeve (**22**).

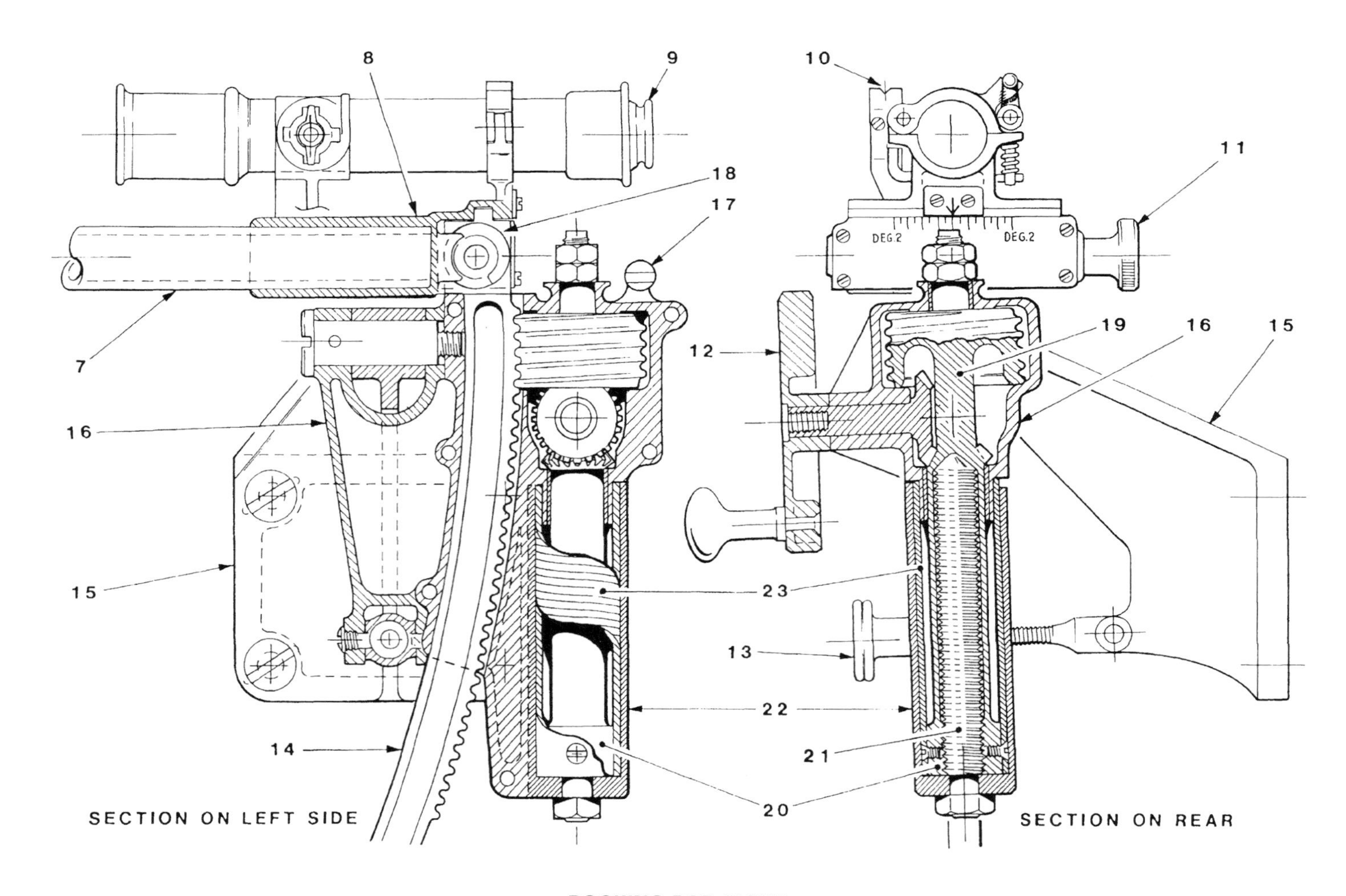

ROCKING BAR SIGHT

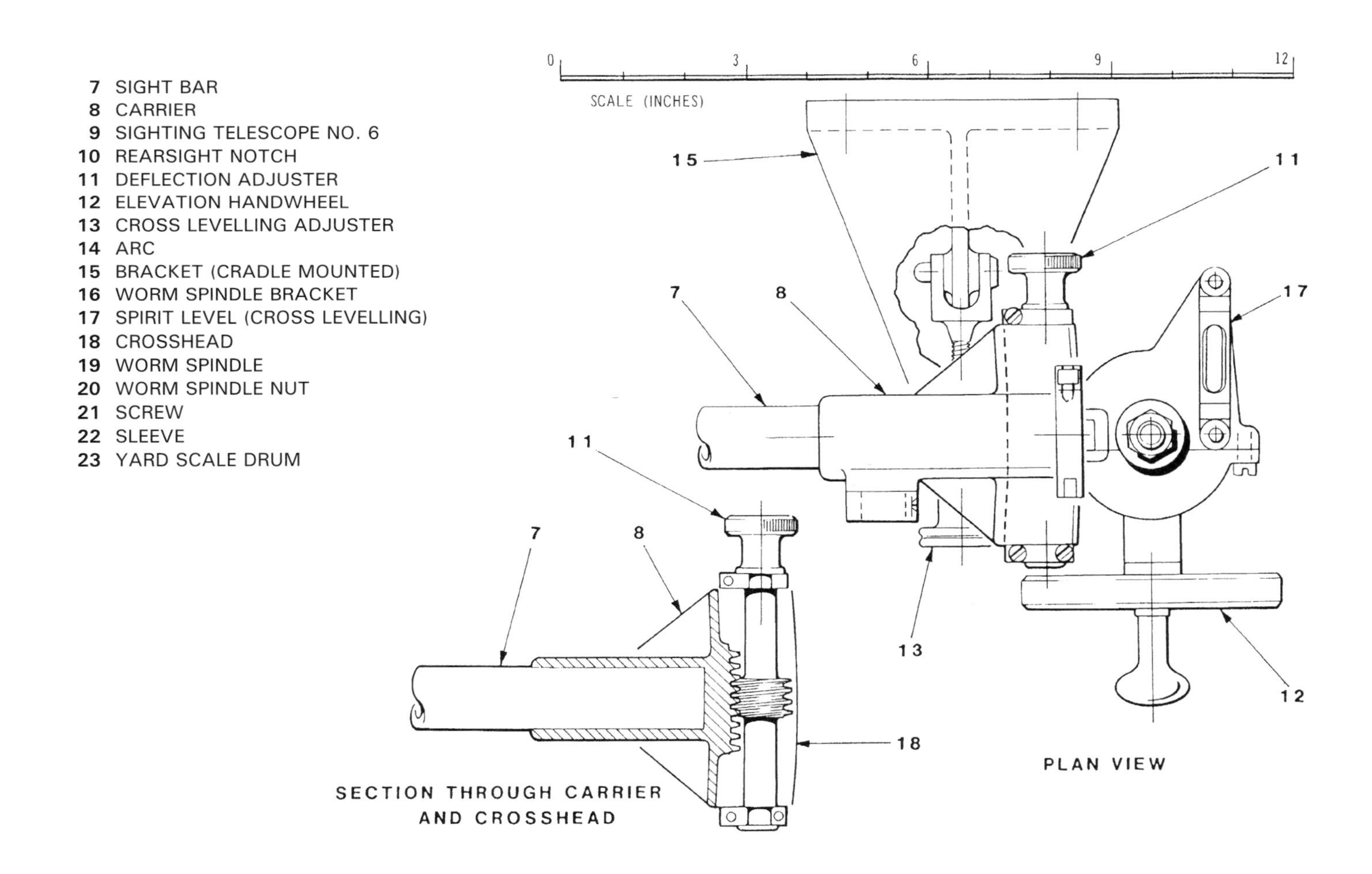

ROCKING BAR SIGHT

Sighting Telescope No. 6 Mk. I

The telescope body was secured centrally into a rectangular frame. A trunnion, projecting from the frame left side, was held in the telescope holder front bearing by a keyed washer and wing nut. A circular boss, at the telescope rear, fitted the telescope holder rear bearing and was secured by a hinged capsquare with spring catch. The front object glass was rotated for focusing, arrows marked on the collar and body would align at infinity.

A diaphragm, in the rear of the telescope, carried a horizontal pointer and was focused by screwing the eye lens in or out. On the frame right side was a gunmetal box holding a longitudinal spirit level, pivoted at the rear and adjusted at the front, up or down, by a milled head screw with a micrometer scale reading to two minutes.

At the spirit level front was a degree scale, graduated to five degrees either way, read against a reader fixed to the frame. A small mirror, hinged to the frame top, was used to read the level.

Sighting Telescope No. 6 Mk. II

This differed from the Mk. I in the pointer, which was vertical and fitted at the focal length of the object glass instead of in the eyepiece. It was adjusted by four capstan head screws. The position of the longitudinal level was reversed.

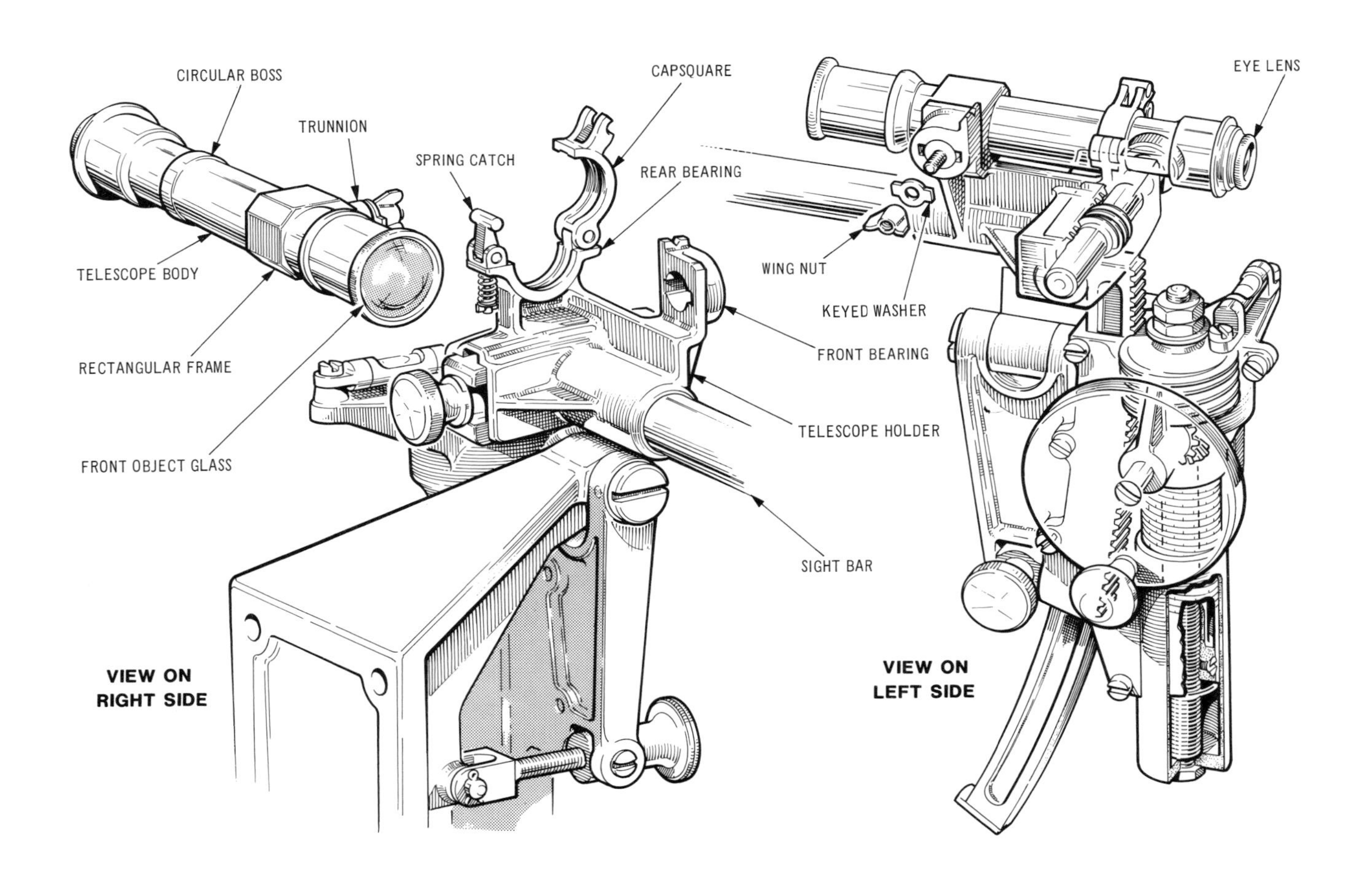

ROCKING BAR SIGHT AND SIGHTING TELESCOPE NO. 6 MK. 1

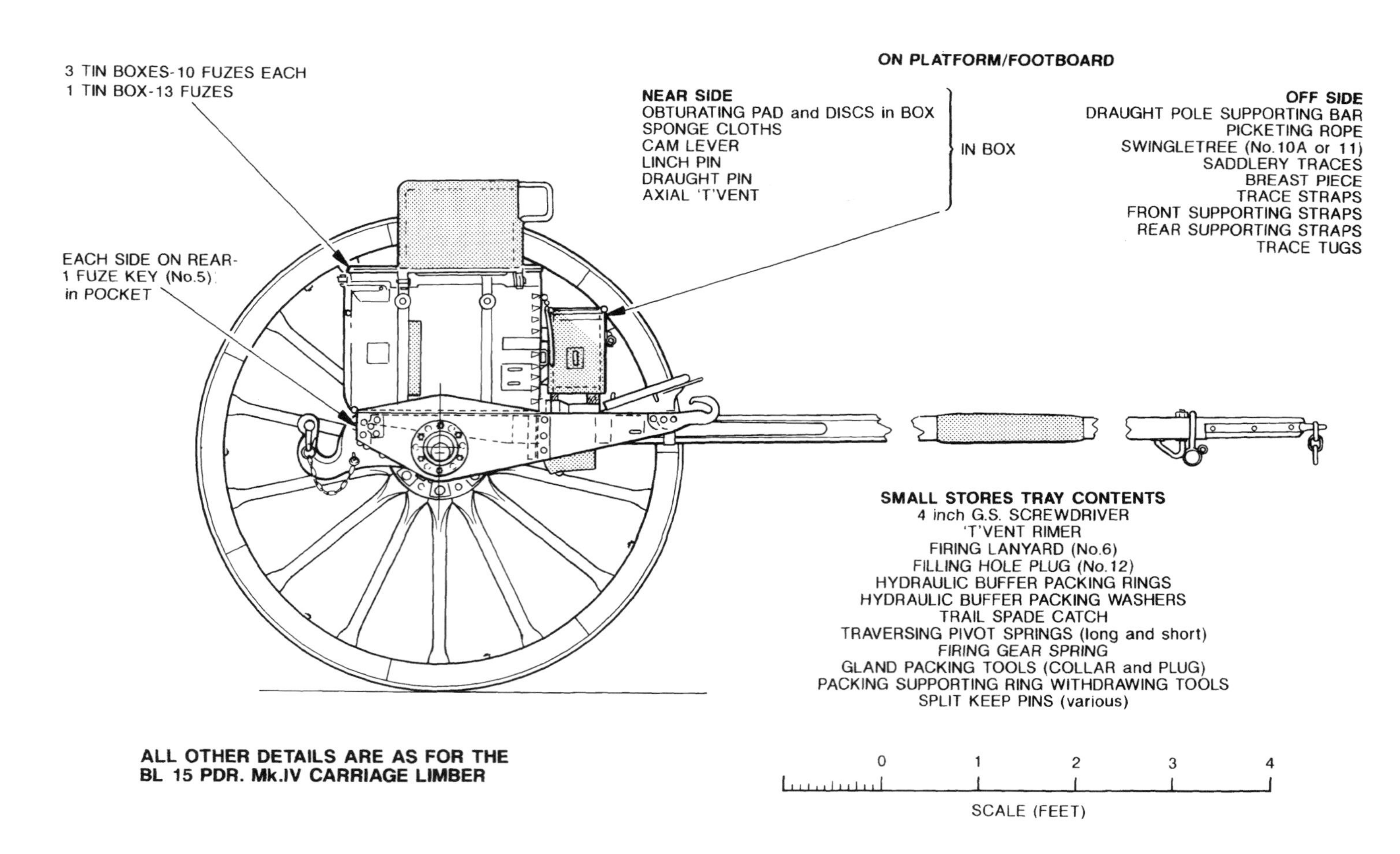

LIMBER (CARRIAGE) STORES AND EQUIPMENT

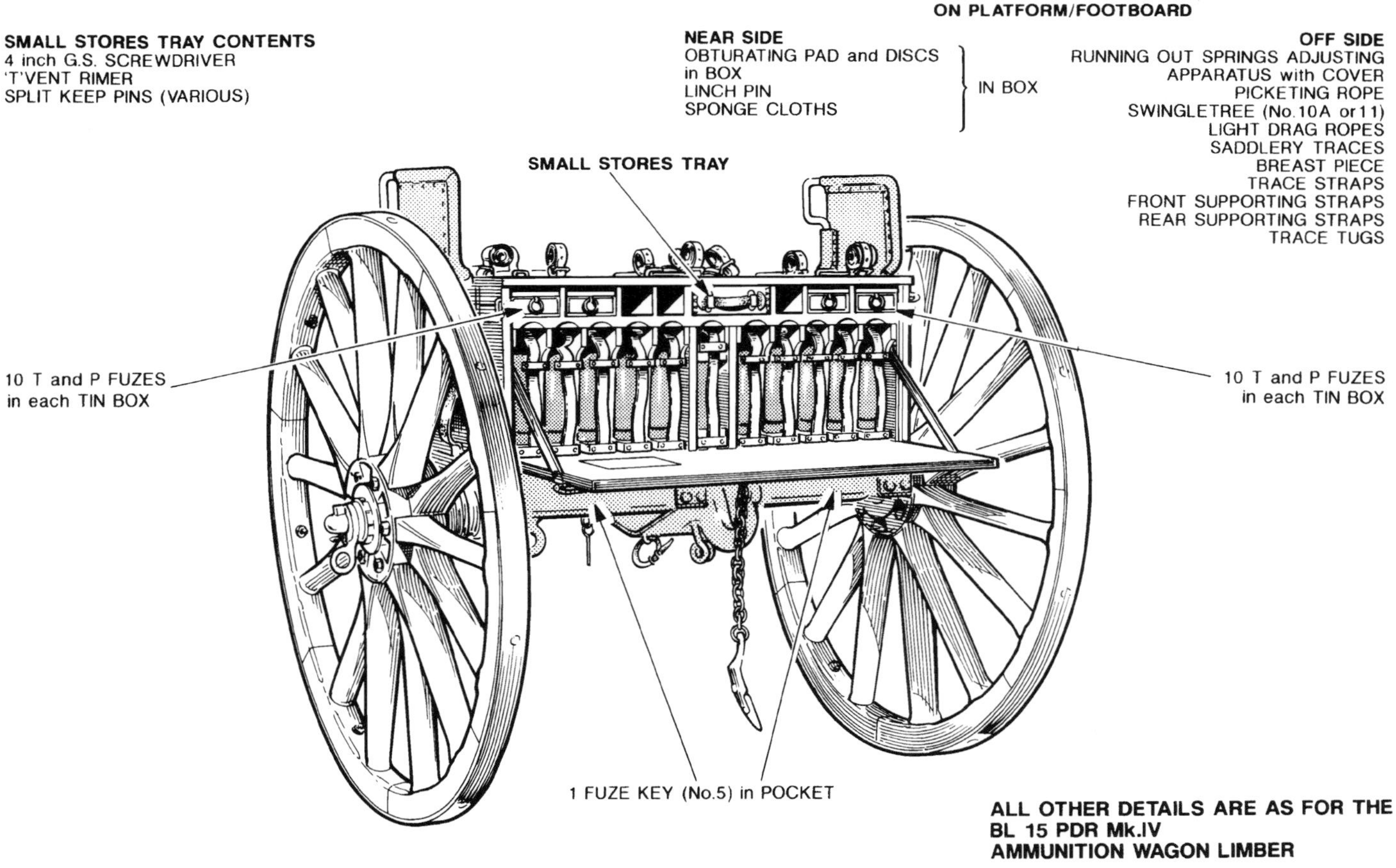

ON PLATFORM/FOOTBOARD

NEAR SIDE
OBTURATING PAD and DISCS in BOX
LINCH PIN
SPONGE CLOTHS
} IN BOX

OFF SIDE
RUNNING OUT SPRINGS ADJUSTING APPARATUS with COVER
PICKETING ROPE
SWINGLETREE (No.10A or 11)
LIGHT DRAG ROPES
SADDLERY TRACES
BREAST PIECE
TRACE STRAPS
FRONT SUPPORTING STRAPS
REAR SUPPORTING STRAPS
TRACE TUGS

SMALL STORES TRAY CONTENTS
4 inch G.S. SCREWDRIVER
'T'VENT RIMER
SPLIT KEEP PINS (VARIOUS)

SMALL STORES TRAY

10 T and P FUZES in each TIN BOX

10 T and P FUZES in each TIN BOX

1 FUZE KEY (No.5) in POCKET

ALL OTHER DETAILS ARE AS FOR THE BL 15 PDR Mk.IV AMMUNITION WAGON LIMBER

LIMBER (AMMUNITION WAGON) STORES AND EQUIPMENT

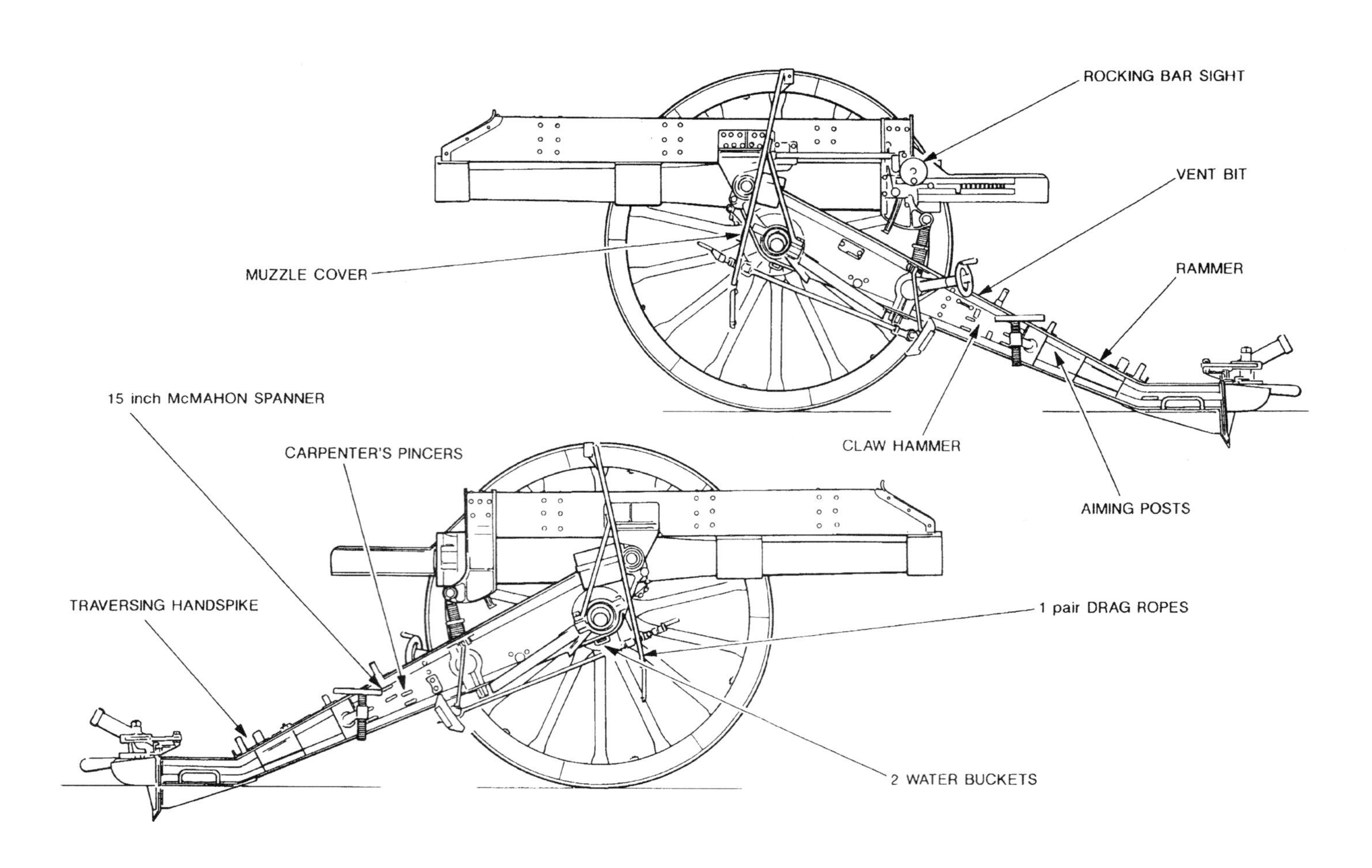

CARRIAGE STORES AND EQUIPMENT

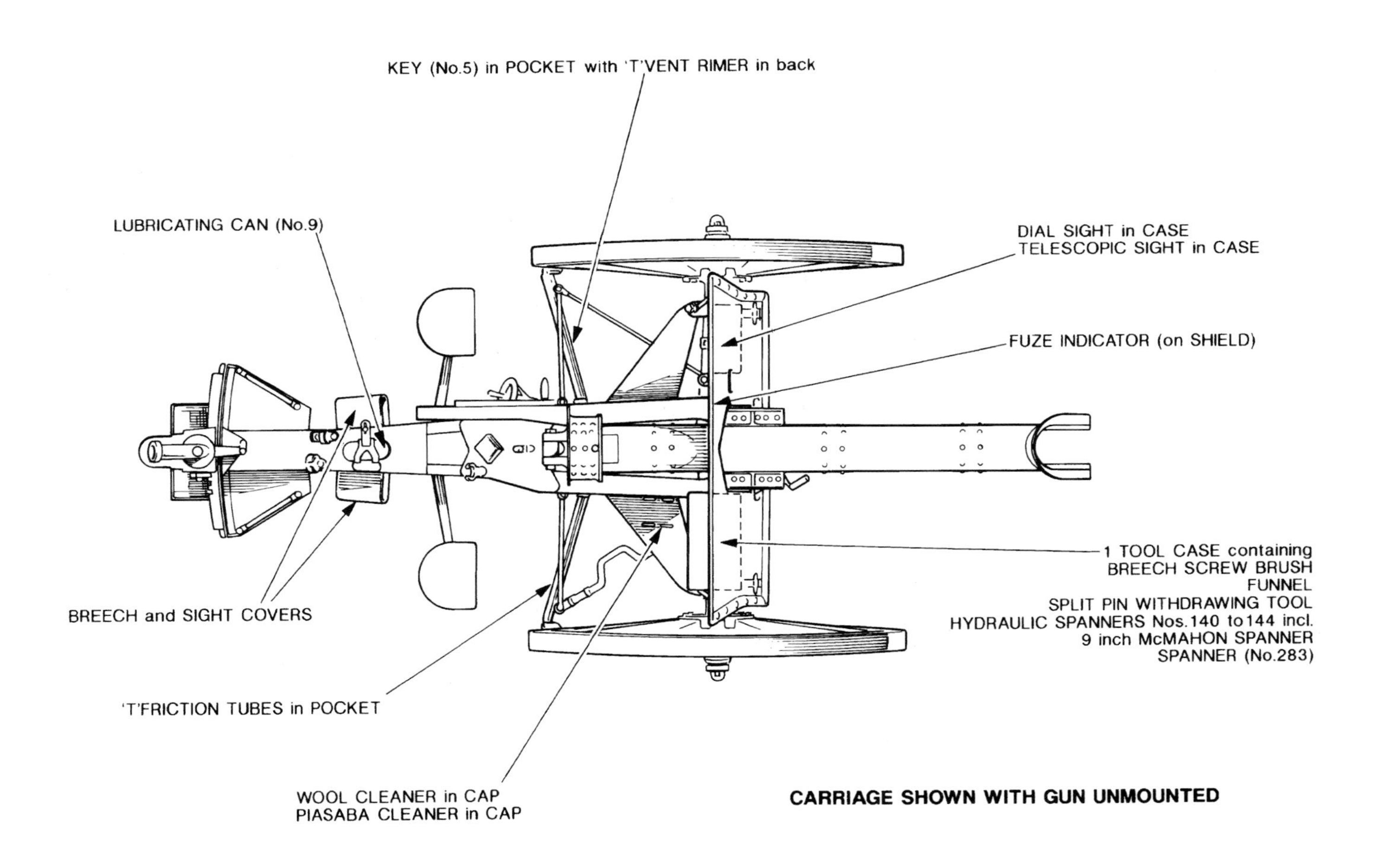

CARRIAGE SHOWN WITH GUN UNMOUNTED

CARRIAGE STORES AND EQUIPMENT

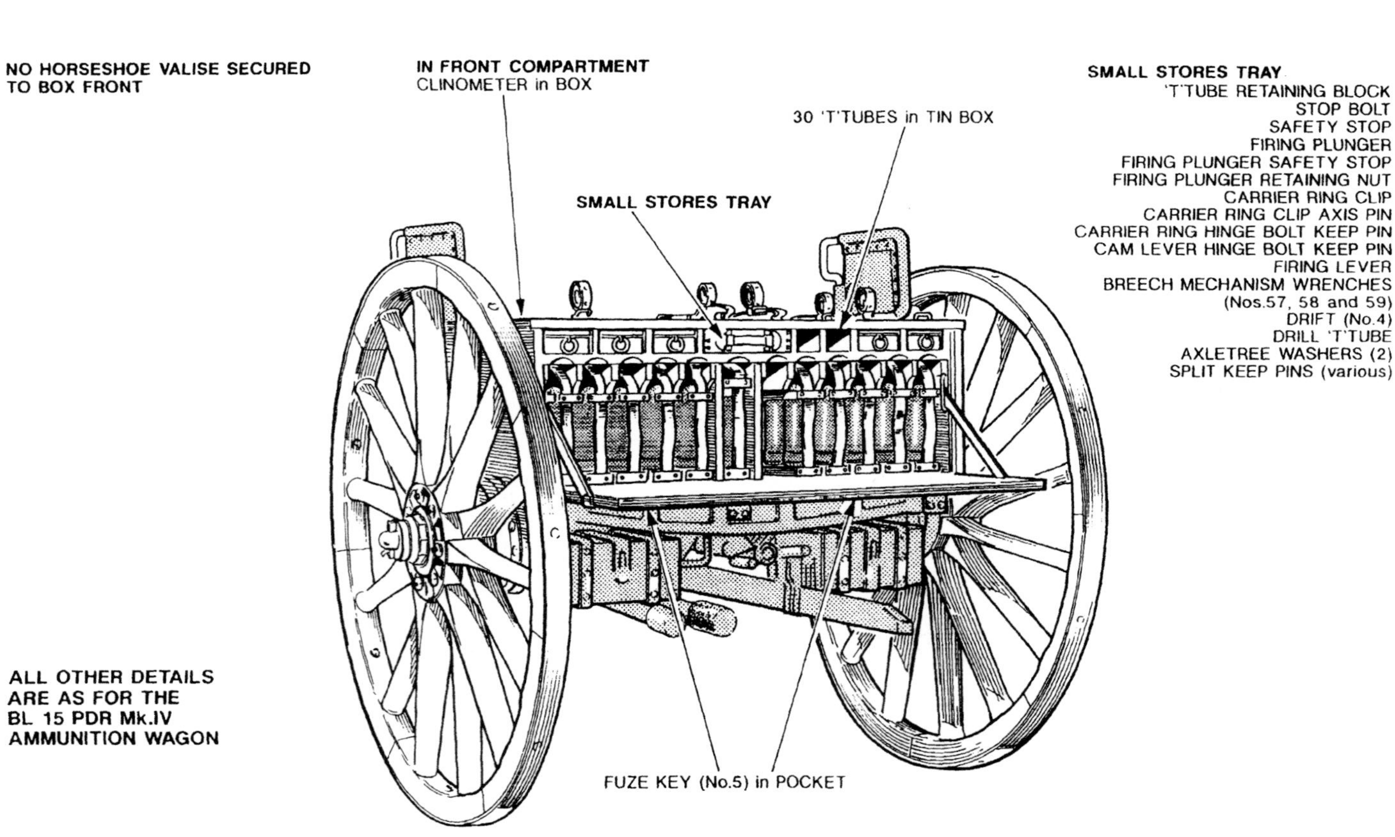

AMMUNITION WAGON STORES AND EQUIPMENT

Messrs. Armstrong, Whitworth Co.

WIRE WINDING A GUN BARREL

QUICK FIRING 15 PDR. MK. I*

QUICK FIRING 15 PDR MK. I

WEIGHTS (as packed)

Carriage with gun	20cwt 1qtr 4lb
Carriage limber	14cwt 2qtr
Ammunition wagon	22cwt 1qtr
Wagon limber	14cwt 2qtr

Trail

The tubular steel trail was originally telescopic on early models, later ones were permanently bolted into the closed position.

At the trail rear end was riveted a trail eye, formed integrally with the spade. Each end of the spade carried a lifting handle. Pivoted to the trail eye right side was a traversing lever. For travelling, the lever was folded over along the carriage right side, where it was secured by a spring clip. Riveted to the trail was a locking band. This prevented damage to the trail tube by the limber wheels when the carriage and limber were turning at maximum lock.

A mounting bracket for the elevating gear was riveted to the trail. Near the trail centre was mounted a seat for use by the gun layer. A mounting for the brake bars was riveted to the trail body, forward of the layer's seat.

A steel saddle, formed with two bearings into which fitted the axletree, was riveted to the trail body. The axletree was secured in the bearings by capsquares and bolts.

A bracket, on which pivoted the brake rocking bar, was riveted to the trail front end. The trail tube was closed at the front end by a hinged flap, secured shut by a hasp and turnbuckle.

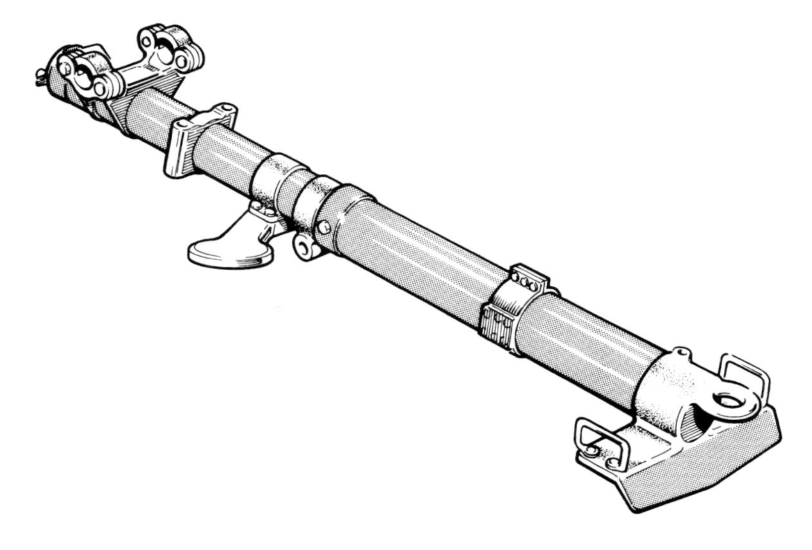

CARRIAGE MK. I FEATURES
TWO AXLETREE SEATS WITH GUARD IRONS
SEPARATE FORE AND REAR TANGENT SIGHTS
NO. 1 DIAL SIGHT SUPPORTING PILLAR
ATTACHMENT BRACKET ON THE CARRIAGE LEFT SIDE

CARRIAGE MK. I* FEATURES
SHIELD AND TRAVERSING INDICATOR
ROCKING BAR SIGHT AND SIGHTING TELESCOPE (NO. 6)
SOME EARLY MK. I* CARRIAGES WERE FITTED WITH SEPARATE FORE AND REAR TANGENT SIGHTS

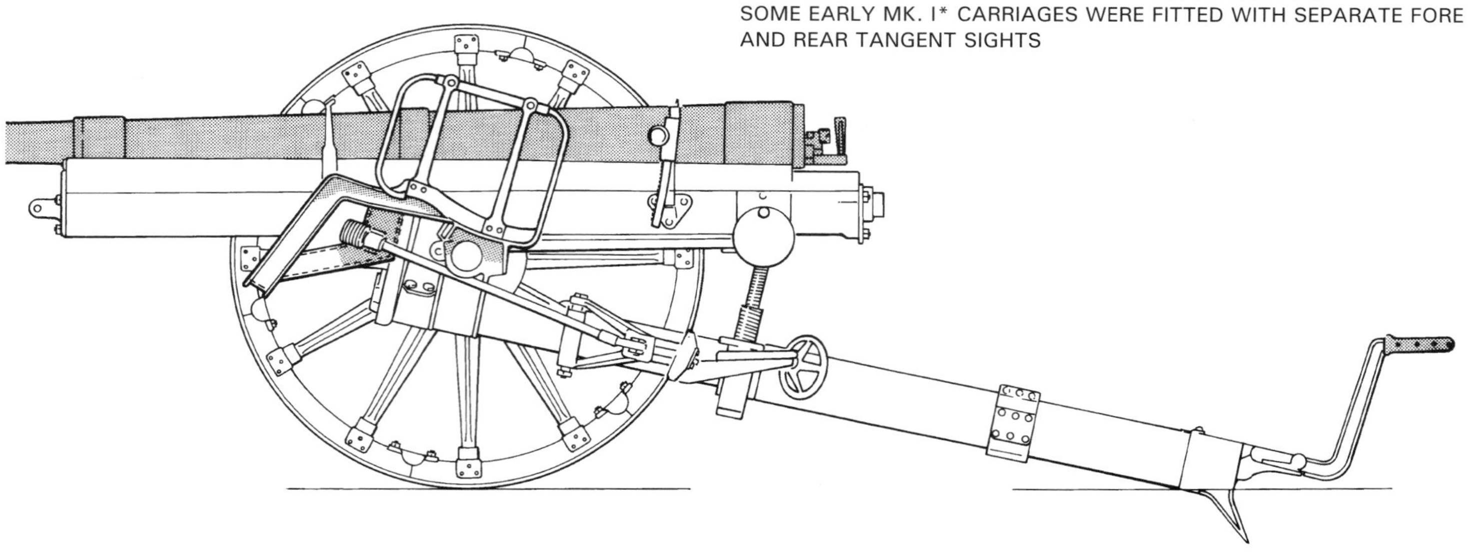

CARRIAGE – QUICK FIRING 15 PDR. MK. I

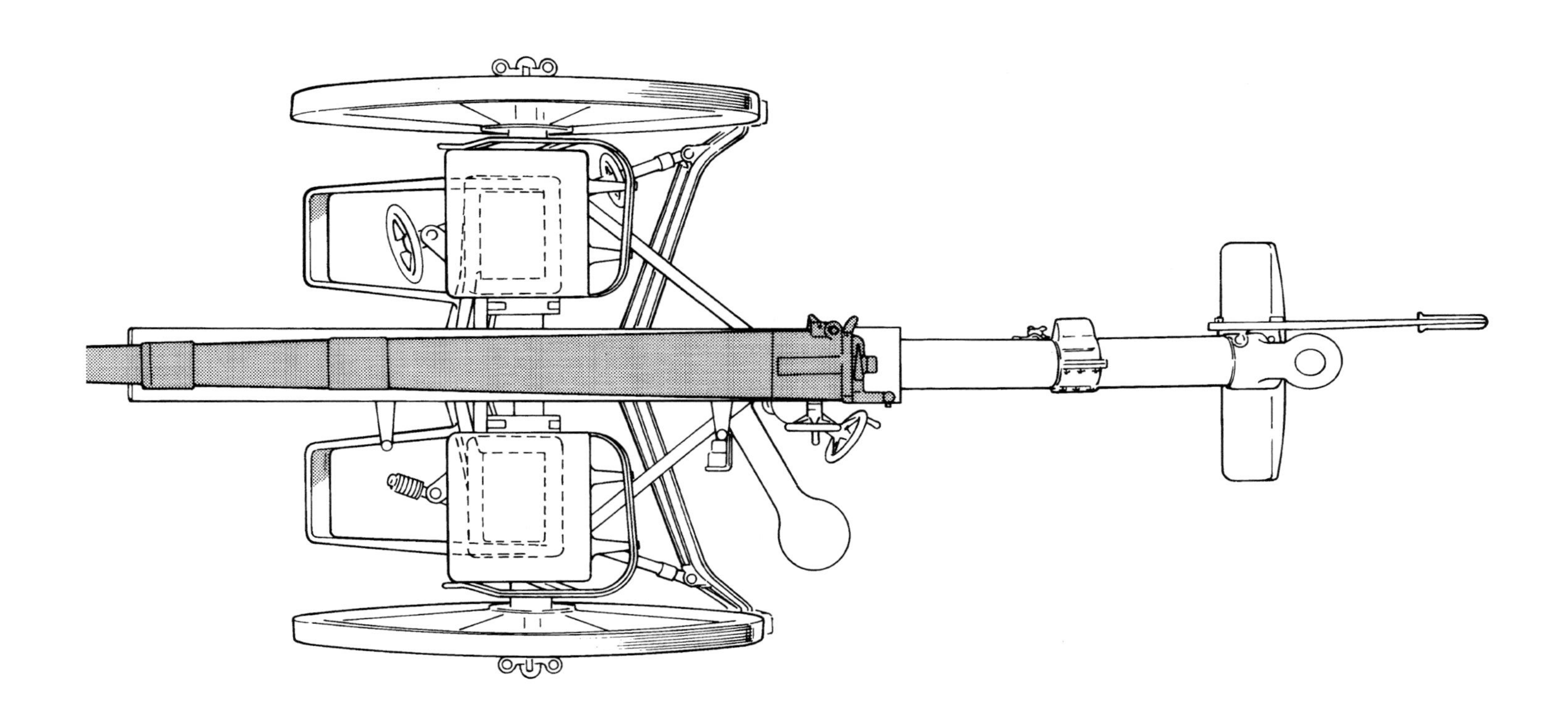

CARRIAGE – QUICK FIRING 15 PDR. MK. I

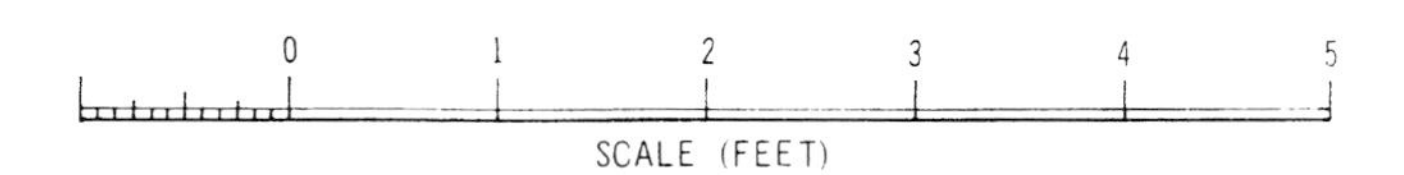

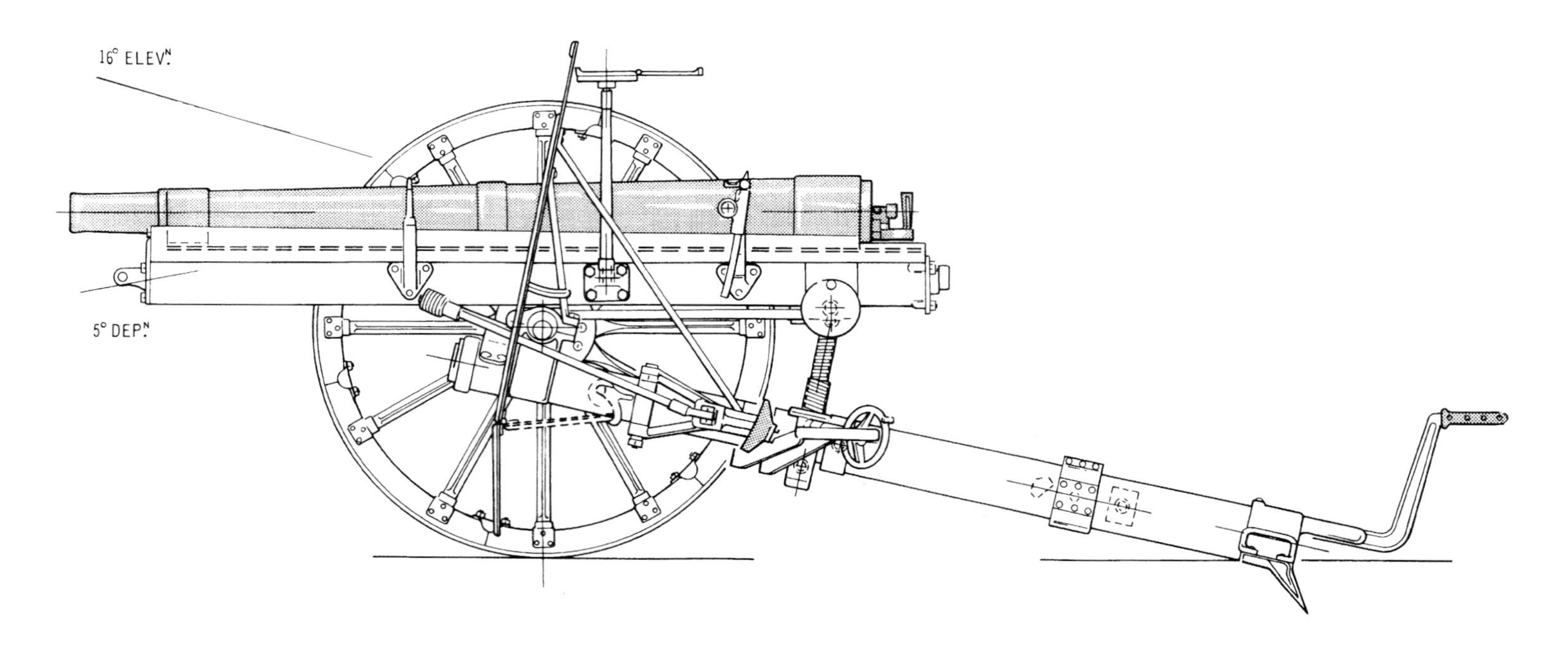

CARRIAGE – QUICK FIRING 15 PDR. MK. I*

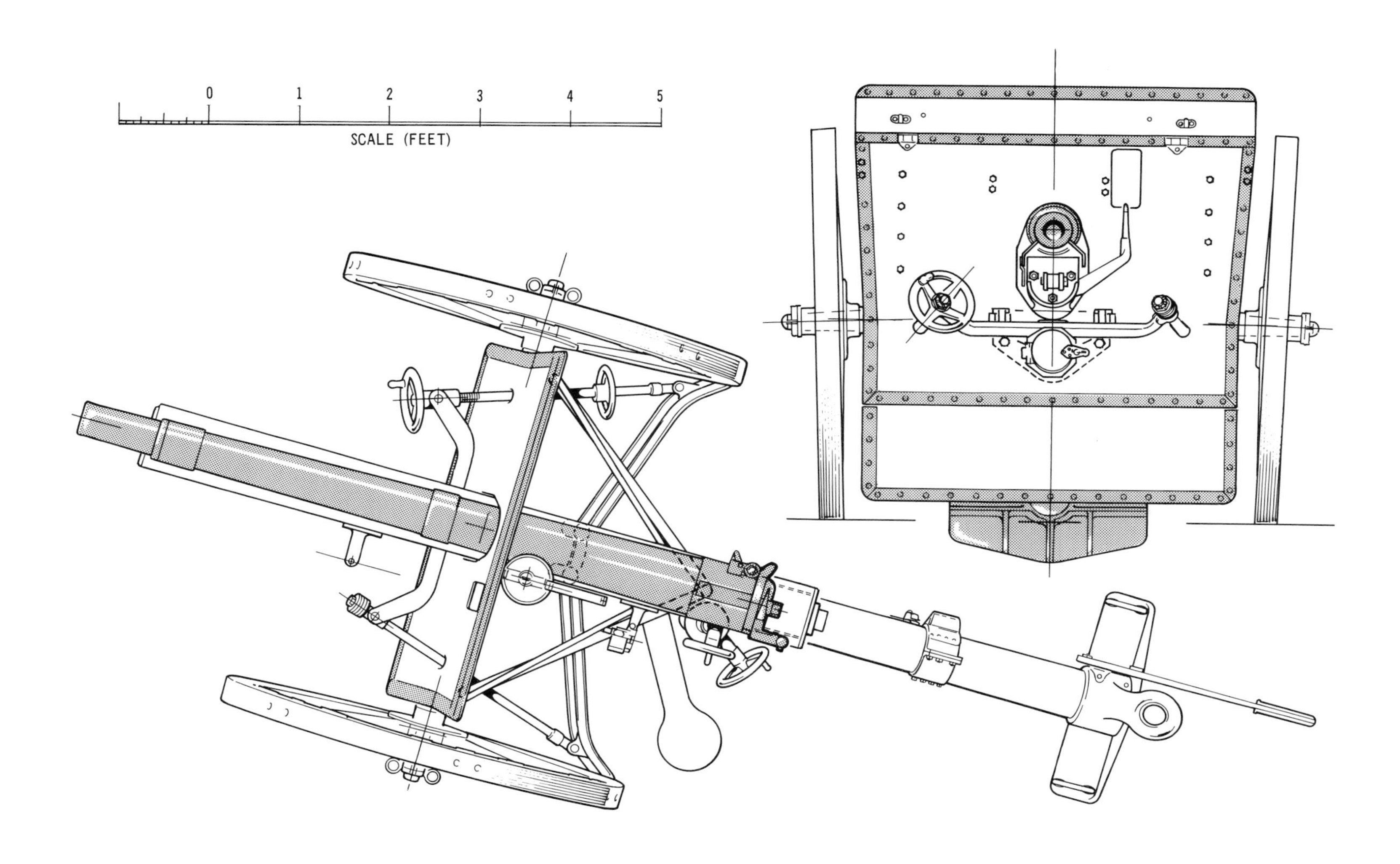

CARRIAGE – QUICK FIRING 15 PDR. MK. I*

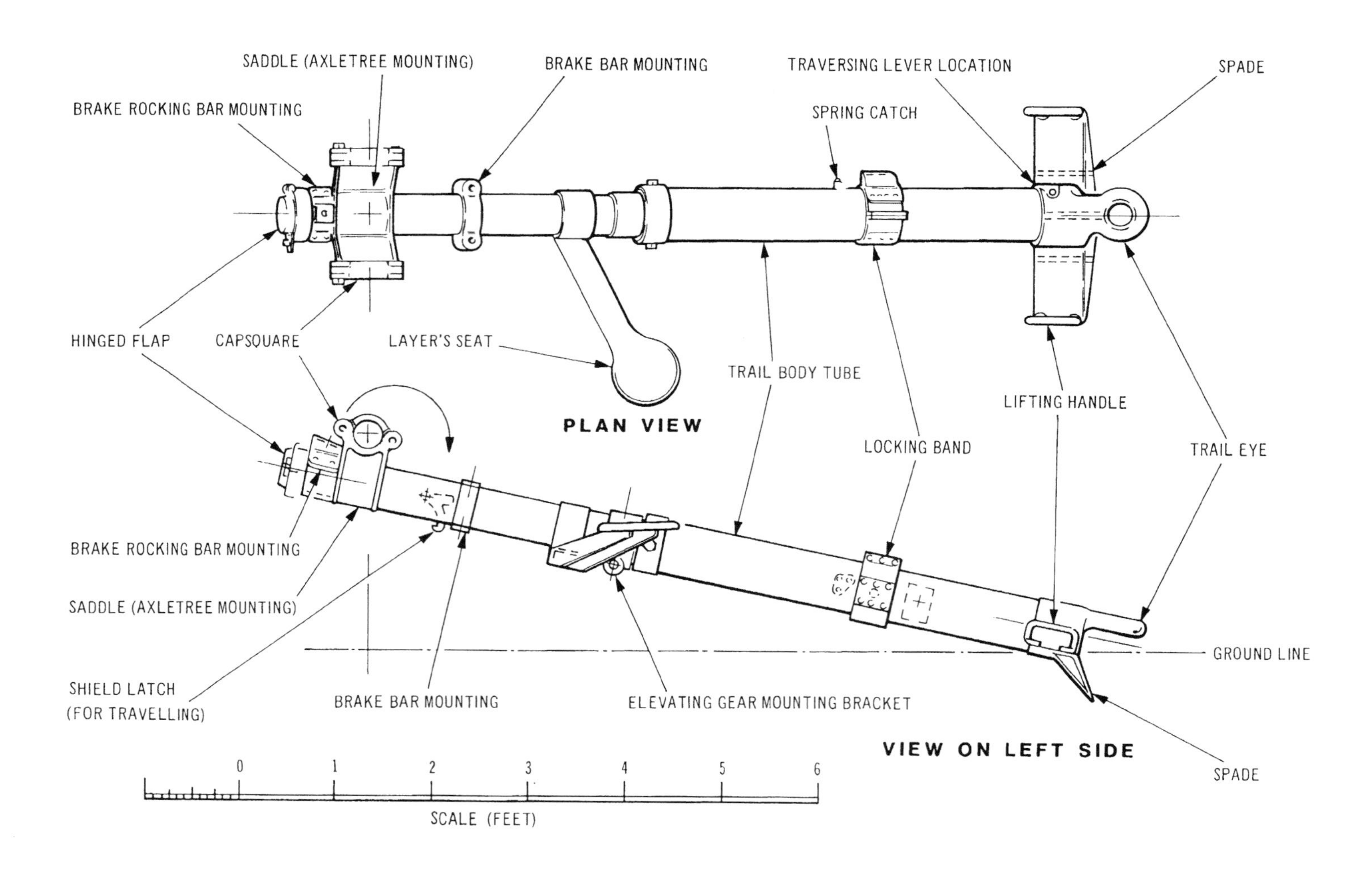
SADDLE (AXLETREE MOUNTING)
BRAKE BAR MOUNTING
TRAVERSING LEVER LOCATION
SPADE
BRAKE ROCKING BAR MOUNTING
SPRING CATCH
HINGED FLAP
CAPSQUARE
LAYER'S SEAT
TRAIL BODY TUBE
PLAN VIEW
LIFTING HANDLE
LOCKING BAND
TRAIL EYE
BRAKE ROCKING BAR MOUNTING
SADDLE (AXLETREE MOUNTING)
GROUND LINE
SHIELD LATCH
(FOR TRAVELLING)
BRAKE BAR MOUNTING
ELEVATING GEAR MOUNTING BRACKET
VIEW ON LEFT SIDE
SPADE
0
1
2
3
4
5
6
SCALE (FEET)

TRAIL

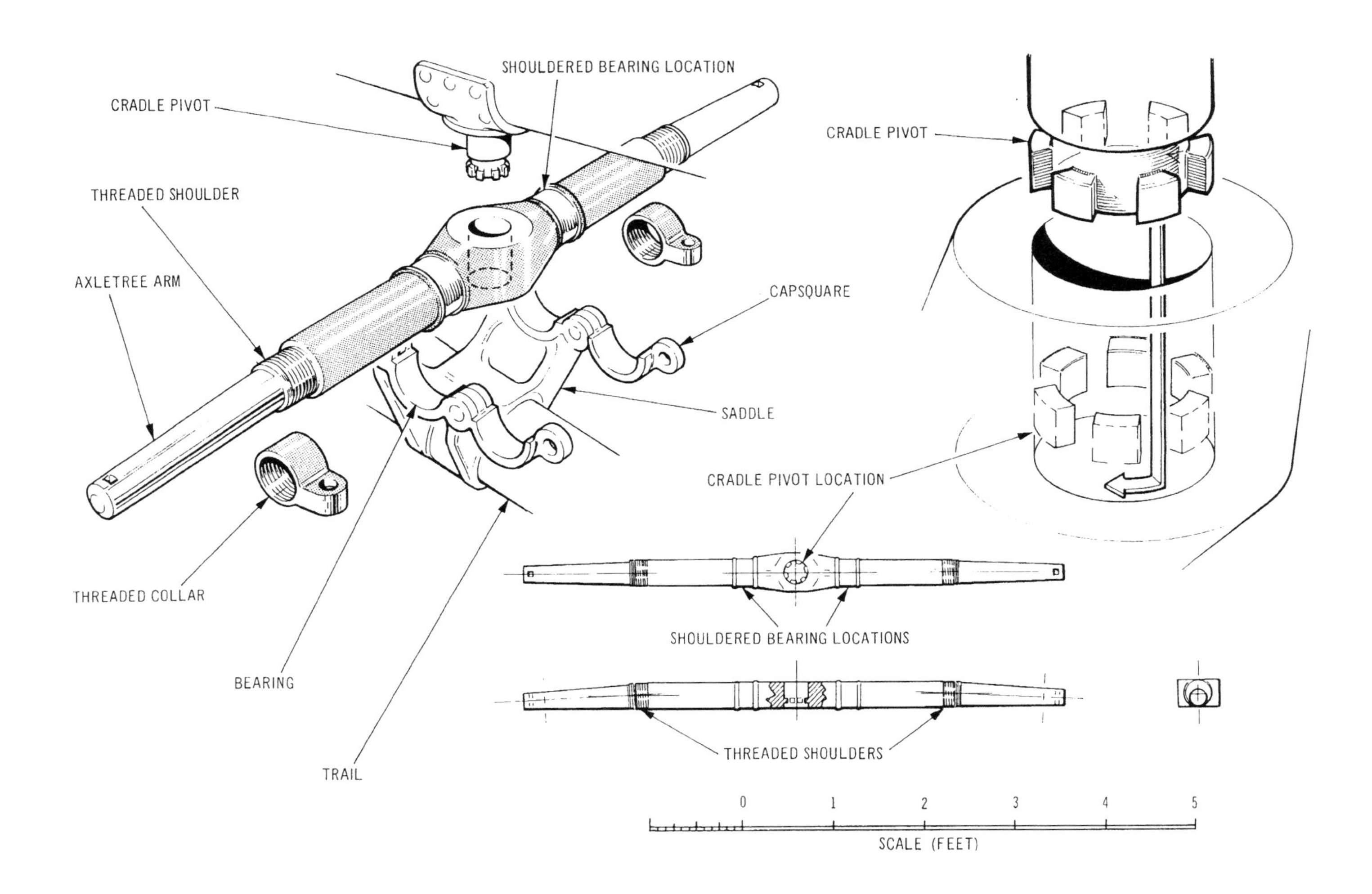
SHOULDERED BEARING LOCATION
CRADLE PIVOT
THREADED SHOULDER
AXLETREE ARM
CAPSQUARE
SADDLE
CRADLE PIVOT
CRADLE PIVOT LOCATION
THREADED COLLAR
SHOULDERED BEARING LOCATIONS
BEARING
THREADED SHOULDERS
TRAIL
0
1
2
3
4
5
SCALE (FEET)

AXLETREE

Axletree

The hollow, forged steel axletree was circular in section, except the central portion which was rectangular and solid. The centre was bored through vertically to provide a housing for the cradle-mounted pivot. Six lugs projected into the pivot housing to engage six projections on the cradle pivot and provide a means of locking the axletree and cradle together, while enabling the cradle some movement for deflection purposes.

The axletree was mounted into two bearings on a saddle riveted to the trail body and secured into the bearings by capsquares. The capsquares were each pivoted at the rear and held closed at the front by a bolt. End movement was prevented by shoulders machined on the axletree at the bearing locations.

At each end of the axletree body was mounted a collar, screwed on, for the attachment of a tensile stay. Each stay rear end was attached to the steel bracket connected to the elevating screw head.

Cradle

The cradle was mounted onto the axletree by a vertical pivot, riveted to the cradle underside, and housed within a vertical hole bored through the axletree centre. To mount the cradle, it would be lowered onto the axletree so that the cradle pivot entered the axletree hole, the six cradle pivot projections passing between the matching lugs in the axletree hole. The cradle would then be turned to position its pivot projections below the axletree lugs and prevent the cradle pivot lifting out. This would lock the cradle and axletree together while allowing the cradle enough horizontal rotation to provide top traverse of three degrees, right or left. The axletree illustration on page 173 shows this arrangement clearly.

The cradle was a steel trough formed with longitudinal ribs, at the top, on either side. These ribs were the sliding surfaces which engaged the gun barrel guide rings and allowed the barrel to move longitudinally during recoil.

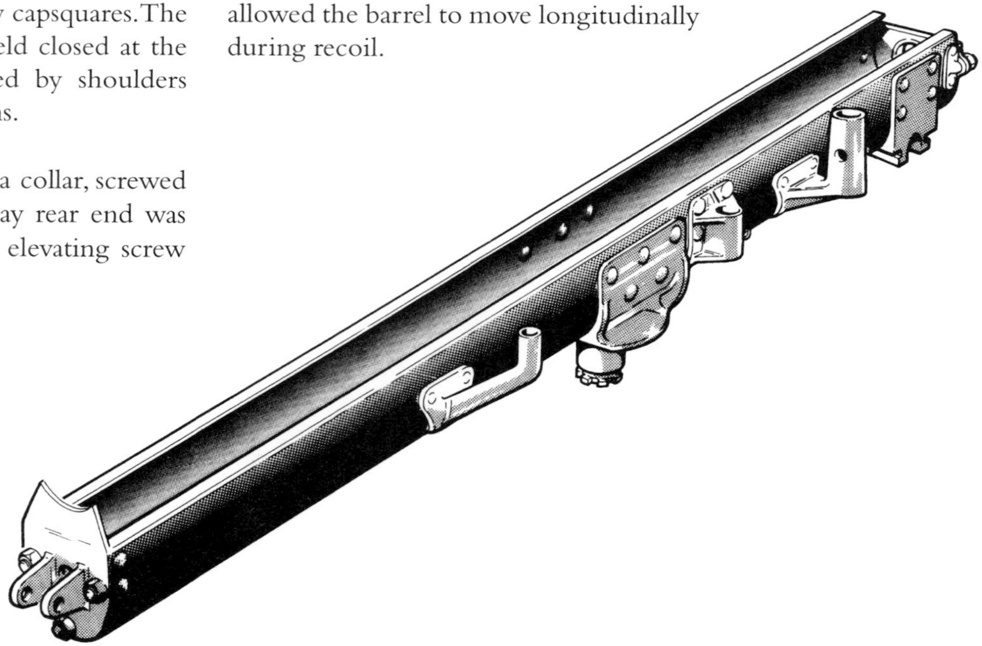

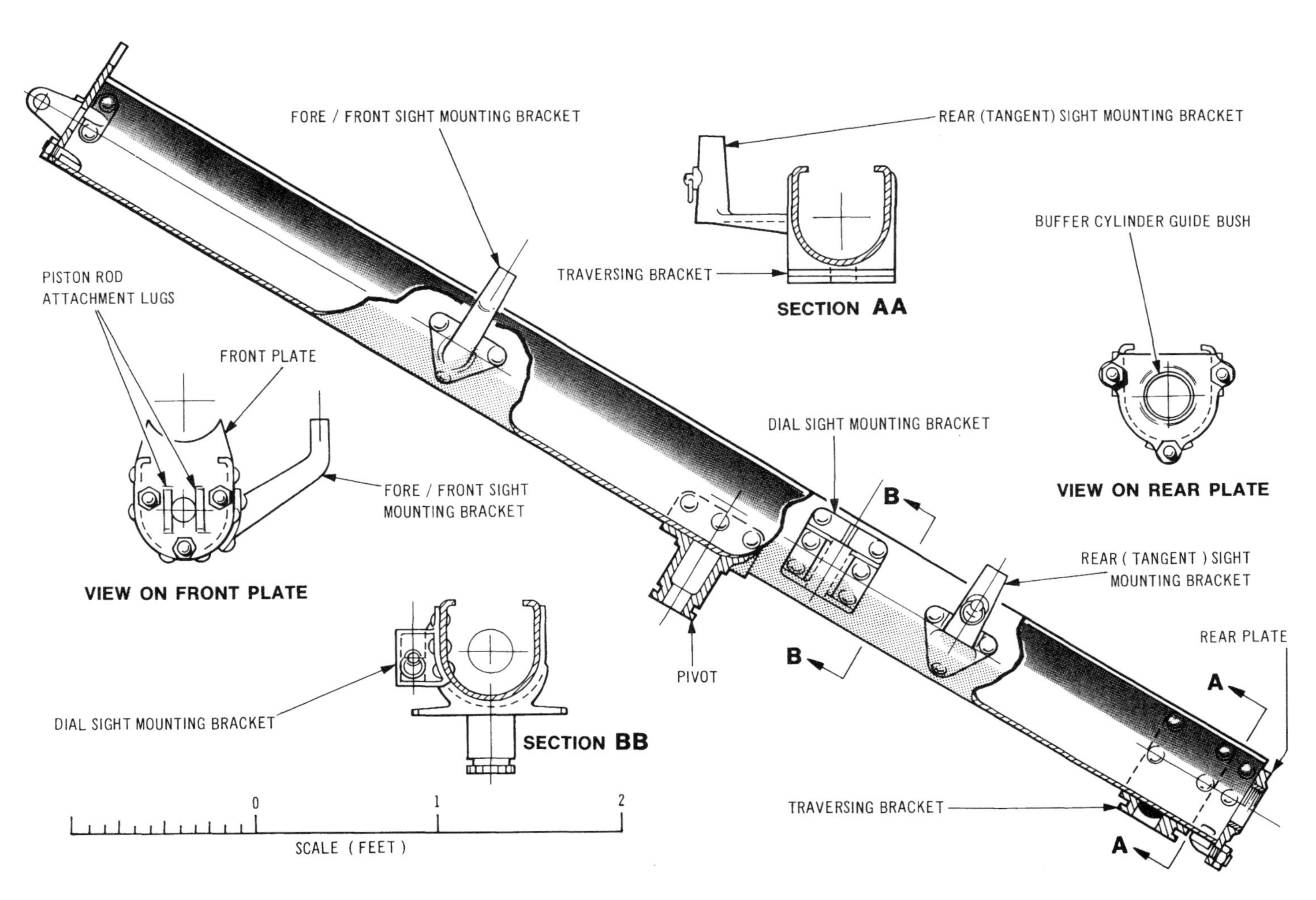
FORE / FRONT SIGHT MOUNTING BRACKET
REAR (TANGENT) SIGHT MOUNTING BRACKET
BUFFER CYLINDER GUIDE BUSH
TRAVERSING BRACKET
SECTION AA
PISTON ROD
ATTACHMENT LUGS
FRONT PLATE
VIEW ON REAR PLATE
DIAL SIGHT MOUNTING BRACKET
FORE / FRONT SIGHT
MOUNTING BRACKET
B
REAR (TANGENT) SIGHT
MOUNTING BRACKET
VIEW ON FRONT PLATE
REAR PLATE
B
PIVOT
A
DIAL SIGHT MOUNTING BRACKET
SECTION BB
0
1
2
TRAVERSING BRACKET
SCALE (FEET)
A

CRADLE

Each end of the cradle was closed by a steel cover plate. The front cover plate had two lugs to which was secured the hydraulic buffer piston rod crosshead. The piston rod passed rearwards through a hole in the front cover plate into the body of the cradle. This housed the hydraulic buffer and spring recuperator, the cylinder of which passed through a bush in the rear cover plate.

The cradle left side carried gunmetal mounting brackets for the fore (acorn) and rear (tangent) sights. Also on the cradle left side was a manganese bronze bracket for mounting a steel pillar to support a No.1 dial sight.

To the cradle underside rear was riveted a traversing bracket. This was machined with grooves which slid in the traversing gear guide located at the elevating screw top end. The spaces between the cradle and barrel were closed in by steel protecting plates.

Hydraulic buffer and spring recuperator

The forged steel buffer cylinder operated within the cradle and was screwed at its front end, into the gun barrel front guide ring, with which it recoiled on firing. The buffer cylinder rear end passed through a guide bush in the cradle rear cover plate. The piston rod was secured, with a crosshead, to attachment lugs on the cradle front cover plate exterior. Situated between the cradle front cover plate and the barrel front guide ring was an India rubber buffer stop.

The recuperator consisted of a single bank of eight spiral springs separated by seven parting plates, housing the hydraulic buffer cylinder. The cradle rear cover plate formed the seating for the rear spring, the front spring bearing against the gun barrel front guide ring.

On recoil (see page 178), the gun barrel front guide ring moved rearwards, pulling with it the buffer cylinder. This compressed the springs between the guide ring and the cradle rear cover plate. Once the hydraulic buffer had arrested all recoil movement, the springs returned the barrel to the firing position, the final travel being cushioned by the control plunger and India rubber buffer stop.

As the buffer cylinder moved rearwards during recoil, it was, in effect, being drawn off the stationary piston rod, forcing the hydraulic fluid to flow from the front of the piston to the rear through the grooves in the buffer cylinder wall. The grooves tapered in width, becoming wider as the buffer cylinder moved to the rear, thus lessening the hydraulic resistance as the spring resistance increased and maintaining carriage stability.

Subsequent to the recoil energy being absorbed by the hydraulic buffer, the springs returned the gun barrel forward to the firing position, the travel being partially controlled by the narrowing cylinder wall grooves progressively increasing resistance to the movement. Final travel of the barrel was cushioned by the control plunger. As the control plunger entered the tube it displaced the fluid within through channels in the plunger which reduced in depth, until the end movement which displaced the remaining tube contents through the small bleed hole. Final cushioning was carried out by the India rubber buffer stop.

The packing gland could be tightened with the hydraulic buffer

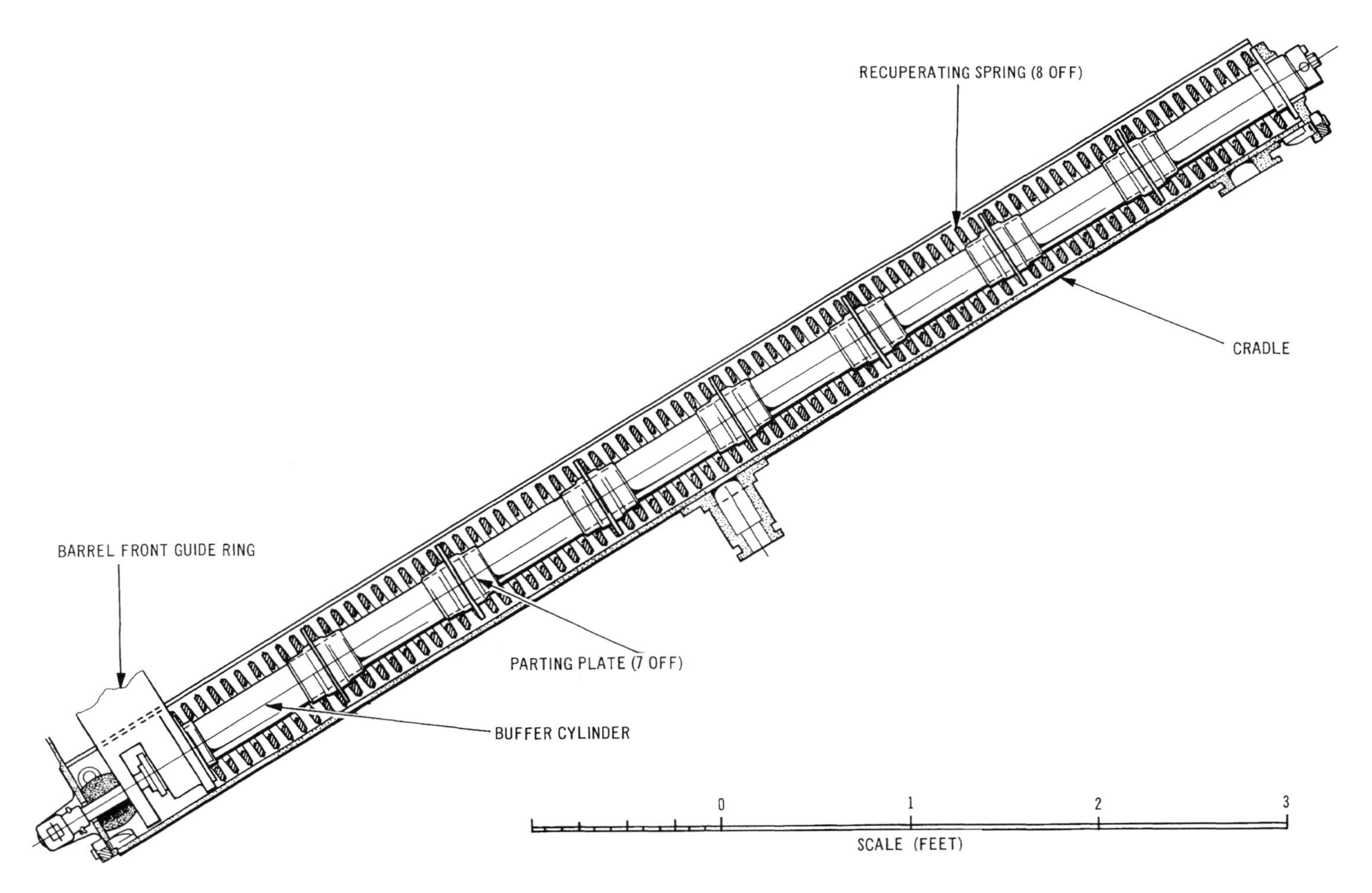

HYDRAULIC BUFFER AND SPRING RECUPERATOR

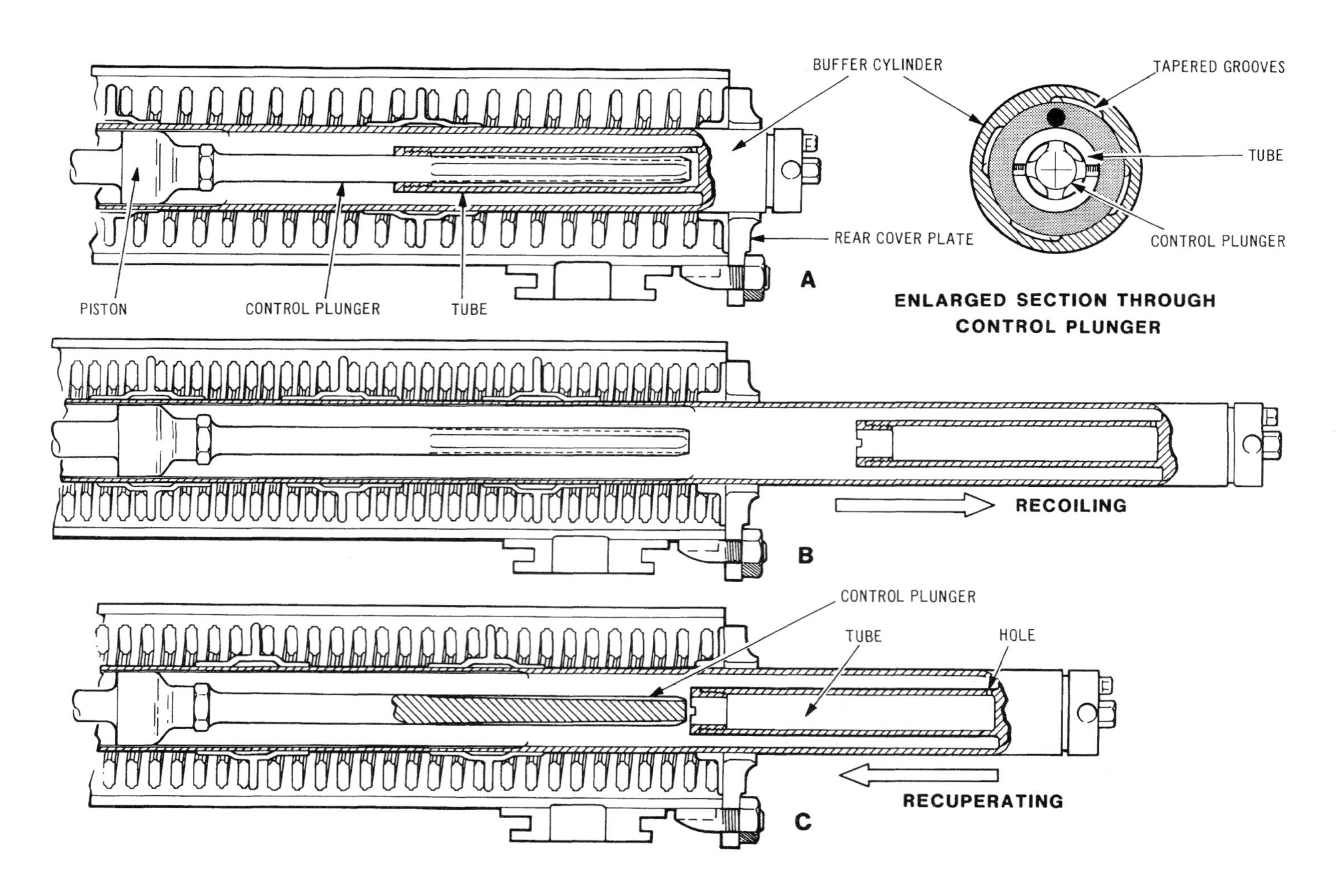

HYDRAULIC BUFFER AND CONTROL PLUNGER – OPERATION

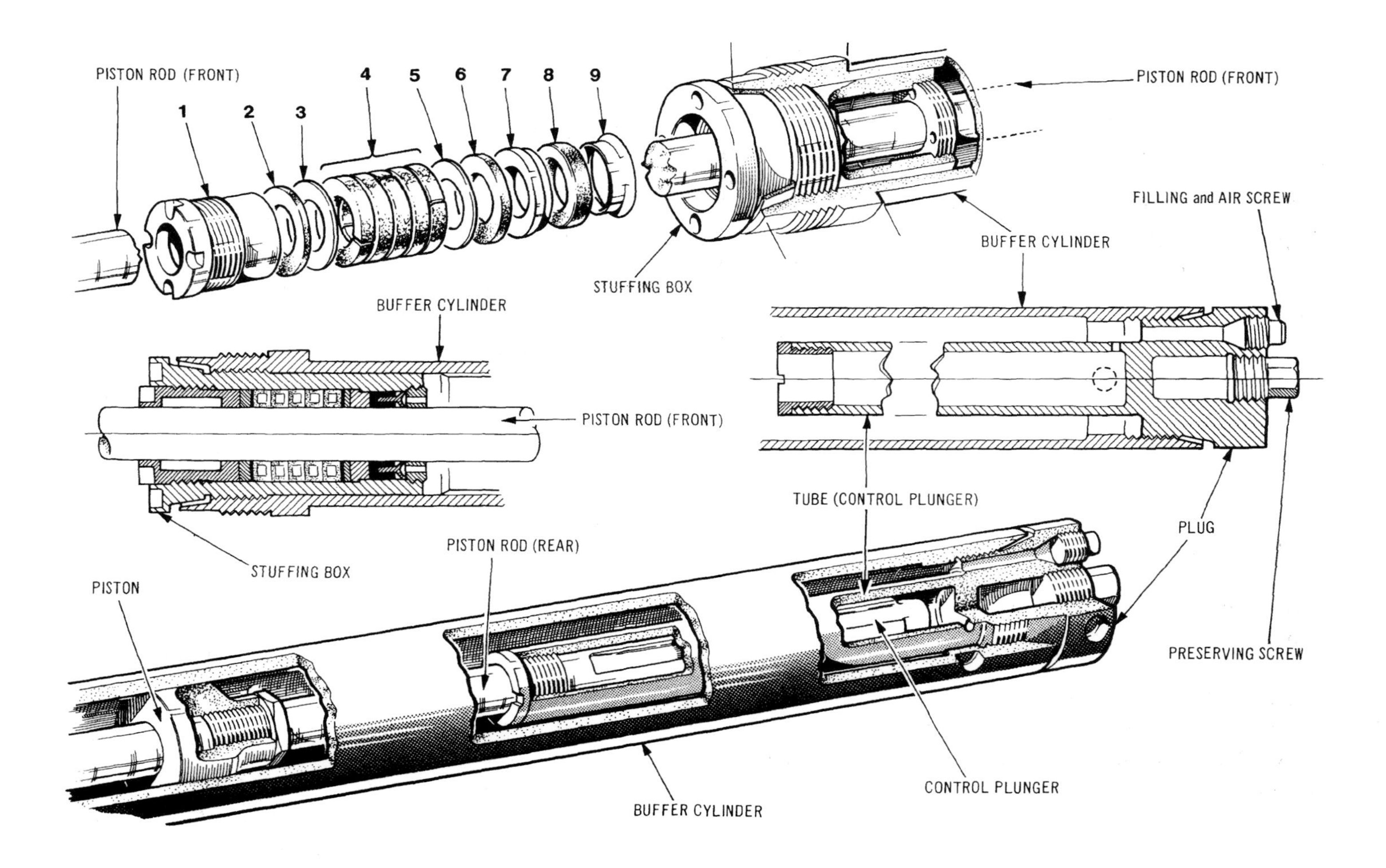

HYDRAULIC BUFFER DETAILS

KEY FOR GLAND PACKING ITEMS

1 GLAND
2 WASHER (LEATHER)
3 RING (MANGANESE BRONZE)
4 HYDRAULIC PACKING
5 RING (MANGANESE BRONZE)
6 WASHER (LEATHER)
7 OUTER PROTECTING RING
8 U LEATHER
9 RING (MANGANESE BRONZE)

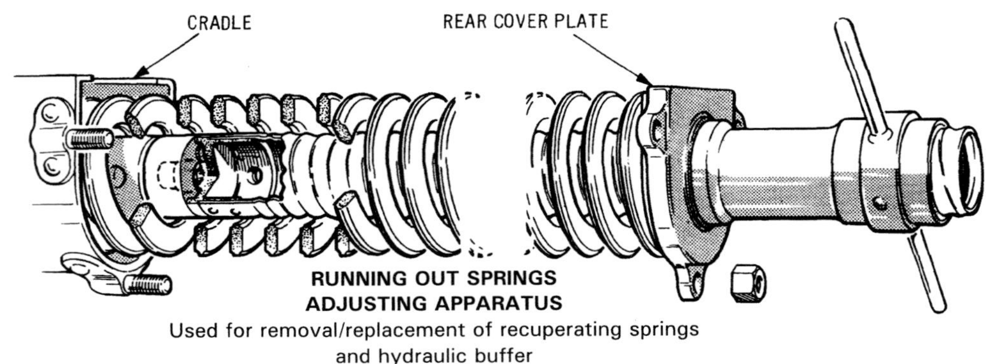

RUNNING OUT SPRINGS ADJUSTING APPARATUS
Used for removal/replacement of recuperating springs and hydraulic buffer

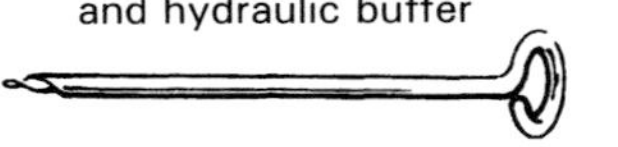

EXTRACTORS
Used for removal of hydraulic packing

in place. This would entail removal of the cradle front cover plate and use of a special key. To fill or empty the hydraulic buffer, also to replace the U leather and hydraulic packing, it was necessary to remove the buffer from the cradle. Special equipment was needed to accomplish these procedures.

The hydraulic fluid used was pure glycerine. Capacity of the buffer cylinder was eight and one-third pints, but the buffer was not totally filled, about seven and three-quarter pints being the usual quantity.

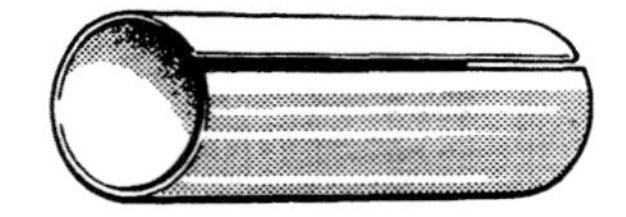

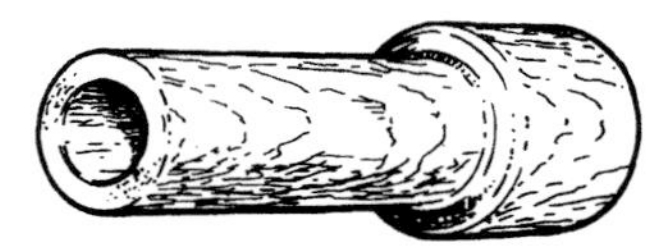

REPACKING CYLINDERS
One tin, one wood, used to repack hydraulic packing

DRIFT AND BUSH
Bronze, used to reform the stuffing box (one set per battery)

Elevating and traversing gear

Elevating gear

The elevating gear was of double screw pattern. Turning the handwheel (**3**) caused the handwheel pinion (**10**) to rotate and turn the bevel wheel (**8**). The drive continued through the keyway (**7**) and turned the outer elevating screw (**6**), causing it to travel up or down through the internal thread of the oscillating bracket (**9**), dependent on the direction of rotation. As the outer elevating screw (**6**) turned, the inner elevating screw (**5**) – being prevented from rotating by attachment of the crosshead (**4**) to the traversing guide (**19**) – travelled up or down through the internal thread in the outer elevating screw (**6**) bore.

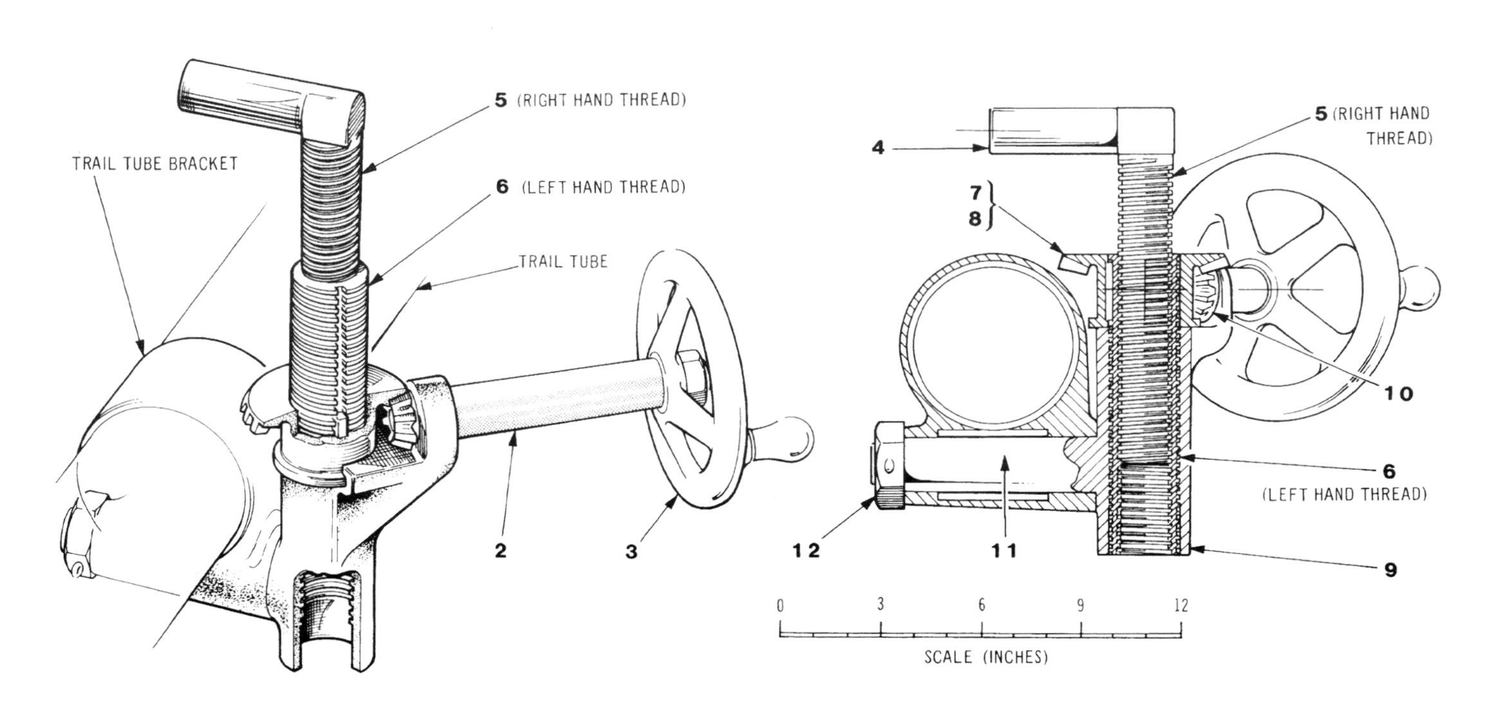

ELEVATING GEAR

1 CRADLE TRAVERSING GUIDE BRACKET
2 SPINDLE AND PIN
3 ELEVATING HANDWHEEL AND NUT
4 CROSSHEAD
5 INNER ELEVATING SCREW
6 OUTER ELEVATING SCREW
7 KEY
8 BEVEL WHEEL
9 OSCILLATING BRACKET AND NUT
10 PINION
11 TRUNNION
12 RETAINING NUT AND SPLIT PIN
13 TRAVERSING HANDWHEEL AND NUT
14 SWIVEL BEARING BUSHES
15 SWIVEL BEARING
16 LOCK NUT
17 TRAVERSING SCREW
18 TRAVERSING SCREW SECURING PIN
19 GUIDE
20 CAPSQUARE

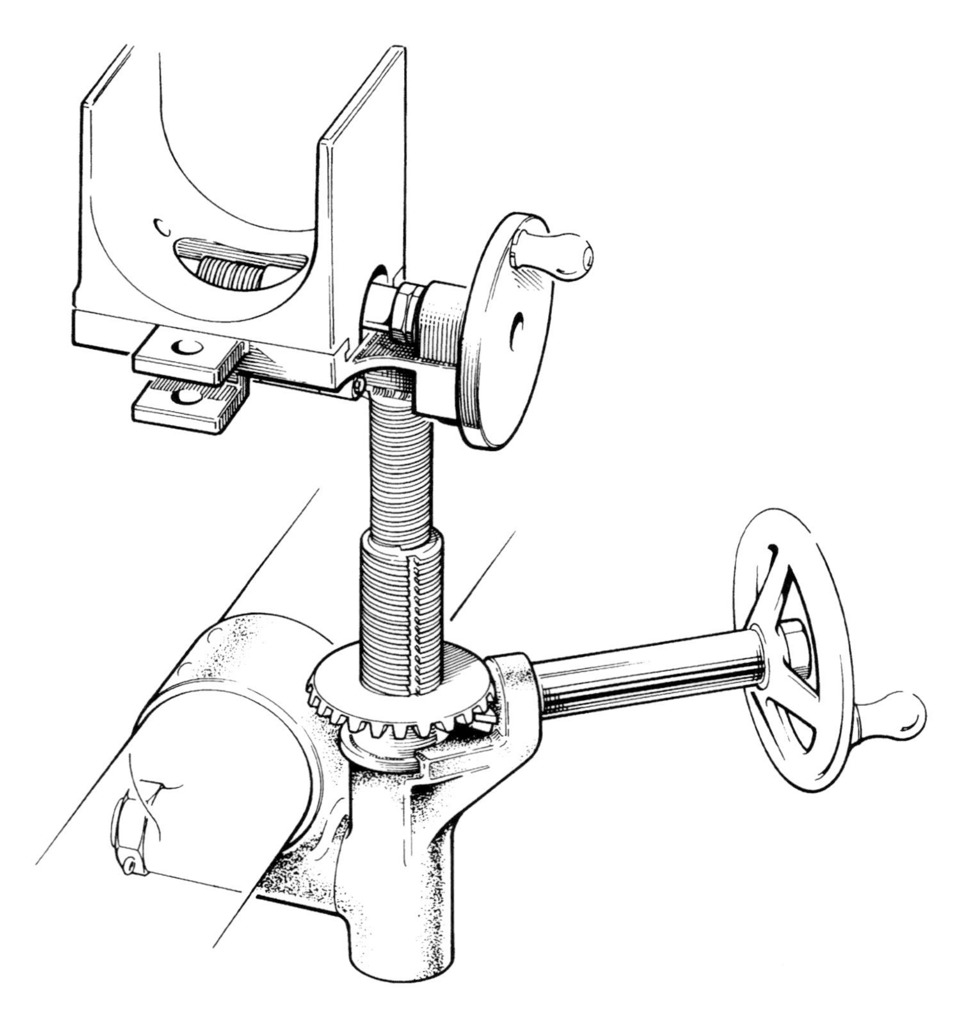

ELEVATING AND TRAVERSING GEAR

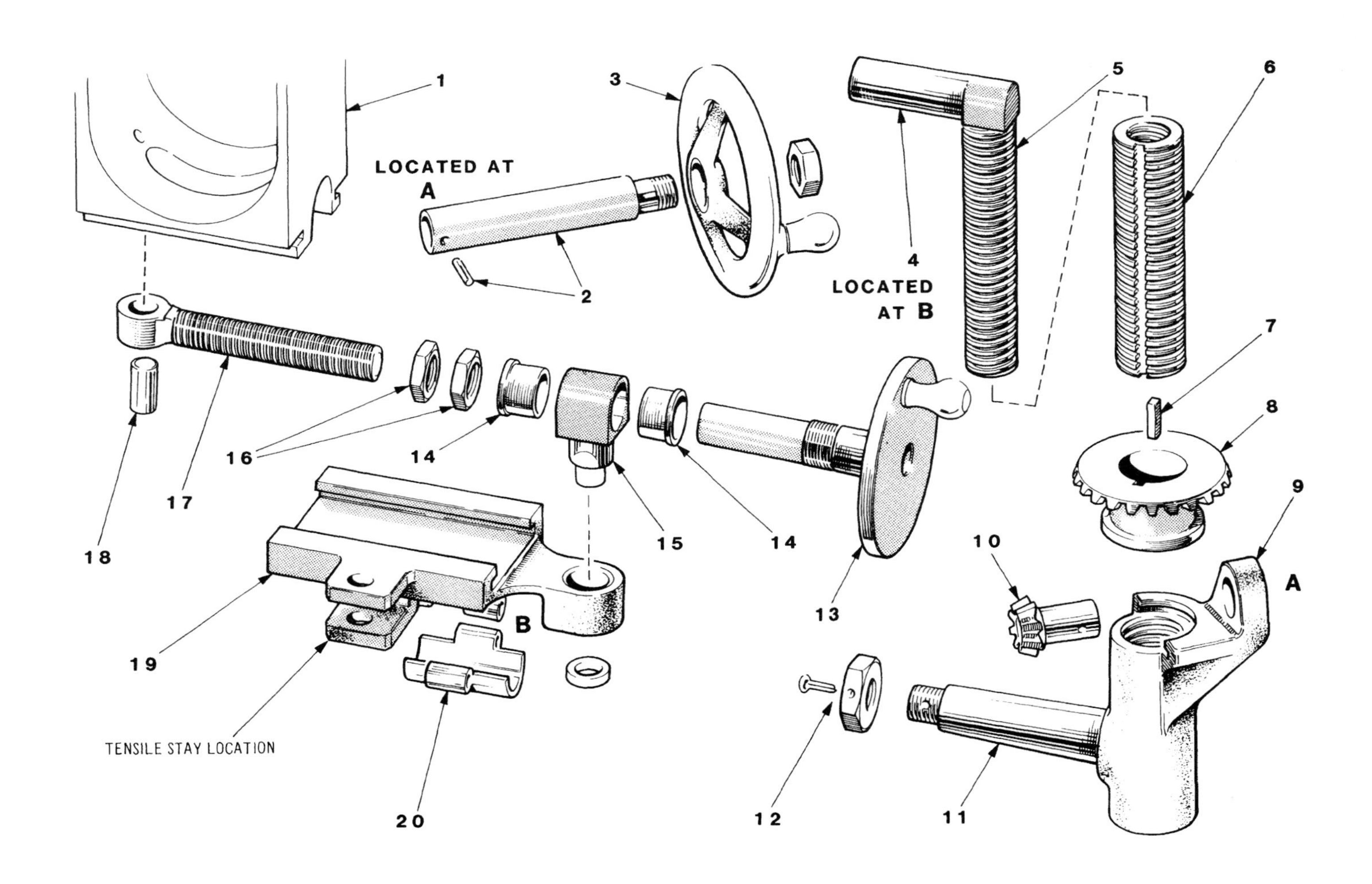

ELEVATING AND TRAVERSING GEAR – COMPONENTS

Traversing gear

The traversing gear was mounted on the elevating gear inner elevating screw crosshead (**4**) and secured by a capsquare (**20**). It was braced to the axletree threaded collars by two tensile stays, attached at their rear ends to the traversing guide bracket (**19**) front face. Top traverse of three degrees, left or right, was provided by the traversing gear.

Turning the handwheel (**13**) caused the traversing screw (**17**) to move in or out of the handwheel threaded bore (**13**) and rotate the cradle (**1**) about its pivot mounting in the axletree centre.

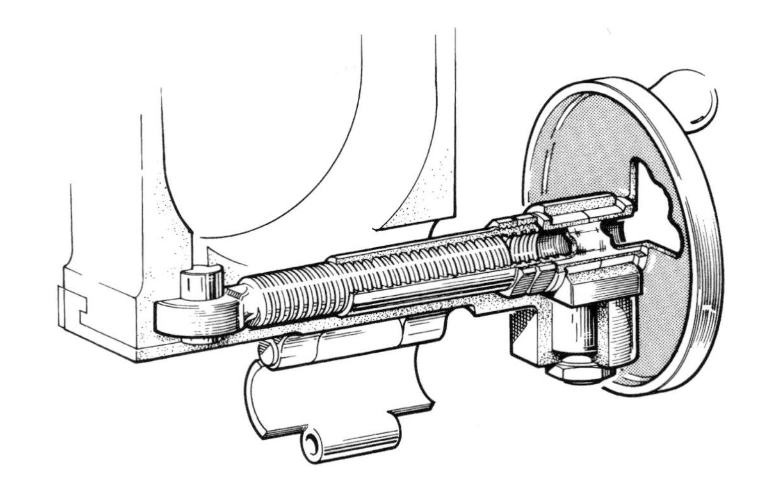

Mk. I* carriages carried a scale plate and pointer on the guide rear face (**19**).

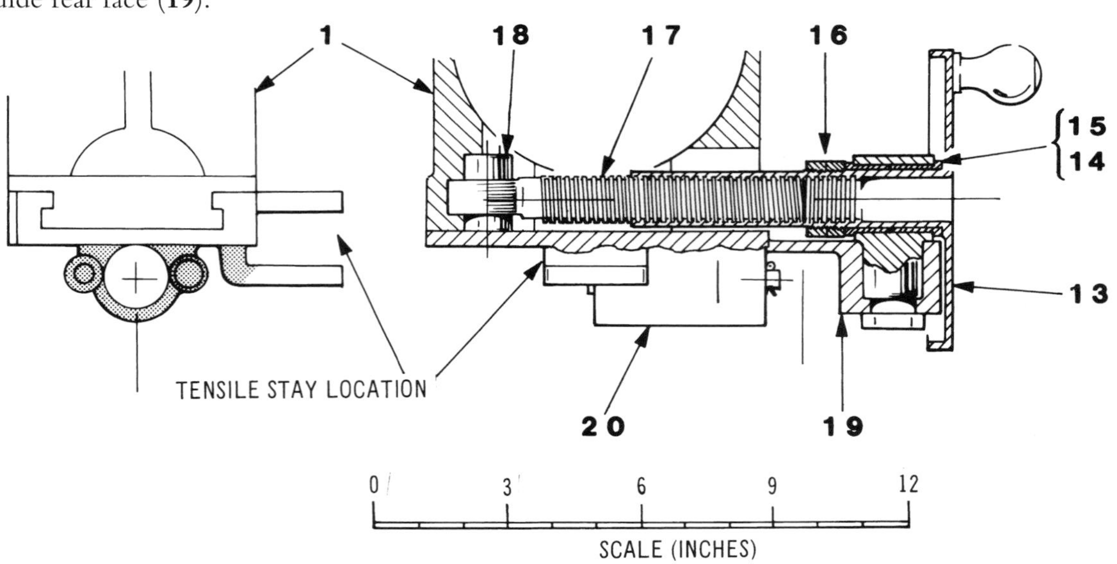

Tensile stays and swinging arm brake

Tensile stays

The tensile stays were secured, at their forward end, to a threaded collar on each end of the axletree body. They converged, at their rear, onto a bracket, formed on the front of the traversing guide. They braced the elevating gear against any strain imposed during traversing.

Swinging arm brake

The brake right-hand elevating rod carried a handwheel at the forward end and another towards the rear, to enable brake operation from before or behind the shield. Turning a handwheel caused the threaded rod to travel forward through a nut – formed with trunnions and mounted on one end of a rocking lever – until the right brake block contacted the wheel. Subsequent turning of the handwheel caused the rocking lever to draw the left-hand rod forward until the left brake block contacted the wheel.

Disc springs were located at the forward end of the left-hand rod to cushion the brake action.

Shield (see page 187)

The bulletproof shield was an assembly of three portions. The centre portion was fabricated from two pieces, joined vertically at the centre-line. Apertures were cut in it to allow clearance for the gun barrel and cradle, the trail and the brake rods. There was also an aperture for the purpose of sighting.

Two flaps were hinged to the centre portion, one each at the top and bottom. The top flap was secured in the upright position by means of sliding bolts. The flap could be hinged down to the horizontal position and secured by sliding bolts in the event of the No. 1 dial sight being employed. The bottom flap hung free in use. For travelling, it would be folded up under the trail and supported by a spring pawl with handle.

The shield was of sheet steel, reinforced with wood slats around the edges. The shield centre portion was secured to the axletree mounting saddle front face by bolts. Its top was braced and supported by vertical stays. A tubular steel stay was attached to each top outer corner of the shield centre portion, each stay rear end being secured to the trail at the gun layer's seat position.

The following equipment was carried on the shield:

- No. 1 dial sight (in case)
- Dial sight pillar
- Breech screw brush (in pocket)
- Clinometer (in leather case)
- Fuze indicator
- Sighting telescope (in case)
- One pair of drag ropes

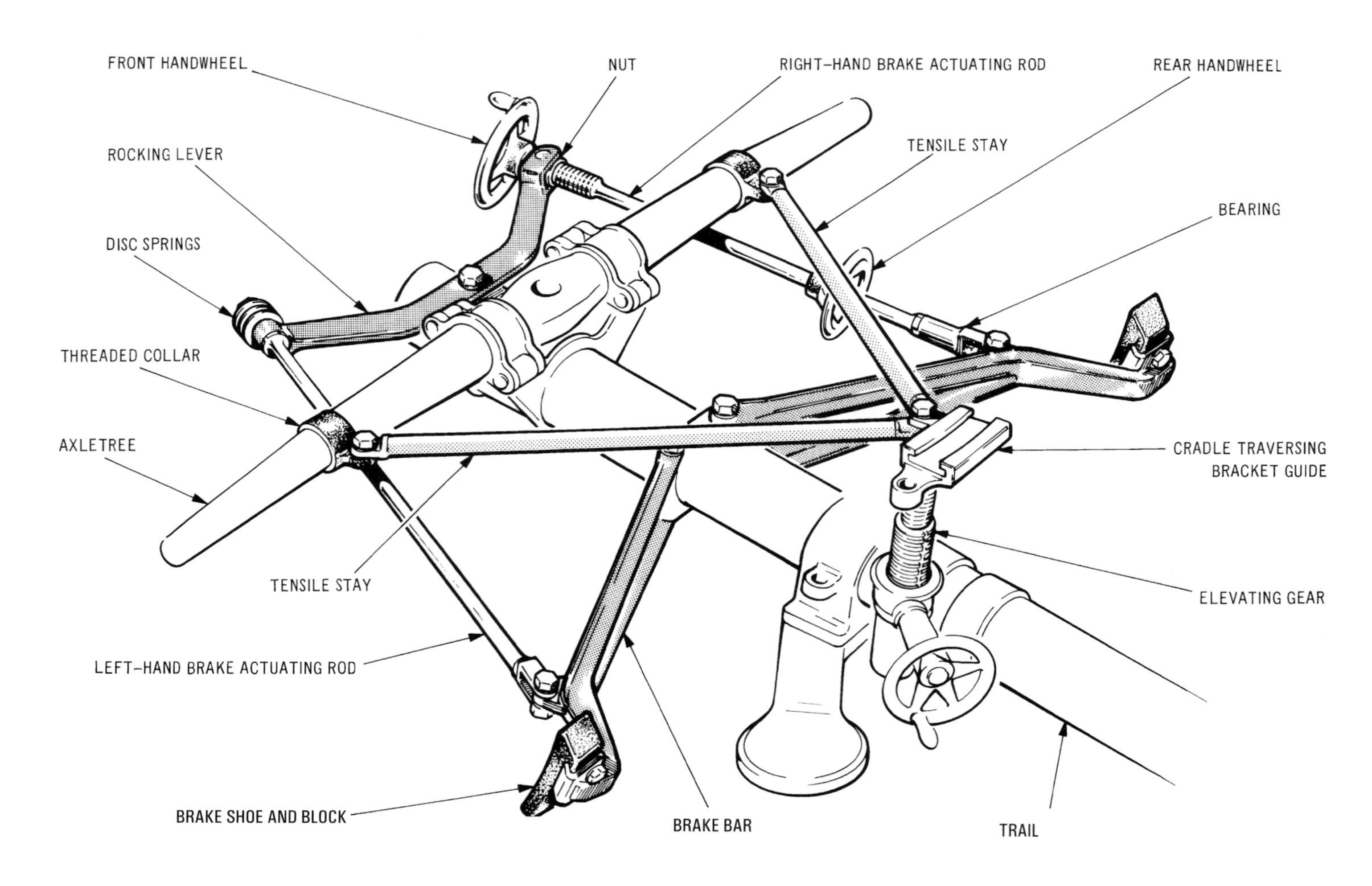

TENSILE STAYS AND SWINGING ARM BRAKE

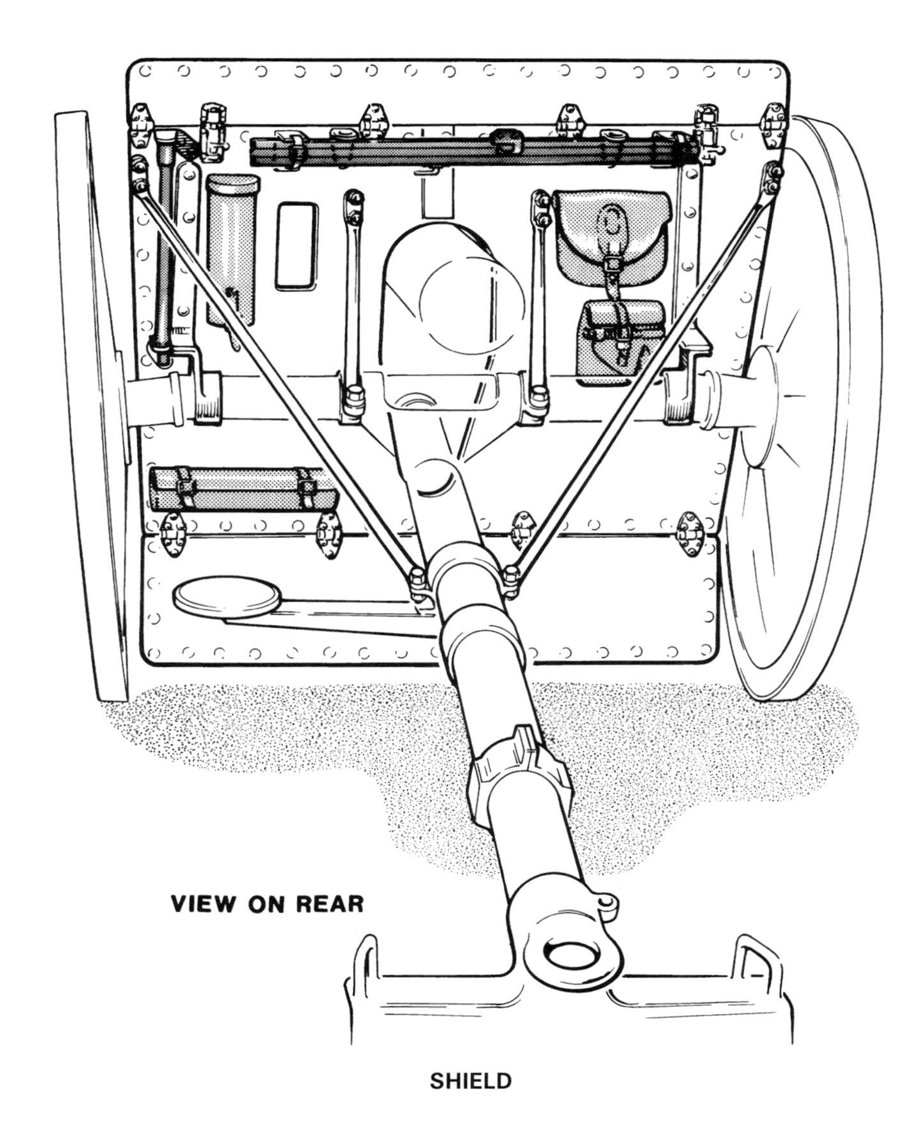

SHIELD

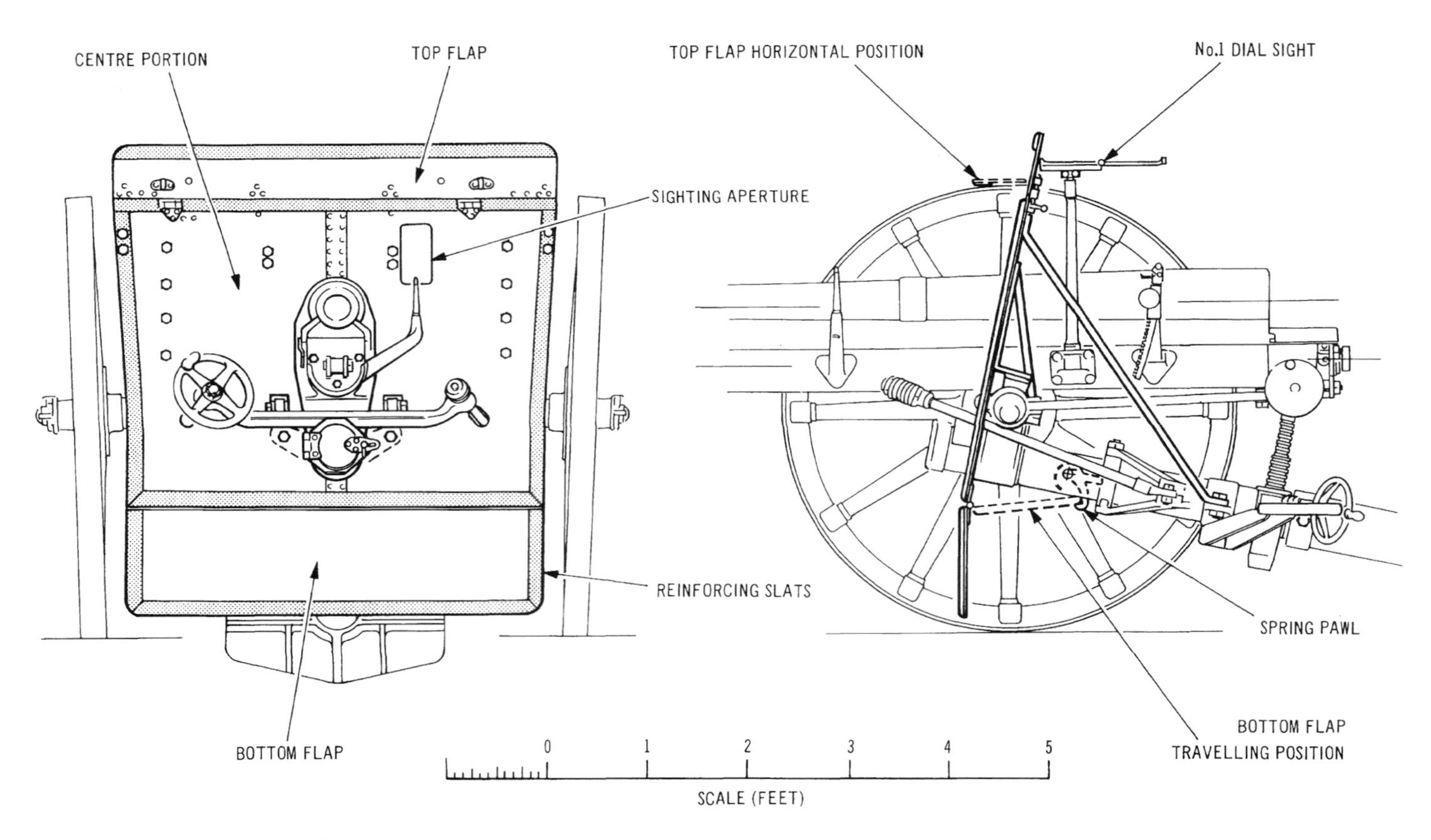

VIEW ON FRONT

VIEW ON LEFT SIDE

SHIELD

Also on the shield, when not fitted to the gun or sights were:

- Rocking bar sight cover
- Breech cover
- Muzzle cover

Sights

The QF 15 pdr had two types of sighting equipment.

Separate foresights and tangent rearsights were issued for use with the Mk. I gun. Rocking bar sights were issued for use with the Mk. I* gun. The rocking bar sights were as fitted to the Breech Loading (Converted) Mk. I gun and described on page 155.

The foresight was a steel pillar, having a pointed apex with a flat portion on the rear. It was fitted to a bracket on the cradle, secured by a taper bolt and nut. The rearsight consisted of a curved sight bar, this having a crosshead with deflection leaf and traversing screw to allow two degrees of deflection, right and left. The sight bar was graduated on the rear face with a yard scale and on the side face with a degree scale. The sight bar front face had a toothed rack which engaged a pinion spindle in the socket. The spindle was keyed to a milled head and drum, by which means it was rotated to raise or lower the sight bar. The drum had yard graduations engraved on it which were read, against an arrow, through an aperture in the sheath.

An adjustable level was fitted to the sight bar, just below the crosshead, moved by a milled head at the sight bar side. This level was used as a clinometer.

Foresight and rearsight were stamped with the gun number to which they would have been adjusted and were not interchangeable with other guns.

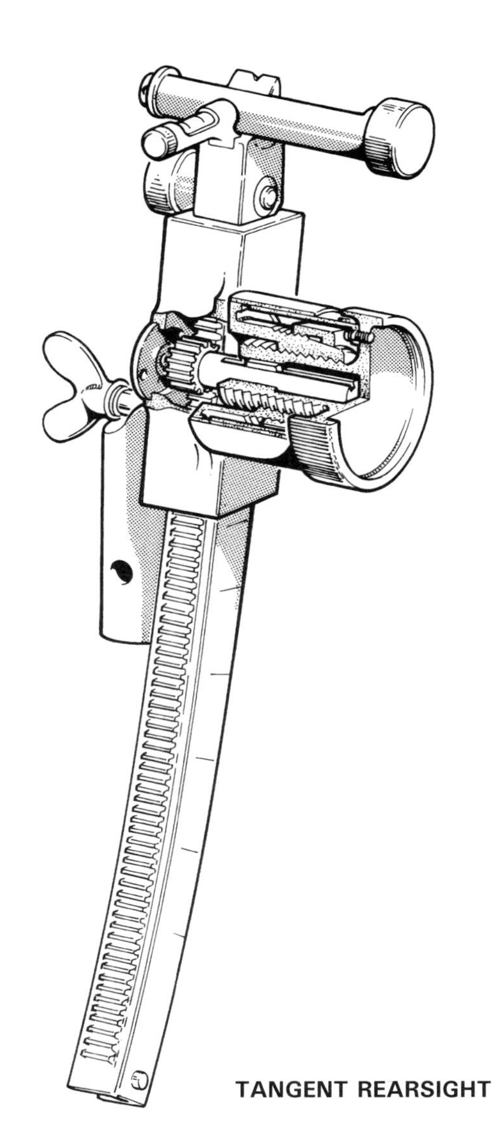

TANGENT REARSIGHT

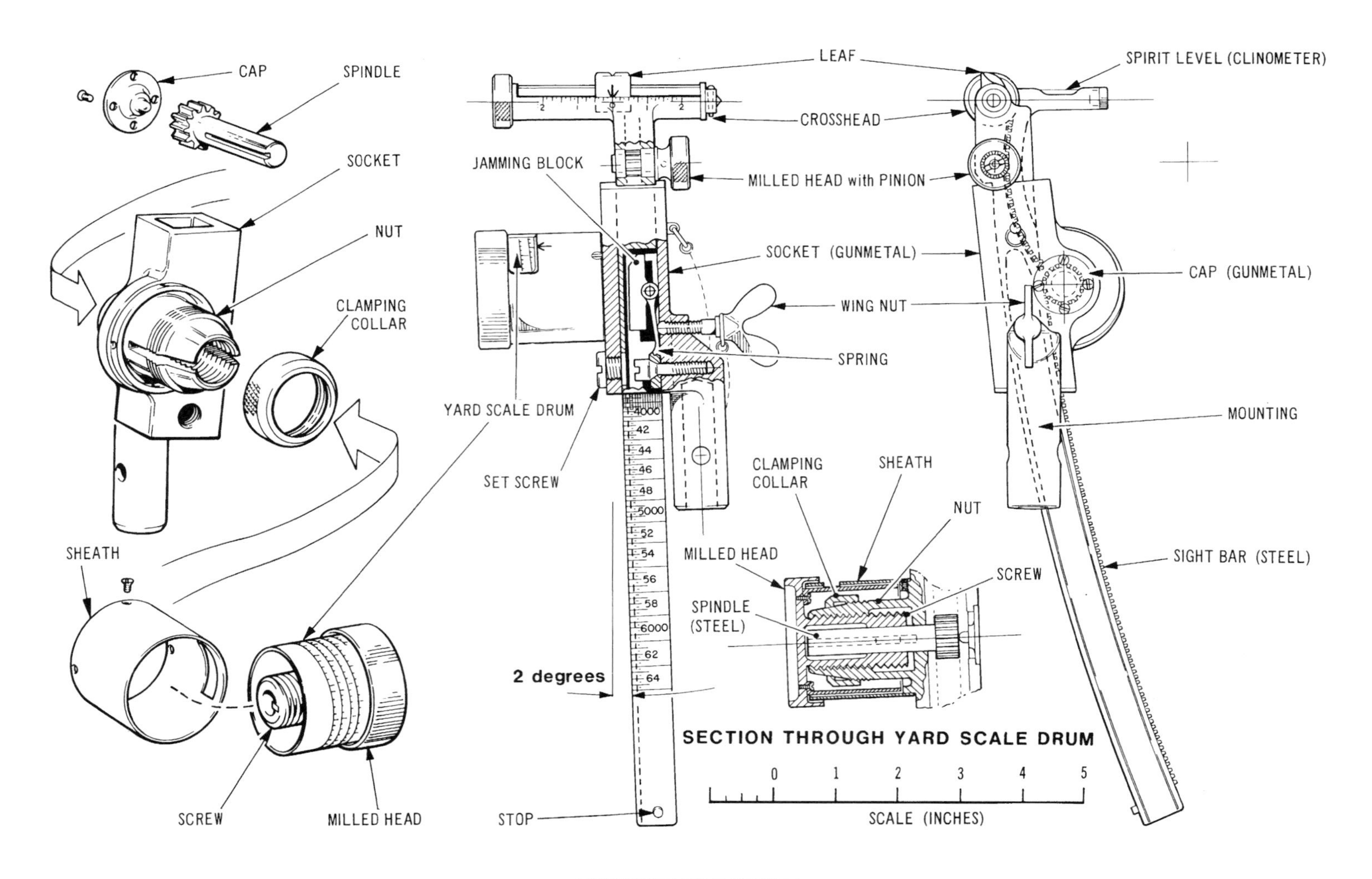

TANGENT REARSIGHT

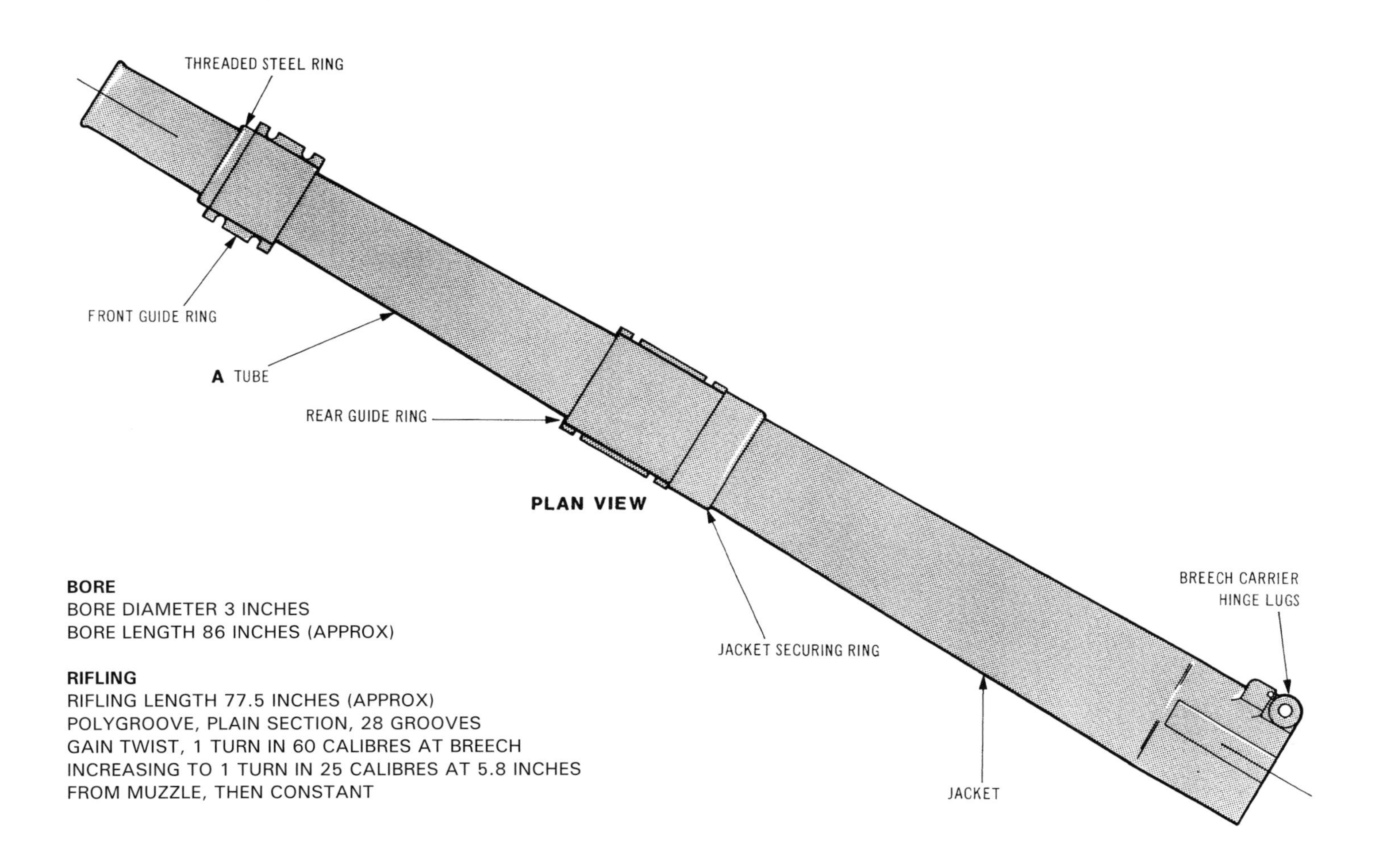

BORE
BORE DIAMETER 3 INCHES
BORE LENGTH 86 INCHES (APPROX)

RIFLING
RIFLING LENGTH 77.5 INCHES (APPROX)
POLYGROOVE, PLAIN SECTION, 28 GROOVES
GAIN TWIST, 1 TURN IN 60 CALIBRES AT BREECH
INCREASING TO 1 TURN IN 25 CALIBRES AT 5.8 INCHES
FROM MUZZLE, THEN CONSTANT

BARREL

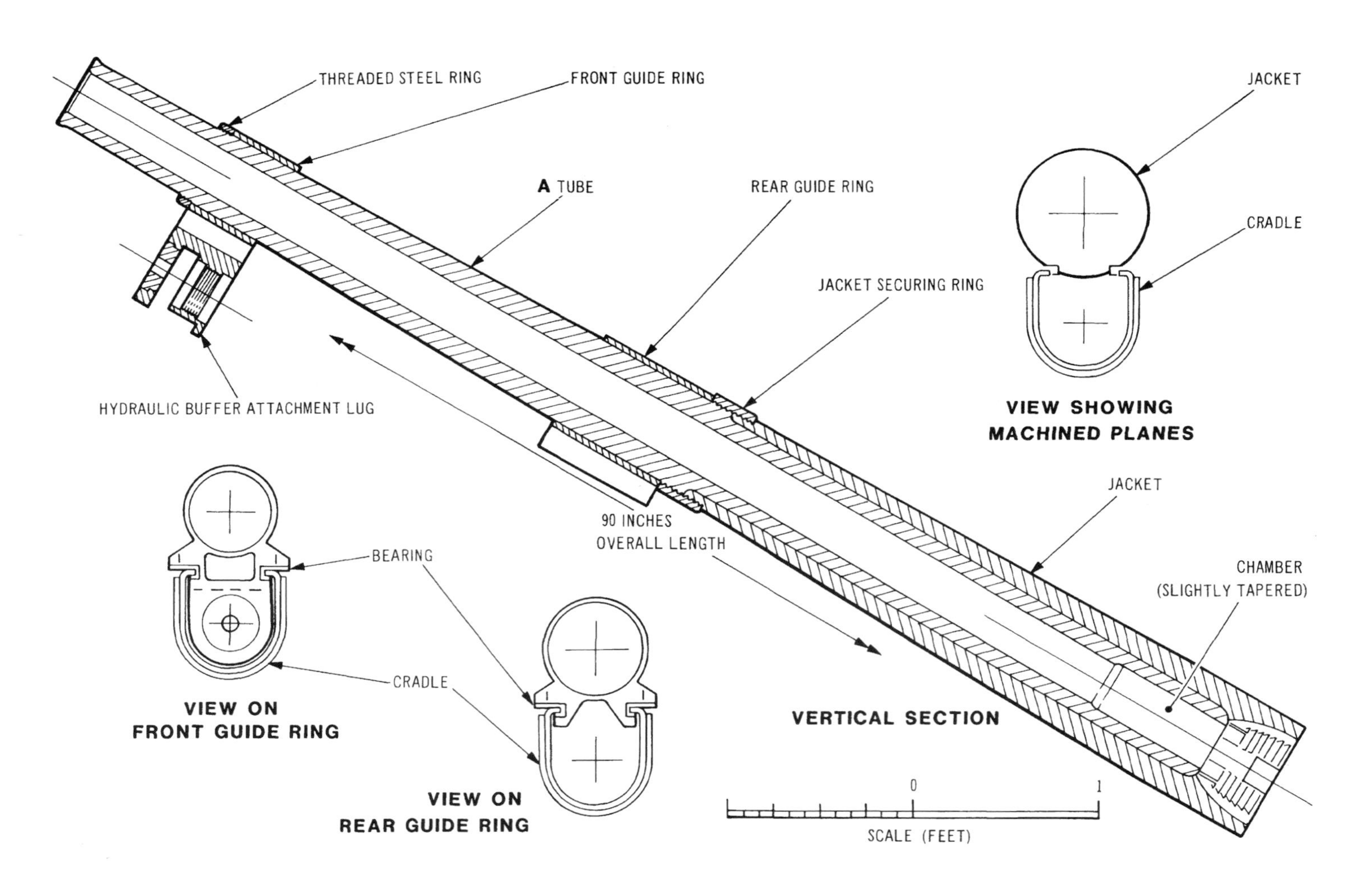

BARREL CONSTRUCTION (SEE PAGE 196)

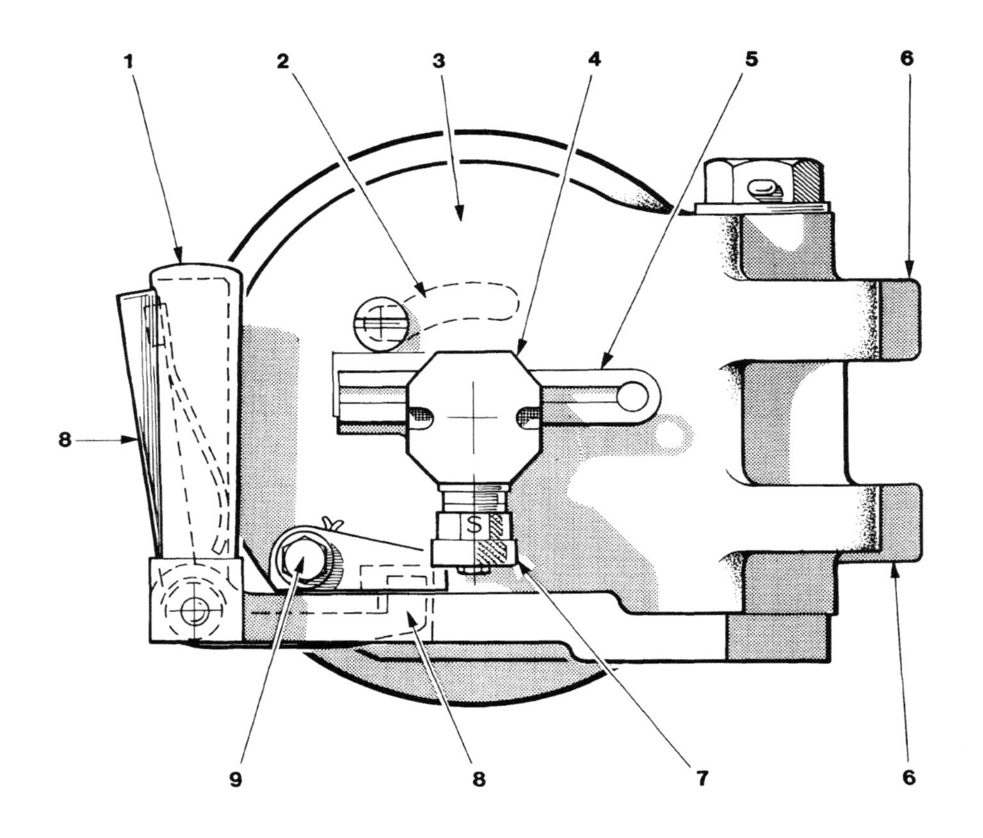

VIEW ON REAR

1 BREECH MECHANISM LEVER
2 SAFETY CATCH
3 CARRIER
4 STRIKER GUIDE CAP
5 FIRING WEDGE
6 EXTRACTOR
7 STRIKER RETAINING CATCH
8 BREECH MECHANISM LEVER RETAINING CATCH
9 BREECH BLOCK RETAINING CATCH
10 BREECH BLOCK
11 FIRING PIN
12 STRIKER GUIDE
13 STRIKER
14 SLEEVE
15 REBOUND SPRING
16 MAIN SPRING
17 BREECH MECHANISM LEVER PINION

BREECH (SEE PAGE 196)

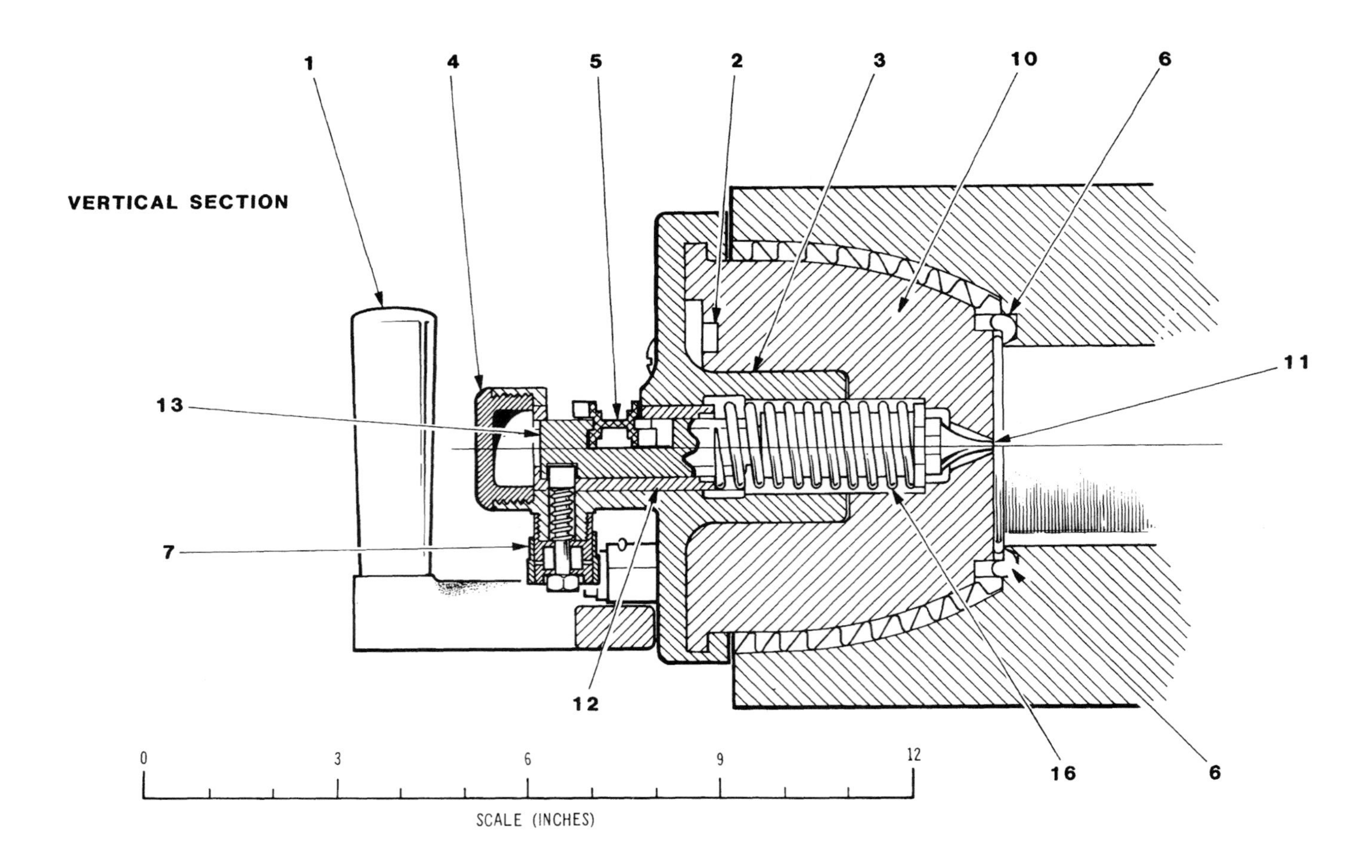

VERTICAL SECTION
1
4
5
2
3
10
6
11
13
7
12
16
6
0
3
6
9
12
SCALE (INCHES)

BREECH

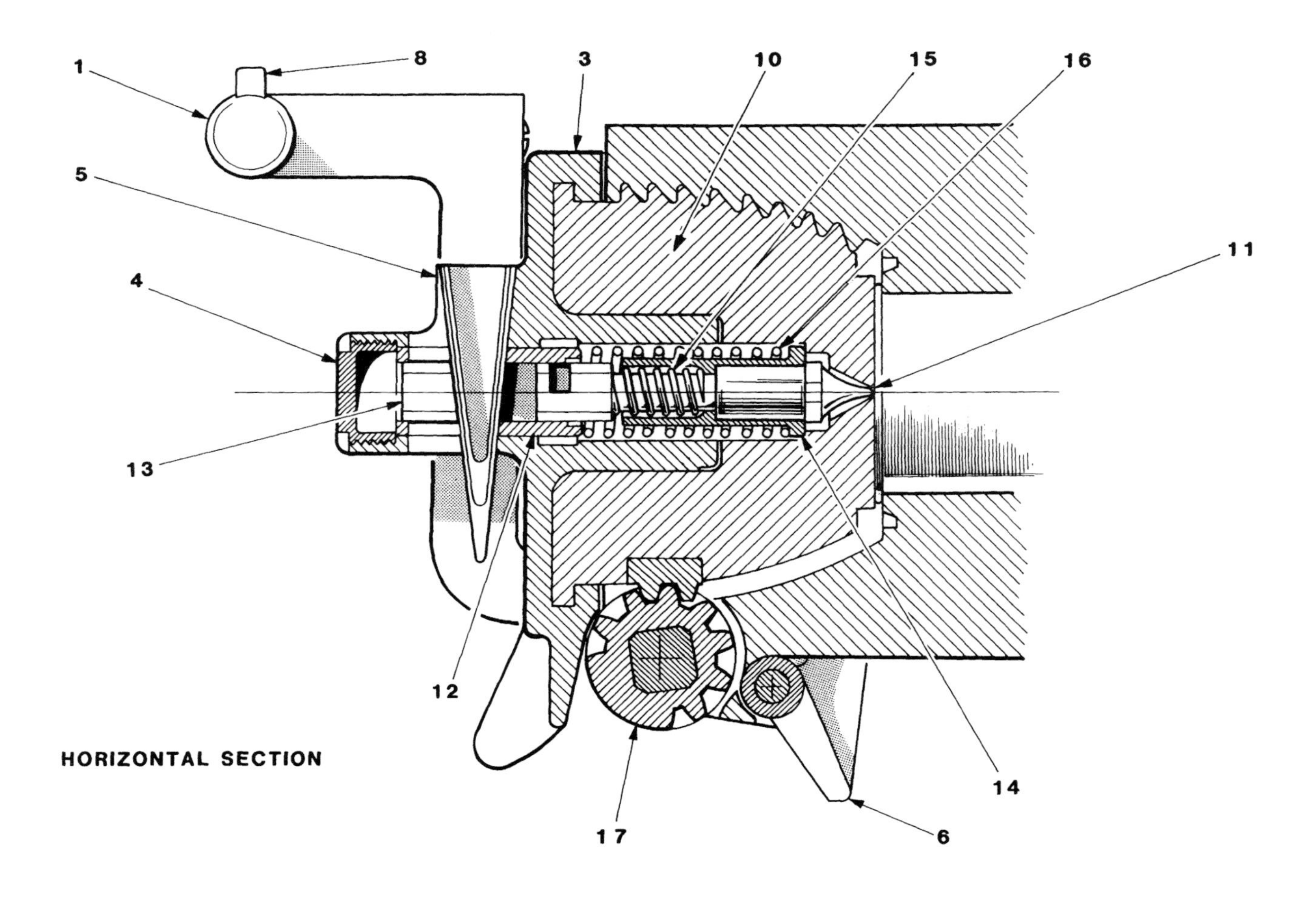

BREECH

Barrel and breech

Barrel

The barrel consisted of an A tube, the rear half reinforced by a jacket which was shrunk on and secured with a threaded steel ring. At the rear, the jacket was internally machined to receive the breech block.

Two steel guide rings were shrunk onto the A tube. The rear one butted against the forward edge of the jacket securing ring. The front one, close to the muzzle, was secured by a steel ring threaded onto the A tube. The front guide ring was formed with a lug on the underside, to which was attached the hydraulic buffer. Both guide rings were formed with bearings carrying bronze liners. These engaged the cradle guides and, together with two plane surfaces machined into the jacket rear lower half, supported the barrel in the cradle.

The jacket was machined with a plane surface at the rear for a clinometer. Vertical and horizontal lines were cut into the breech and muzzle faces.

Breech

The steel, tapered breech block (**10**) had, on its exterior surface, annular collars. These were machined with five interruptions, each being one-tenth of the circumference. The barrel breech was machined in a similar manner to allow the breech block to be pushed home and locked by one-tenth of a turn.

The breech block (**10**) was supported by a steel carrier (**3**), hinged to the barrel exterior on the right side. The breech block (**10**) had an interrupted rear flange which engaged a corresponding recess in the carrier (**3**).

A breech block retaining catch (**9**) was located in the carrier (**3**) and served to lock carrier and block together as the breech was opened. The catch (**9**) would disengage automatically when the breech was closing.

The breech mechanism lever (**1**), hinged to the barrel exterior right side, carried a pinion (**17**) engaging a toothed, steel segment on the breech block (**10**). Movement of the breech mechanism lever (**1**) rotated the pinion (**17**), which turned the breech block (**10**) to disengage the interrupted collars and allow the breech block to withdraw from the breech. The breech mechanism lever (**1**) was retained in the closed position by a catch (**8**), pivoted in the lever (**1**) and spring loaded to engage a recess in the carrier rear face (**3**).

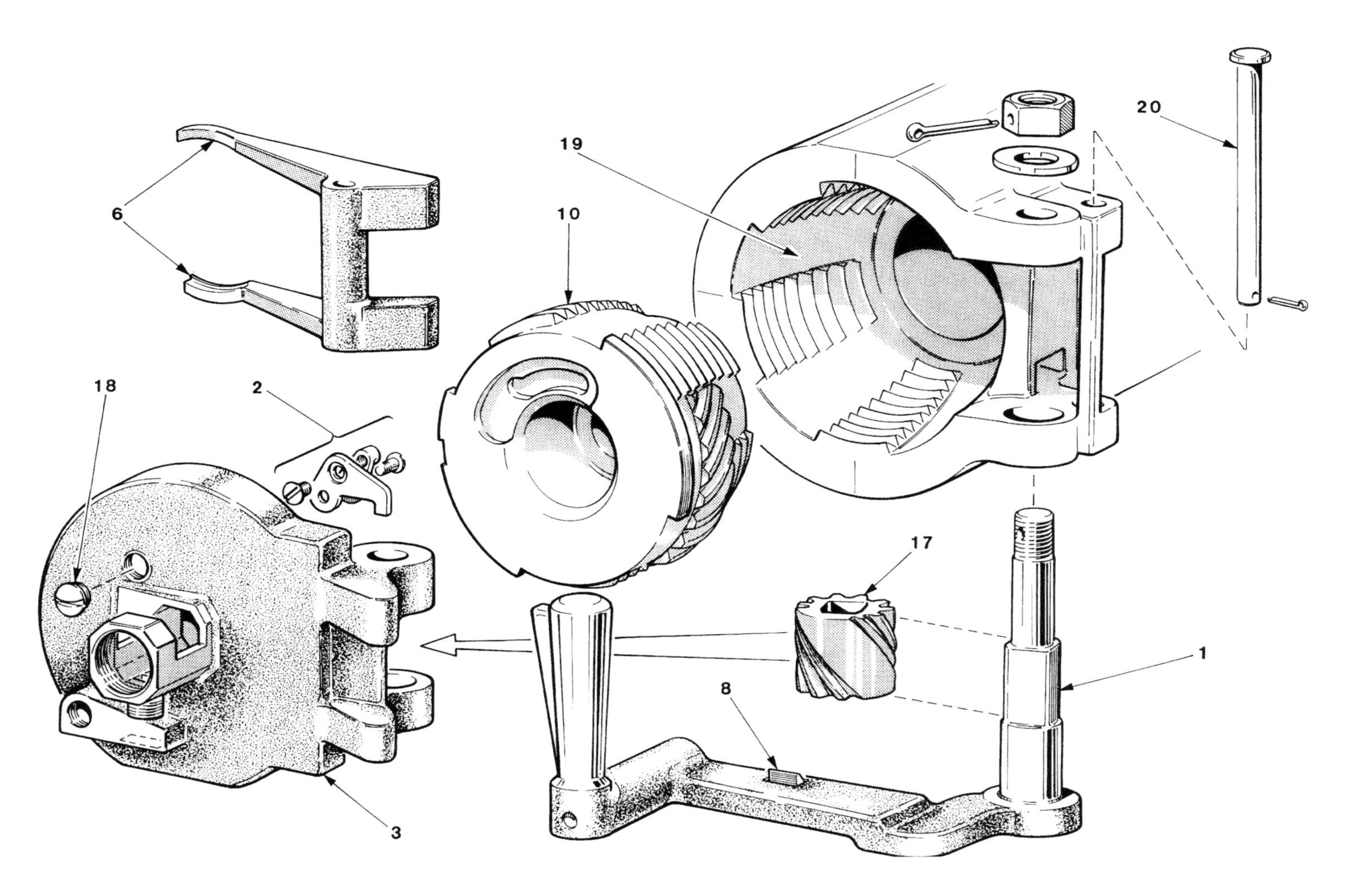

BREECH COMPONENTS

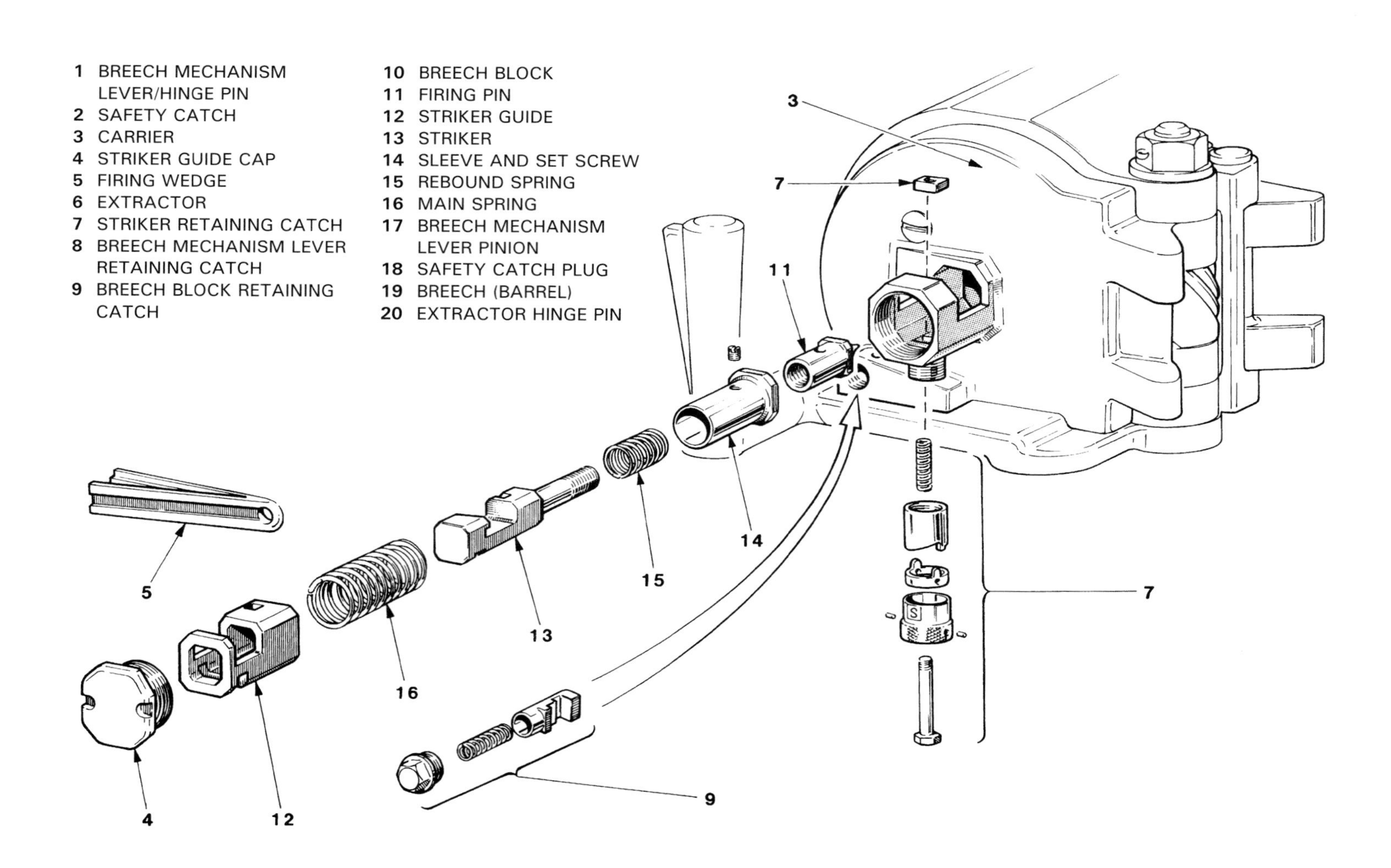

BREECH COMPONENTS

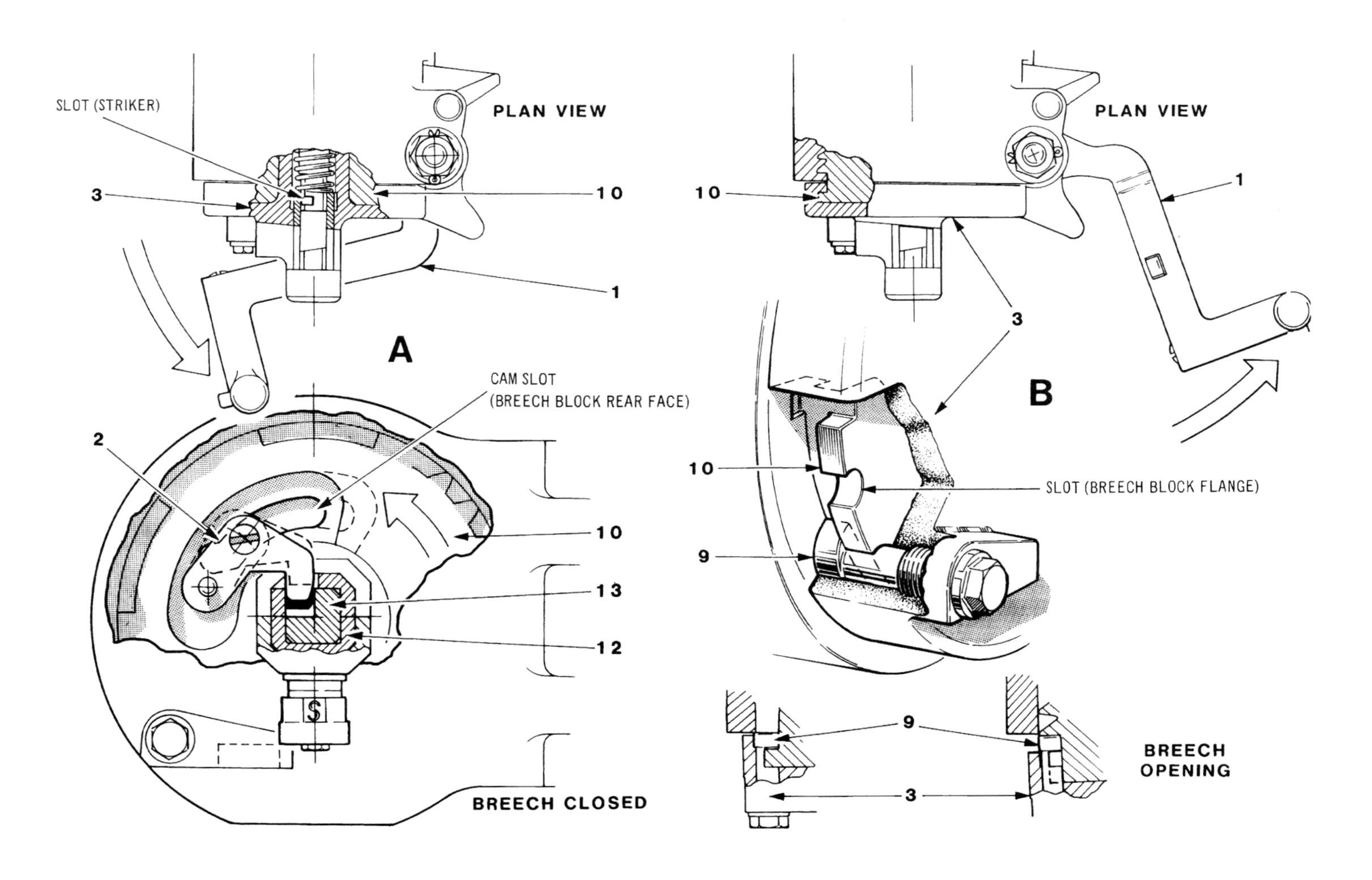

BREECH OPERATION

Breech operation

A On opening the breech, the first few degrees of breech block rotation caused the safety catch (**2**) to move into a slot in the striker (**13**) and lock the striker (**13**) and striker guide (**12**) together, preventing any movement of the firing mechanism while the breech was open.

B Rotation of the breech block (**10**) through one-tenth of a turn aligned the breech block thread interruptions with the thread segments in the barrel breech. At that point the carrier mounted breech block retaining catch (**9**), being spring loaded, engaged a slot in the breech block flange and locked breech block (**10**) and carrier (**3**) together, further movement of the breech mechanism lever (**1**) causing withdrawal of the breech block (**10**) from the breech opening (**19**).

At the end of the lever travel, lugs formed on the carrier (**3**) struck the extended external arms formed on the extractor (**6**) causing the extractor to pivot about the hinge pin (**20**) and the extractor arms within the breech to move rapidly rearwards, ejecting the cartridge case.

On closing the breech, the breech block (**10**) would enter the breech opening until the breech block retaining catch (**9**) contacted the breech face, further movement pushing the catch out of engagement with the breech block flange (**10**) and allowing the block thread segments to rotate into engagement with the barrel breech segments.

The final movement of breech rotation withdrew the safety catch (**2**) from the striker (**13**), leaving it ready to fire.

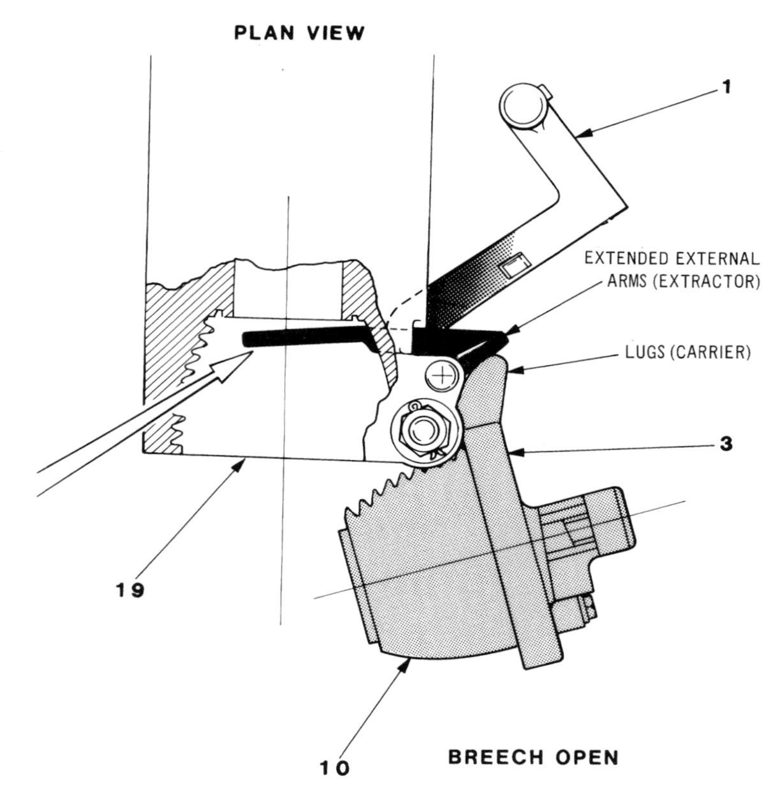

BREECH OPERATION

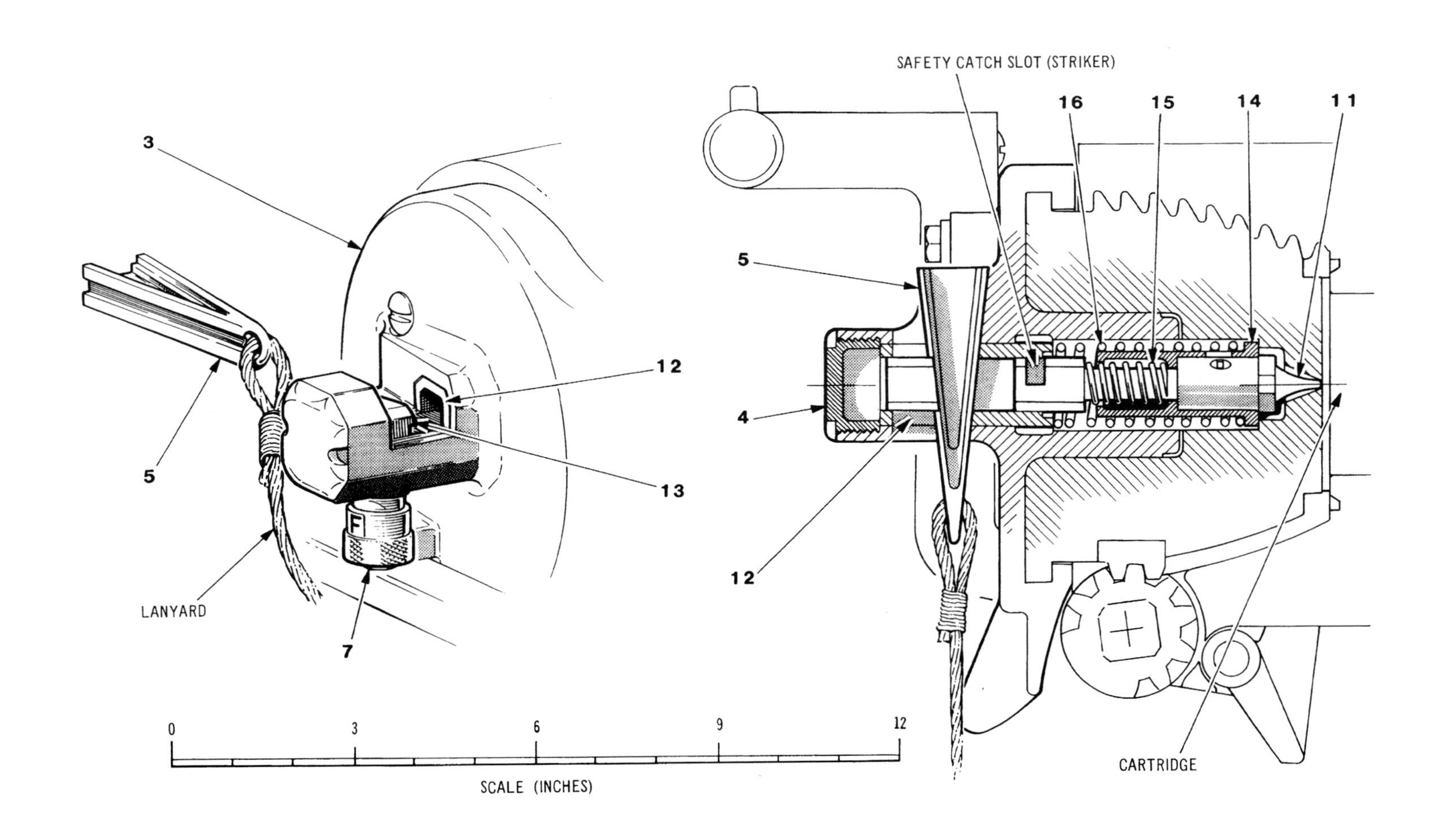

FIRING MECHANISM

Firing mechanism

The mechanism was for 'percussion' firing and embodied a safety catch (**2**), which prevented the gun being fired until the breech block (**10**) was sufficiently turned into the closed and locked position to be safe. This limiting position was with the elbow of the breech mechanism lever (**1**) being within two inches of its home position against the carrier rear face (**3**).

C The firing mechanism was actuated by means of a firing wedge (**5**) on a lanyard, being pulled through the transverse slot in the carrier (**3**). As the wedge (**5**) moved through the slot, it forced the striker (**13**) to move rearwards, together with the firing pin (**11**), the sleeve (**14**) and the rebound spring (**15**), compressing the main spring (**16**).

D As the firing wedge (**5**) pulled clear of the slot, the main spring (**16**) threw the striker assembly (**11, 13, 14** and **15**) forward and the firing pin (**11**) emerged through the breech block front face (**10**) to strike the cartridge primer/percussion cap.

E The rebound spring (**15**), having been compressed by the final part of the firing assembly forward travel (**11, 14, 15** and **13**), then returned the firing pin (**11**) to a position where it did not protrude from the breech block front face (**10**) and so could not cause premature firing of a live cartridge when the breech was being closed.

The striker retaining catch (**7**) could be set to the 'S' (safe) position to prevent the firing mechanism being operated with the gun loaded. Turning the knurled nut to display 'F' (fire) freed the mechanism to operate when required.

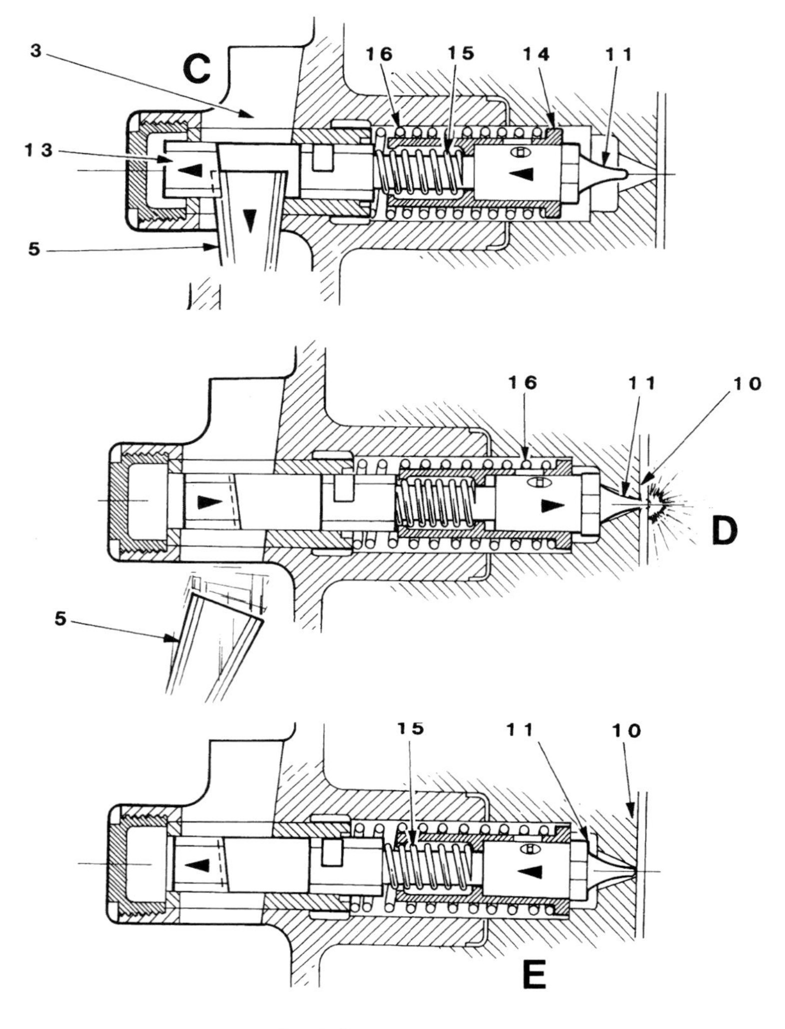

FIRING MECHANISM

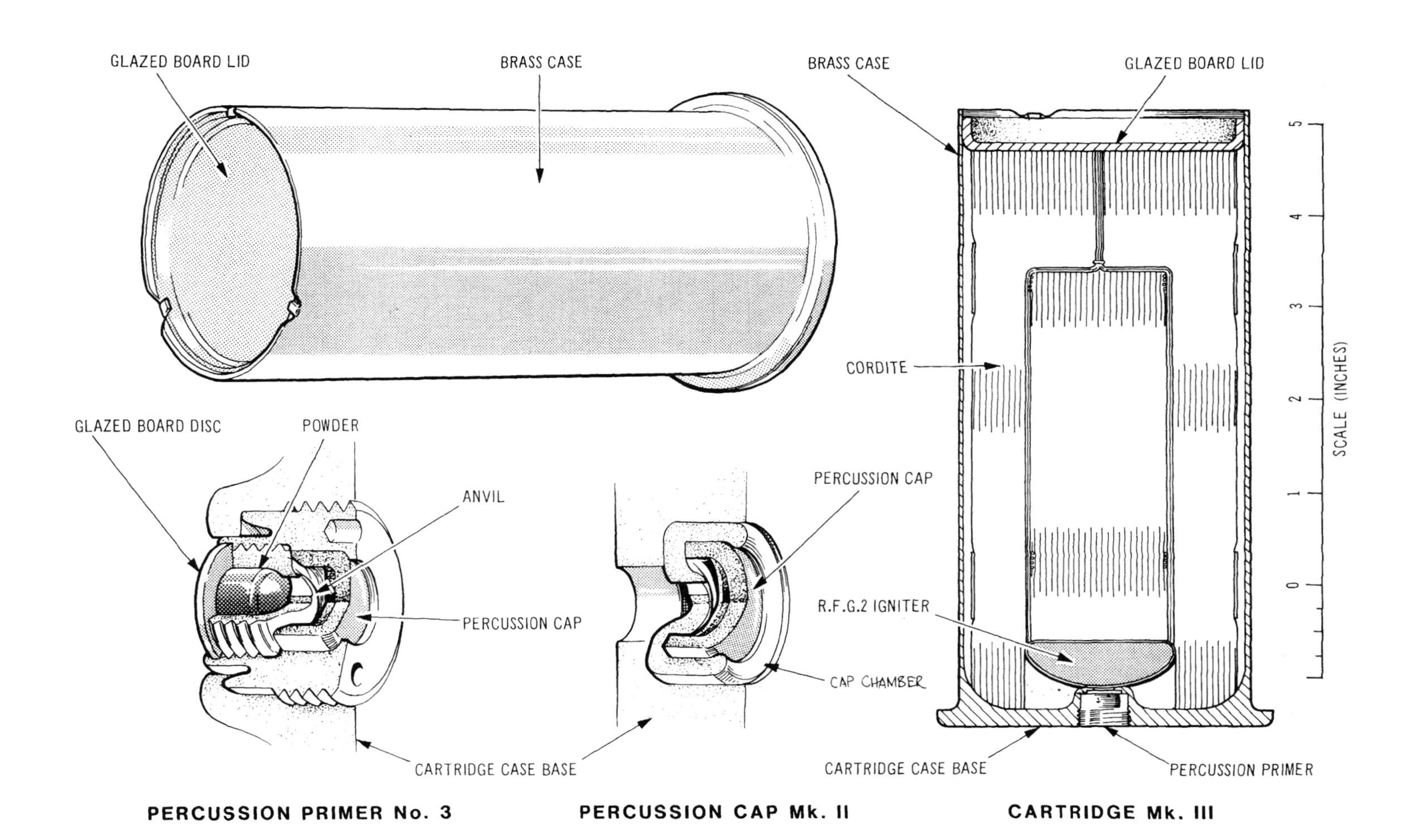
GLAZED BOARD LID
BRASS CASE
BRASS CASE
GLAZED BOARD LID
CORDITE
SCALE (INCHES)
5
4
3
2
1
0
GLAZED BOARD DISC
POWDER
ANVIL
PERCUSSION CAP
PERCUSSION CAP
R.F.G.2 IGNITER
CAP CHAMBER
CARTRIDGE CASE BASE
CARTRIDGE CASE BASE
PERCUSSION PRIMER
PERCUSSION PRIMER No. 3
PERCUSSION CAP Mk. II
CARTRIDGE Mk. III

CARTRIDGES

Cartridges

Cartridge – 1lb 2oz 10 drams, cordite MDT Size 20/10

Cartridge Mk. I★. This consisted of a brass case containing a charge of 1lb 2oz 10 drams, MDT Cordite size 20/10. The case was recessed in the base to take a cap chamber and cap which were pressed into the case from the outside.

The charge was cylindrical in shape, the bottom being shaped to take an igniter consisting of 4 drams RFG 2 powder (new or converted). The igniter was made in two parts to cover the bottom of the charge, one part being a ring which fitted around the boss in the cartridge base and the other a disc to rest on the boss. The charge was held in the case by a glazed board lid secured with Pettman's cement.

Cartridge Mk. II. This was similar to the Mk. I★ cartridge, except that it was fitted with a percussion primer instead of a cap.

Cartridge Mk. III (illustrated). This differed from the Mk. II in the manner in which the charge was built up, and also in having a Mk. III igniter, consisting of 4 drams of RFG 2 gunpowder, contained between two discs of undyed shalloon.

Cartridge – 1lb ½oz, cordite size 15

Cartridge Mk. I. This differed from the Mk. I 1lb 2oz 10 drams cartridge in the charge being made up of two different lengths of cordite, contained in a shalloon bag. It had an igniter consisting of two drams of guncotton yarn.

Cartridge Mk. II. This had an igniter consisting of 4 drams of SFG 2 powder. Cartridges of later manufacture had a primer instead of a cap.

Blank cartridge Mk. I

The blank cartridge consisted of a capped service case containing a charge of 1lb blank LG powder in a No. 1 class silk cloth bag, enclosed within a felt jacket. The mouth of the cartridge was closed with a half inch felt disc, to which was stitched a felt washer.

Drill cartridge Mk. I

The drill cartridge consisted of a service case lined with teak. It was closed at the mouth with a lid soldered to the case.

The cartridge base was fitted with a dummy primer containing a spiral spring and rubber pad for the firing pin to strike against. Two holes were drilled through the cartridge at right angles to each other to aid identification.

Projectiles

These were the same shrapnel shell and case shot as were employed with both the BL 15 pdr. and the BLC 15 pdr.

LIMBER

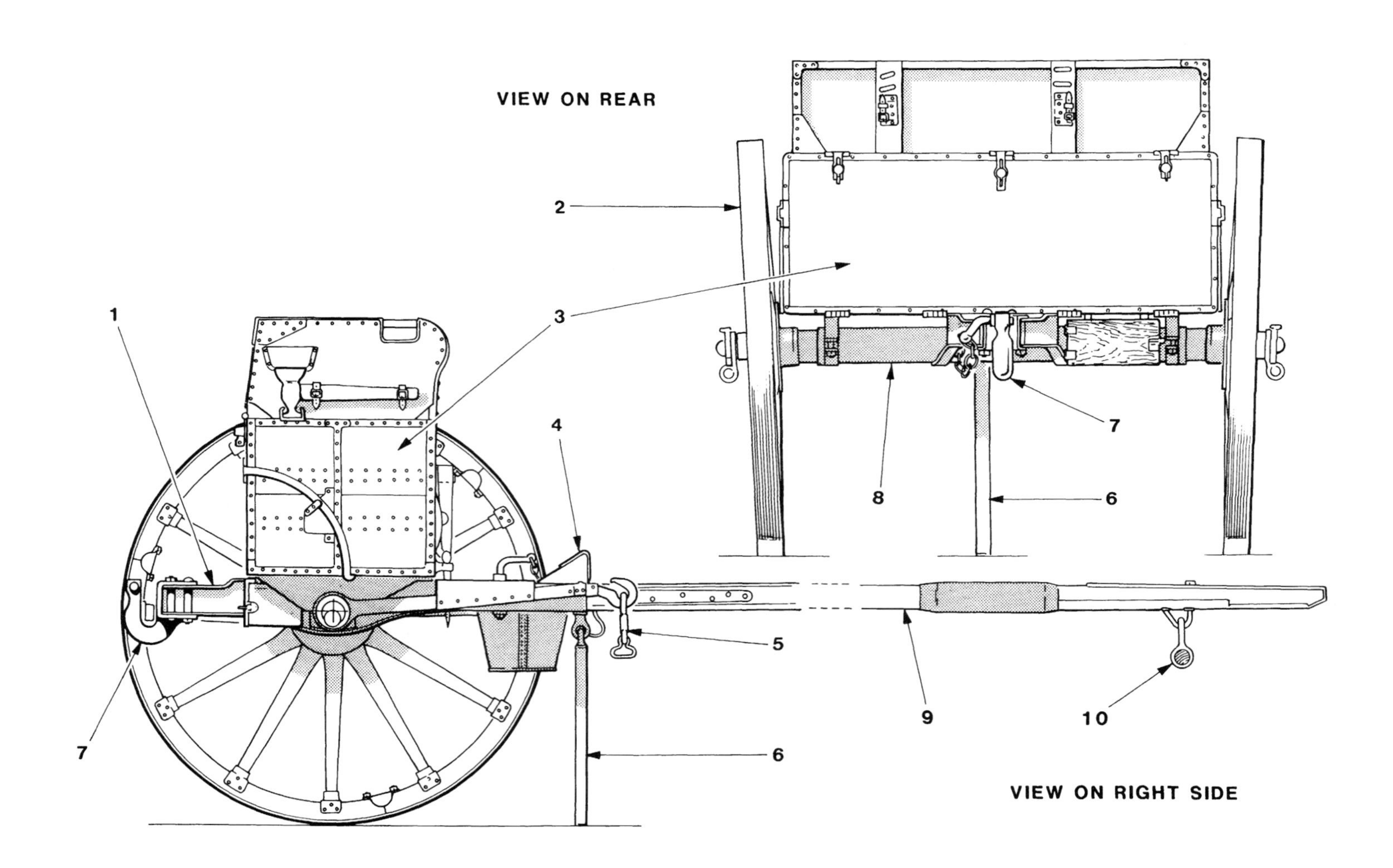

LIMBER

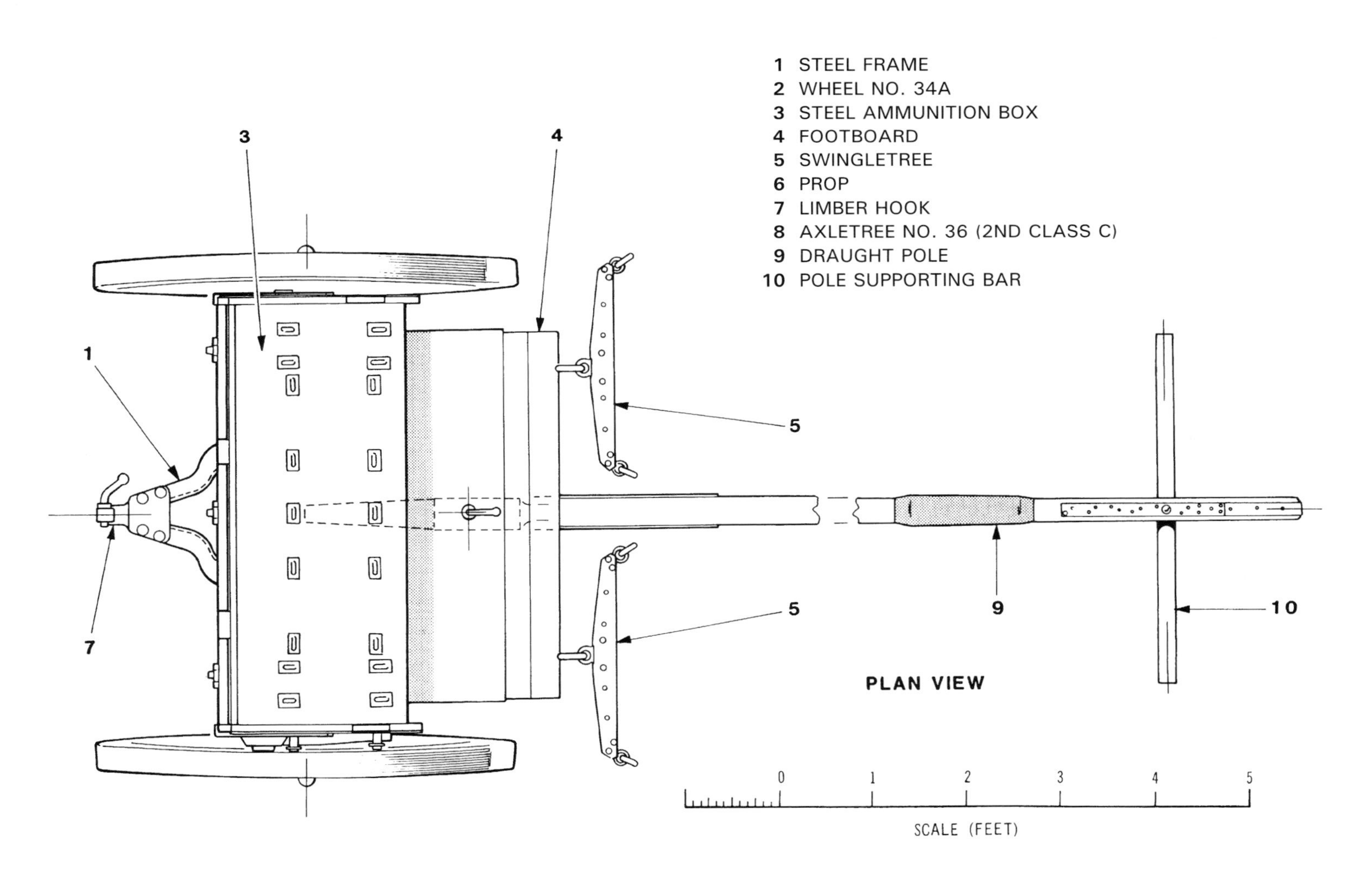
1 STEEL FRAME
2 WHEEL NO. 34A
3 STEEL AMMUNITION BOX
4 FOOTBOARD
5 SWINGLETREE
6 PROP
7 LIMBER HOOK
8 AXLETREE NO. 36 (2ND CLASS C)
9 DRAUGHT POLE
10 POLE SUPPORTING BAR
3
4
1
5
5
7
9
10
PLAN VIEW
0
1
2
3
4
5
SCALE (FEET)

LIMBER

Limber

The Mk. I limber would be equipped with one of two alternative sets of draught fittings. For the Territorial Force the fittings consisted of a No. 17 Mk. III pole, No. 3 supporting bar and two No. 1OA or No. 11 swingletrees.

For Moveable Armament the fittings consisted of a No. 17 Mk. II pole, No. 2 supporting bar and two No. 10A swingletrees.

Some limbers had loop plates provided on the front for bullock draught fittings.

The steel ammunition box lid served as a shelf for fuzing shells and was fitted with a fuze and turnscrew socket for the removal of shell plugs.

The box was divided internally into nine compartments, eight of which contained a wicker basket ammunition carrier, the ninth being fitted with a steel tray for the carriage of small stores. Each carrier held four cartridges and projectiles. The carriers containing case shot were painted light blue on their sides, ends and top. Carriers containing shrapnel shells were left uncoloured.

An ammunition carrier sling could be used by one of the gun detachment, if necessary, to support the carriers when being carried to the gun. It consisted of a two-piece, adjustable leather strap, to pass around the man's shoulders, with a hook at each end which engaged with the carrier handles. A connecting piece held the two hooks in the required position.

Limbers for use by the Territorial Force were also provided with fittings for carrying rifles.

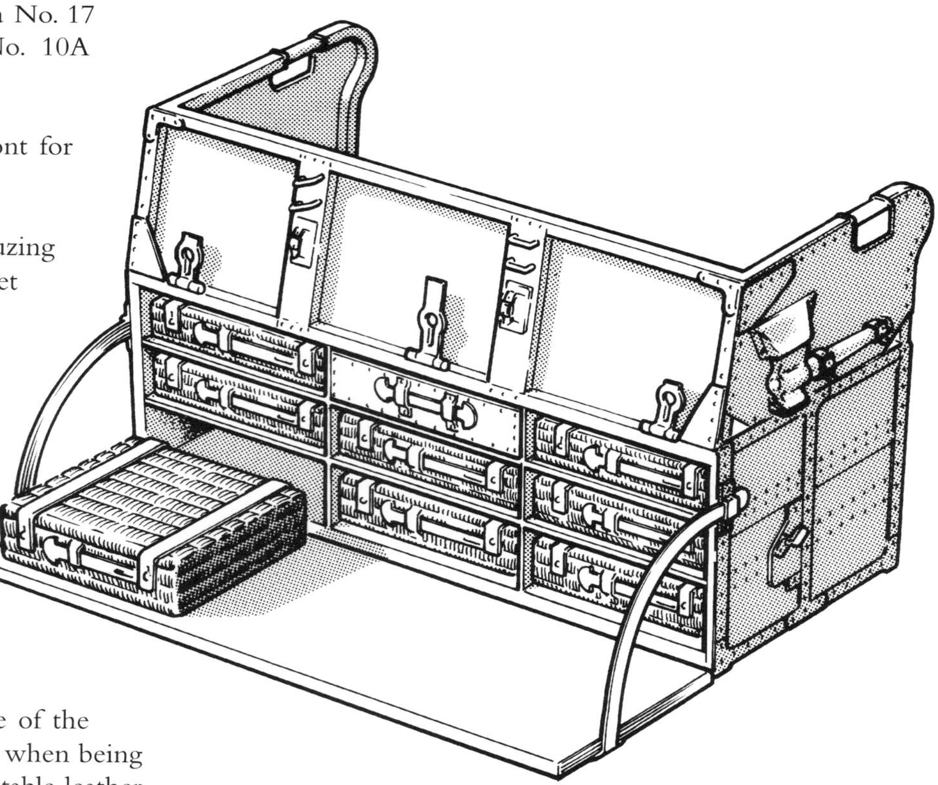

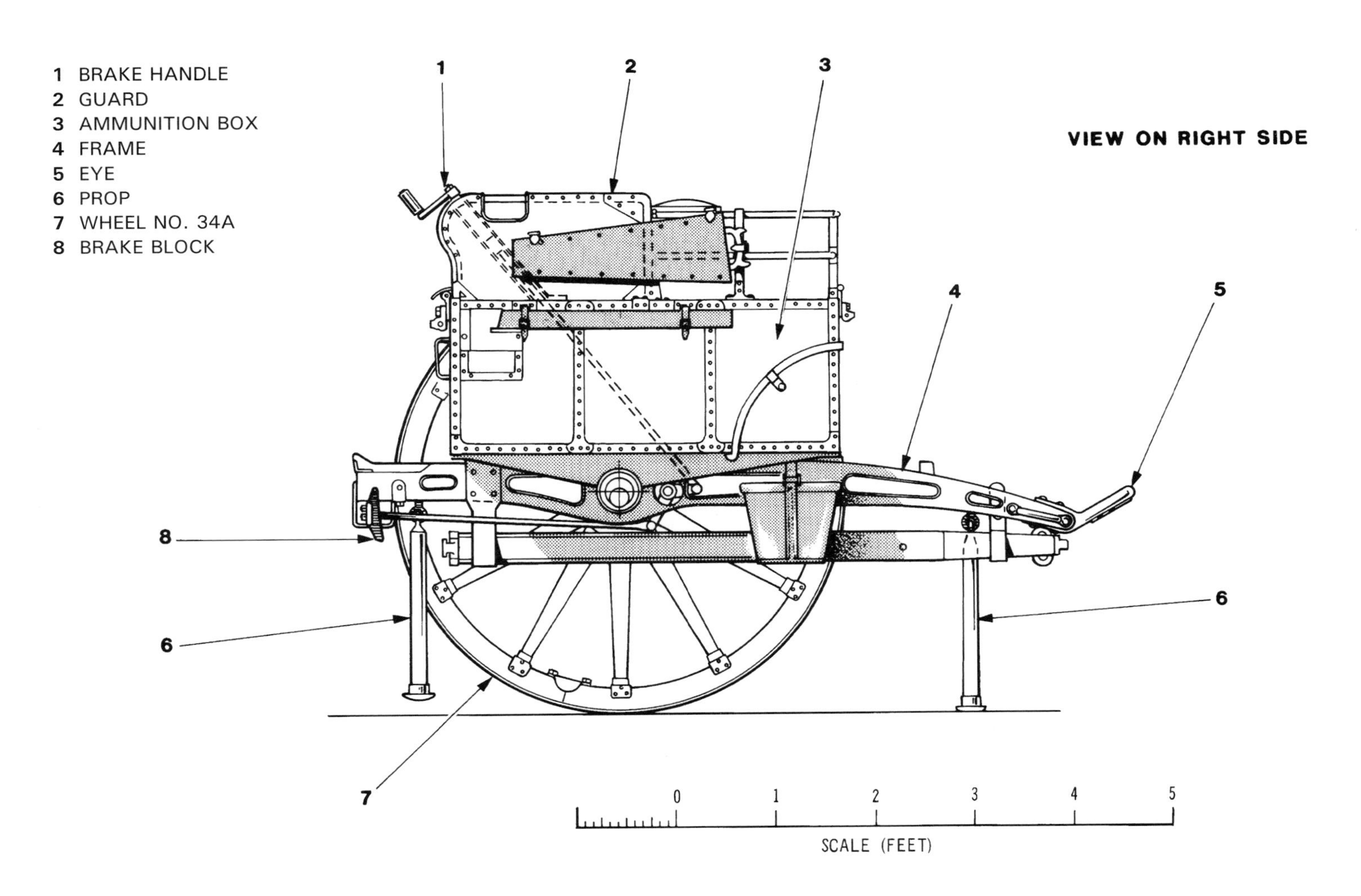

AMMUNITION WAGON

Ammunition wagon box

The front compartment conformed closely to that of the limber ammunition box. The rear compartment contained nine wicker basket ammunition carriers and no parts tray.

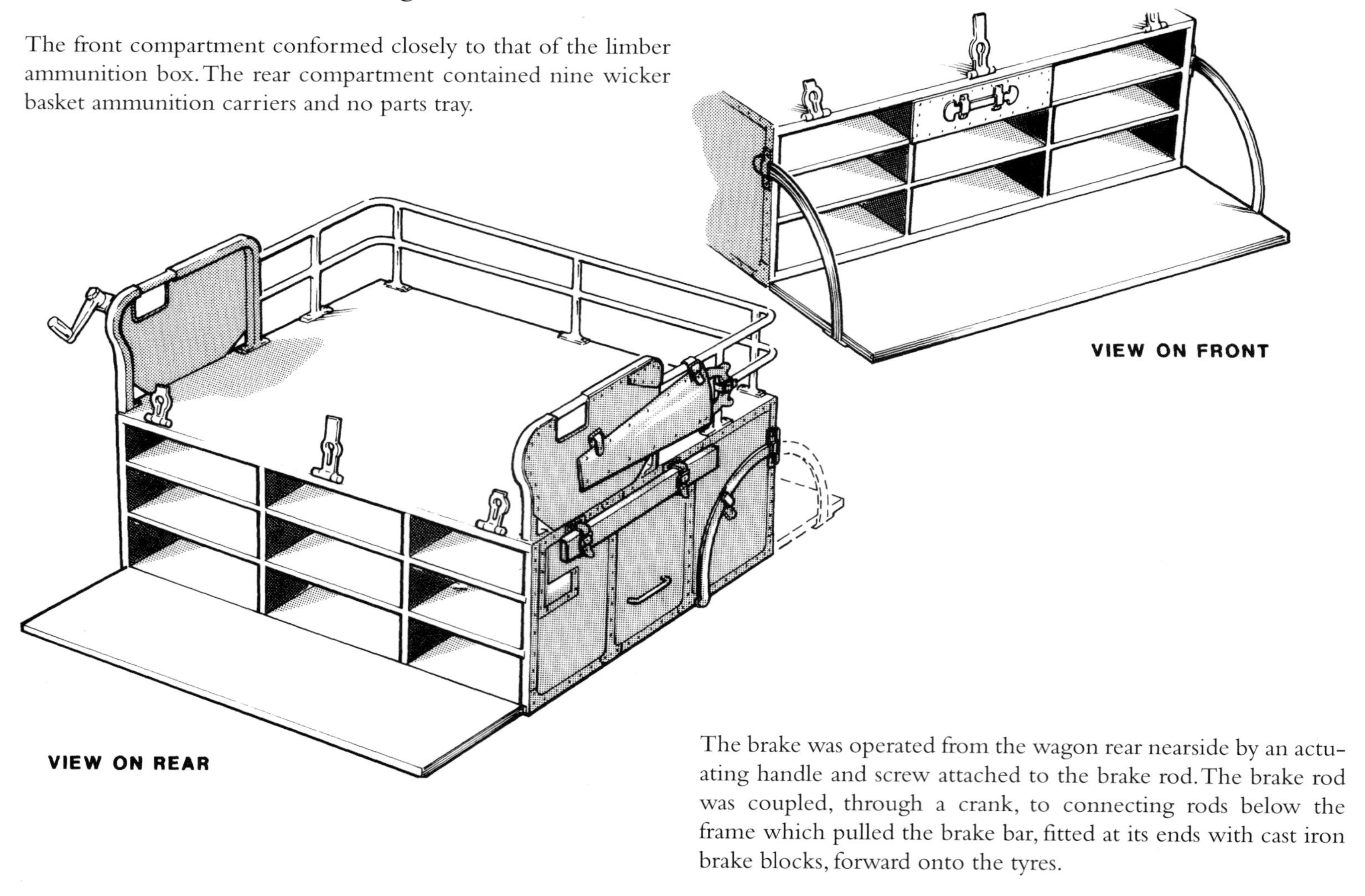

The brake was operated from the wagon rear nearside by an actuating handle and screw attached to the brake rod. The brake rod was coupled, through a crank, to connecting rods below the frame which pulled the brake bar, fitted at its ends with cast iron brake blocks, forward onto the tyres.

Stores and Equipment

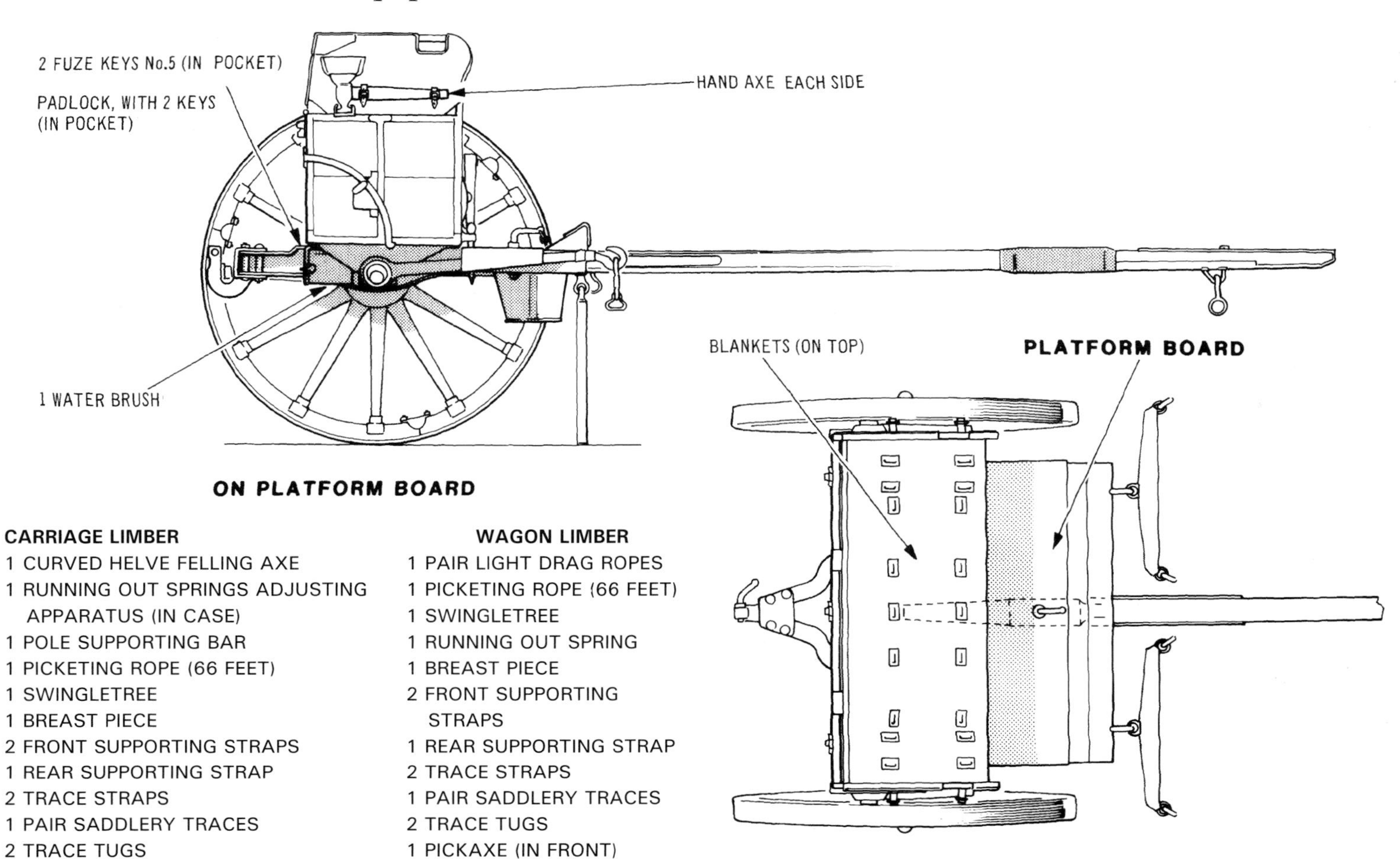

ON PLATFORM BOARD

CARRIAGE LIMBER

1 CURVED HELVE FELLING AXE
1 RUNNING OUT SPRINGS ADJUSTING APPARATUS (IN CASE)
1 POLE SUPPORTING BAR
1 PICKETING ROPE (66 FEET)
1 SWINGLETREE
1 BREAST PIECE
2 FRONT SUPPORTING STRAPS
1 REAR SUPPORTING STRAP
2 TRACE STRAPS
1 PAIR SADDLERY TRACES
2 TRACE TUGS
1 PICKAXE (IN FRONT)
2 SHOVELS (IN FRONT)

WAGON LIMBER

1 PAIR LIGHT DRAG ROPES
1 PICKETING ROPE (66 FEET)
1 SWINGLETREE
1 RUNNING OUT SPRING
1 BREAST PIECE
2 FRONT SUPPORTING STRAPS
1 REAR SUPPORTING STRAP
2 TRACE STRAPS
1 PAIR SADDLERY TRACES
2 TRACE TUGS
1 PICKAXE (IN FRONT)
2 SHOVELS (IN FRONT)

LIMBER STORES AND EQUIPMENT

SPARE PARTS TRAY CONTENTS

CARRIAGE LIMBER
2 STRIKER RETAINING CATCH BOLTS
3 TIN BOXES (GLYCERINE ETC.)
1 CAN (RANGOON OIL)
1 BREECH BLOCK CATCH
2 SAFETY CATCHES
- SPONGE CLOTHS
1 CUP (GLYCERINE)
1 EXTRACTOR
1 FILE
1 STRIKER PROTRUSION GAUGE (NO. 1)
1 HAMMER
1 BREECH APPARATUS KEY
1 FIRING PIN KEY
1 HYDRAULIC BUFFER KEY
3 LINCH PIN SECURING KEYS
3 FIRING PINS
1 LINCH PIN
1 SCREWDRIVER (3 INCH)
1 SCREWDRIVER (4 INCH)
1 SPECIAL SCREWDRIVER
1 AMMUNITION CARRIER SLING
1 MCMAHON SPANNER (15 INCH)
1 HYDRAULIC BUFFER SPANNER NO. 112
1 HYDRAULIC BUFFER SPANNER NO. 113
1 HYDRAULIC BUFFER SPANNER NO. 114
2 BREECH BLOCK CATCH SPRINGS
1 BREECH MECHANISM LEVER CATCH SPRING
2 STRIKER CATCH SPRINGS
1 MAIN SPRING
1 STRIKER REBOUND SPRING
2 STRIKERS
6 LINCH PIN TIES
4 AXLETREE WASHERS
1 DRAG WASHER
1 FIRING WEDGE

WAGON LIMBER
3 TIN BOXES (GLYCERINE ETC.)
1 CAN (RANGOON OIL)
- SPONGE CLOTHS
3 LINCH PIN SECURING KEYS
1 HAMBRO' LINE
1 WHITE LINE
1 LINCH PIN
1 AMMUNITION CARRIER SLING
6 LINCH PIN TIES
4 AXLETREE WASHERS
1 DRAG WASHER

8 AMMUNITION CARRIERS, EACH CONTAINED 4 CARTRIDGES AND 4 ROUNDS (SHRAPNEL OR CASE SHOT)

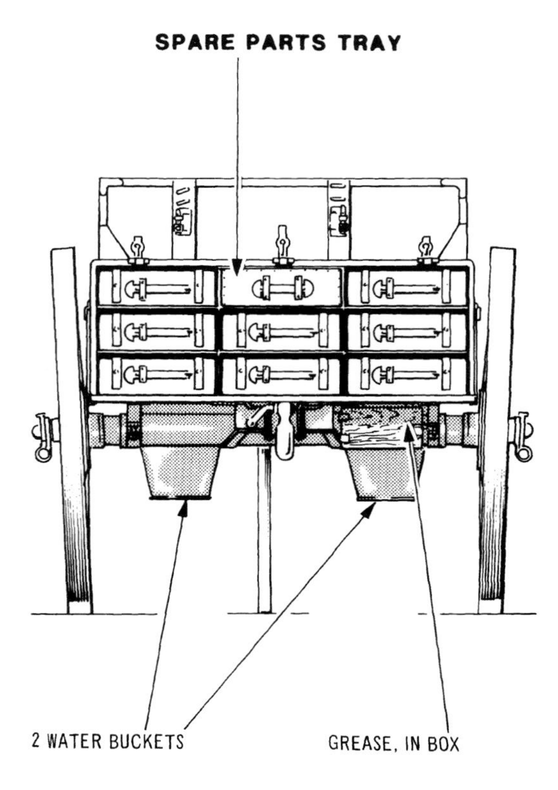

LIMBER STORES AND EQUIPMENT

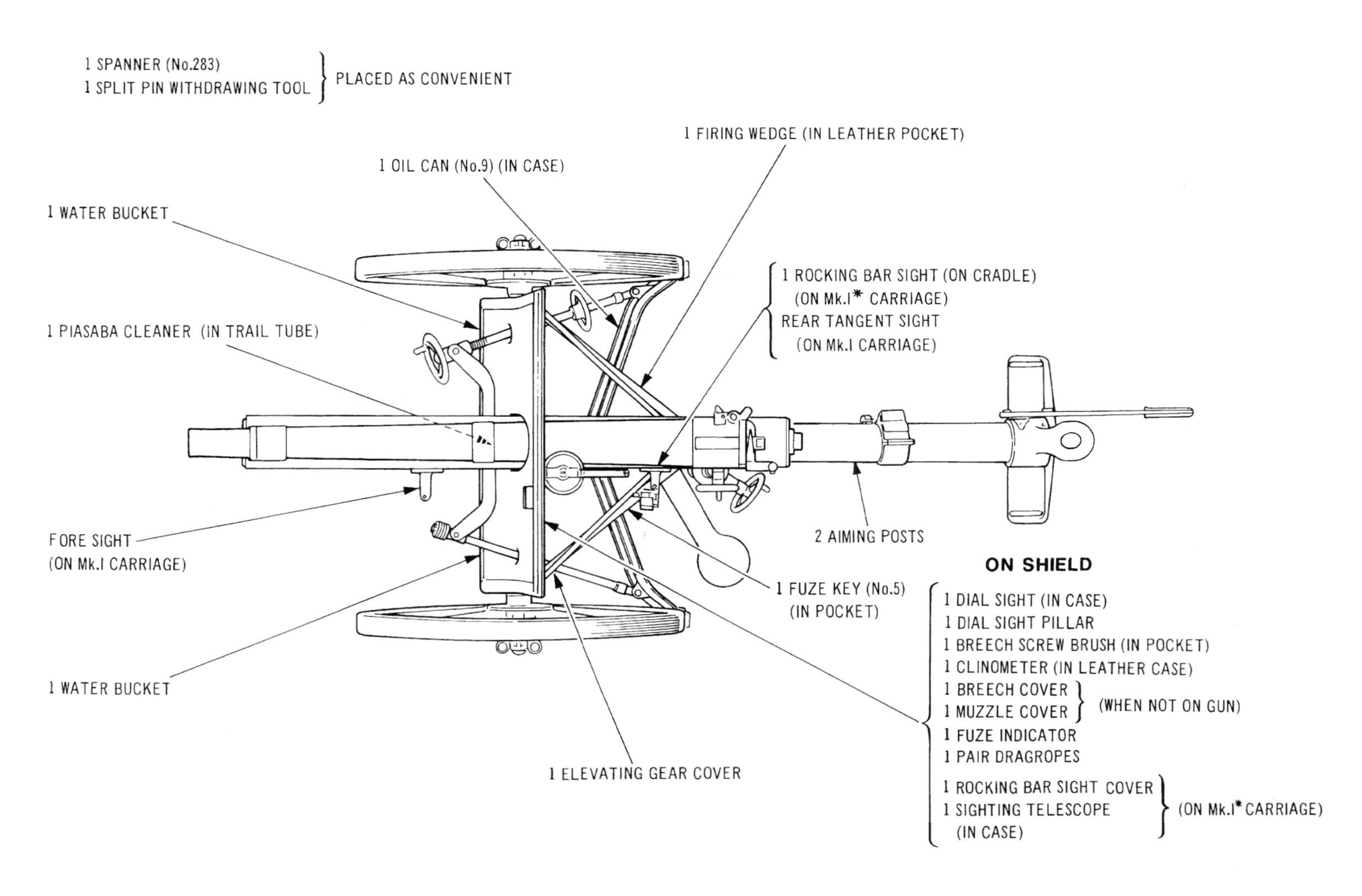

CARRIAGE STORES AND EQUIPMENT

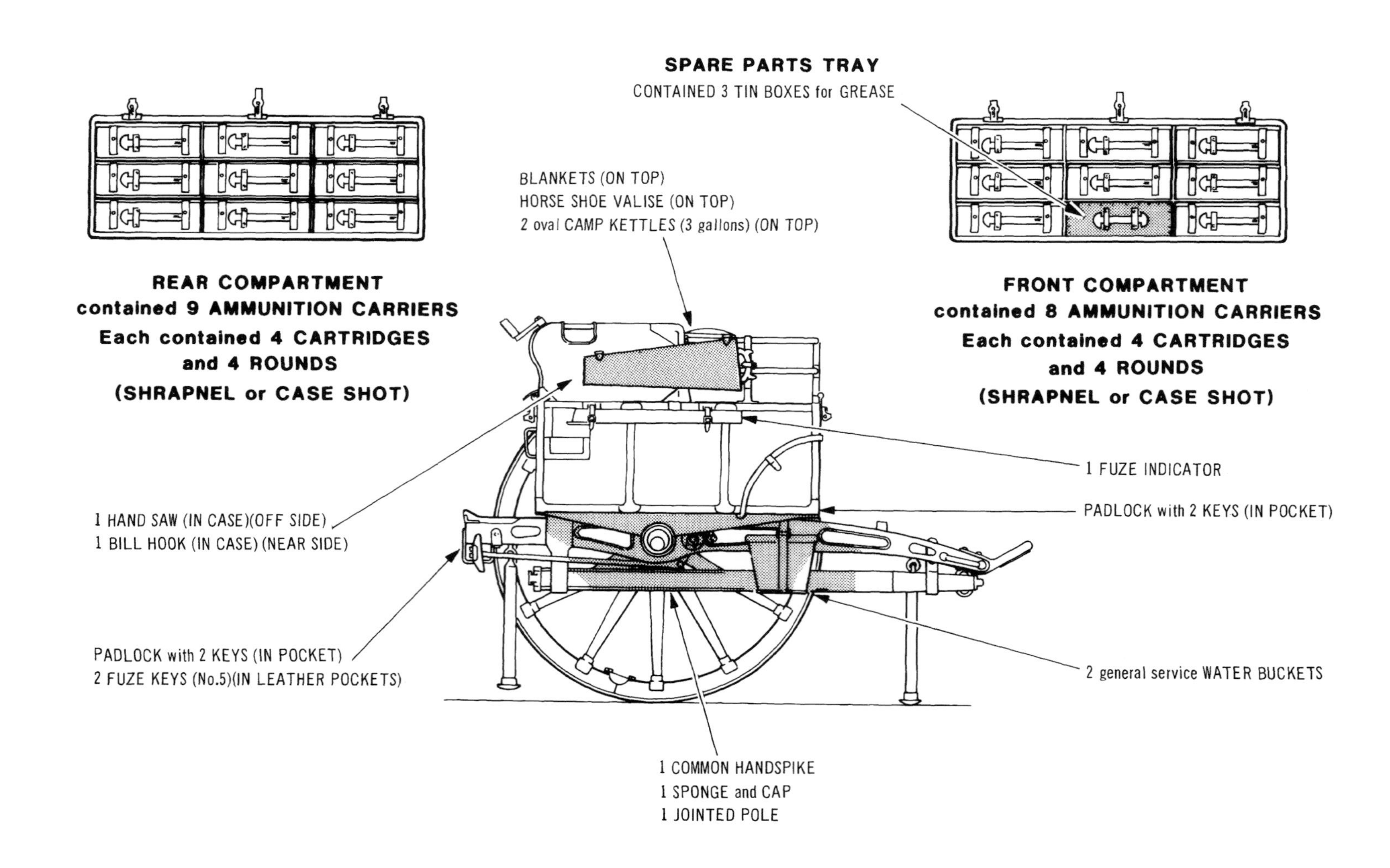

AMMUNITION WAGON STORES AND EQUIPMENT

QUICK FIRING 18 PDR. MK. I

QUICK FIRING 13 PDR MK. 1

The details of this gun, used by The King's Troop, Royal Horse Artillery to this day for ceremonials, saluting and displays, were similar in all functional respects to the Quick Firing 18 pdr Mk. I described hereafter, differing in some dimensional details only.

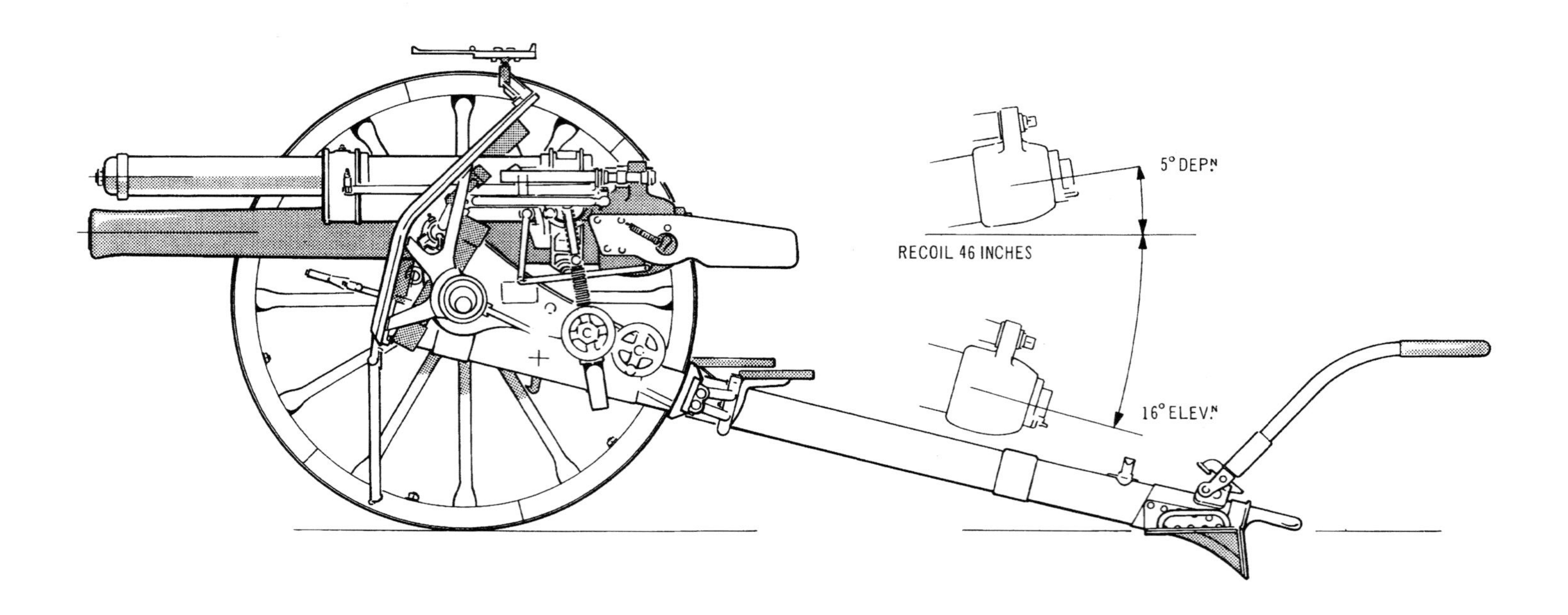

WEIGHTS (as packed)

Carriage with Gun	19 cwt	1 qtr	8 lb
Carriage Limber	12 cwt	1 qtr	4 lb
Ammunition Wagon (with Spare Jointed Pole)	15 cwt	3 qtr	9 lb
Wagon Limber	14 cwt	3 qtr	4 lb

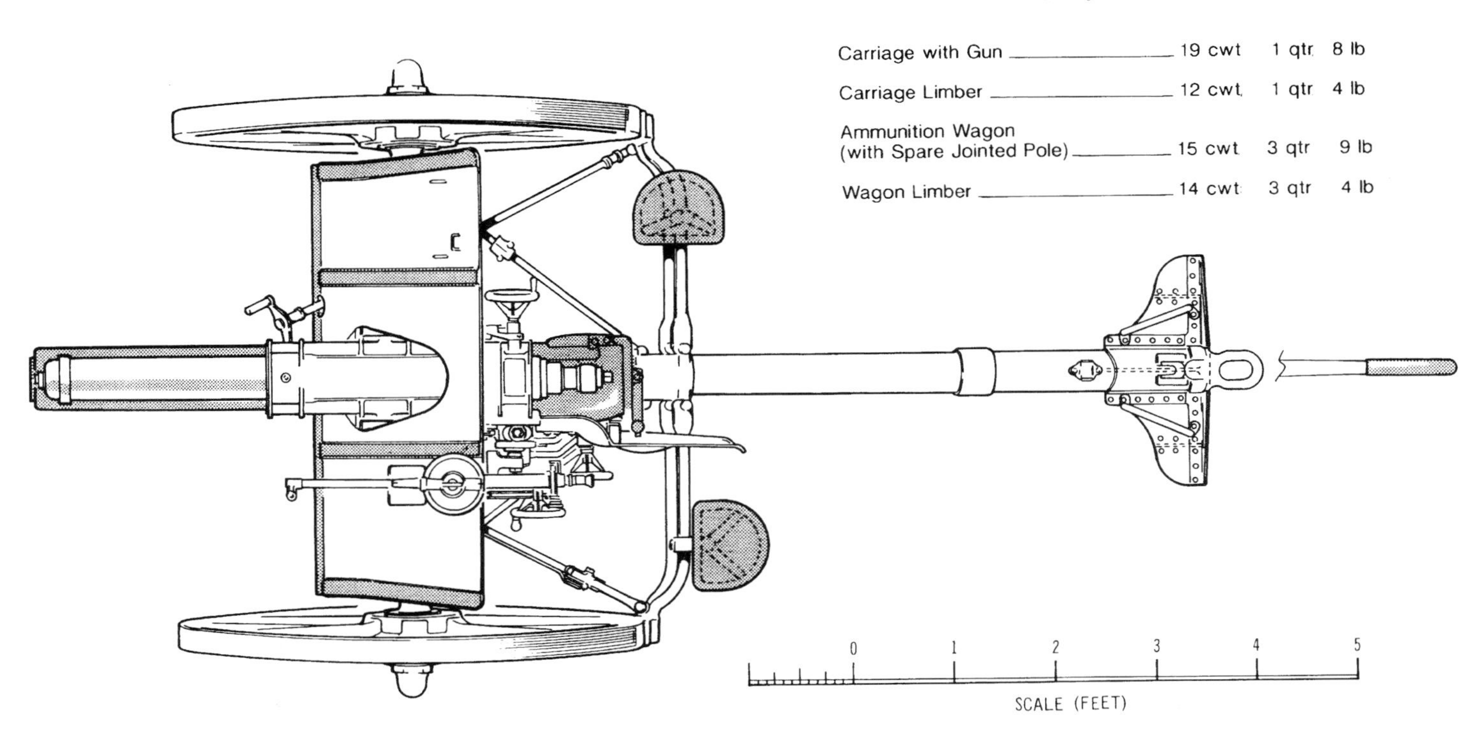

QUICK FIRING 13 PDR. MK. I

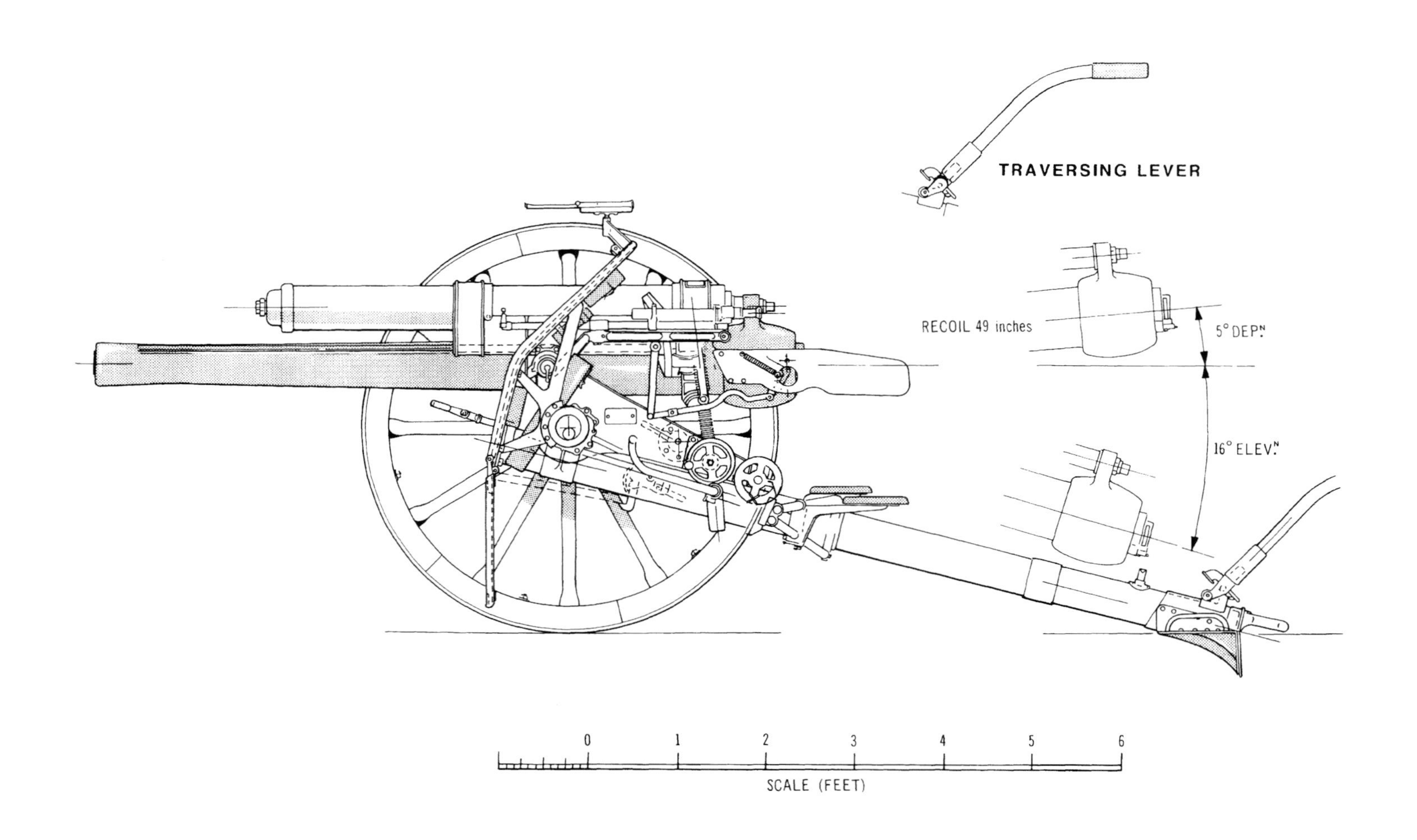

CARRIAGE – QUICK FIRING 18 PDR. MK. I

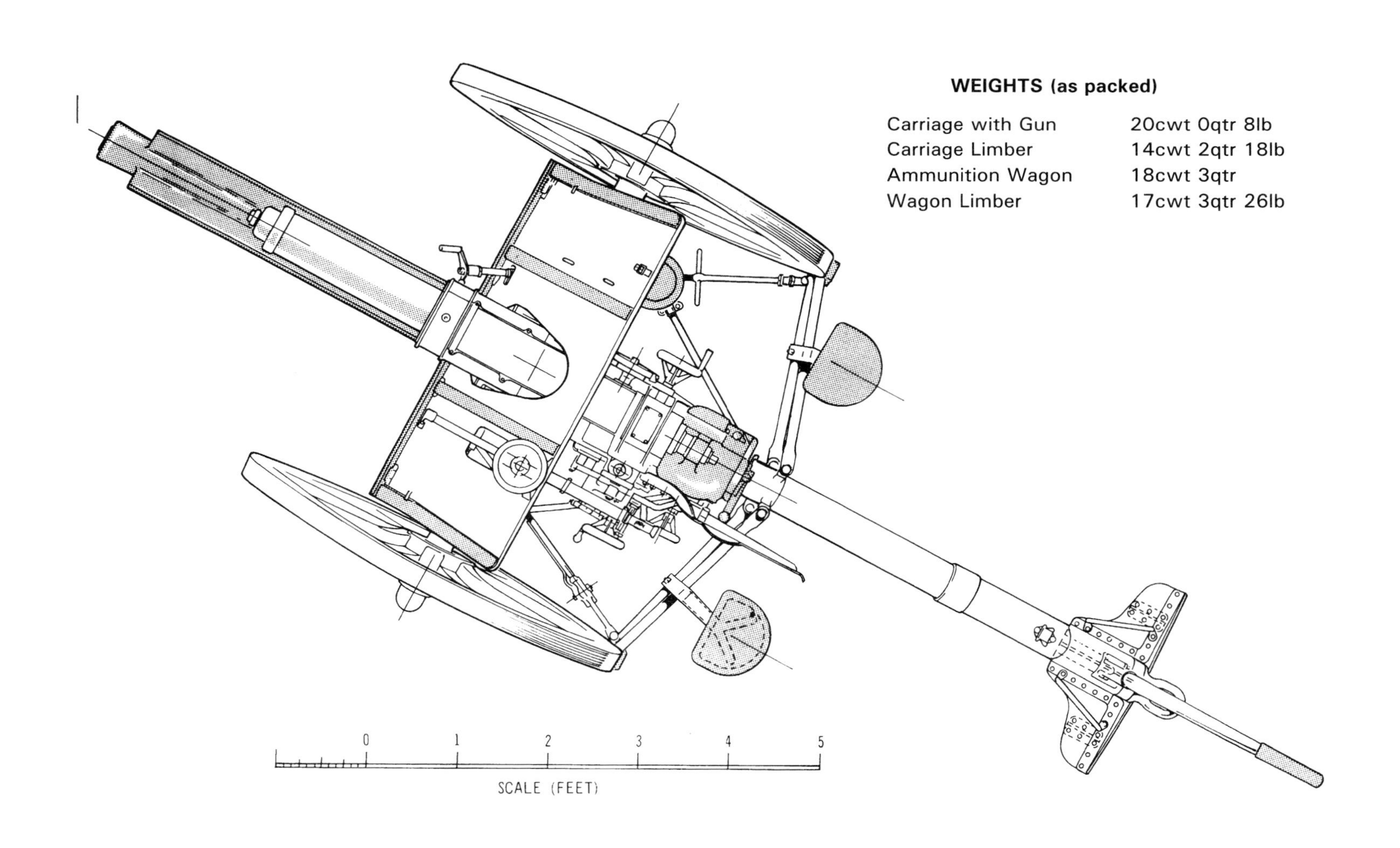

CARRIAGE – QUICK FIRING 18 PDR. MK.I

QUICK FIRING 18 PDR MK. I

This gun, introduced into service during 1904, replaced the Quick Firing 15 pdr. A mainstay of the Royal Field Artillery, some 8,000 were built in Great Britain. With a range of 6,525 yards and firing either shrapnel shells, high explosive or smoke producing ammunition, it was a very versatile piece of ordnance.

This gun was also built under licence and used by the Americans as a 75mm, to use the French ammunition of that calibre.

Trail

The trail was a steel tube of five inches outside diameter and one-quarter inch wall thickness.

A steel eye was secured to the rear end by countersunk rivets. Early eyes were fitted with a hardened steel insert, but later examples were case hardened. Angle steel brackets, riveted to the trail eye sleeve, carried a nickel steel spade. This was strengthened by a rear spade bracket. A lifting handle was riveted to the top of each spade bracket.

A traversing lever mounting bracket was riveted above the spade. For travelling, the traversing lever was folded over forward and retained by a spring clip. The steel locking band prevented damage being caused to the trail by the limber wheels when turning tightly.

Lugs, formed on the brake band, carried the brake arms and tensile stay rear ends.

The carriage body guide bracket had, formed on the top surface, an undercut guide in which could slide the carriage body rear end. The left side of the bracket was drilled to house the traversing gear crosshead pivot. Forward of this, on the trail right side, was pivoted a spring pawl to support the shield lower, hinged half for travelling.

The axletree connecting bracket was a double loop. The upper loop was shaped to receive the axletree centre section, this being retained in the bracket by a tapered pin. At right-angles to the top loop was the lower loop, which encircled the trail and was secured to it by rivets.

Inside the trail tube was secured a bulkhead, or stop. This formed a receptacle, some two feet in length, to house cleaners. It was closed by a hinged lid on a flanged frame riveted to the front end of the trail tube. The lid was secured by a hasp and turnbuckle. The shield was bolted to the frame flange.

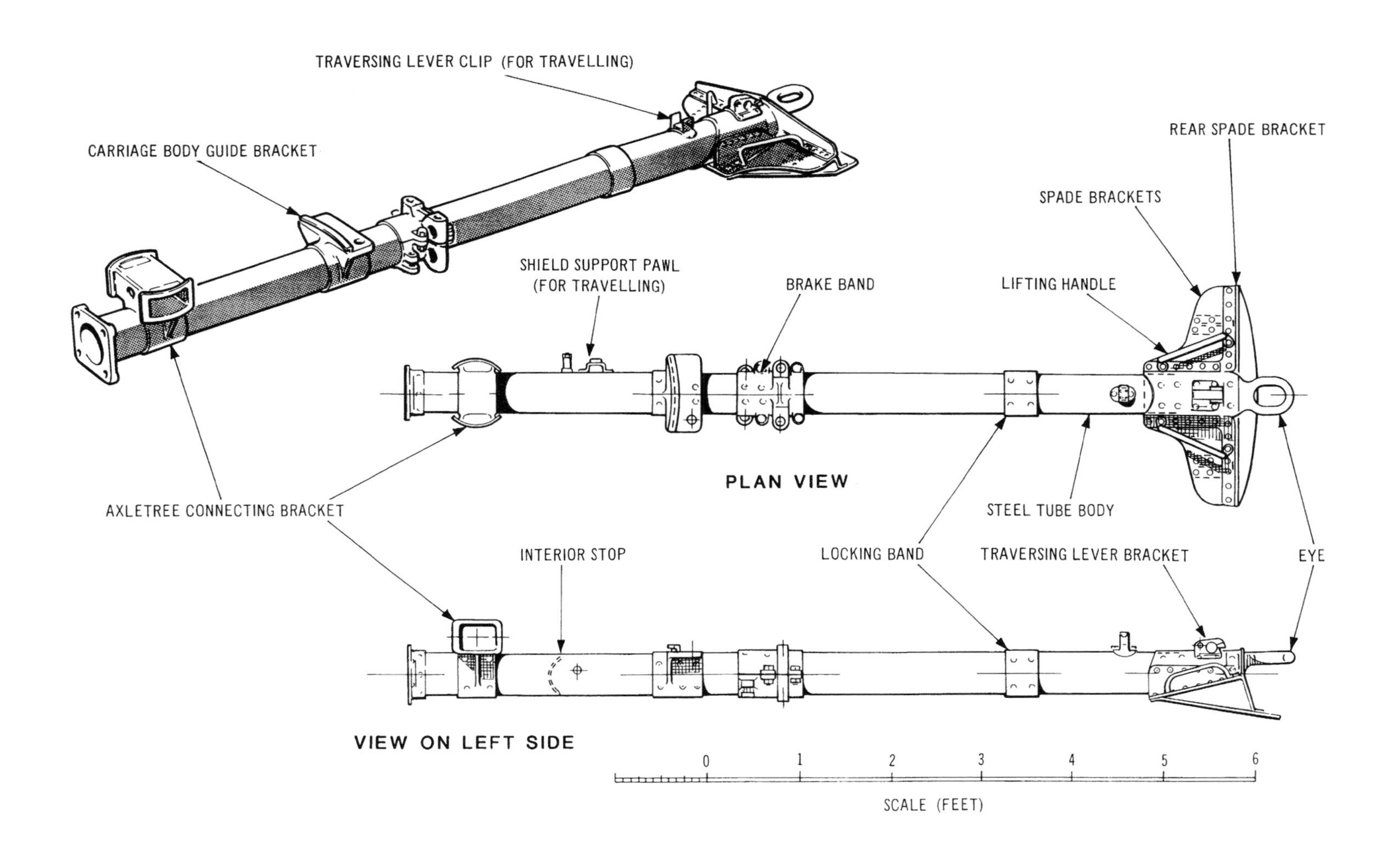
TRAVERSING LEVER CLIP (FOR TRAVELLING)
CARRIAGE BODY GUIDE BRACKET
REAR SPADE BRACKET
SPADE BRACKETS
SHIELD SUPPORT PAWL
(FOR TRAVELLING)
BRAKE BAND
LIFTING HANDLE
PLAN VIEW
AXLETREE CONNECTING BRACKET
STEEL TUBE BODY
INTERIOR STOP
LOCKING BAND
TRAVERSING LEVER BRACKET
EYE
VIEW ON LEFT SIDE
0
1
2
3
4
5
6
SCALE (FEET)

TRAIL

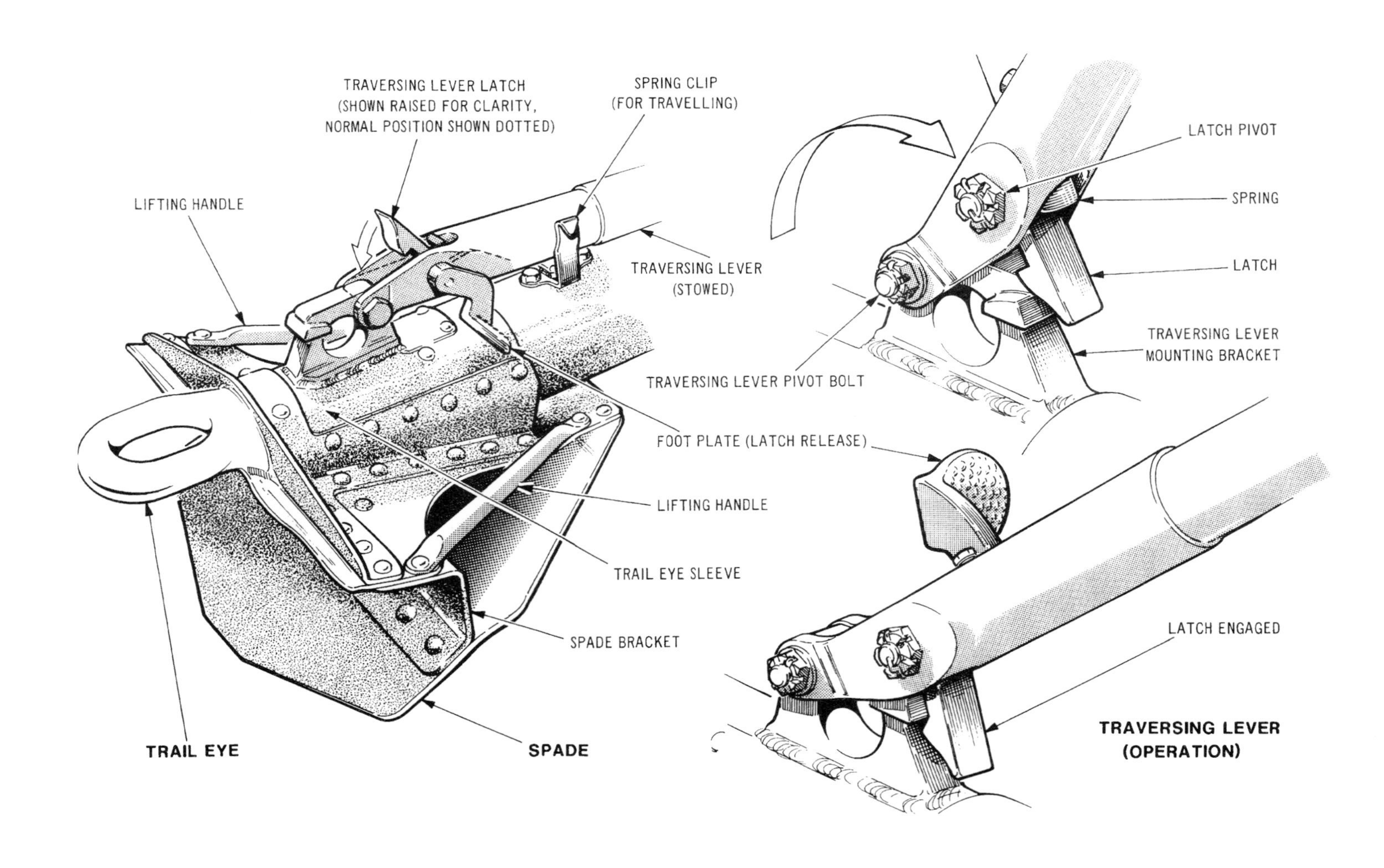

TRAIL EYE, SPADE AND TRAVERSING LEVER

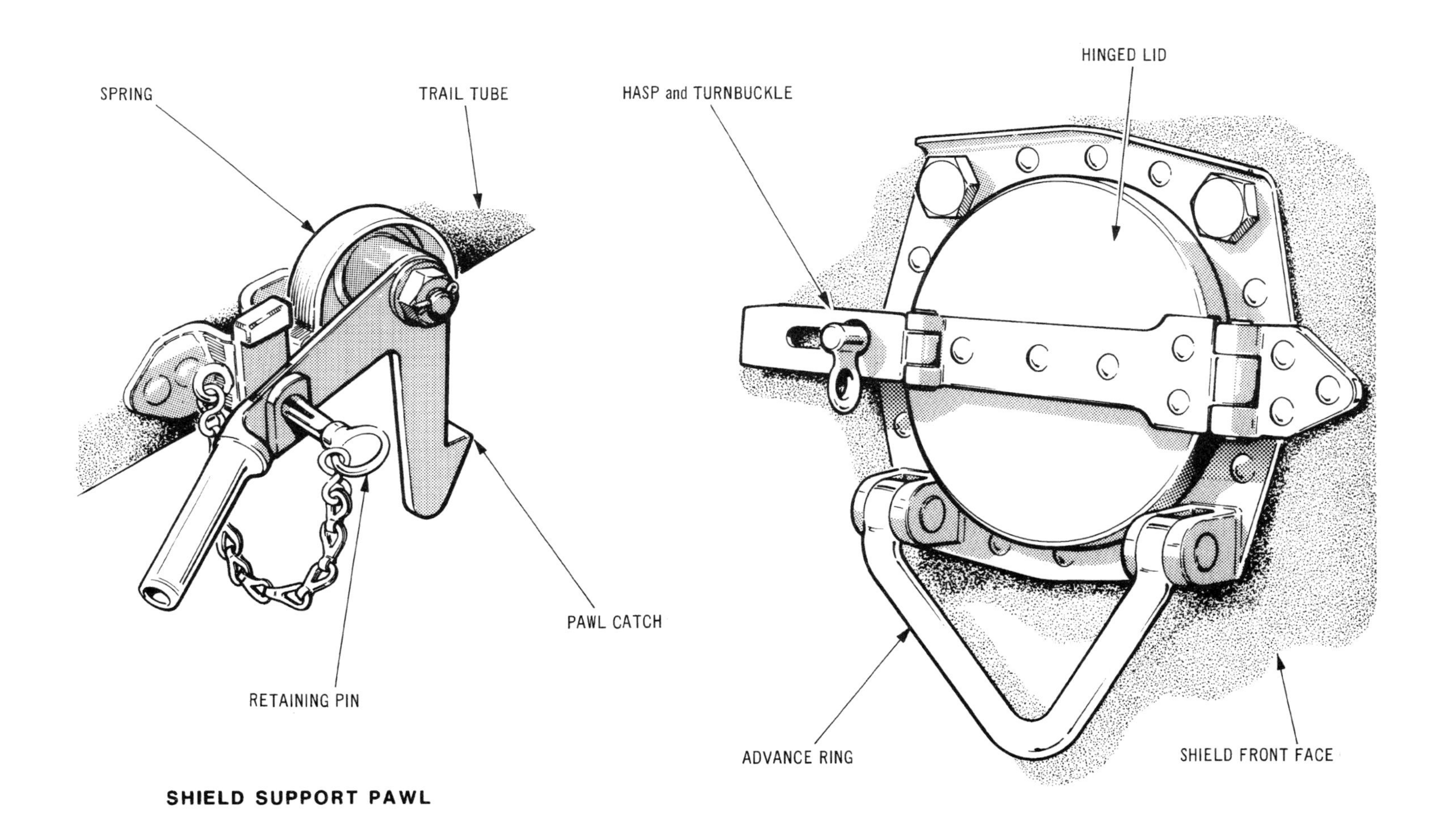

SHIELD SUPPORT PAWL

SHIELD SUPPORT PAWL AND TRAIL FRONT LID

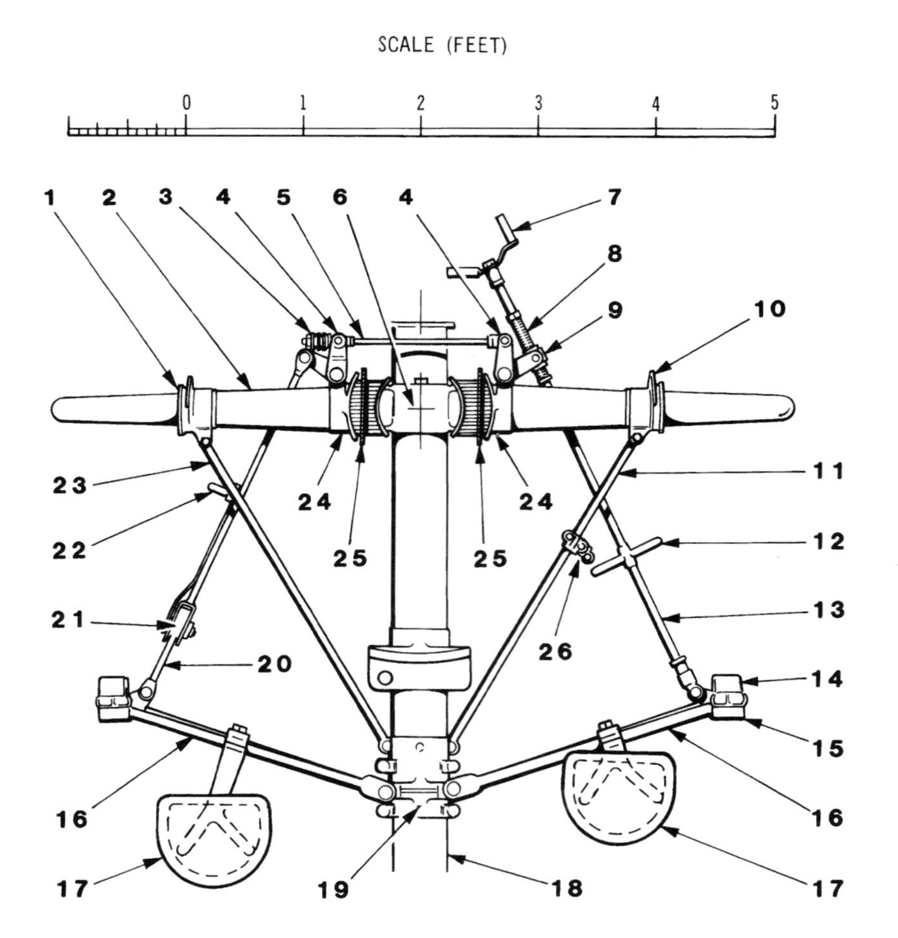

1 AXLETREE BRACKET
2 AXLETREE
3 DISC SPRINGS
4 BRAKE BELL-CRANK LEVER
5 BRAKE CONNECTING ROD
6 AXLETREE CONNECTING BRACKET
7 BRAKE HANDLE
8 THREAD (LEFT-HAND, SQUARE SECTION)
9 NUT
10 SHIELD STAY MOUNTING FLANGE
11 TENSILE STAY (RIGHT-HAND)
12 BRAKE CROSS-HANDLE
13 BRAKE RIGHT-HAND ACTUATING ROD
14 BRAKE BLOCK
15 BRAKE SHOE
16 BRAKE SWINGING ARMS
17 SEAT
18 TRAIL TUBE BODY
19 TRAIL BRAKE BAND
20 BRAKE LEFT-HAND ACTUATING ROD
21 BRAKE QUICK-RELEASE ECCENTRIC
22 QUICK-RELEASE OPERATING LEVER
23 TENSILE STAY (LEFT-HAND)
24 AXLETREE FLANGE
25 CARRIAGE BODY SUPPORT BEARINGS
26 FUZE INDICATOR MOUNTING BRACKET

AXLETREE AND SWINGING ARM BRAKE

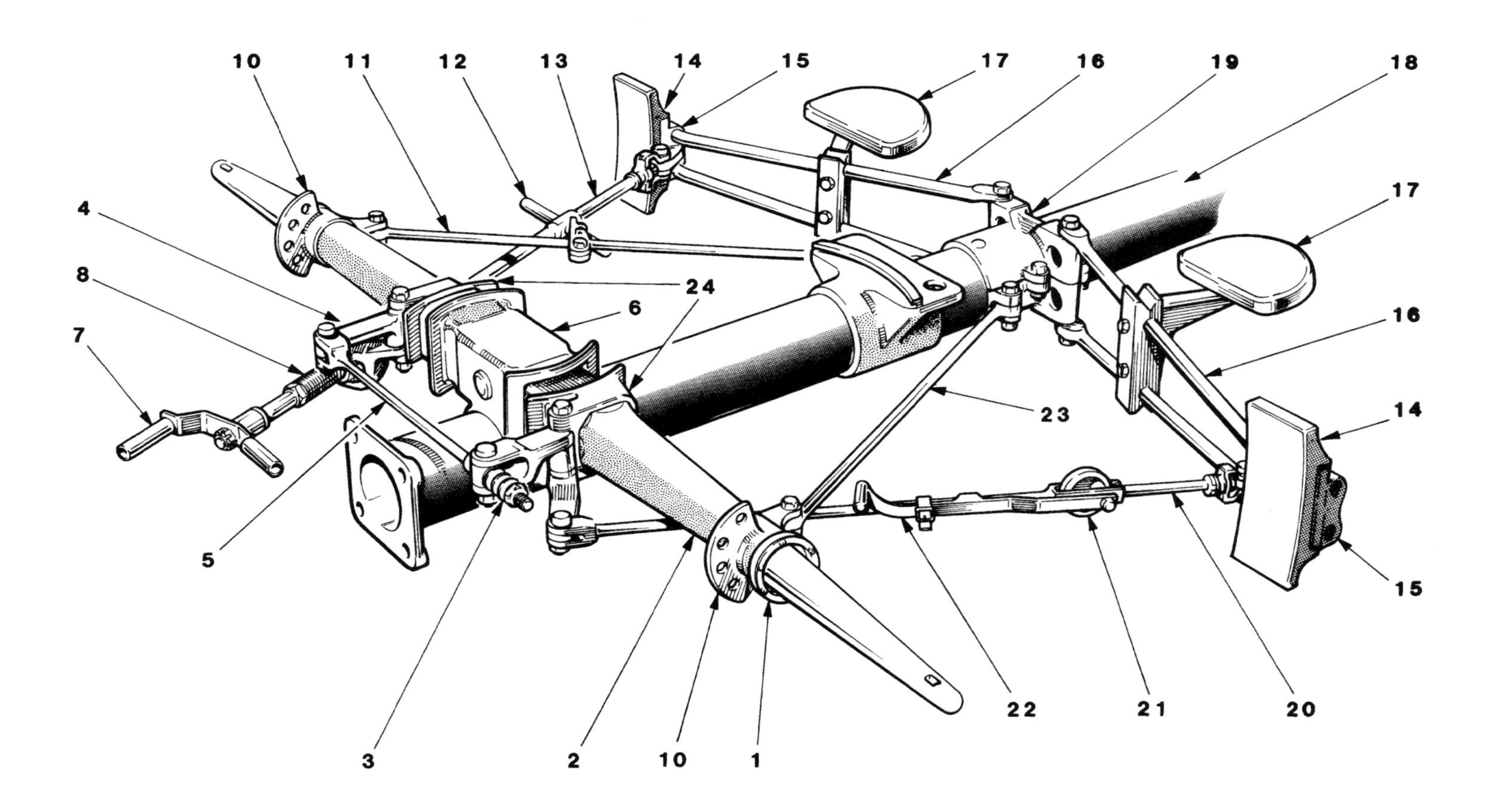

AXLETREE AND SWINGING ARM BRAKE

Axletree and swinging arm brake

The axletree (**2**) was a hollow steel forging, with ends drawn down and tapered to 13.5 inches long forming 2nd class C pattern arms, these to carry 2nd class C pattern No. 45 wheels, 4 feet 8 inches in diameter. The shoulders were circular and had keyways cut to receive keys formed within the axletree bracket bores (**1**).

Each bracket (**1**) had a circular recess fitted with an L leather seal retained by a steel ring, to avoid contamination of the pipebox grease by grit and dust. The brackets (**1**) were formed externally with tensile stay (**11** and **23**) attachment lugs and mounting flanges (**10**) for the shield support stays.

The axletree centre portion (**2**) fitted into the trail connecting bracket (**6**) top loop and was retained by a tapered pin.

Spaced three inches outboard from the connecting bracket (**6**) on each side was an axletree flange (**24**), secured by a tapered pin. The spaces were to accommodate the carriage body support bearings (**25**). The connecting bracket outer flanges (**6**) and each axletree flange inner flange (**24**) were curved to allow the carriage body bearings (**25**) to slide between them when being traversed. Both axletree flanges (**24**) had lugs formed to carry the pivot pins of the brake bell-crank levers (**4**).

The axletree (**2**) was braced by tensile stays (**11** and **23**). At the rear these were secured to the trail brake band (**19**) front lugs and at the front to the axletree brackets (**1**). The bolt heads were grooved to form bearings for a lifting jack.

A bracket (**26**), to support a fuze indicator, was clipped by screws to the right-hand tensile stay (**11**) and incorporated a hinge to allow the fuze indicator to be secured in an upright position.

The swinging arm brake comprised four tubular steel brake arms (**16**), pivoted in pairs on each side of the brake band (**19**) at their inner ends. Each pair terminated in a steel brake shoe (**15**) at their outer ends, the brake shoe fitted with a cast iron brake block (**14**) which acted against the wheel tyre.

The brake right-hand actuating rod (**13**) carried a handle (**7**) at the forward end and a cross handle (**12**) behind the shield to enable brake operation from either end. Turning the handle (**7**) caused the threaded rod (**8**) to travel forward through a nut (**9**), formed with trunnions and mounted in the forked end of a rocking bell-crank lever (**4**), until the right brake block (**14**) contacted the wheel. Subsequent turning of the handle (**7**) caused the bell-crank lever (**4**) to draw the left-hand actuating rod (**20**) forward until the left brake block contacted the wheel. Four disc springs (**3**) were fitted at the left-hand bell-crank lever end of the steel connecting rod (**5**).

Forming part of the left-hand actuating rod (**20**) was a quick-release eccentric (**21**) and operating lever (**22**). For normal use the lever (**22**) was housed in the forward position and secured by a strap. In action, when small changes of position were required rapidly, without limbering up, the lever (**22**) would be swung to the rear, thus lengthening the left-hand actuating rod (**20**) by the amount of throw of the eccentric (**21**) and releasing the brake. Once the required movements were completed the lever (**22**) would be returned to the forward position, restoring the normal brake action. A leather cover was provided to protect the eccentric from grit and dust.

Seats (**17**), for the use of the gun layers, were clamped to the brake arms (**16**).

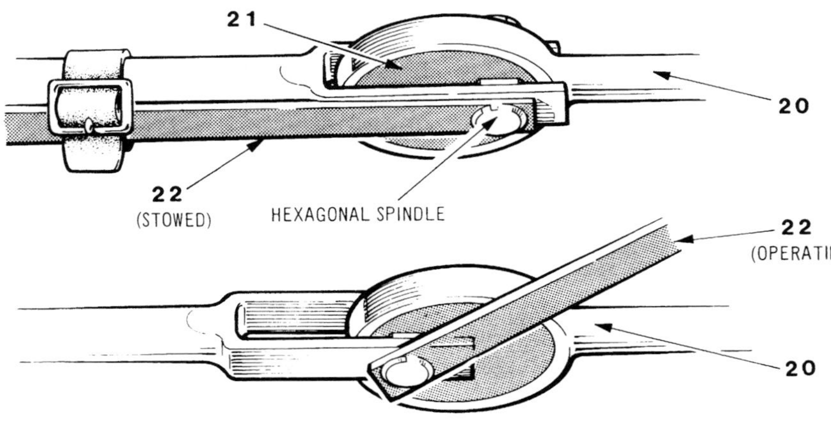

BRAKE QUICK RELEASE OPERATION

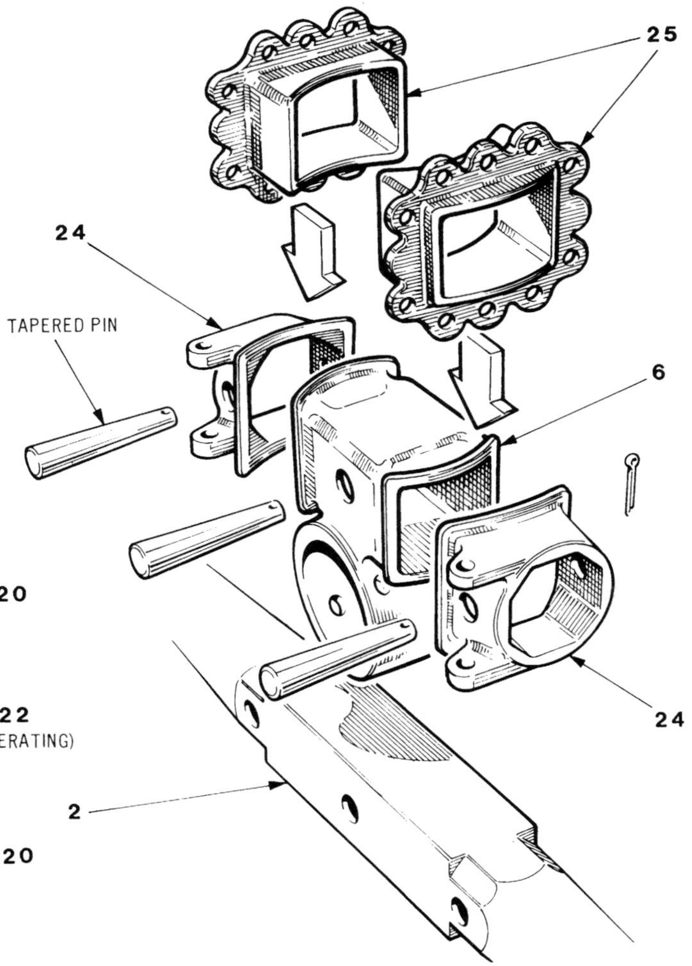

Carriage body

The carriage body consisted of two flanged, nickel steel side brackets or cheeks (**10**) connected by three transoms (**4**, **6** and **7**). Riveted to each side bracket (**10**) was a cradle trunnion support bearing (**9**) of steel, fitted with sliding capsquares (**8**) and retaining pins.

Below each trunnion bearing (**9**) was a rectangular aperture, in which was secured a carriage body support bearing (**13**) of manganese bronze. The top of each bearing (**13**) was drilled and fitted with a lubricating cap (**11**).

A manganese bronze traversing bracket (**12**) was riveted to the carriage body rear. The bracket (**12**) had, machined into the underside, an undercut groove which engaged the undercut guide on the trail carriage body support bracket. Excess wear at this point was remedied by sweating a brass strip onto the traversing bracket (**12**).

Riveted to the carriage body rear left side was a steel bracket (**5**), to house the elevating gear lower portion. Attached to the left side bracket (**10**) was a description plate, bearing details of the registered number and Mk. number of the carriage, manufacturer's initials and date.

1 CRADLE CLAMPING GEAR HANDLE
2 TRAVERSING CROSSHEAD ATTACHMENT BRACKET
3 CRADLE CLAMPING CLUTCHES
4 REAR TRANSOM
5 ELEVATING GEAR LOWER SUPPORT BRACKET
6 CENTRE TRANSOM
7 FRONT TRANSOM
8 SLIDING CAPSQUARE
9 TRUNNION BEARING
10 SIDE BRACKET
11 LUBRICATING CAP
12 TRAVERSING BRACKET
13 SUPPORT BEARING

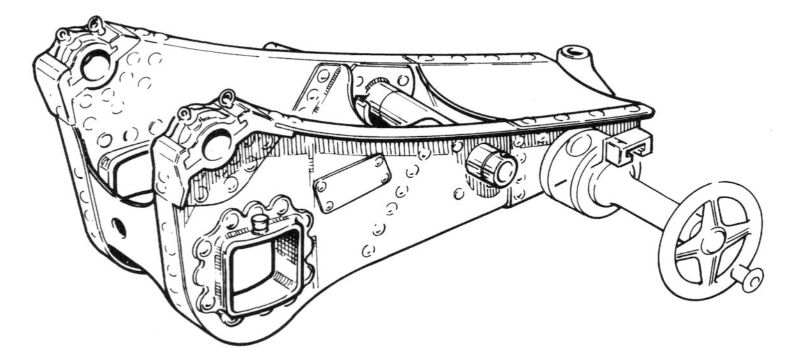

CARRIAGE BODY

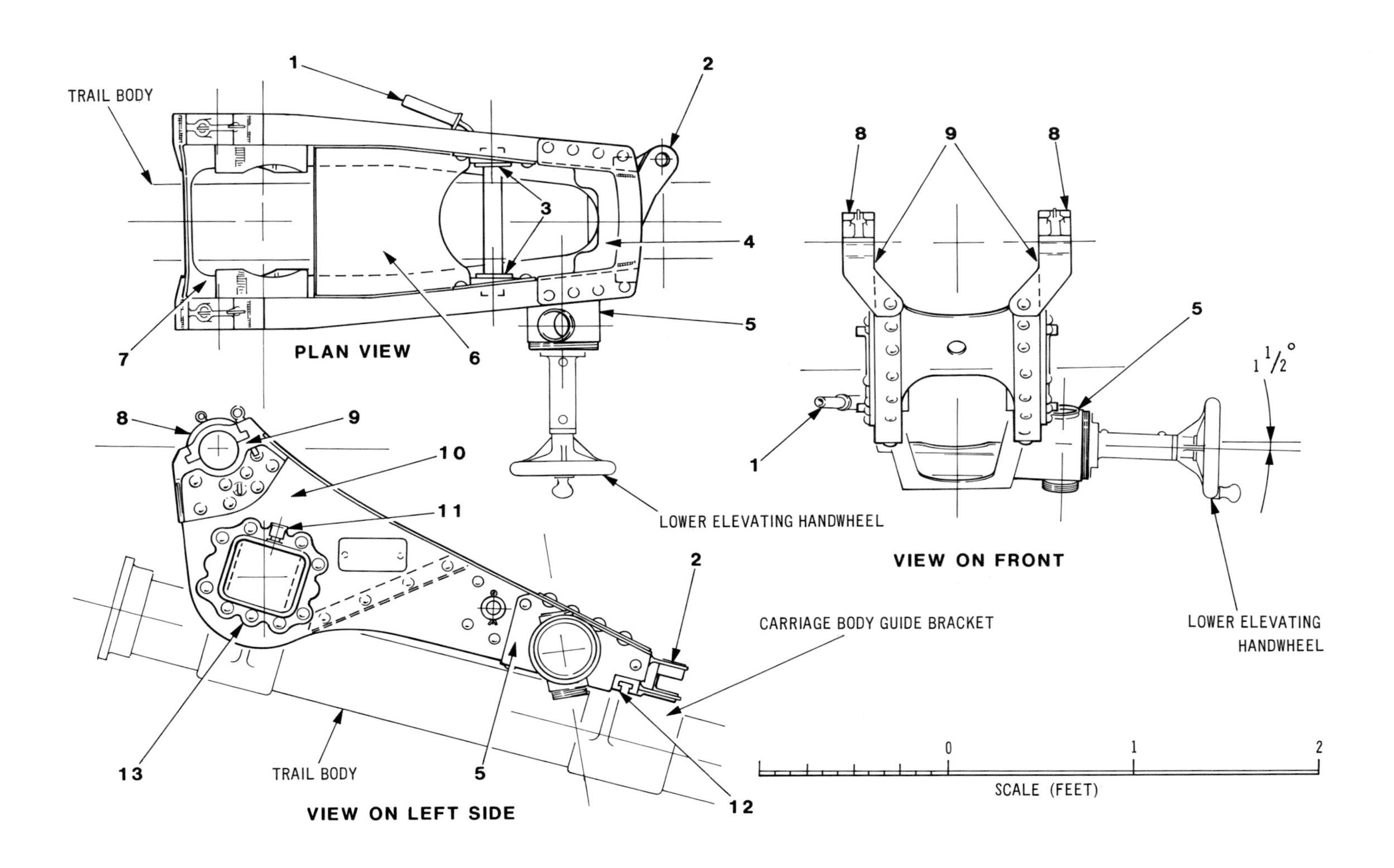

CARRIAGE BODY

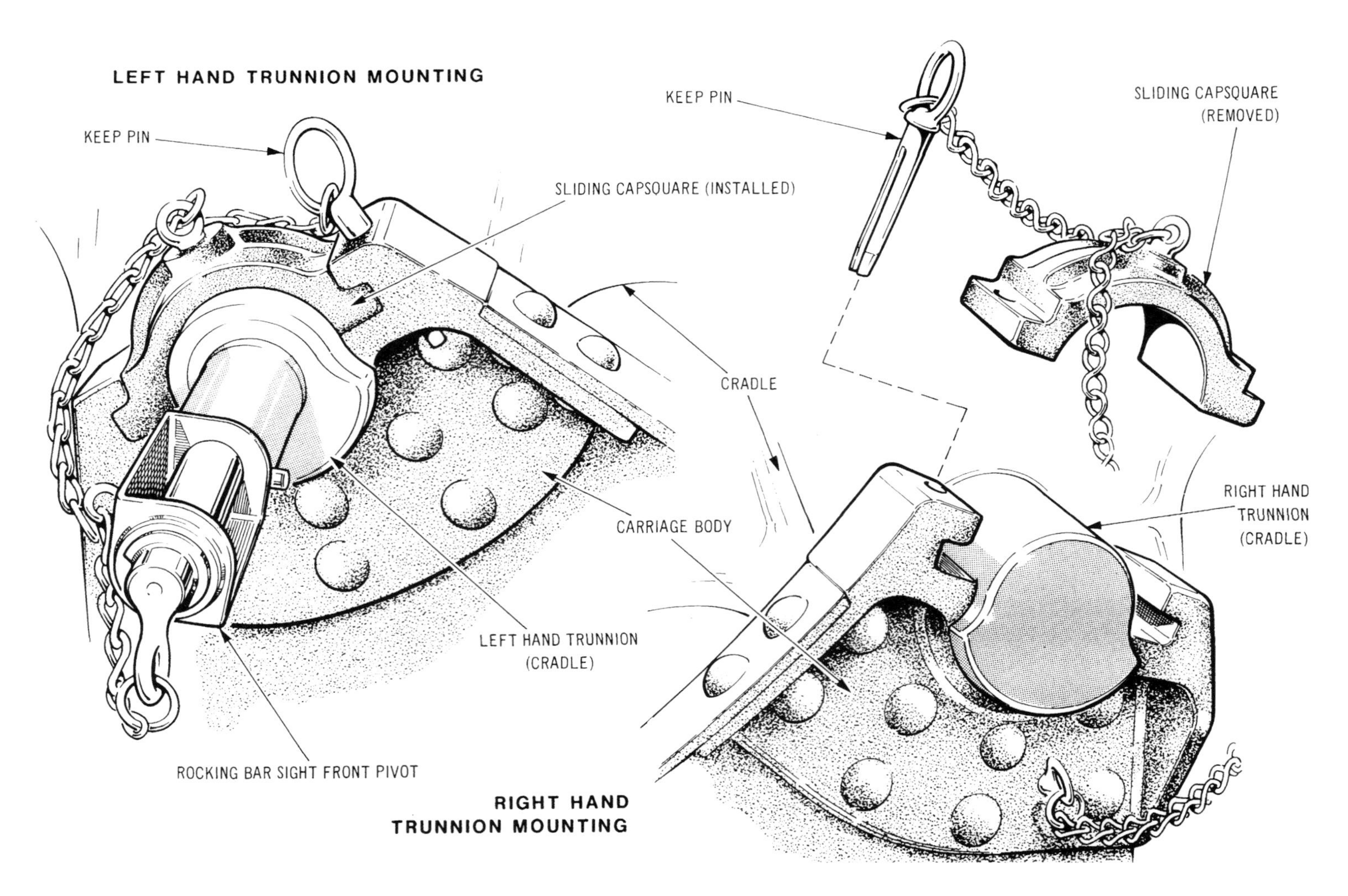

TRUNNION MOUNTINGS

PLAN VIEWS

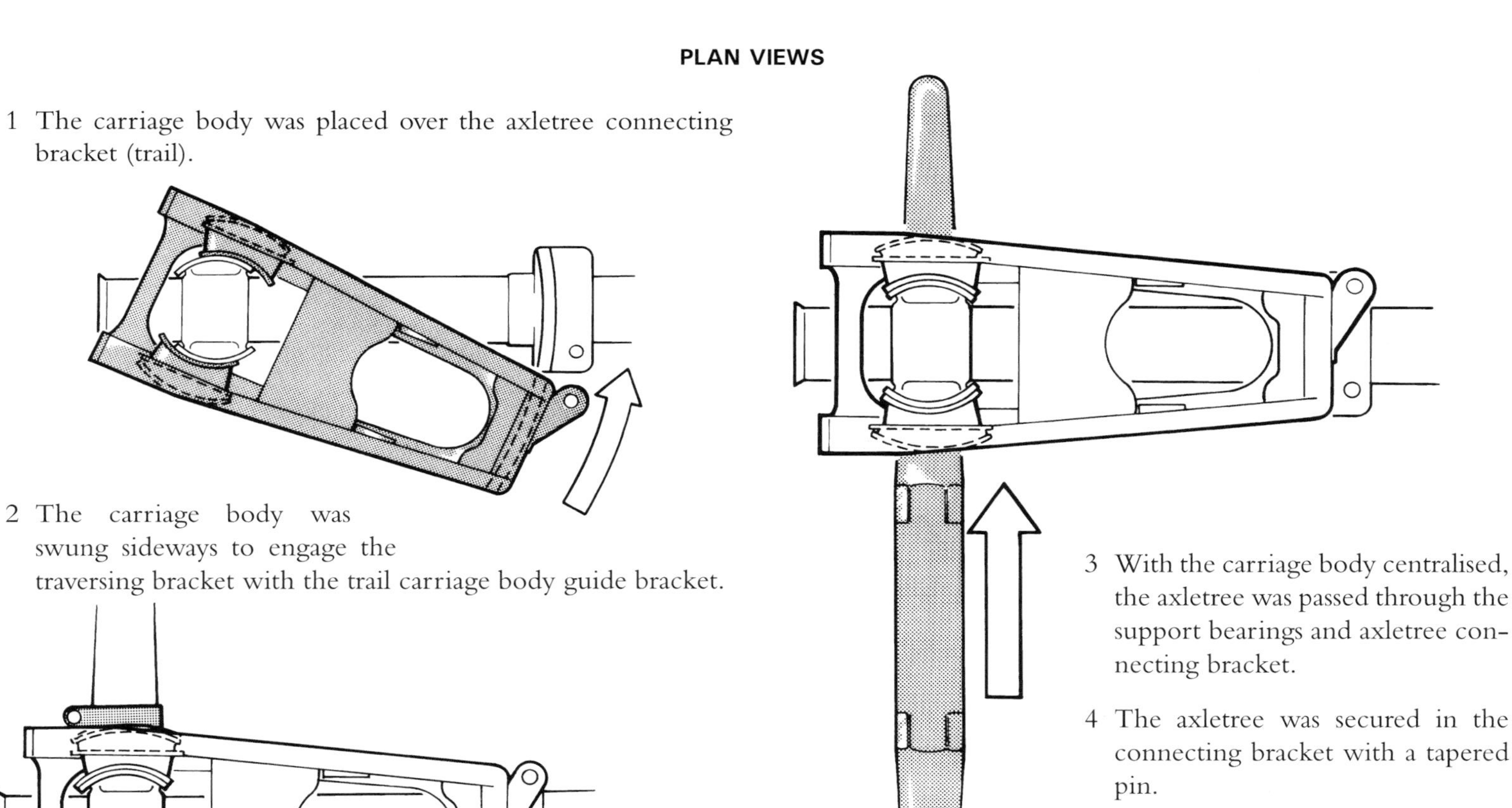

1 The carriage body was placed over the axletree connecting bracket (trail).

2 The carriage body was swung sideways to engage the traversing bracket with the trail carriage body guide bracket.

3 With the carriage body centralised, the axletree was passed through the support bearings and axletree connecting bracket.

4 The axletree was secured in the connecting bracket with a tapered pin.

5 An axletree flange was passed over each arm of the axletree and secured at its location with a tapered pin.

ASSEMBLY OF TRAIL, CARRIAGE BODY AND AXLETREE

Traversing gear

The traversing gear enabled lateral movement of the carriage body over four degrees either side of the trail centre line. The crosshead (**8**) was a steel tube, pivoted to the traversing bracket (**12**) and secured by a washer, nut and split pin.

Sliding inside the body (**8**) was a manganese bronze nut (**7**) running on the traversing screw (**10**) and pinned at the right-hand end to the carriage body rear (**2**).

1	HANDWHEEL	7	NUT
2	CARRIAGE BODY	8	CROSSHEAD BODY
3	GRADUATED SCALE	9	TRAIL BODY
4	SCREW CAP	10	TRAVERSING SCREW
5	STOP COLLAR (ADJUSTMENT)	11	CROSSHEAD PIVOT
6	POINTER	12	TRAVERSING BRACKET

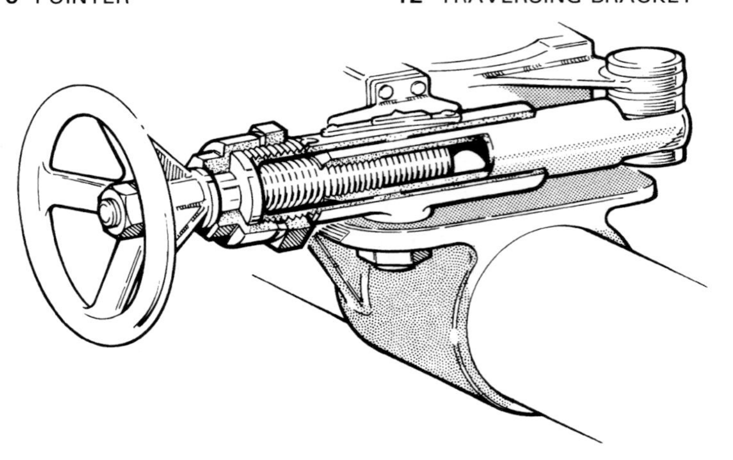

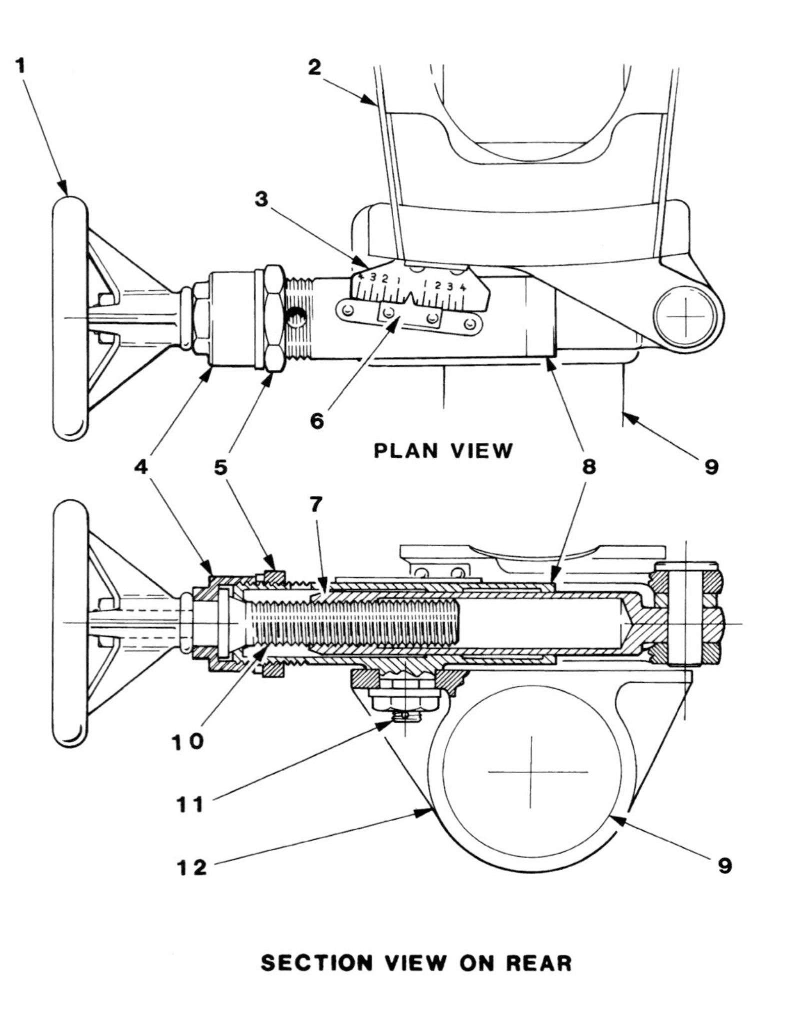

TRAVERSING GEAR

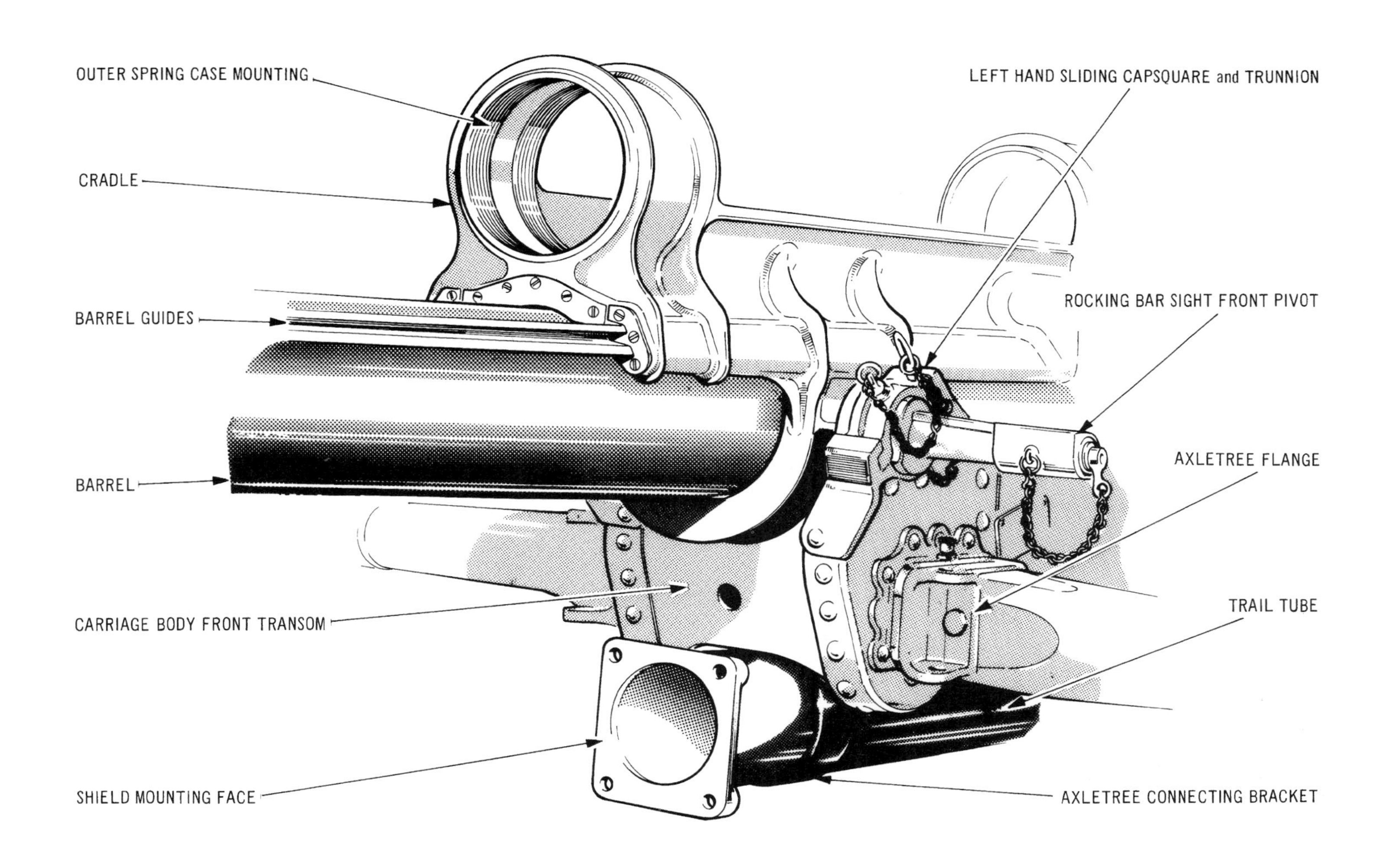

FRONT VIEW OF MAJOR ASSEMBLIES

Cradle

The cradle was a one-piece, manganese bronze casting. It was formed by two single front collars (**5** and **13**) and a double rear collar (**8**), connected by two sides (**6**). The sides were formed with wedge-shaped grooves (**1**) to carry the barrel supporting wings. Both the front, upper, single collar (**5**) and the upper portion of the rear double collar (**8**) were screw-threaded, to receive the outer spring case.

Trunnions (**2** and **3**) formed on either side of the front, lower, single collar (**13**) had their axis inclined to an angle of one and a half degrees, left trunnion down (**3**), to compensate automatically for projectile drift at all elevations.

The left trunnion (**3**) was internally screw-threaded axially. On early patterns this thread received a steel arm pivoting the rocking bar sight, which was secured by a key and split pin. Later patterns had the steel arm replaced by a conical one which was secured to the cradle trunnion interior by a nut and split pin. To the outer end of the arm, a sight bar was secured by a nut and split pin.

Shaped brass protectors were fitted front and rear to the cradle and leather pads protected the guide grooves from the ingress of grit and dirt.

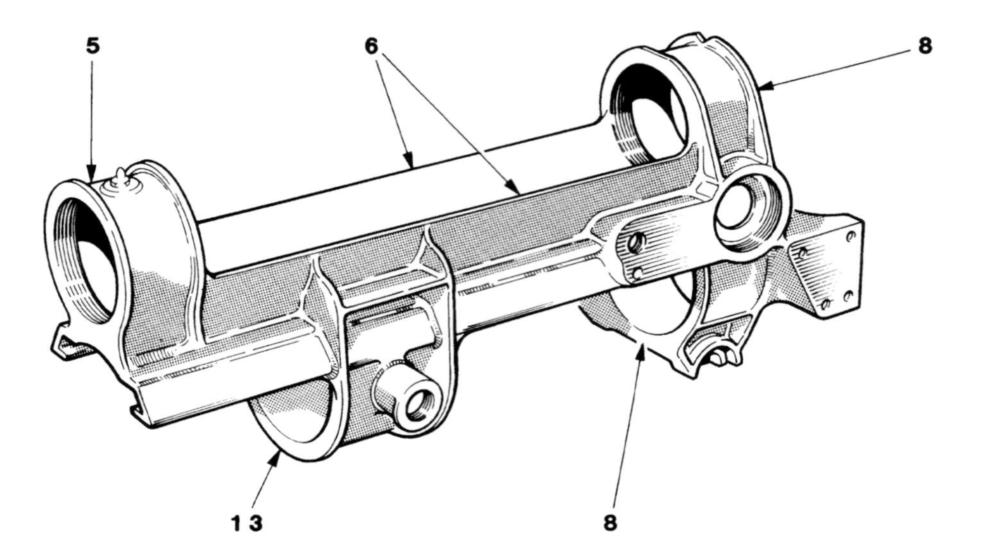

1 BARREL SUPPORTING WING GUIDE GROOVE
2 RIGHT SIDE TRUNNION
3 LEFT SIDE TRUNNION
4 ACORN FORESIGHT
5 UPPER SINGLE COLLAR (FRONT)
6 SIDES
7 ELEVATING GEAR CROSS SPINDLE LOCATION
8 DOUBLE COLLAR (REAR)
9 REARSIGHT NOTCH
10 LAYER'S GUARD MOUNTING FACE
11 CLAMPING PROJECTIONS
12 RANGE GEAR CROSS SPINDLE LOCATION
13 LOWER SINGLE COLLAR (FRONT)

CRADLE

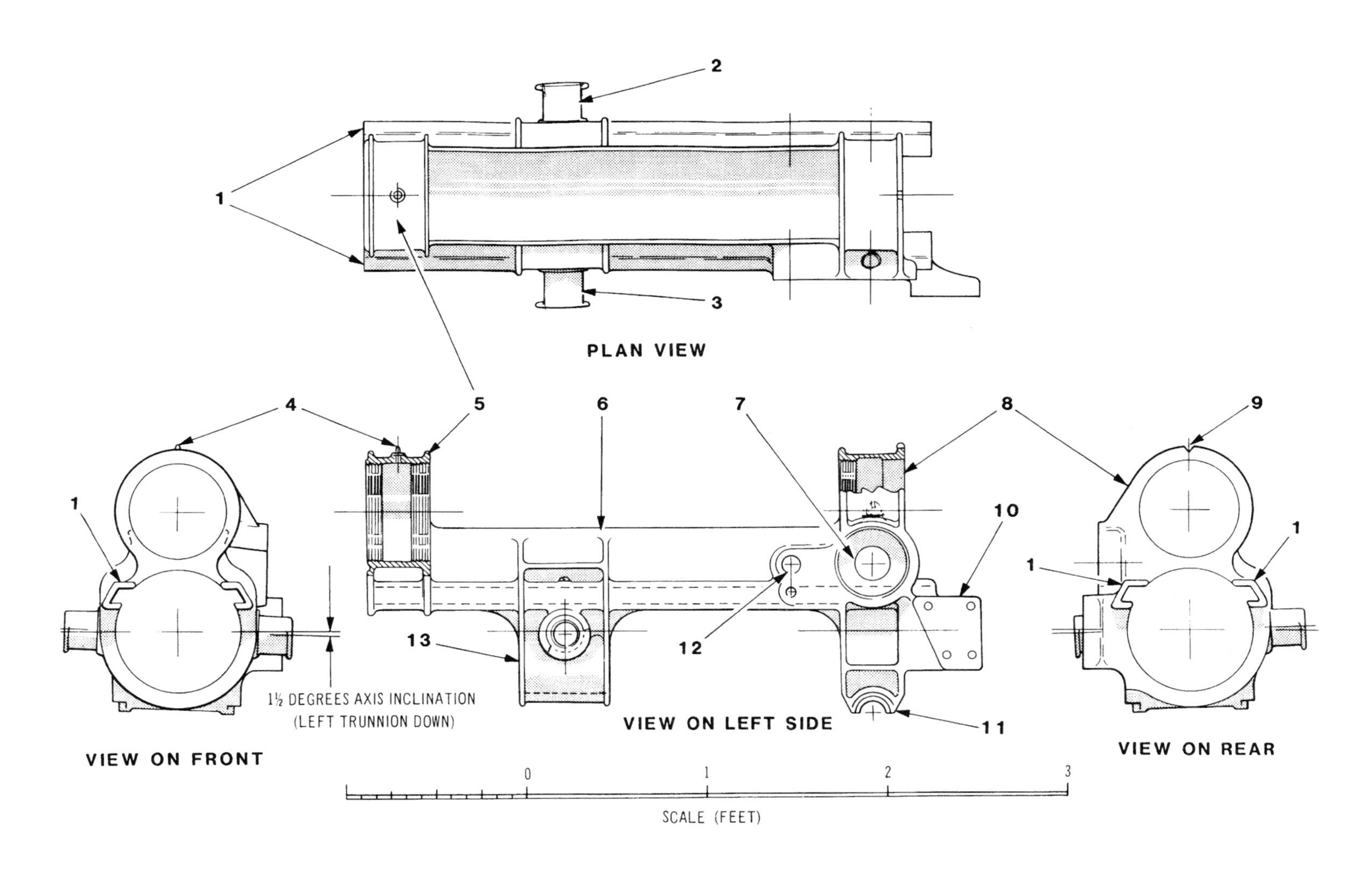
2
1
3
PLAN VIEW
4
5
6
7
8
9
1
10
1
1
1½ DEGREES AXIS INCLINATION
(LEFT TRUNNION DOWN)
13
12
VIEW ON LEFT SIDE
11
VIEW ON FRONT
VIEW ON REAR
0
1
2
3
SCALE (FEET)

CRADLE

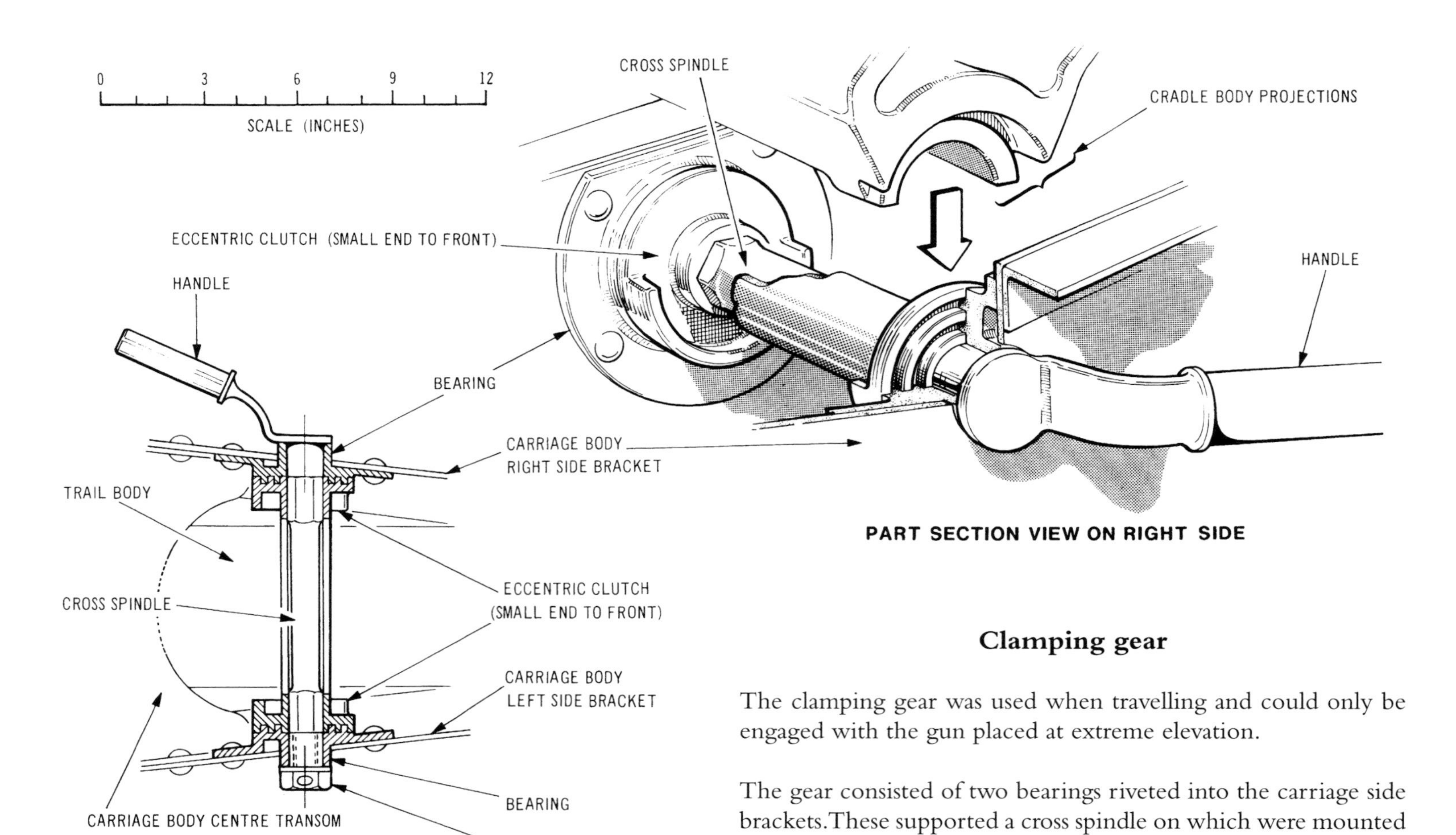

CRADLE CLAMPING GEAR

Clamping gear

The clamping gear was used when travelling and could only be engaged with the gun placed at extreme elevation.

The gear consisted of two bearings riveted into the carriage side brackets.These supported a cross spindle on which were mounted the clutches, which engaged projections on the cradle.

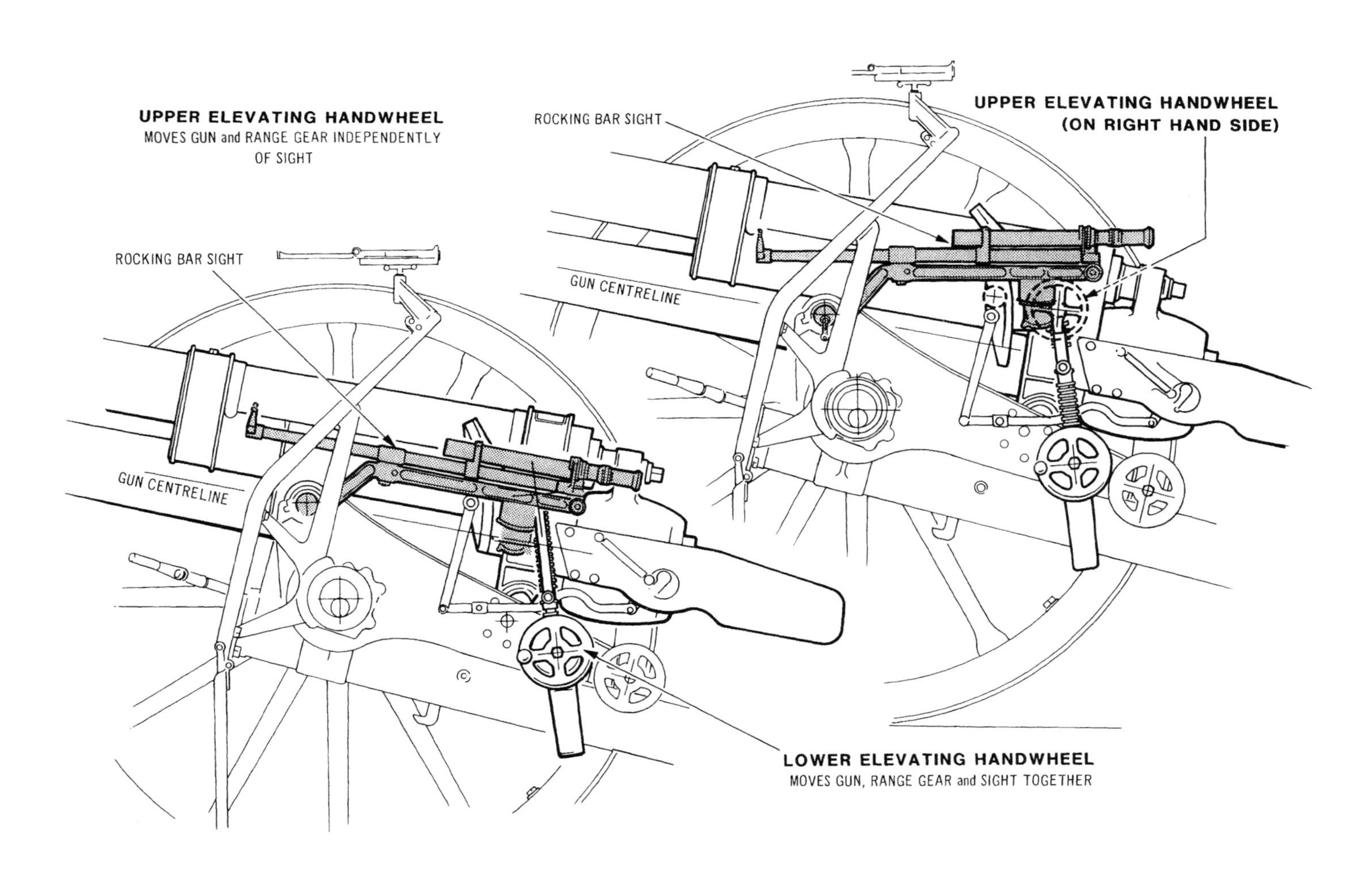

INDEPENDENT LINE OF SIGHT

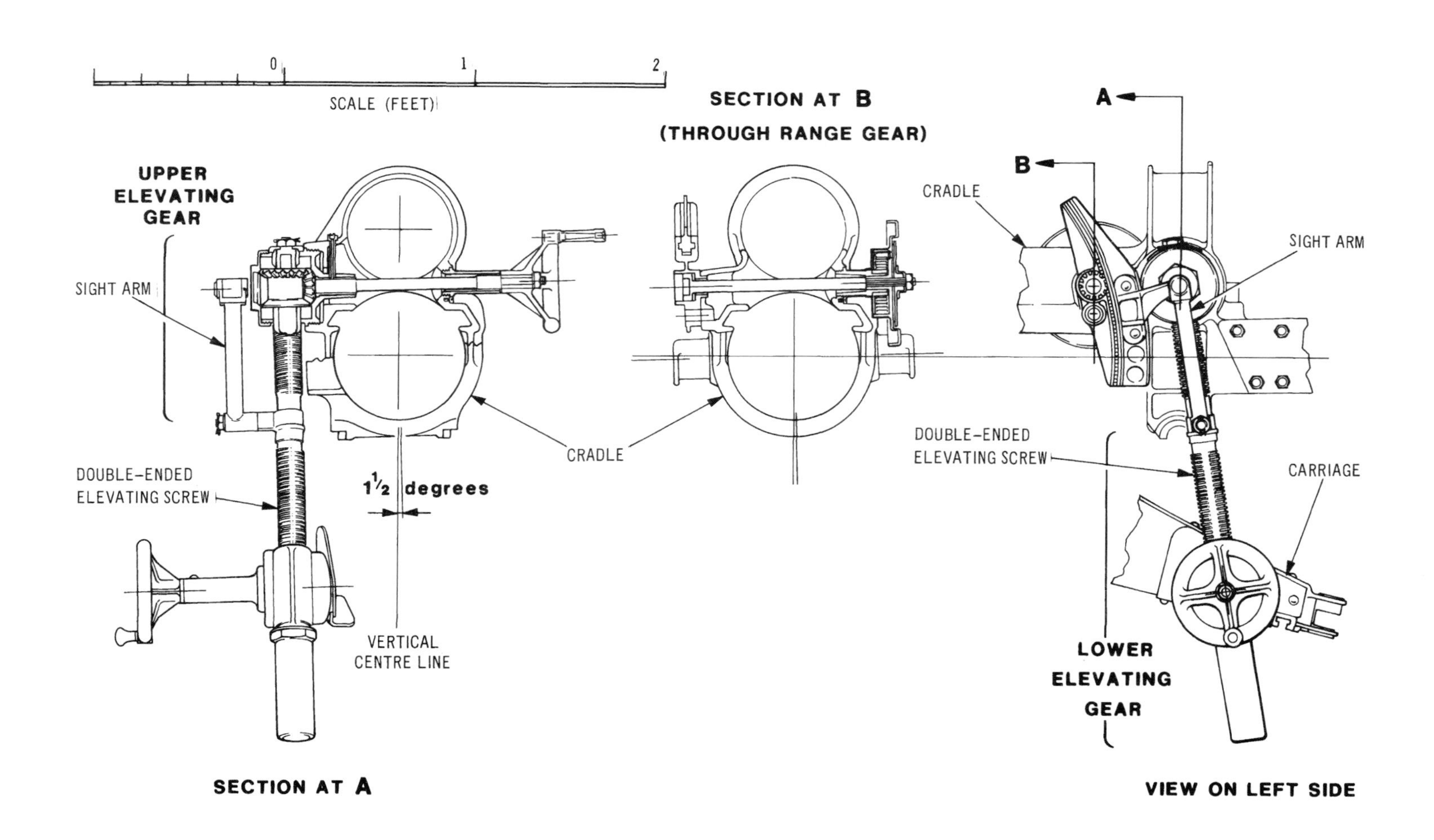

ELEVATING AND RANGE GEAR

Elevating and range gear

This equipment embodied the principle known as 'independent line of sight', in which the angle of sight adjustment (i.e. the angle between the line of sight and the horizontal) was separate from the angle of elevation adjustment (i.e. the angle between the axis of the gun and line of sight). The elevating gear was divided into upper and lower portions by means of a double-ended elevating screw, at the centre of which was attached an arm to carry the sight. The upper portion moved the gun relative to the line of sight and regulated the elevation angle to the range required. The angle of elevation applied by the upper elevating gear was measured by the range gear in degrees and yards. The lower portion moved the line of sight and gun together relative to the horizontal and regulated the angle of sight according to the line of fire being up or down hill.

By this method, alterations of range did not affect the position of the sight bar, only moving the gun relative to it.

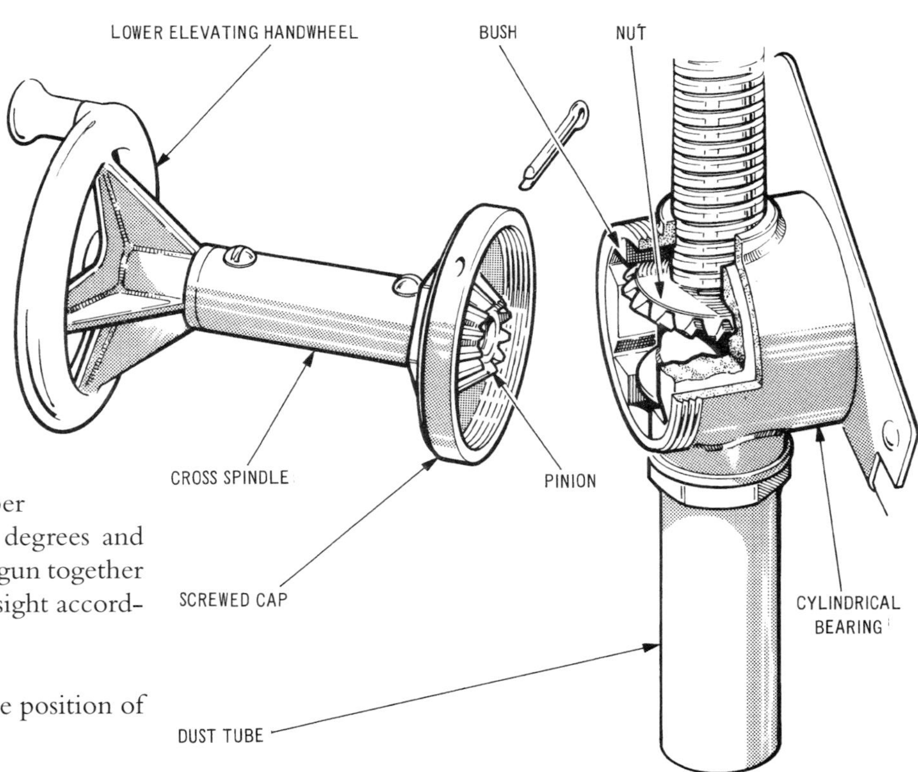

LOWER ELEVATING GEAR

Lower elevating gear

The lower portion of the elevating gear consisted of a handwheel mounted on the outer end of a cross spindle, the inner end of which carried a pinion. The pinion engaged gear teeth formed on the exterior of a steel nut housed within a manganese bronze bush. The bush was carried in a cylindrical bearing riveted to the carriage body, the bearing being closed by a steel screwed cap locked with a split pin.

When the handwheel was turned, the nut turned and moved the elevating screw up or down, this moving the cradle and sight simultaneously.

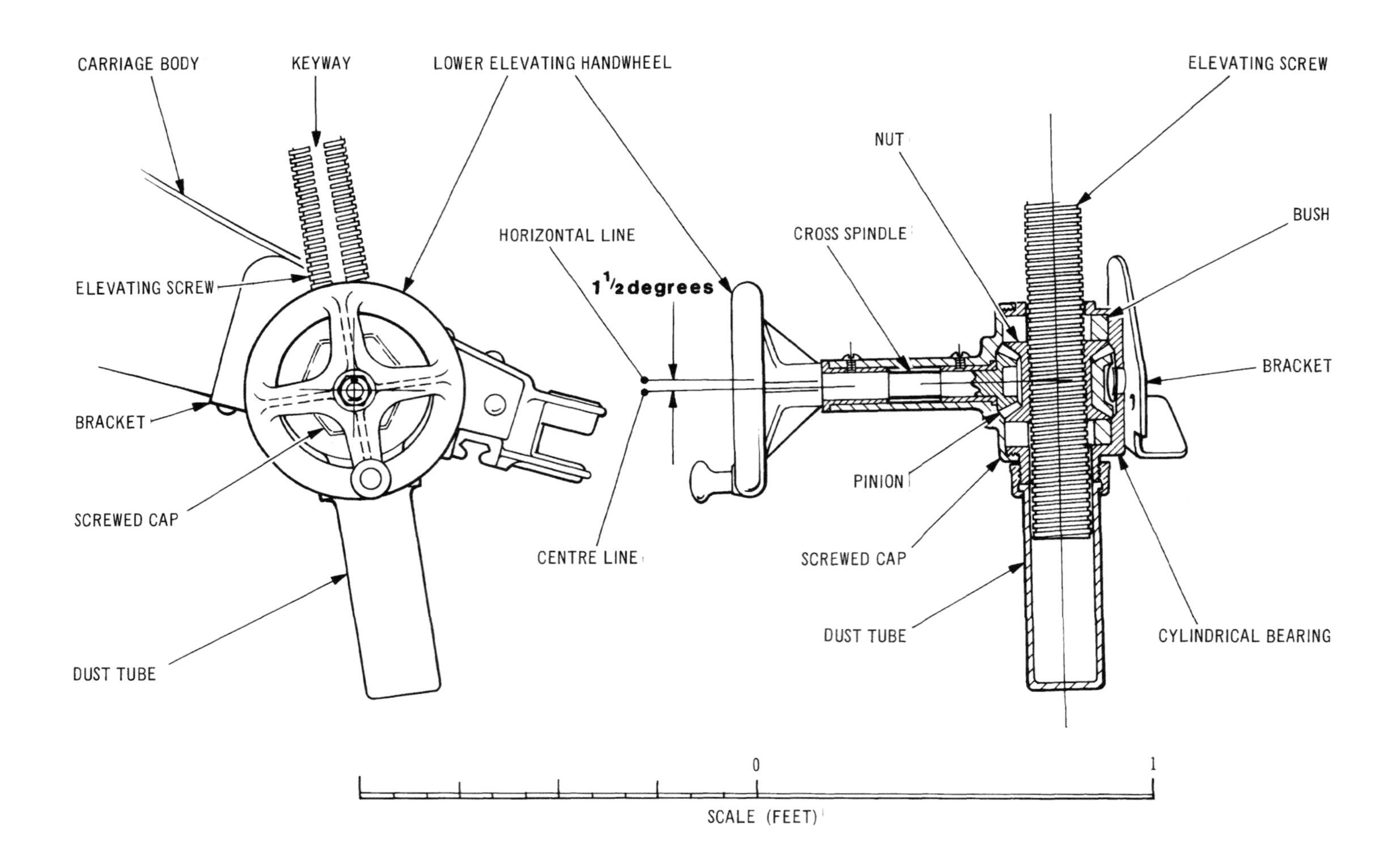

LOWER ELEVATING GEAR

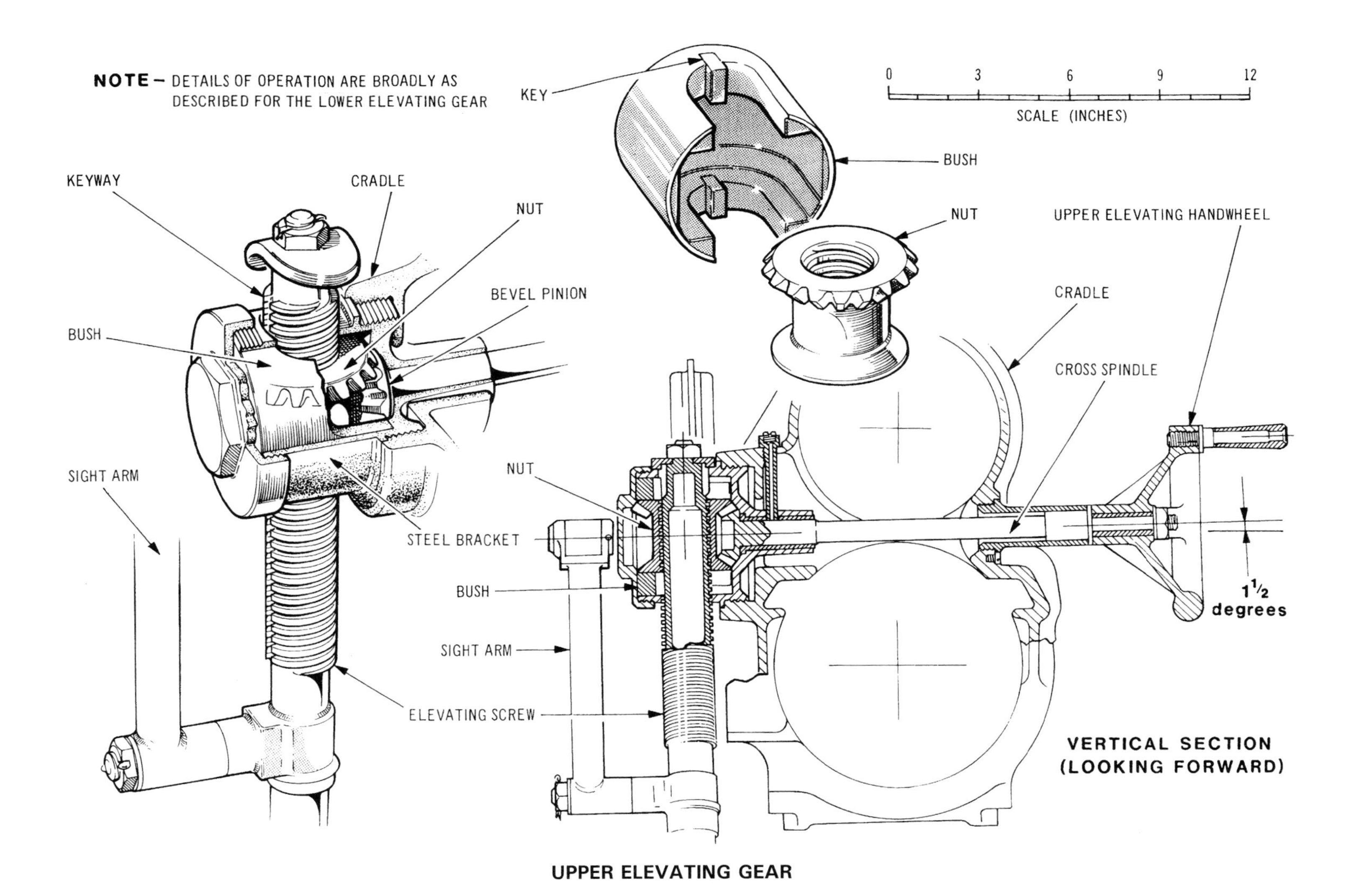

UPPER ELEVATING GEAR

Range gear

The range gear consisted of a spindle, passing through the cradle from the left side, having a spur pinion on the left-hand end engaging a toothed arc attached to the sight bracket.

RANGE GEAR

Rotation of the upper elevating gear handwheel caused the cradle-mounted spur gear to roll along the toothed arc. The gear rotation was transmitted, via the spindle, to the range gear mounted on the cradle right-hand side.

The spindle passed through a cradle-mounted bearing, the outer end of which was externally hexagonal in section, onto which was mounted a spring barrel. The spindle right-hand end was also hexagonal in section, onto which was mounted a spring case.

Engaging both barrel and case was a clock spring to prevent any backlash between the two. Mounted on the spring case was an aluminium scale ring, graduated in degrees and yards. It was held against the spring case by a jamming plate, woodite washer and nut. The elevation angle of the gun was read from the scale by a pointer, mounted on the cradle.

Any excess wear between the spindle spur gear and toothed arc could be corrected by turning the adjustable bush. The bush was eccentric, its rim notched and numbered, a stud in the cradle engaging whichever notch gave the correct operation. A few early bushes were made with five notches, most were produced with eight, the numbers one and eight representing the low and high setting limits.

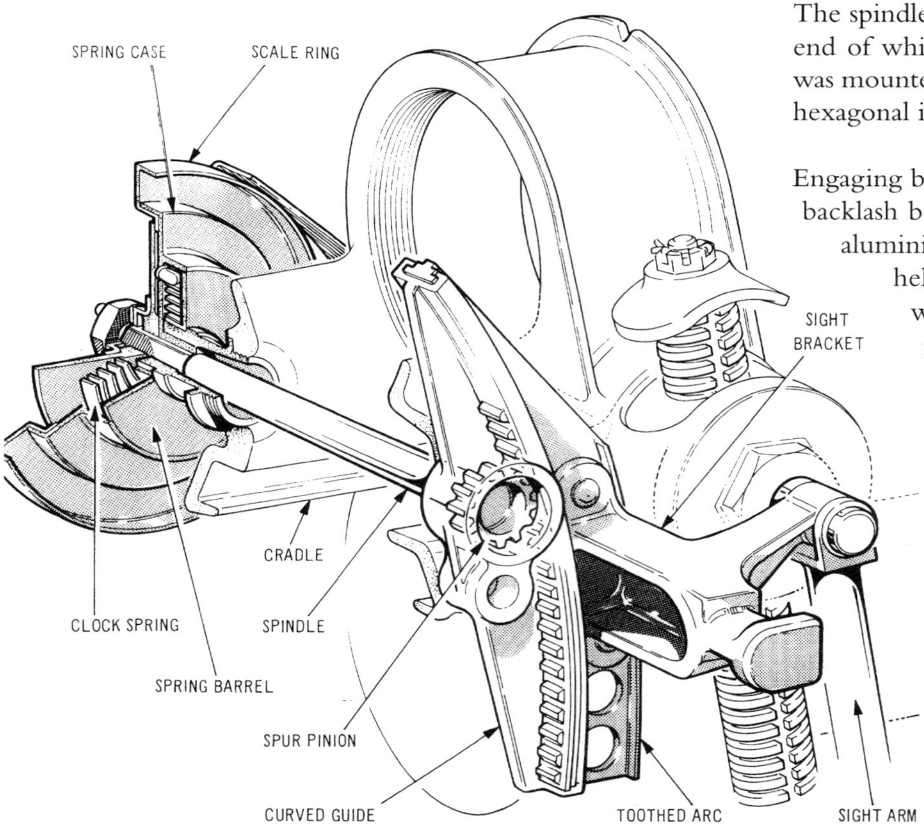

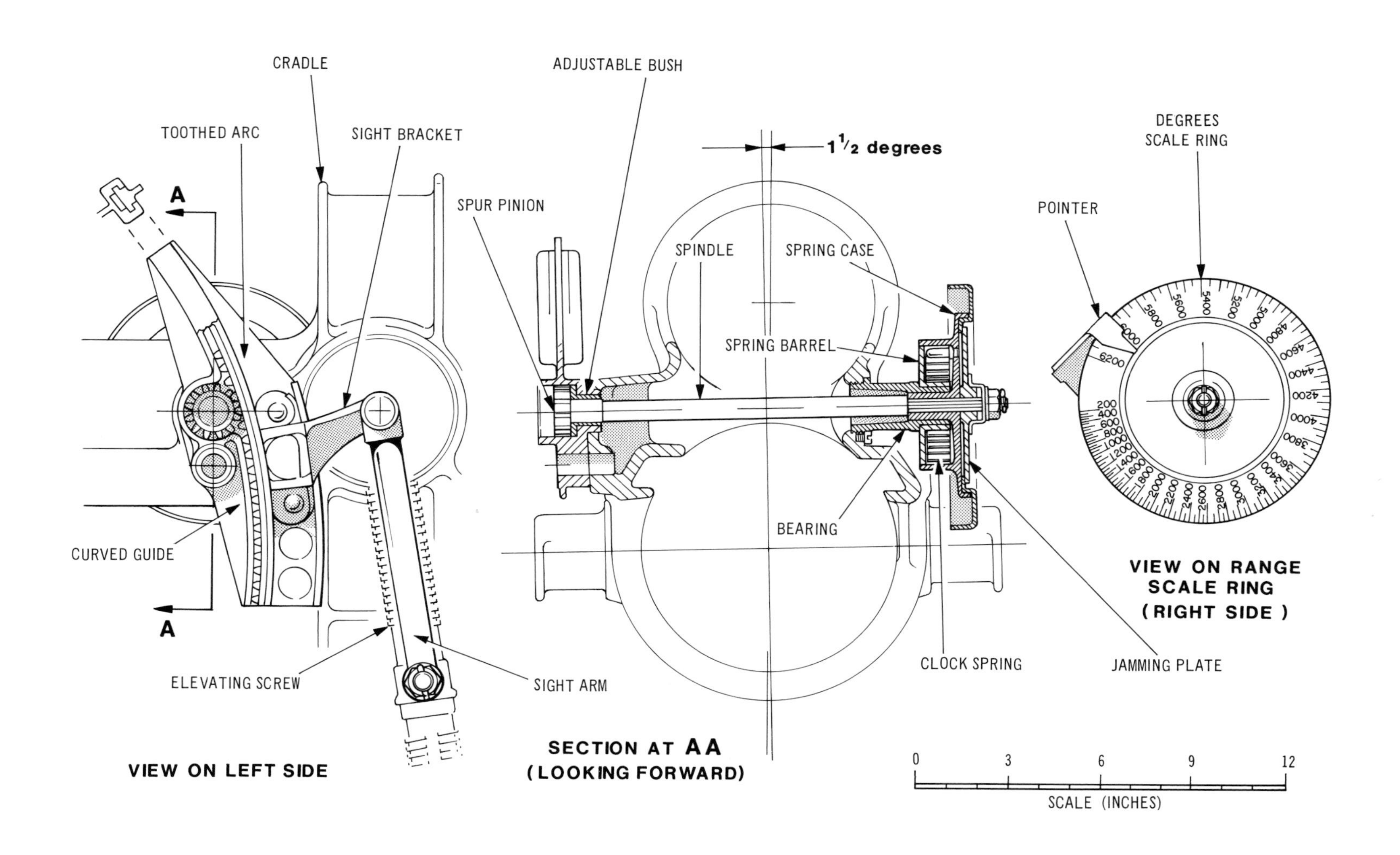
CRADLE
ADJUSTABLE BUSH
TOOTHED ARC
SIGHT BRACKET
1 1/2 degrees
DEGREES
SCALE RING
A
SPUR PINION
POINTER
SPINDLE
SPRING CASE
SPRING BARREL
BEARING
CURVED GUIDE
VIEW ON RANGE
SCALE RING
(RIGHT SIDE)
A
ELEVATING SCREW
SIGHT ARM
CLOCK SPRING
JAMMING PLATE
SECTION AT AA
(LOOKING FORWARD)
VIEW ON LEFT SIDE
0
3
6
9
12
SCALE (INCHES)

RANGE GEAR

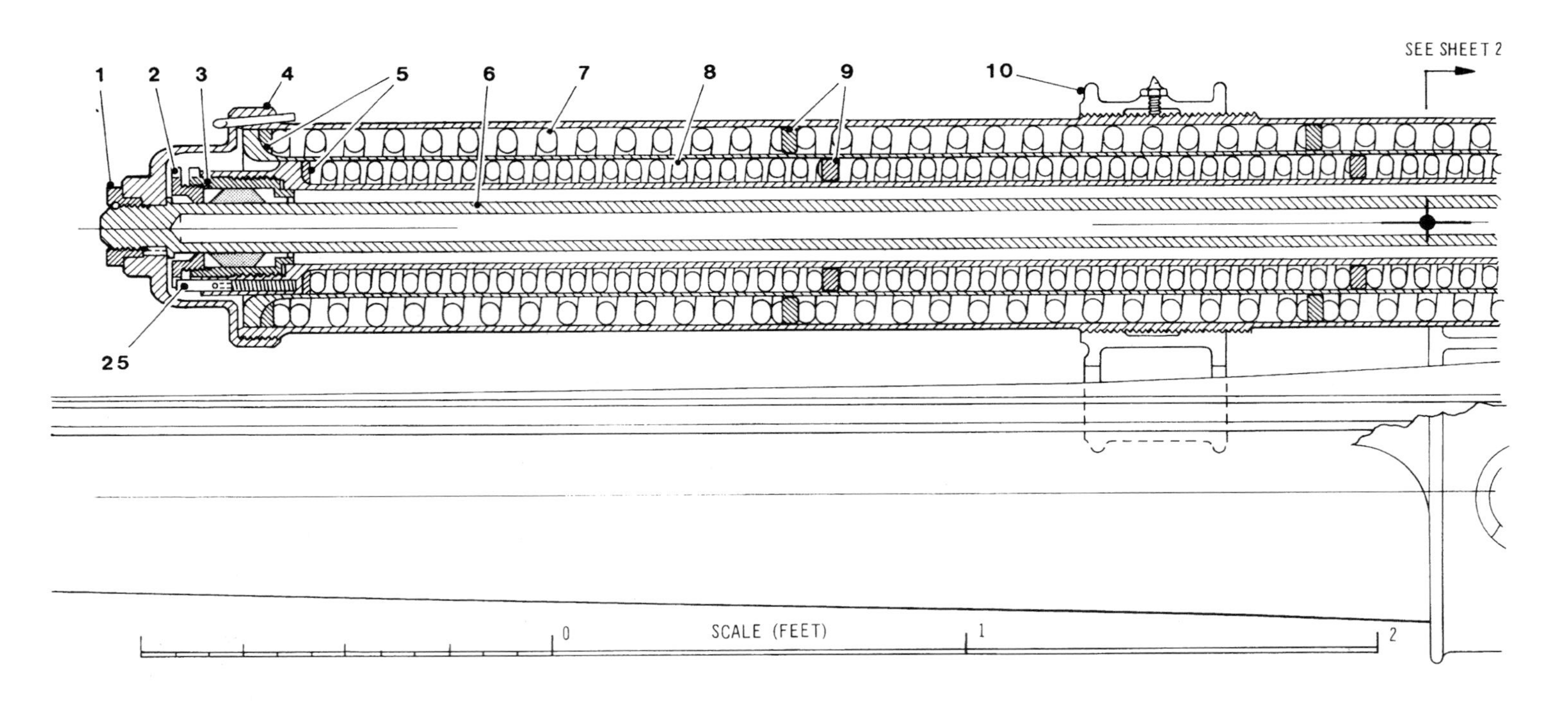

1 NUT (PISTON ROD)
2 GLAND
3 STUFFING BOX AND PACKING
4 FRONT CAP (OUTER SPRING CASE)
5 FRONT END PLATES
6 PISTON ROD
7 OUTER SPRINGS
8 INNER SPRINGS
9 PARTING PLATES
10 CRADLE UPPER SINGLE COLLAR (FRONT)
11 OUTER SPRING CASE
12 INNER SPRING CASE
13 BUFFER CYLINDER
14 SCREWED PLUG AND COPPER WASHER
15 RECESS (CONTROLLING PLUNGER)
16 CONTROLLING PLUNGER
17 PISTON
18 CRADLE DOUBLE COLLAR (REAR)
19 REAR END PLATES
20 FILLER HOLE PLUG
21 INNER SECURING NUT
22 BARREL LUG
23 OUTER SECURING NUT
24 CONNECTING PIECE
25 STUD WITH KEEP PIN AND SPRING

HYDRAULIC BUFFER AND SPRINGS

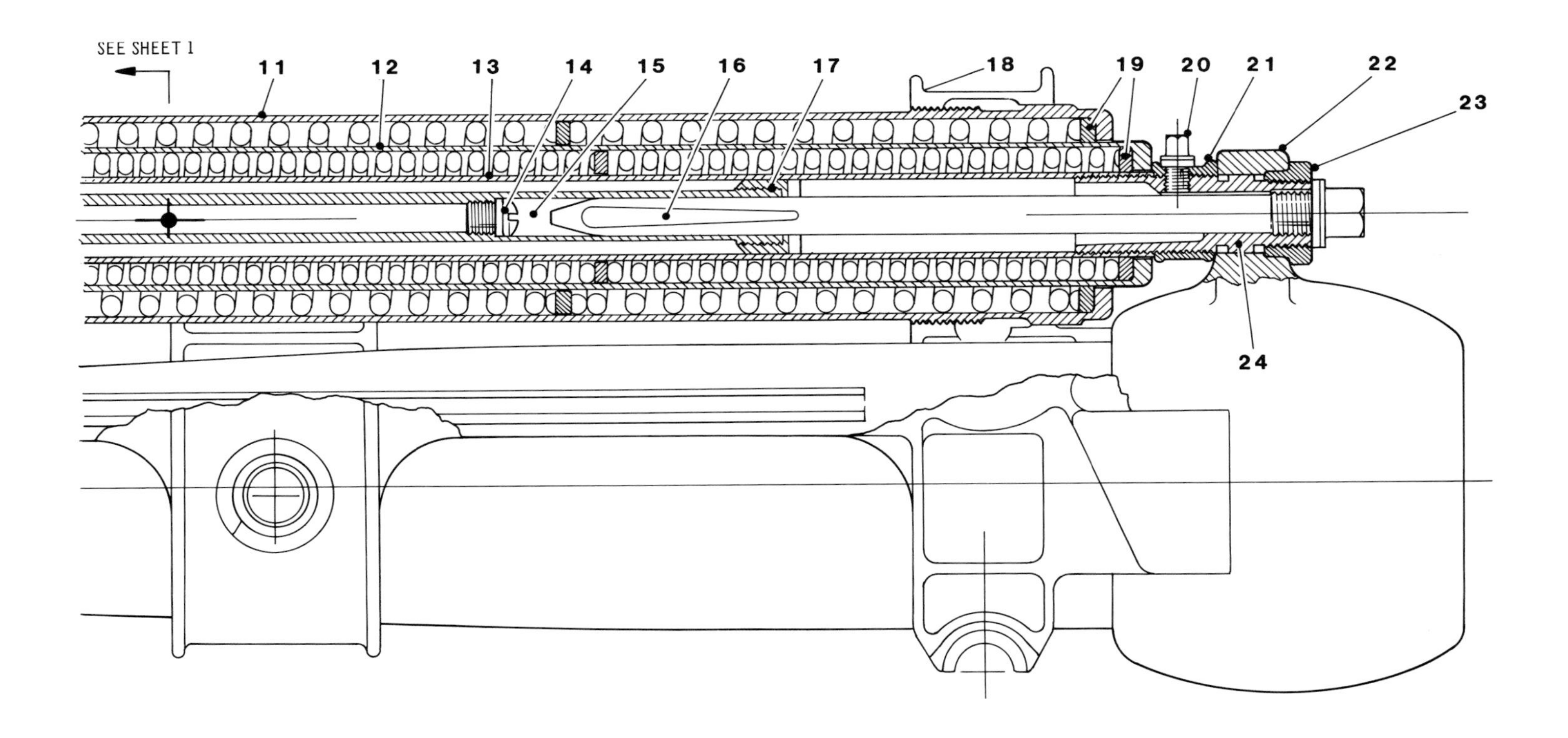

Hydraulic buffer and springs

The hydraulic buffer (**13**) was a forged steel tube, the rear end closed by a steel connecting piece (**24**) screwed and soldered into place. The connecting piece (**24**) was secured to the barrel lug (**22**) by flanged inner (**21**) and outer (**23**) securing nuts. The unthreaded portion of the connecting piece (**24**) which passed through the barrel lug (**22**) had two keys, fitted into keyways cut into the lug bore. The inner securing nut (**21**) had a vertical circular hole bored through to coincide with the filler hole in the connecting piece (**24**), this being threaded to admit a filler hole plug (**20**) and copper sealing washer. The plug was provided with a chain and keep pin. The connecting piece bore (**24**) was threaded at the rear to take a steel controlling plunger (**16**),

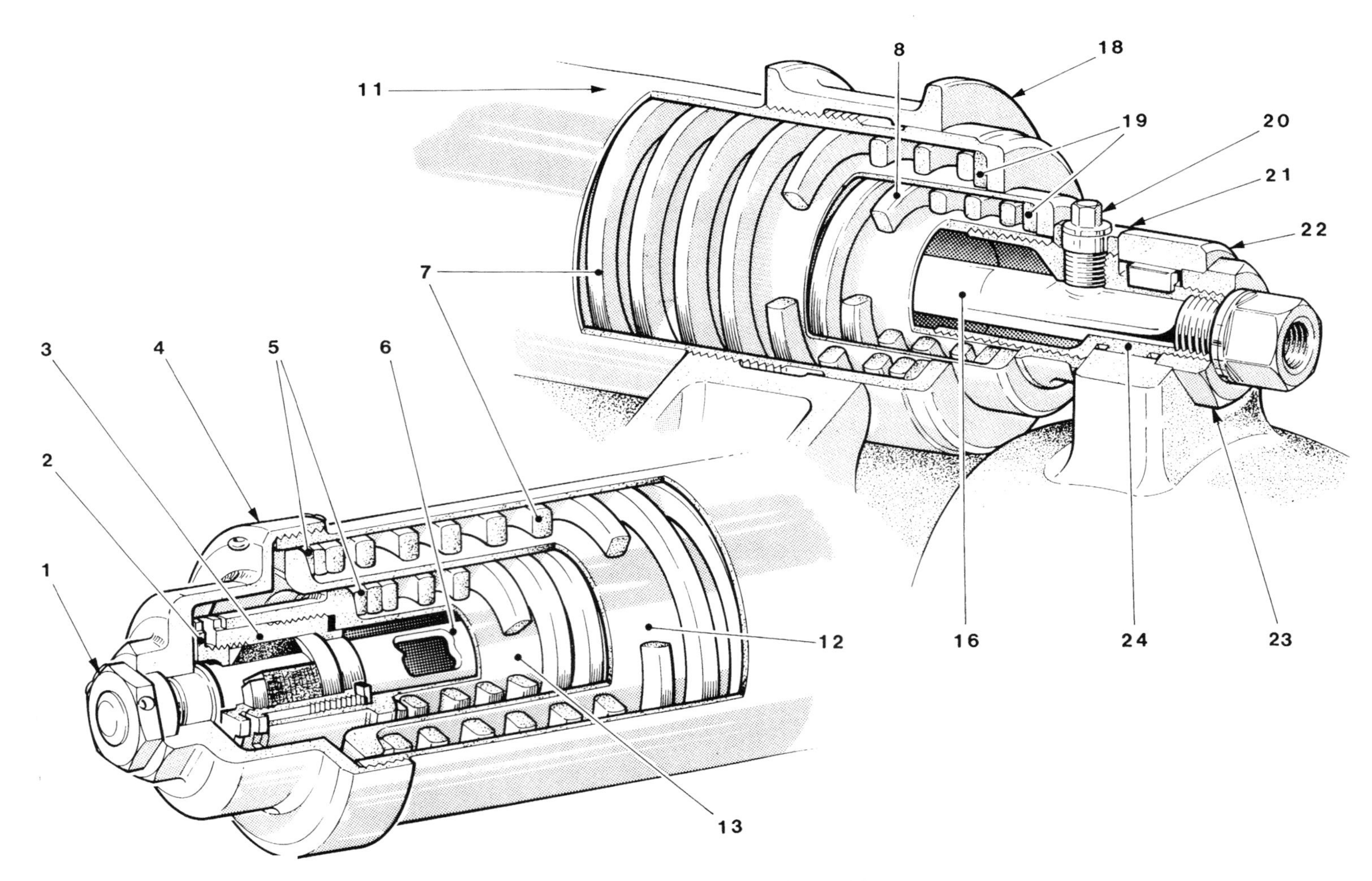

HYDRAULIC BUFFER AND SPRINGS

screwed up against a copper sealing washer, the bore thread being grooved longitudinally to enable air to vent, during filling of the buffer, with the plunger unscrewed through two turns.

Screwed into the front of the buffer cylinder (**13**) was a manganese bronze stuffing box (**3**) butting against a sealing washer of anhydrous leather. The stuffing box (**3**) held two manganese bronze, coned supporting rings. These trapped a packing ring of asbestos and mutton suet enclosed in a canvas cover and pressed to shape. Rings and packing were pressed into the stuffing box by a manganese bronze gland (**2**), a spring stud with keep pin (**25**), housed in a recess in the front end of the buffer cylinder (**13**), prevented the stuffing box (**3**) and gland (**2**) from becoming unscrewed.

Ten longitudinal grooves, tapering in depth, were cut into the bore of the buffer cylinder (**13**) to graduate hydraulic pressure during recoil.

The tubular steel piston rod (**6**) was screwed to the front cap (**4**) at the forward end and keyed to prevent rotation. The piston rod (**6**) rear end carried a manganese bronze piston (**17**) which was screwed on.

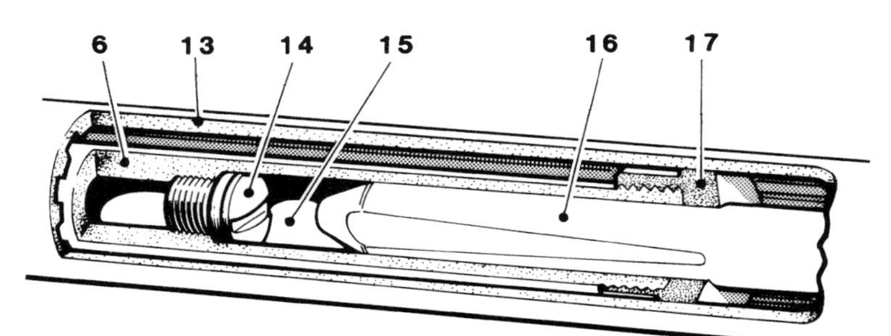

A recess (**15**), formed by a plug and copper sealing washer (**14**) within the piston rod (**6**) had, operating within it, the controlling plunger (**16**). This was tapered at its front and had two filed flats to control the hydraulic oil during the final running out. A threaded recess in the rear end of the controlling plunger (**16**) was for use during operation of the running out springs adjusting apparatus.

Two banks of springs, an outer bank (**7**) and inner bank (**8**), surrounded the buffer cylinder (**13**), contained within steel cases (**11** and **12**). The outer spring case (**11**) was screwed into the cradle upper collars (**10** and **18**) and secured by a set screw. The outer spring case (**11**) had a rear inner flange bearing against the outer springs (**7**). The inner spring case (**12**) was a sliding fit between the buffer cylinder (**13**) and outer spring case (**11**). It had a front outer flange and rear inner flange bearing against the outer springs (**7**) and inner springs (**8**) respectively. The buffer cylinder (**13**) had a front external flange bearing against the inner springs (**8**).

There were four springs in each bank, separated by manganese bronze parting plates (**9**). Each inner spring (**8**) had a left-hand pitch and normal free length of 18.58 inches. Each outer spring (**7**) had a right-hand pitch and normal free length of 19.65 inches. Any spring with a permanent set of 1.25 inches below standard length would be replaced. The spring ends were finished off to a thickness of 0.125 inch.

On firing, the gun barrel recoiled towards the rear, drawing the buffer cylinder (**13**) over the piston (**17**) and forcing the hydraulic oil rearwards through the clearance between the two. The increasing depth of the cylinder wall grooves graduated the flow in such a manner as to give the required hydraulic resistance without allowing the carriage to lift about the point of the trail.

With recoil energy absorbed, the springs (**7** and **8**) returned the barrel to the firing position.

The controlling plunger (**16**) displaced the oil in the piston rod recess (**15**) and cushioned the final movement, bringing the barrel gradually to rest.

The full working recoil was forty-nine inches.

Shield

The shield was of Boynton steel, strengthened with ash slats, made in two portions. The upper portion was bolted to a flange secured to the trail tube front end. Additional support was given by stays attached to the axletree brackets. The lower portion was hinged to the upper portion. In action it hung vertically almost to the ground. For travelling it was swung back under the trail and secured by a pawl with releasing handle and keep pin.

Shields would be tested with a service rifle bullet at a range of four hundred yards and should not be pierced, cracked or distorted.

Fitted to the shield top edge were two sighting blades. These indicated, approximately, the field covered by the traversing gear to a man standing to the traversing handspike, equal to eight degrees.

At the shield top edge rear were fittings for a Fuze Indicator Mk. II. An advance ring was fitted centrally to the shield front face.

A lifting jack could be applied, from the front of the carriage, under the outer hinges of the shield. Leather cases and fittings were provided, on the shield and axletree, for carriage of the following stores: a dial sight, field clinometer, sight clinometer, spare parts, fuze keys, shovel, aiming posts, breech and muzzle covers, oil can, fuze indicator, tool case, telescope and drag ropes.

Sights

These sights operated on the **independent line of sight** principle.

Rocking bar sight

The steel **rocking bar** (**16**) was bent downwards at its front end and pivoted, by a manganese bronze key (**14**) secured by a split pin, to a steel arm screwed into the cradle left trunnion.

A crosshead (**3**), formed on the rocking bar rear end (**16**), carried the deflection gear (**2**). Riveted to the underside of the rocking bar (**16**) was a bracket (**1**) which engaged a projection on the range gear arc bracket. Lugs, formed on the lower portion of the bracket (**1**), were mountings for the sight clinometer.

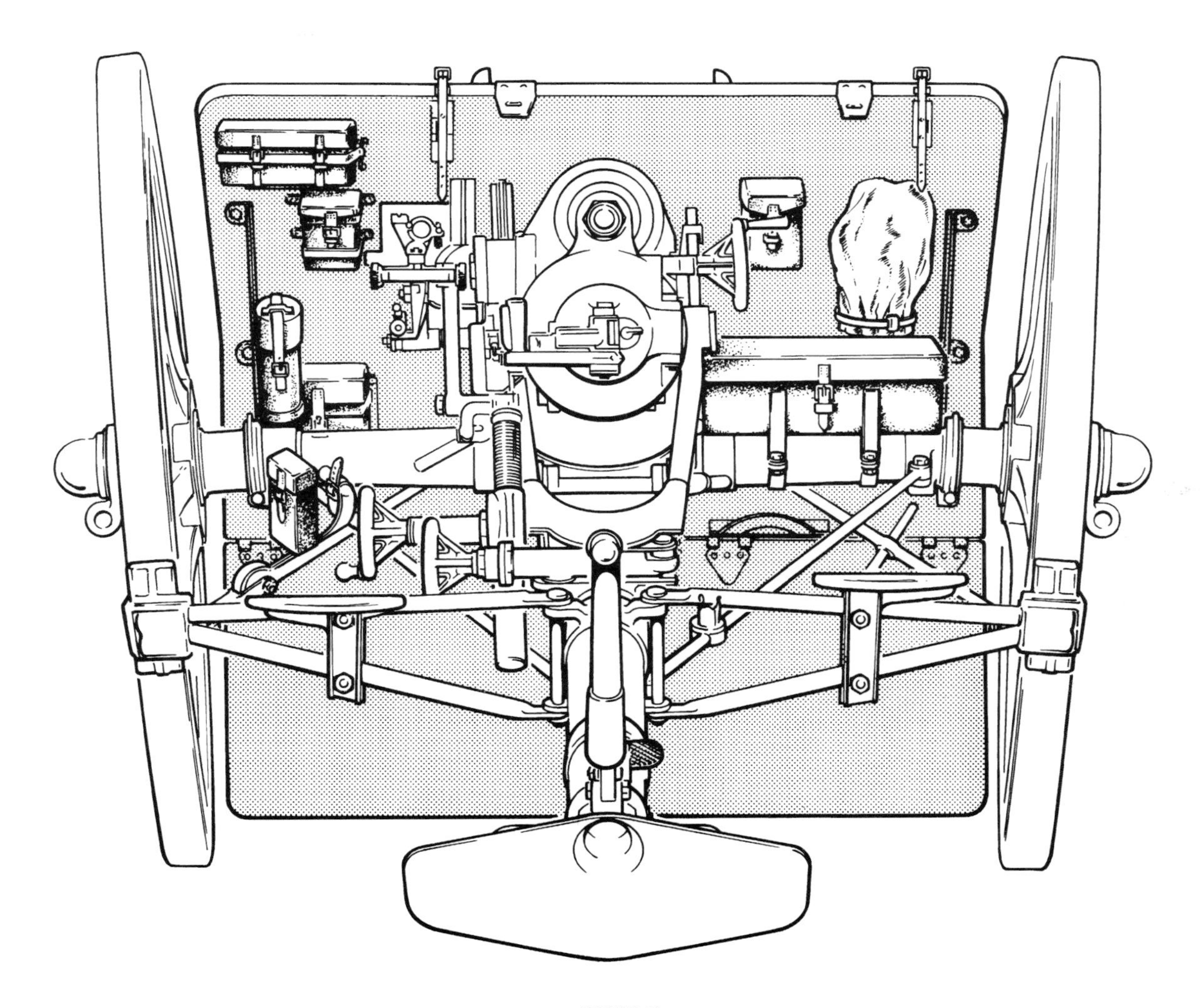

SHIELD

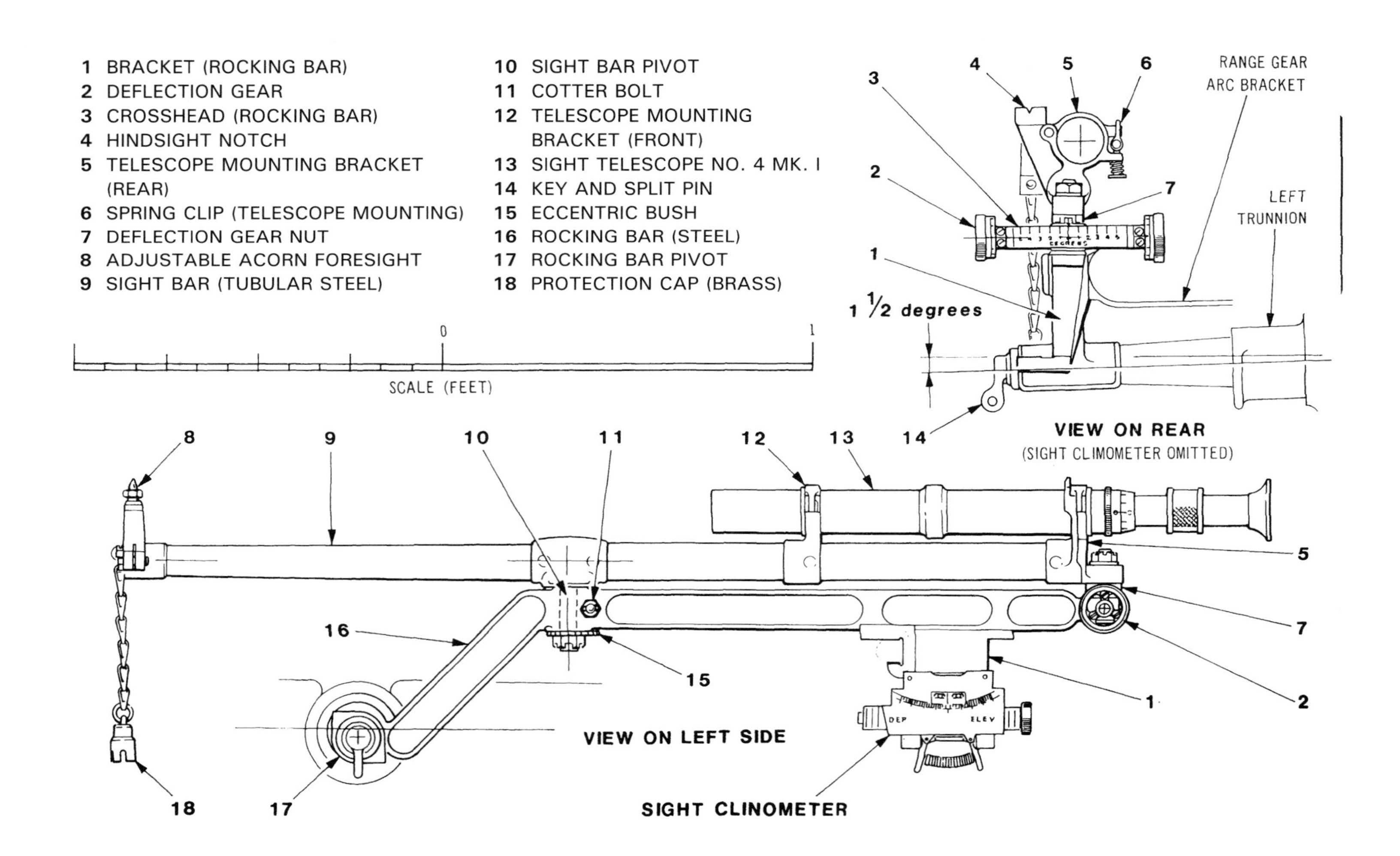

ROCKING BAR SIGHT

The rocking bar (**16**) was bored through vertically, near its front end, to house an eccentric bush (**15**). This bush received the sight bar pivot (**10**) and had its lower edge flanged and shaped to take a spanner. The bush provided horizontal adjustment.

The tubular steel **sight bar** (**9**) was pivoted to the rocking bar (**16**) and secured by a nut, with washer and split pin.

The rear telescope mounting bracket (**5**) had an elongated slot, for attachment to the deflection gear nut (**7**), and a hind sight with notch (**4**). The sight bar (**9**) carried an adjustable acorn foresight (**8**) at the front end.

The **deflection gear** (**2**) consisted of a screw, with milled heads attached at each end, supported in the rocking bar crosshead (**3**), operating a nut (**7**) with a projection on its upper side which passed through the elongated slot in the rear telescope mounting bracket (**5**) and was secured by a nut and split pin. The nut was made in two parts and contained a spiral spring, this to prevent backlash in the screw thread. Degrees were marked on a scale on the crosshead rear face (**3**) and subdivisions of five minutes on the milled heads (**2**).

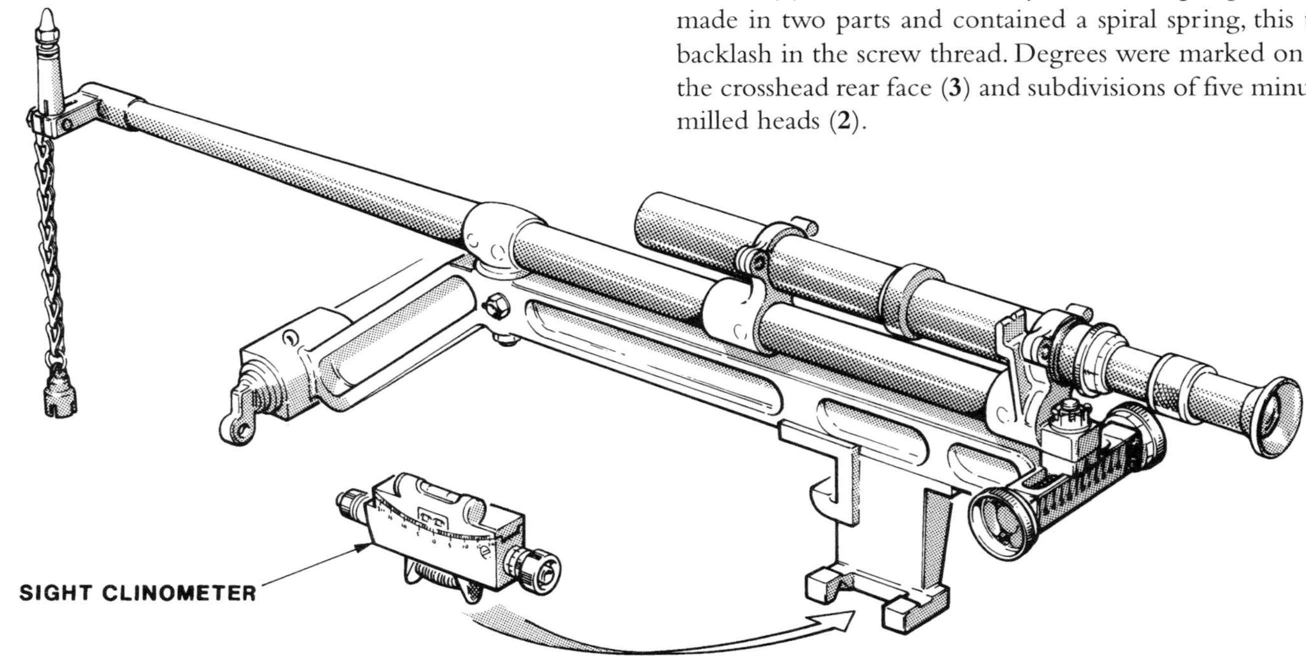

ROCKING BAR SIGHT

Later cradles had the left trunnion modified to carry a different pattern sight supporting arm, this being held in the cradle by an internal nut and split pin, the sight being secured to the supporting arm outer end by a nut and split pin.

The **telescope** No. 4 Mk. I (**13**) had two gunmetal collars which fitted into the mounting brackets (**5** and **12**), the rear collar having a projecting pin which prevented the telescope turning in the mountings. The telescope had a magnification of five and a half diameters and a five and a half degree field of view. The object glass was positioned for infinite focus (all distances over four hundred yards). The pointer was fixed in a diaphragm at the object glass focal length and was adjustable through seven settings for individual requirements. The diaphragm was centrally adjusted by eccentric rings in the object glass cell.

The telescope length was 17.25 inches overall and it weighed 2 pounds 12 ounces.

Protective leather caps were provided for the telescope ends. They were joined by a sling which was attached to the telescope body by a small strap with buckles.

Sight clinometer

The sight clinometer was used to give the angle of sight. The cradle (**26**) was secured by spring clips (**27**) to lugs on the sight rocking bar bracket (**1**) and had, on its upper face, a curved, grooved track in which slid the spirit level (**22**). The spirit level had worm teeth (**31**) on its underside which engaged the actuating worm (**23**) in the centre of the worm spindle (**30**).

The spindle (**30**) was supported by movable bearings (**21** and **24**) in the cradle (**26**).

A flat spring (**29**) kept the worm (**23**) in mesh with the spirit level worm teeth (**22**), as the pivot bearing (**24**) was so arranged that the worm (**23**) could be pulled out of engagement and the spirit level (**22**) moved by hand for rapid setting. The flat spring (**21**) would be tested by suspending a six pound weight from the front milled collar (**20**). If this disengaged the worm (**23**) from the spirit level worm teeth (**31**), the flat spring (**29**) would be renewed.

An adjustable reader (**32**) on the spirit level (**22**) read against a degree scale on the cradle (**26**) to twenty degrees either way. Micrometer heads (**20**) on either end of the worm spindle (**30**) were graduated to five minutes. The micrometer heads (**20**) were clamped by milled collars (**19**).

Dial Sight No. 7 Mk. I

The No. 7 dial sight Mk. I replaced the No. 1 dial sight originally fitted to a mounting bracket on the shield front face. Details of the No. 1 dial sight can be found on page 152.

The No. 7 dial sight Mk. I was provided for indirect laying of the gun when the target could not be seen. The eyepiece was fixed, but the top portion could be turned through 360 degrees and set to any angle ordered, the angle being that between a line to the

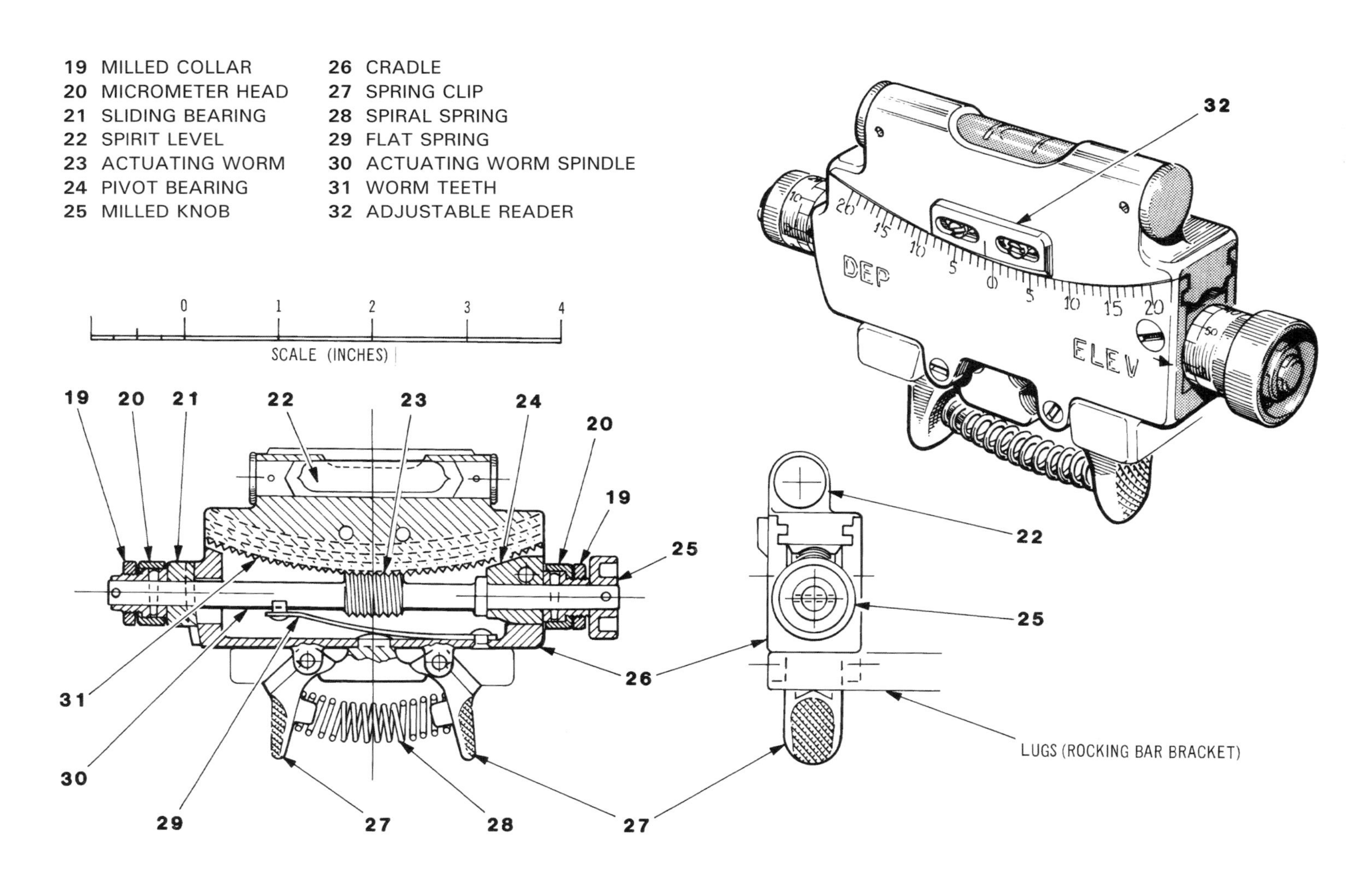

SIGHT CLINOMETER

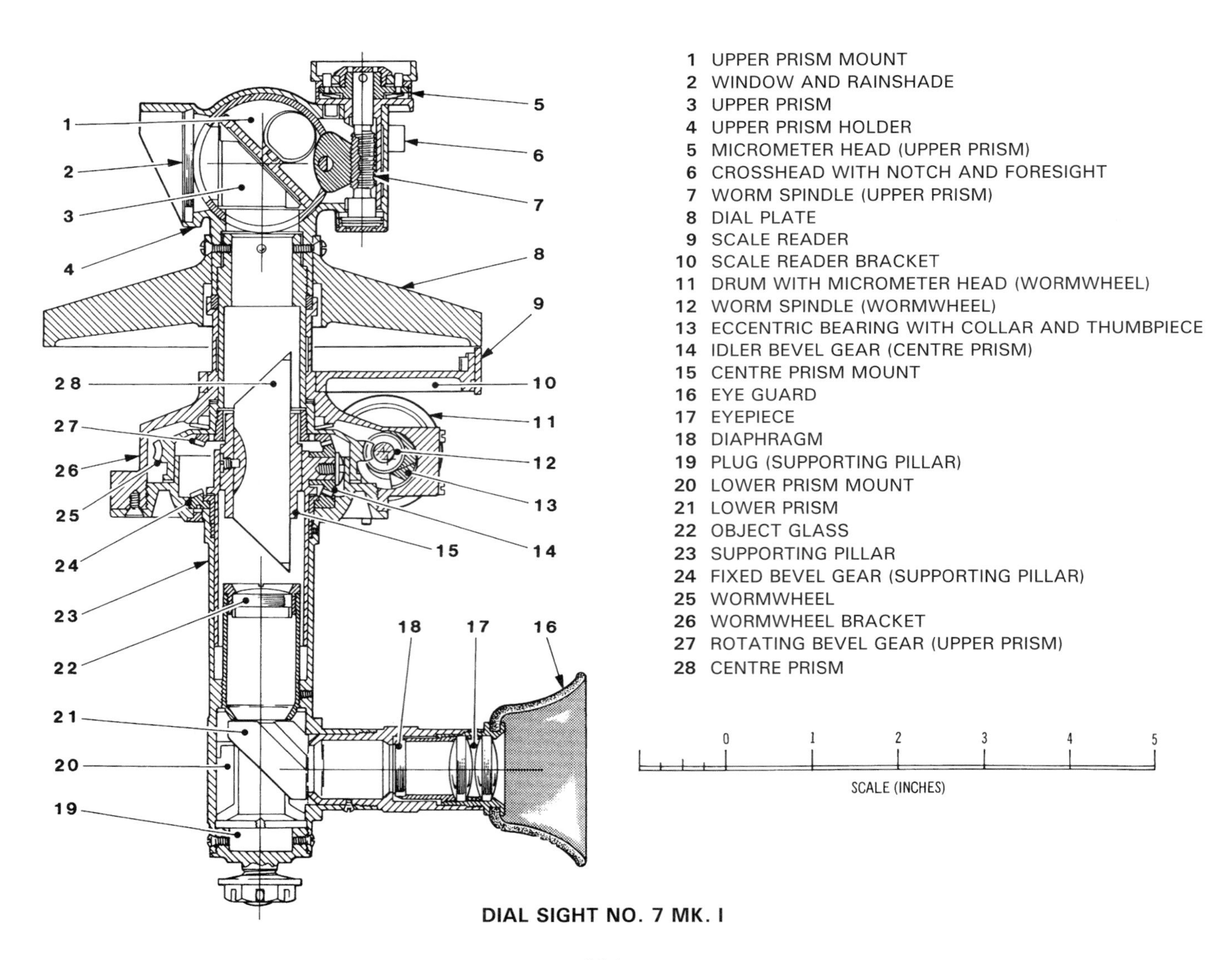

DIAL SIGHT NO. 7 MK. I

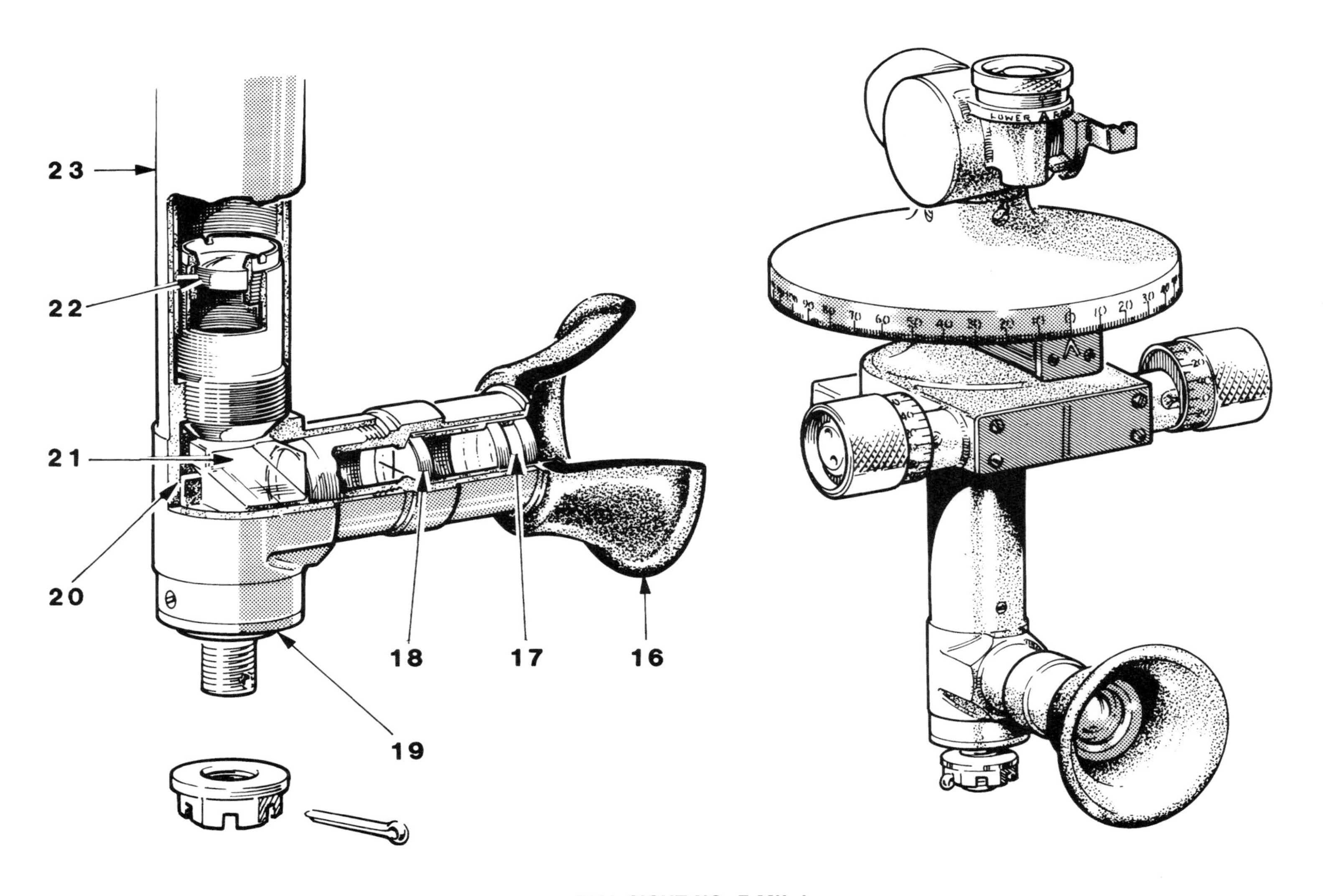

DIAL SIGHT NO. 7 MK. I

target and a line to an aiming point. The sight had a magnification of four diameters with a ten-degree field of view.

The optical combination was of an erecting type, comprising an object glass (**22**) and eyepiece (**17**) with erecting (**28**) and reflecting prisms (**3** and **21**). A diaphragm (**18**) in the horizontal section of the sight had cross lines marked on it. In order to keep the image constantly erect, the centre prism (**28**) revolved at half the rate of the upper prism (**3**), this being controlled by the internal bevel gearing (**14**, **24** and **27**).

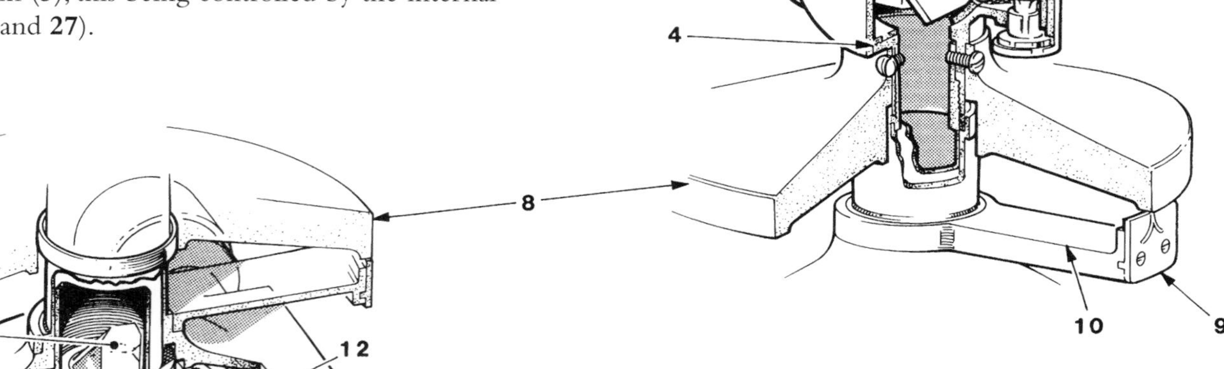

DIAL SIGHT NO. 7 MK. I

Rotation of the upper prism holder (**4**) was controlled by the worm spindle (**12**) and wormwheel (**25**). The worm spindle (**12**) was housed in an eccentric bearing (**13**) fitted with an actuating collar and thumbpiece. Moving the thumbpiece upwards disengaged the worm spindle (**12**) from the wormwheel (**25**) allowing the dial plate (**8**) to be moved rapidly to any required setting of whole degrees. At each end of the worm spindle (**12**) was a drum (**11**) graduated in divisions of ten minutes, each complete revolution of the drum representing a five-degree movement of the dial plate (**8**). The right-hand drum markings were in white on a black ground, the left-hand drum markings were in black on brass.

Attached to the wormwheel (**25**) were the dial plate (**8**) and upper prism holder (**4**).The dial plate was graduated to read from 0 to 180 degrees 'Right' (white markings on a black ground) and 'Left' (black markings on brass).

The upper prism holder (**4**) had a crosshead (**6**), with notch and foresight for rough laying, pivoted to it.

The upper prism (**3**) and crosshead (**6**) had vertical adjustment of fifteen degrees elevation and depression controlled by a worm spindle (**7**) with micrometer head (**5**).The micrometer head had a graduated drum engraved in divisions of ten minutes. Each revolution of the worm spindle (**7**) indicated a five-degree elevation or depression on the crosshead (**6**). Below the crosshead (**6**) was a scale with five-degree graduations read by an arrow on the prism holder (**4**). Indicating arrows and the words 'higher' and 'lower' on the worm spindle bearing showed the direction of turn for the micrometer head to effect the vertical line of sight, up or down.

For carriage purposes, a holder and waterproof cover were provided for the No. 7 dial sight and the No. 2 carrier on the inside of the shield.

Dial Sight No. 7 Mk. II

The Mk. II sight had only a zero and index marks on the crosshead (**6**) and micrometer head (**5**).The wormwheel (**25**) and worm spindle bearings (**12**) were of manganese bronze instead of steel. Springs and spring washers were nickel plated.

Barrel and breech

Barrel construction

The steel A tube had successive layers of steel wire wound around it surrounding the chamber and a portion of the bore.

An outer steel jacket was shrunk on over the wire and A tube, being secured longitudinally by internal shoulders and a breech ring screwed over the jacket rear end. The breech ring was machined for the reception of the breech mechanism and secured by a set screw.

Longitudinal projections, or wings, along both sides of the jacket, formed the sliding mountings which were engaged by the guide grooves of the cradle. The chamber was slightly coned throughout its length to facilitate cartridge case extraction.

The total barrel length was 96.96 inches, of which the bore, of 3.3 inches diameter, took up 92.62 inches from the breech screw face.

The bore was rifled, for a length of 80.232 inches, with eighteen grooves of polygroove, modified plain section, 0.04 inch deep x 0.384 inch wide. The rifling was a right-hand uniform twist, one turn in thirty calibres (99 inches).

The breech ring had a lug, on the top surface, to which attached the hydraulic buffer cylinder rear end. A surface for a clinometer was machined on the breech ring upper surface. An axis line was cut at the breech right-hand side. Horizontal lines were cut on

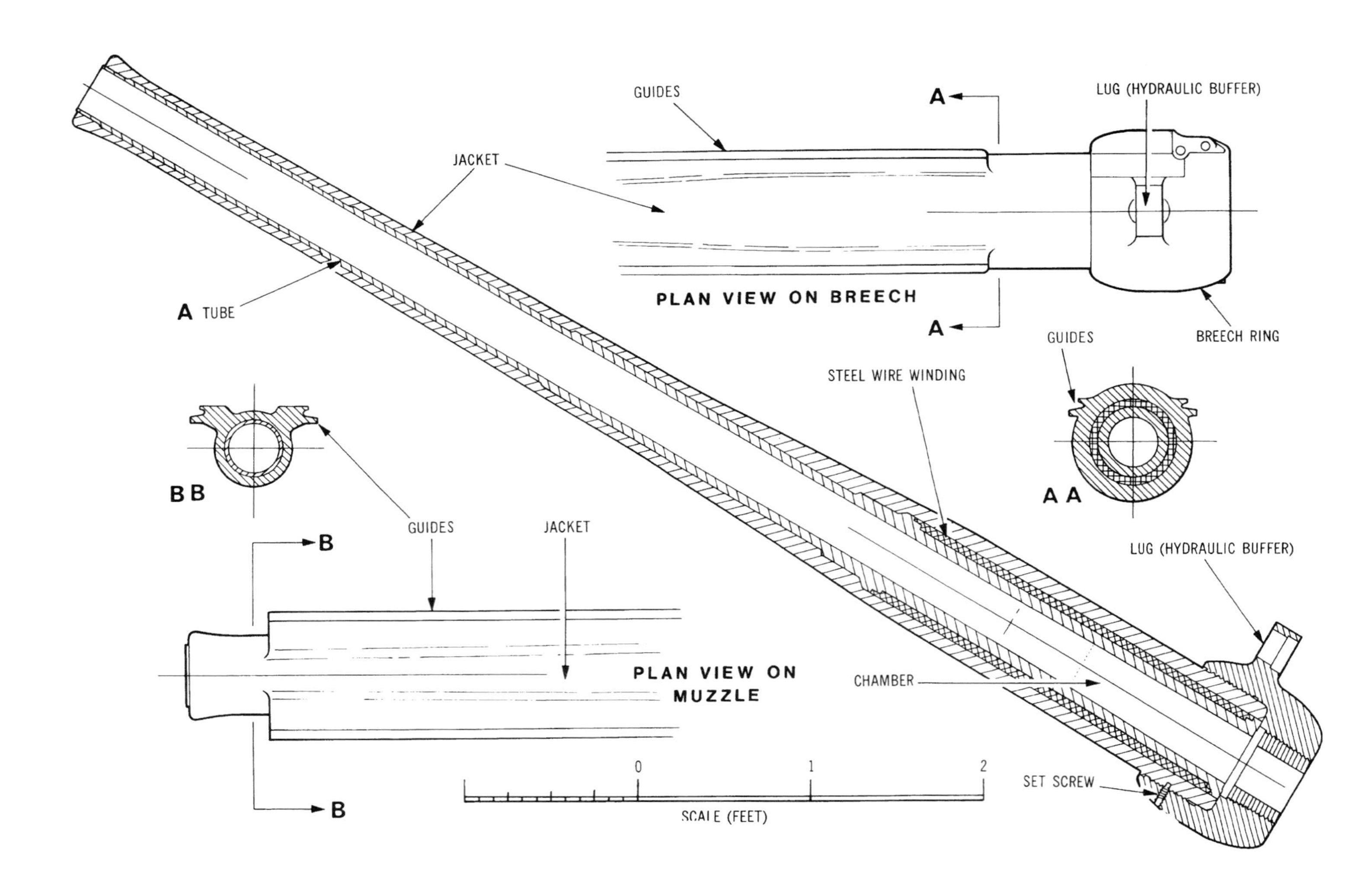

BARREL CONSTRUCTION

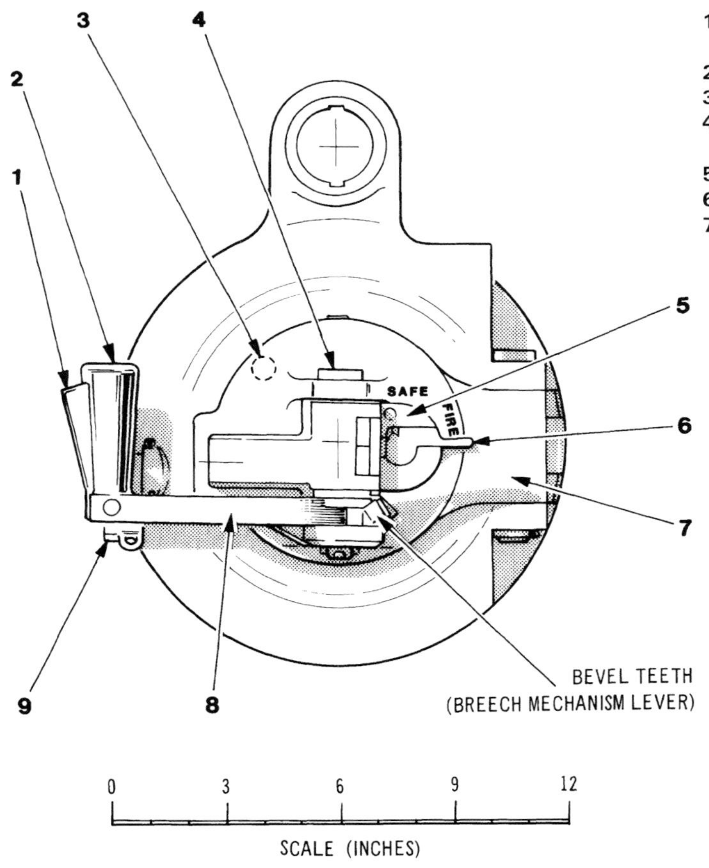

1 BREECH MECHANISM LEVER RELEASE CATCH
2 HANDLE
3 BREECH SCREW RETAINING CATCH
4 BREECH MECHANISM LEVER HINGE BOLT
5 STRIKER GUIDE BLOCK
6 SAFETY CATCH
7 CARRIER
8 BREECH MECHANISM LEVER
9 TRIGGER
10 BREECH SCREW
11 STRIKER (FIRING MECHANISM)
12 EXTRACTOR
13 FIRING HOLE BUSH
14 FIRING LEVER
15 EXTRACTOR HINGE BOLT
16 CARRIER HINGE BOLT

BREECH

the breech face and vertical and horizontal lines were cut on the muzzle face.

Barrel weight, with breech fittings, was 9cwt (1,008 pounds).

The Mk. I gun barrel described above, when repaired by renewal of the A tube, became a Mk. I★ barrel. The repair consisted of fitting a new A tube and wire winding into an existing jacket, the A tube exterior and wire winding being slightly tapered, the jacket bore being coned to suit. The operation was performed using hydraulic pressure.

Mk. II barrels were manufactured as above, but with the use of a new jacket.

Breech

The breech mechanism was of the **single motion** type, so arranged that one pull on the handle (**2**) unlocked the breech and swung the breech screw (**10**) and carrier (**7**) into the loading position. After loading, one thrust on the handle (**2**) inserted the

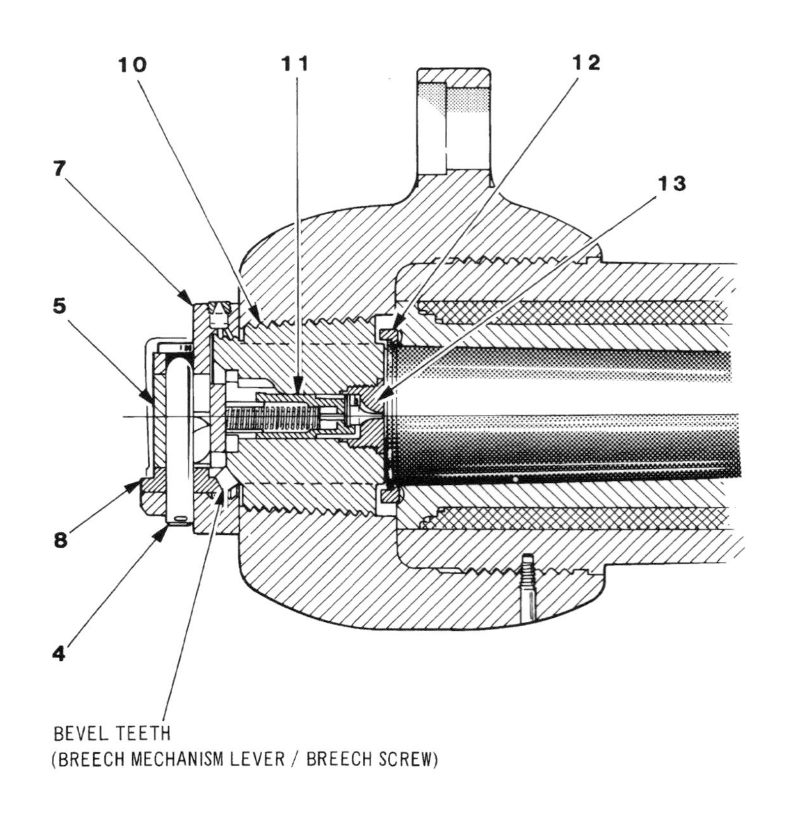

VERTICAL SECTION

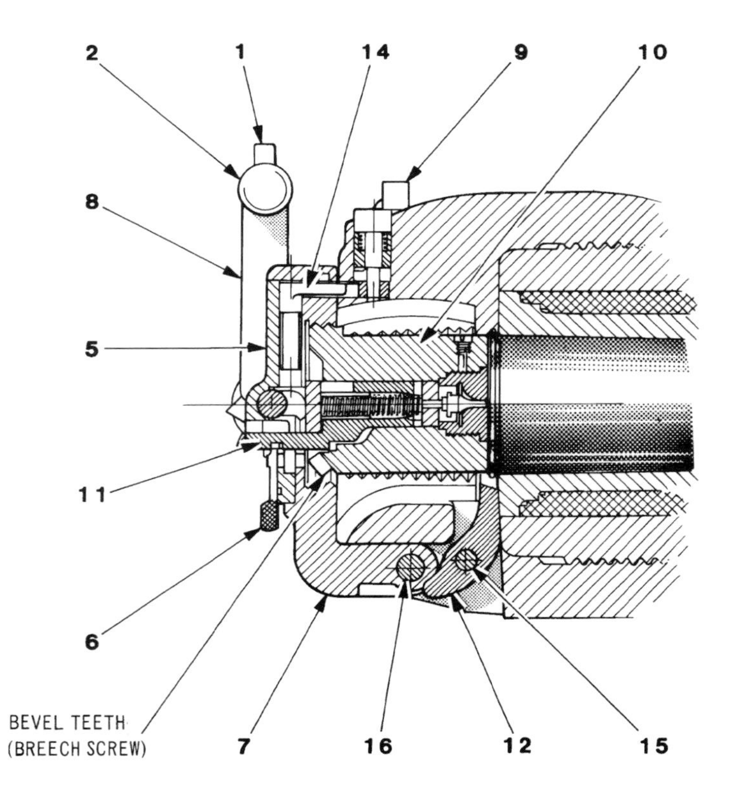

HORIZONTAL SECTION

BREECH

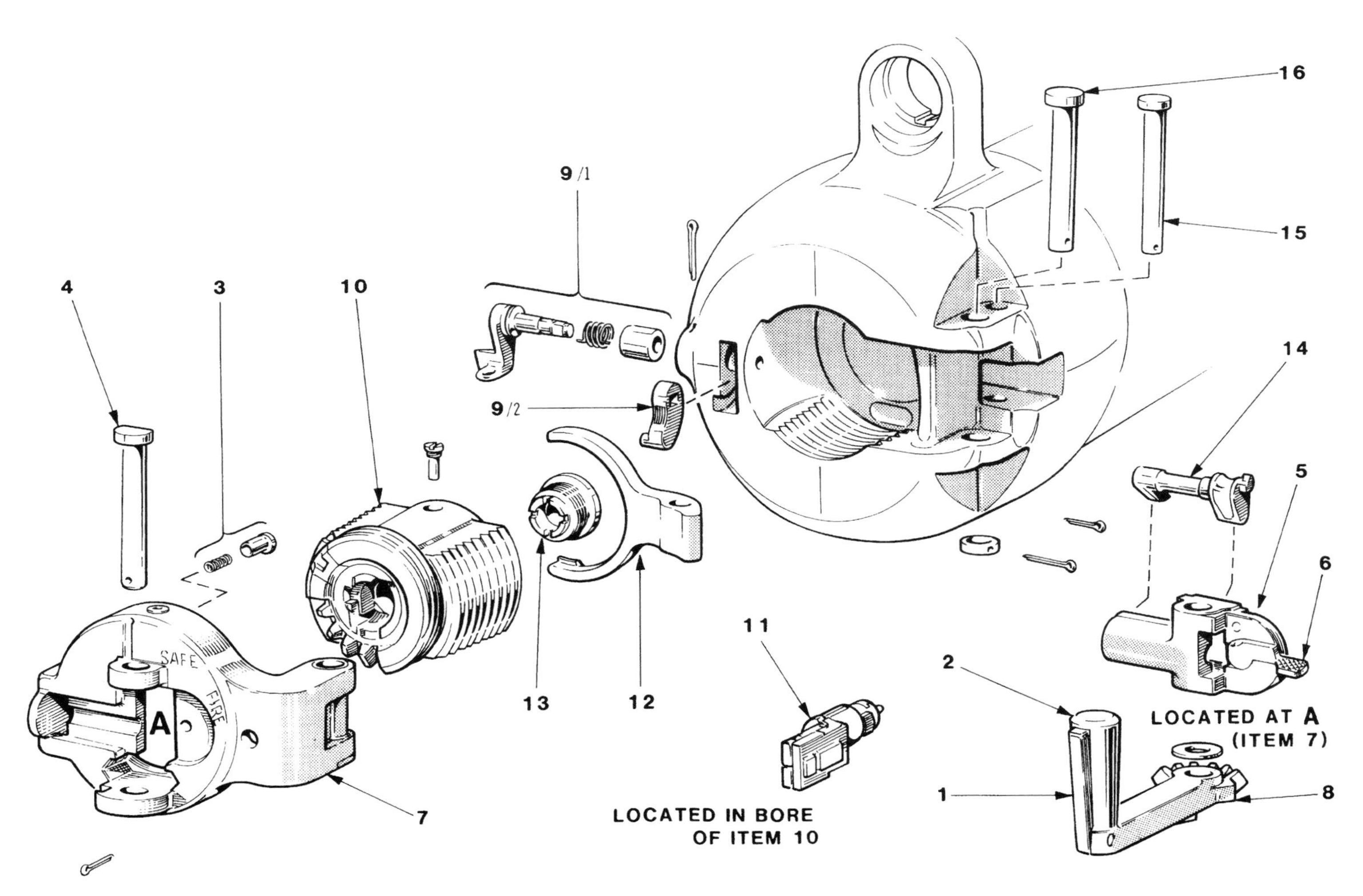

BREECH COMPONENTS

breech screw (**10**) into the breech opening and turned it into the locked position.

The breech screw (**10**) tapered towards the rear and had opposite sides machined away, allowing the screw to lock or unlock with one quarter of a turn. Bevel teeth on the rear of the breech screw (**10**) were engaged by bevel teeth on the breech mechanism lever (**8**), the lever being hinged to the carrier rear face (**7**).

The breech screw (**10**) was secured in the carrier (**7**) by a left-hand screw thread. Housed in the carrier rear face (**7**) was the striker guide block (**5**) containing the firing mechanism (**11**).

Firing mechanism operation (see page 263)

VIEW A This shows the firing mechanism at rest with the breech screw closed and locked. Note that the firing pin was withdrawn and not projecting from the breech screw front face.

VIEW B Pulling on the firing handle rotated the trigger (**9/1**) on its spindle, causing the lever (**9/2**), housed within the barrel breech rear face, to rotate the firing lever spindle and cam (**14**) mounted within the striker guide block (**5**). Clockwise rotation of the firing lever spindle and cam (**14**) caused the cam lower portion to push the main-spring guide forward, while the projection on the cam upper portion engaged the tripping piece, this drawing the tripping piece with the striker to the rear, compressing the main-spring.

VIEW C Clockwise rotation of the firing lever spindle and cam (**14**) continued until the cam upper projection slipped past the tripping piece, this releasing the striker to be thrown forward under the pressure of the main-spring. Near the end of the striker travel, the rebound block stopped against a face machined within the breech screw bore, the striker body continuing to travel forward, the firing pin emerging from the breech screw front face to strike and detonate the cartridge percussion cap.

VIEW D Forward return movement of the firing handle allowed the firing lever spindle and cam to rotate counter-clockwise, allowing main-spring pressure to push the main-spring guide rearwards, the final movement pushing the striker body rearwards, this withdrawing the firing pin within the breech block front face. The cam upper projection rotated past the tripping piece, the tripping piece spring returning the tripping piece to the position shown in VIEW A.

The configuration of the breech screw rear face ensured that the main-spring guide could not move forward until the breech screw was fully turned into the closed position.

Fuze indicators

Fuze Indicator Mk. I (see page 267)

The range ring (**6**) was graduated on its outer edge in hundreds of yards, subdivided to read 50s. A portion of the inner edge was graduated from 0 to 300 to form a corrector scale. The fuze setting disc (**7**) was graduated on its outer edge from 2 to 22, these numbers representing the fuze divisions, each division being

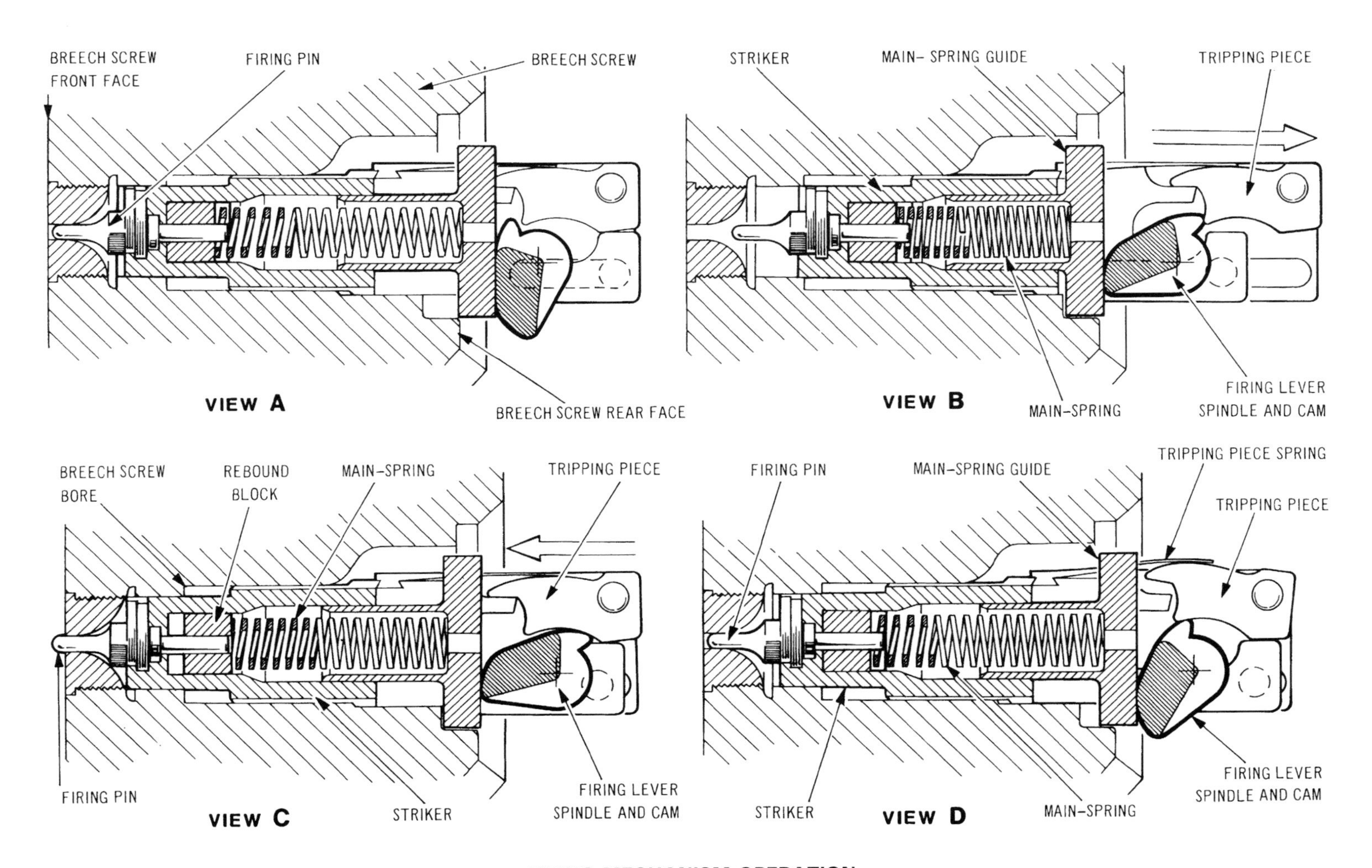

FIRING MECHANISM OPERATION

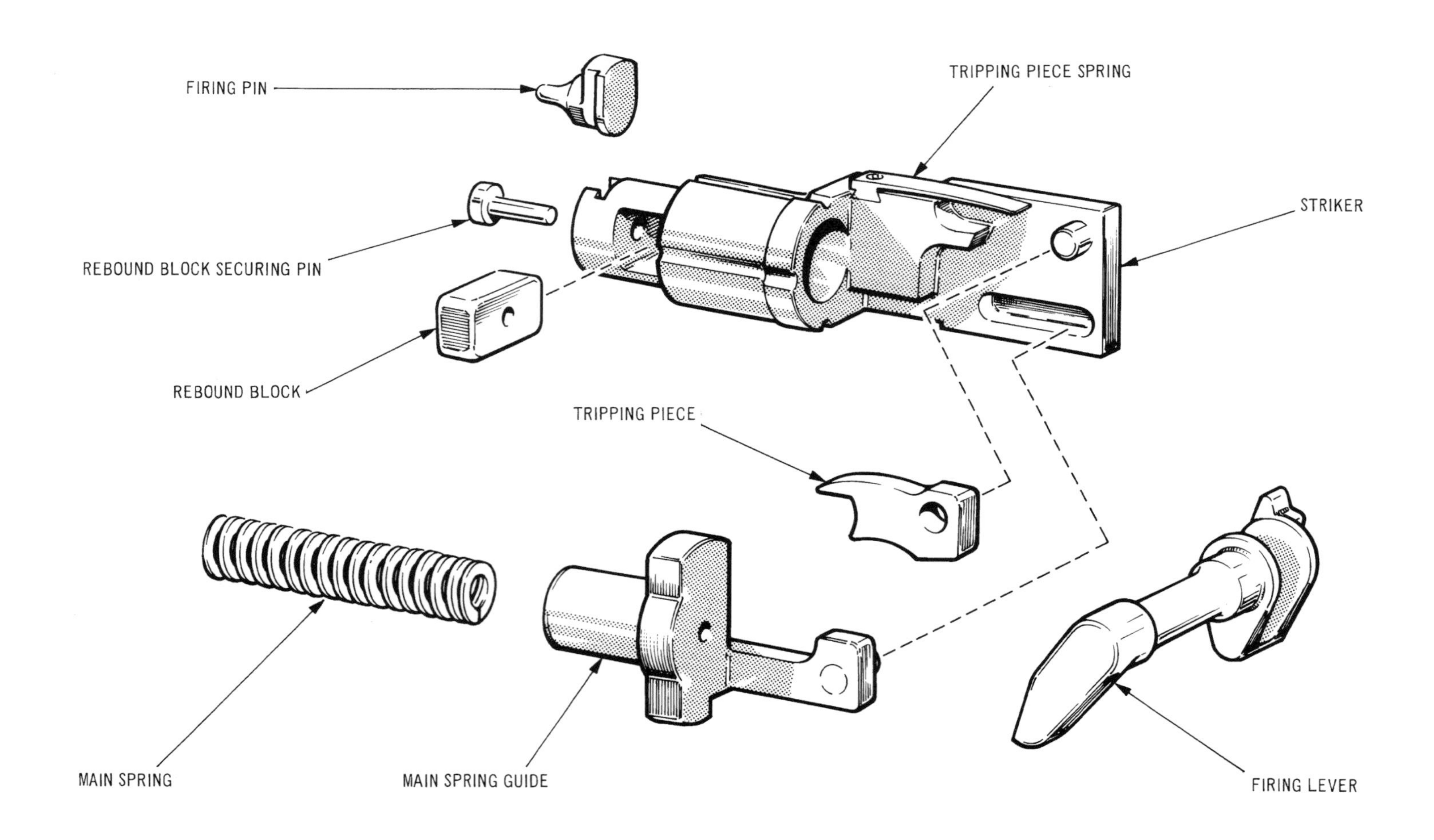

FIRING MECHANISM COMPONENTS

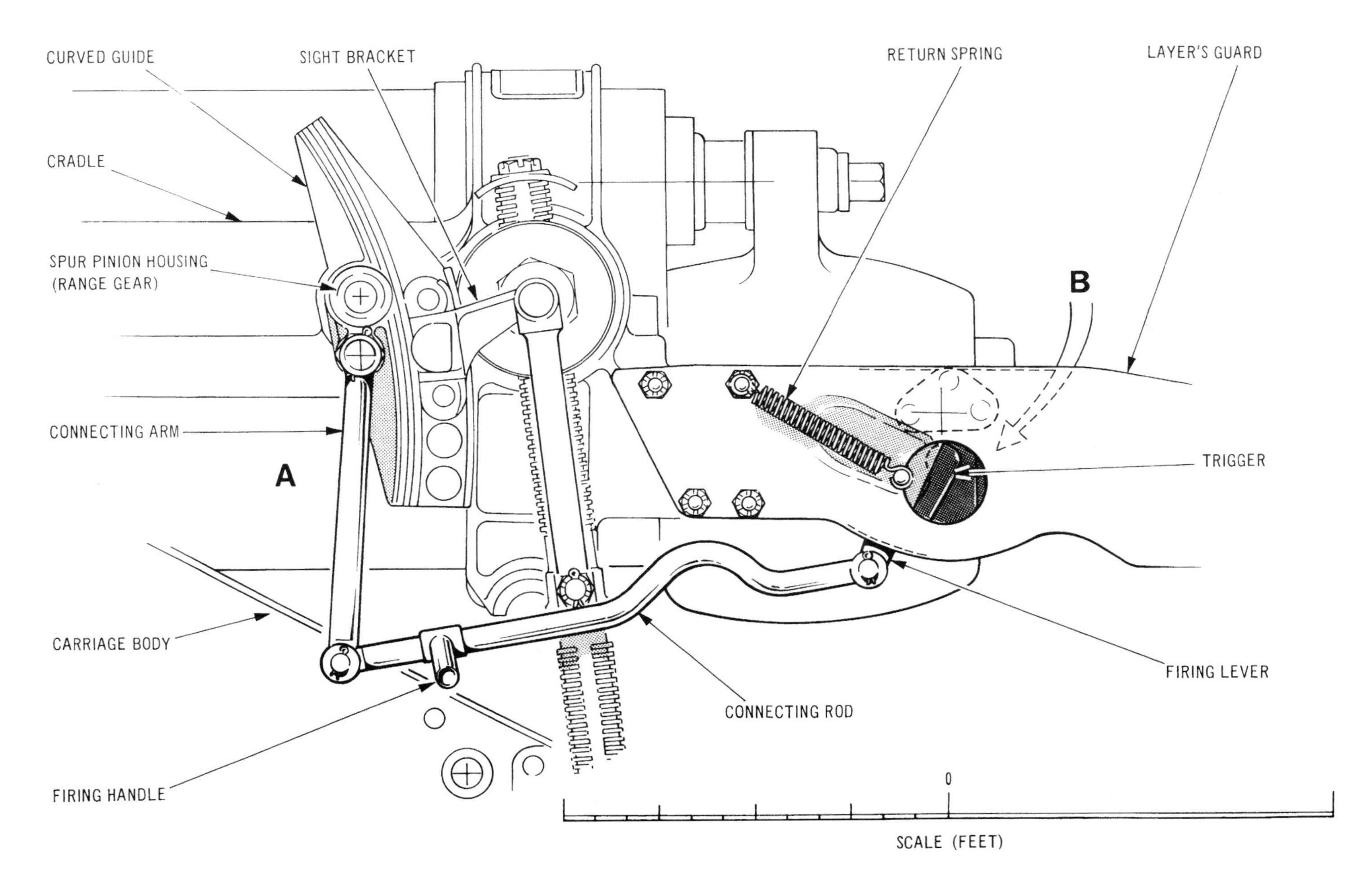

CURVED GUIDE
SIGHT BRACKET
RETURN SPRING
LAYER'S GUARD
CRADLE
SPUR PINION HOUSING
(RANGE GEAR)
B
CONNECTING ARM
A
TRIGGER
CARRIAGE BODY
FIRING LEVER
CONNECTING ROD
FIRING HANDLE
0
SCALE (FEET)

FIRING GEAR

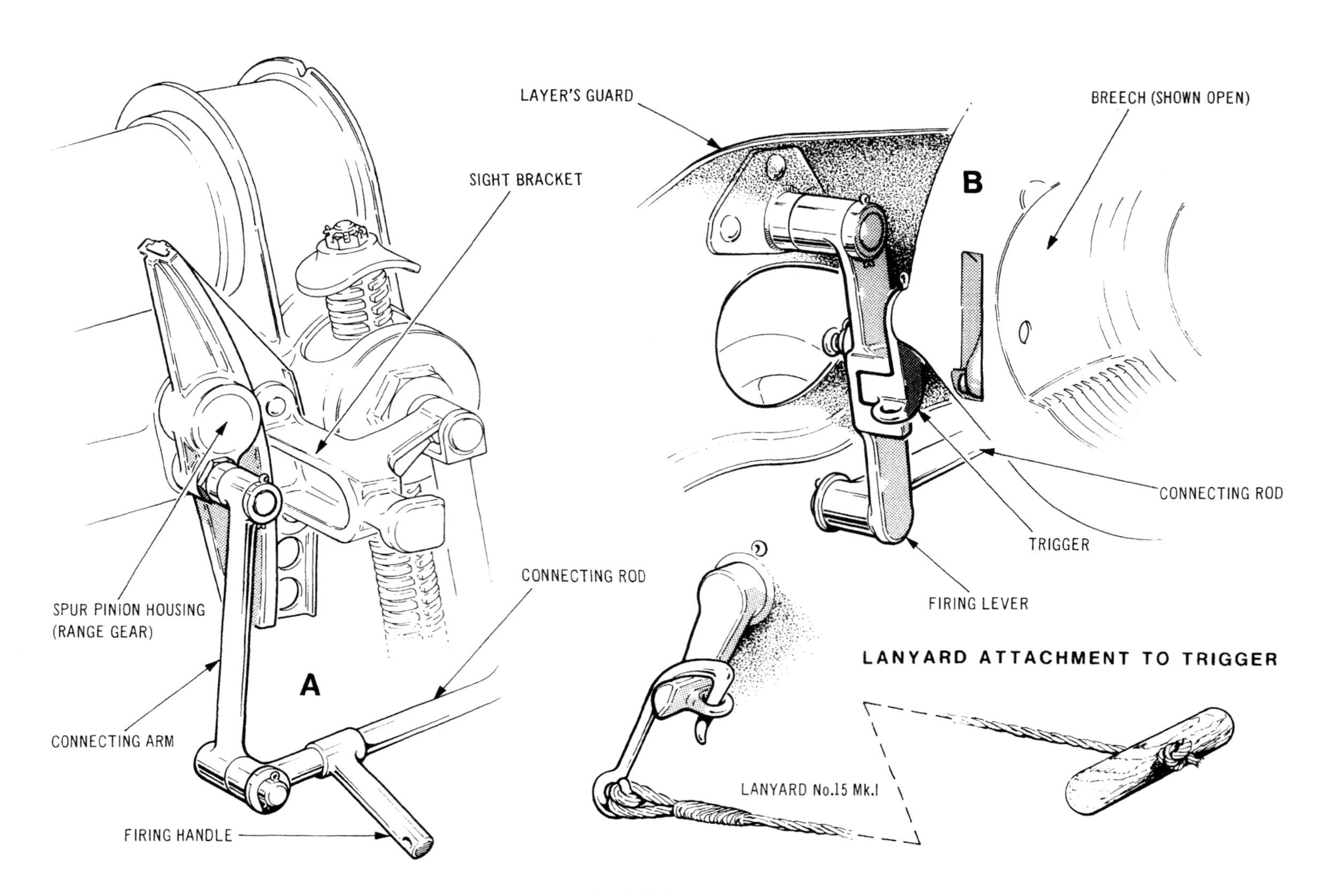
LAYER'S GUARD
BREECH (SHOWN OPEN)
SIGHT BRACKET
B
CONNECTING ROD
TRIGGER
CONNECTING ROD
FIRING LEVER
SPUR PINION HOUSING
(RANGE GEAR)
A
LANYARD ATTACHMENT TO TRIGGER
CONNECTING ARM
LANYARD No.15 Mk.I
FIRING HANDLE

FIRING GEAR

subdivided to give settings of 0.1. An arrow head on the setting disc (**7**) coinciding with an arrow head on the range ring (**6**) indicated the normal setting position. The arrow heads were filled with red wax. A hinged pointer (**2**), when set to the required range, indicated the fuze setting to 'point of burst'. A disc spring minimised involuntary movement of the range ring (**6**).

To use the corrector scale, the adjusting nut (**10**) would be turned to move the setting disc (**7**) position relative to the range ring (**6**), the setting being maintained by tightening the jamming screw (**14**).

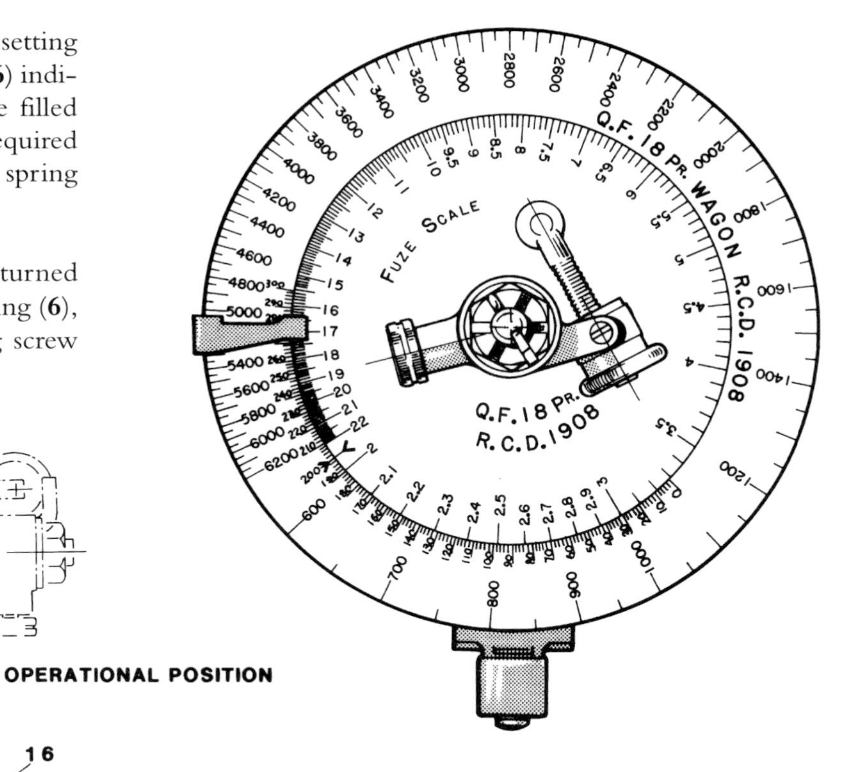

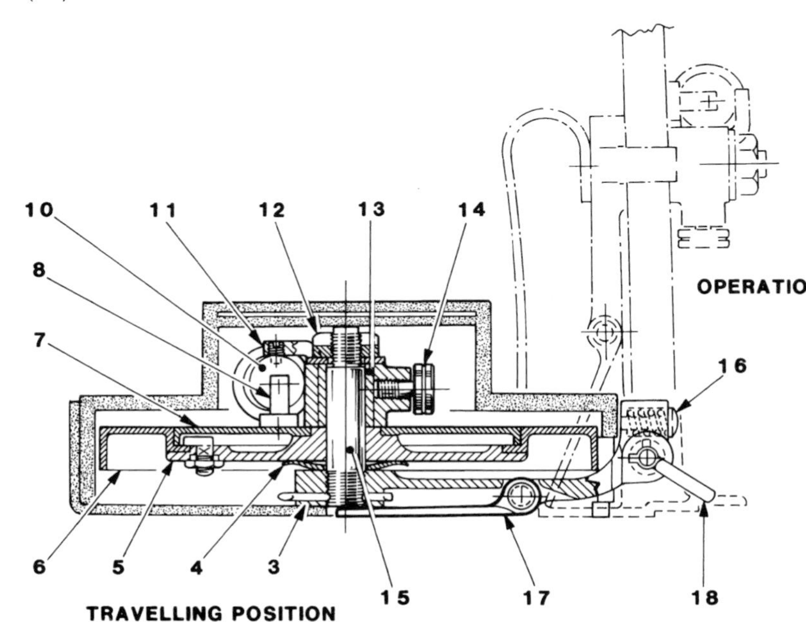

TRAVELLING POSITION

FUZE INDICATOR MK. I

In use, the indicator was supported upright by the hinge plate (**17**) working in opposition to the spring stud (**16**). When not in use the indicator was laid horizontal and protected by a leather cover secured by a strap (**1**).

The fuze indicator was a separate store and not a component of the carriage, limber or ammunition wagon. It was not carried on the carriage during travelling.

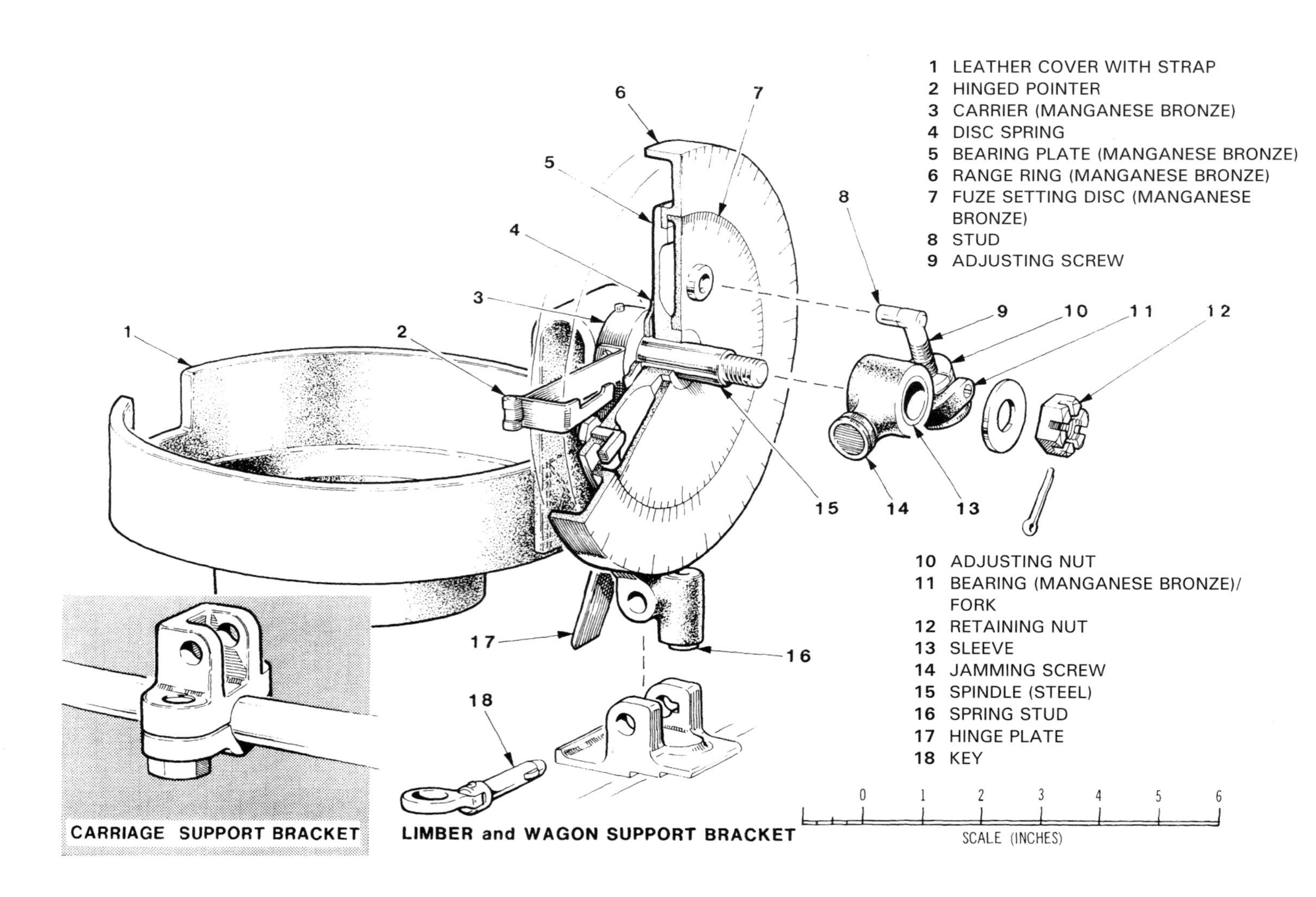

FUZE INDICATOR MK. I

Fuze Indicator Mk. II (see page 270)

Handbooks of 1911 quote Fuze Indicators either Mk. I or Mk. II as being fitted. By 1913 the Mk. II had completely replaced the Mk. I.

The grooved base plate was graduated on the upper portion with a range scale reading from 1600 to 6200 yards and on the lower portion with a corrector scale graduated from 0 to 200.

The slide, which fitted into the base plate central groove, was graduated with a fuze scale numbering from 4.5 to 22, these numbers corresponding with the graduations on a Time and Percussion Fuze No. 80. An arrow, engraved on the slide lower edge, coinciding with No. 150 on the corrector scale, indicated the normal setting position. The slide could be clamped in any required position by use of the clamping handle. The range and fuze scales were read by the sliding reader. The reader movement could be dampened by adjustment of the top screw tensioning the friction spring.

The fuze indicator was suspended by two hooks, attached to the rear face of the base plate, being steadied by the two base plate studs. Two indicators were carried per sub-section, one on the gun carriage shield and one on the rear of an ammunition wagon.

Fuzes

Percussion and Time Fuze No. 80 Mk. IV

The fuze major components were of aluminium unless otherwise stated in the key on page 271.

The body (**11**) lower portion was threaded to house the percussion fuze holder (**18**); the body upper portion forming a stem containing the time fuze pellet (**9**) and stirrup spring (**10**). The body base was fitted with a brass ring (**15**), the upper part of which was graduated from 0 to 22, the graduations being subdivided into 10 divisions. A square notch was cut into the ring for the Fixing Key No. 17 Mk. II. An engraved cross indicated the safety point.

The leather washer (**16**) to fit between fuze and shell was soaked in mineral jelly.

The bottom time ring (**14**) had a projecting pin to engage the Setting Key No. 18. A setting mark was cut on the ring. The percussion fuze holder (**18**) held the needles (**3**) for both time and percussion detonators.

The brass fuze cover (**22**) was held in place by a tearing off strip (**20**) soldered to both the cover (**22**) and lower edge of the graduated ring (**15**). To remove the fuze cover (**22**), the ring was released from the securing strip (**21**) and pulled to tear off the strip (**20**), when the cover (**22**) would fall off and expose the fuze.

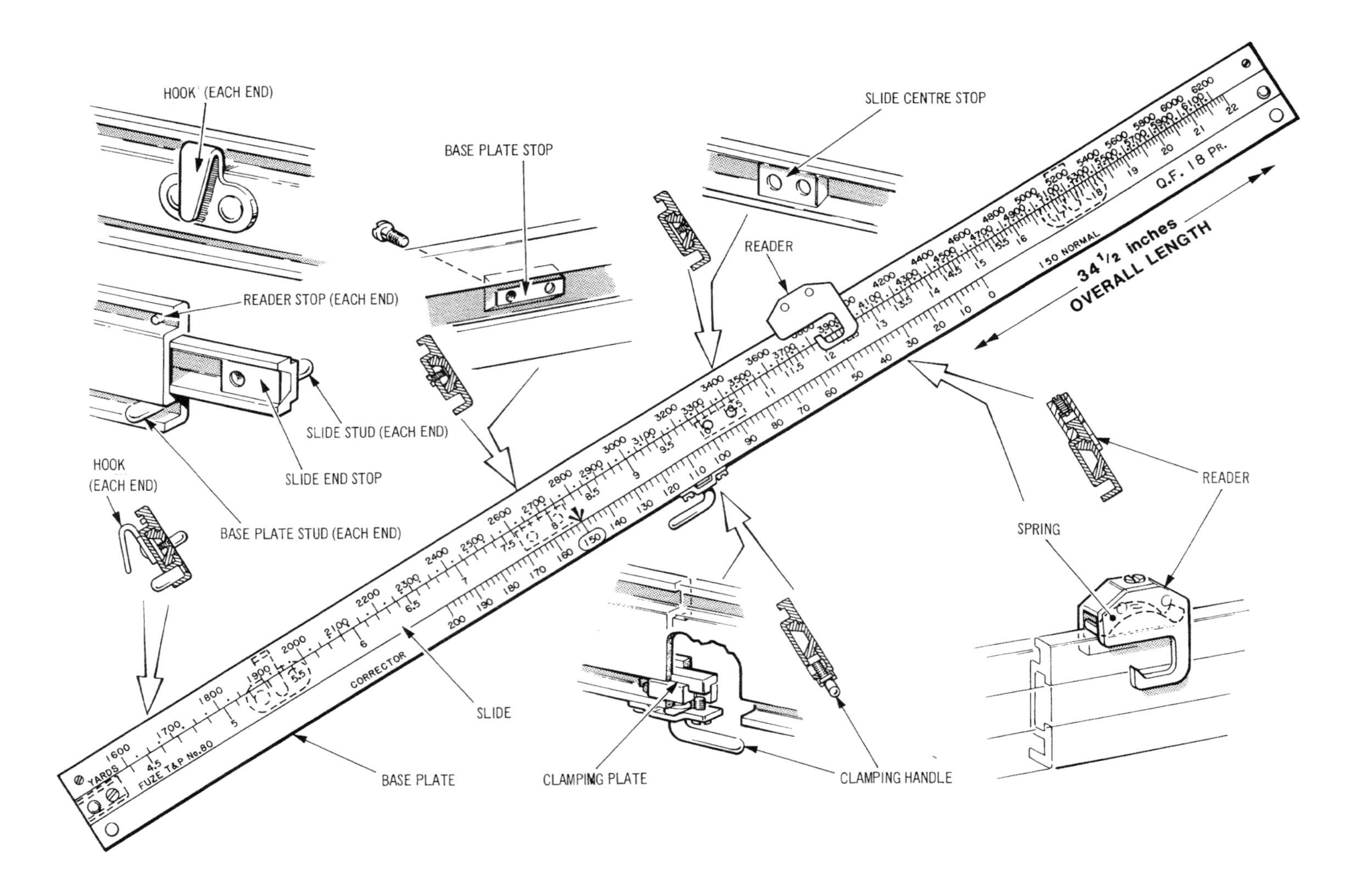

FUZE INDICATOR MK. II

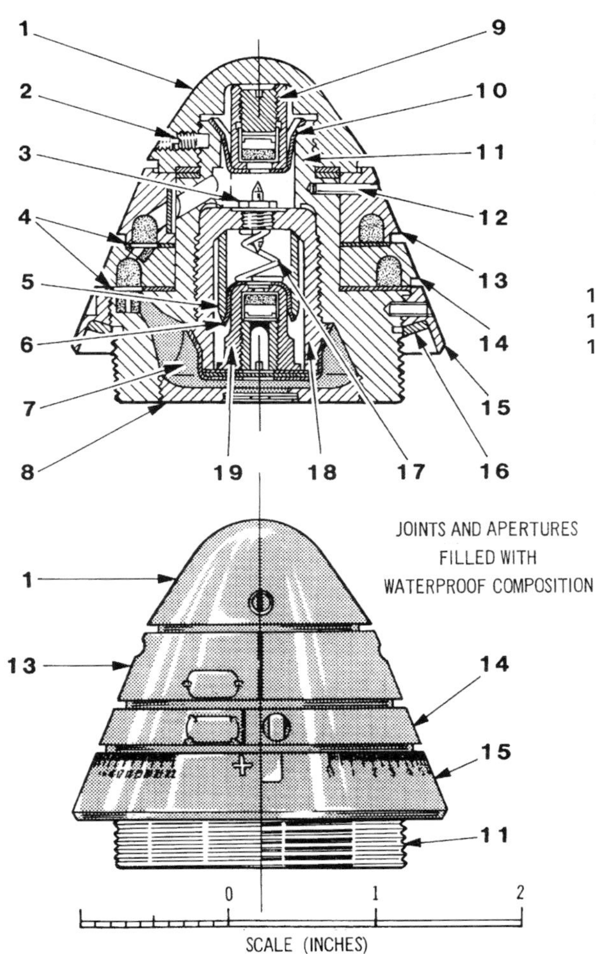

PERCUSSION AND TIME FUZE NO. 80 MK. IV

1 CAP
2 SET SCREW (CAP)
3 NEEDLES
4 WASHERS (WATERPROOF CLOTH)
5 FERRULE
6 STIRRUP SPRING (PERCUSSION FUZE)
7 POWDER MAGAZINE
8 BASE PLUG
9 TIME FUZE PELLET
10 STIRRUP SPRING (TIME FUZE)
11 BODY
12 PIN (2)
13 TOP COMPOSITION (TIME) RING
14 BOTTOM COMPOSITION (TIME) RING
15 GRADUATED RING (BRASS)
16 WASHER (LEATHER)
17 SPIRAL SPRING
18 PERCUSSION FUZE HOLDER
19 PERCUSSION DETONATOR PELLET
20 TEARING OFF STRIP
21 RING SECURING STRIP
22 CAP (BRASS)
23 RING

To set the fuze, the bottom time ring (**14**) would be turned to position the setting line opposite the required mark on the graduated ring (**15**).

The weight of the fuze was 10.25 ounces.

Time fuze operation (see page 273)

The time fuze was set by turning the bottom time ring until the setting line coincided with the required mark on the graduated ring (**A**).

On discharge, inertia caused the time fuze pellet to move rearwards (**B**), straightening the clips of the stirrup spring, allowing the detonator housed within the pellet to strike the forward facing needle (**C**).

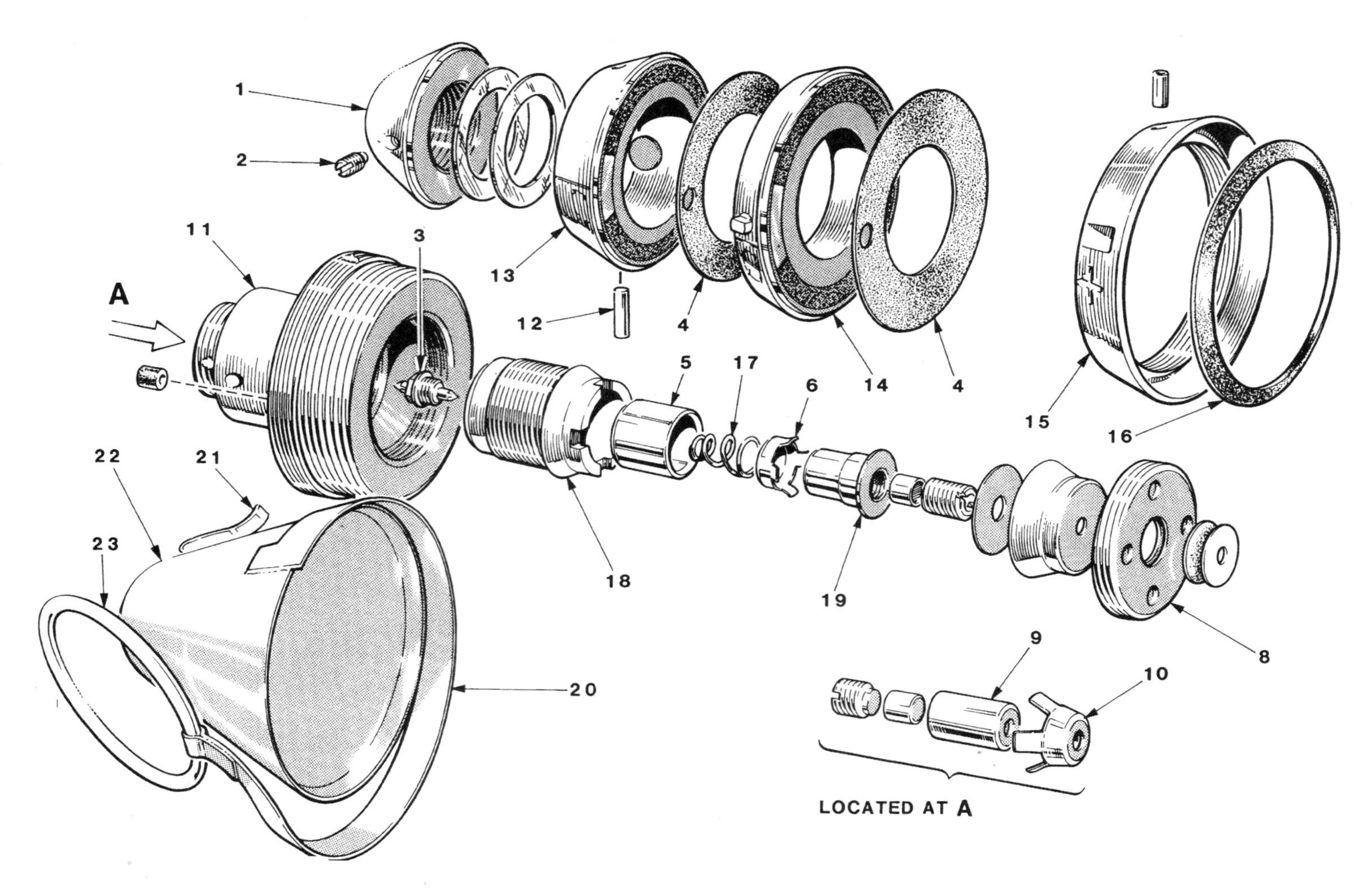

PERCUSSION AND TIME FUZE NO. 80 MK. IV

Ignition of the detonator composition fired through and ignited the composition of the top ring (**D**) which burned around and in turn ignited the composition of the bottom ring (**E**). This burned around until the flame passed through the channel (**F**) and ignited the charge contained in the powder magazine (**G**), this firing through the fuze base plug into the shell bursting charge.

The fuze, on full setting and at rest, would burn for 22 seconds.

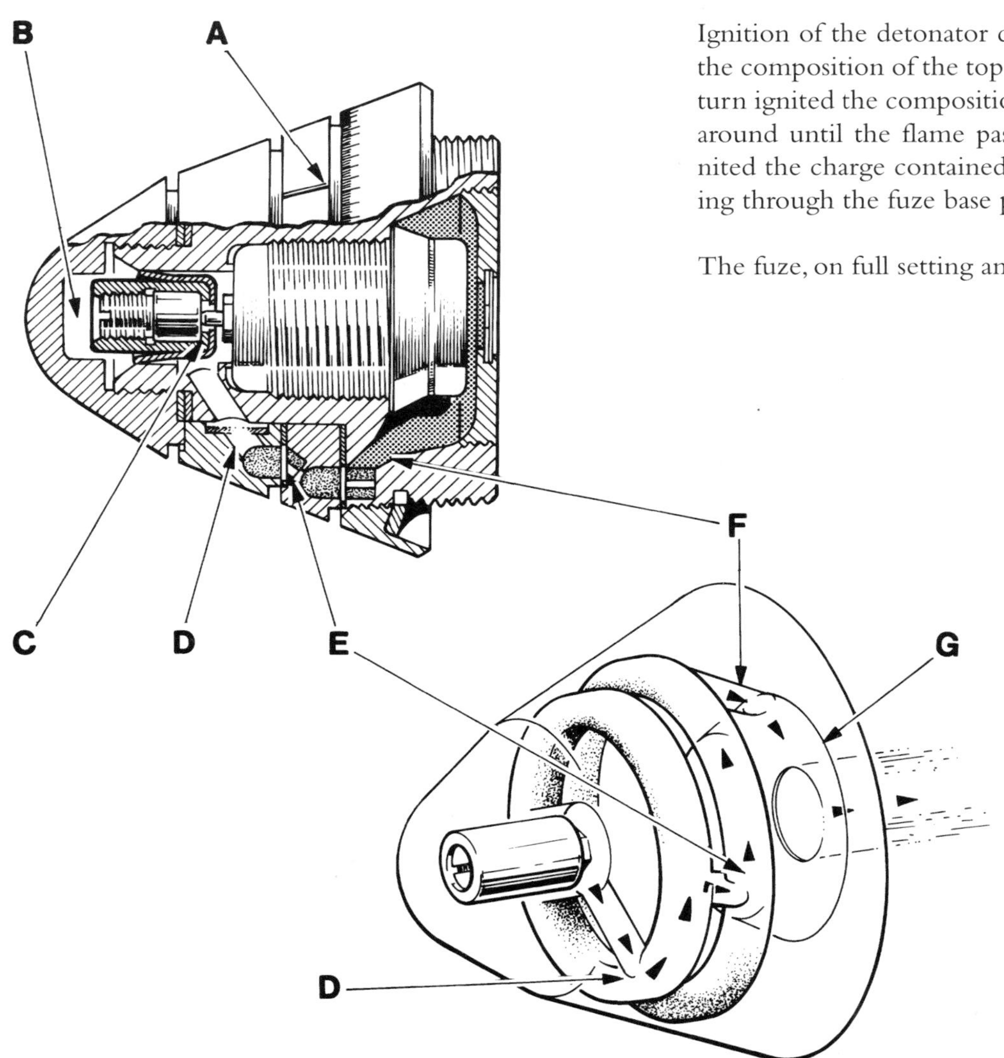

TIME FUZE OPERATION

Percussion fuze operation

On discharge, inertia caused the ferrule to move rearwards over the detonator pellet (**A**) straightening the clips of the stirrup spring.

On impact, the ferrule and detonator pellet moved forwards (**B**), compressing the light spiral spring and allowing the detonator housed within the pellet to strike the rearward facing needle (**C**).

Ignition of the detonator composition fired through into the charge contained in the powder magazine (**D**), this firing through the fuze base plug into the shell bursting charge.

A number of fuzes were issued which bore no numeral, lot number or date of manufacture. They were marked only on the cover with the design number 16603A. These fuzes differed from the MK. IV fuze in the shape of the brass ring and other minor details.

The **Mk. III** fuze had no brass ring around the body flange for fitting a cap. The **Mk. II** fuze was identical to the Mk. III except that the external joints were not waterproofed. Existing Mk. II fuzes which were subsequently waterproofed were known as Mk. II*. Fuzes Mks. II and III were fitted with a cover, No. 80 Mk. II. This was a brass cap, shaped to fit over the fuze and attached with a screwed ring and tin band. Tearing off the tin band caused the cap to fall off, exposing the fuze. The weight of the cover was 2.5 ounces.

Fuzes were issued in tin cylinders, one fuze per cylinder. The cylinders were known as Cylinder No. 80F and were painted green with yellow labels.

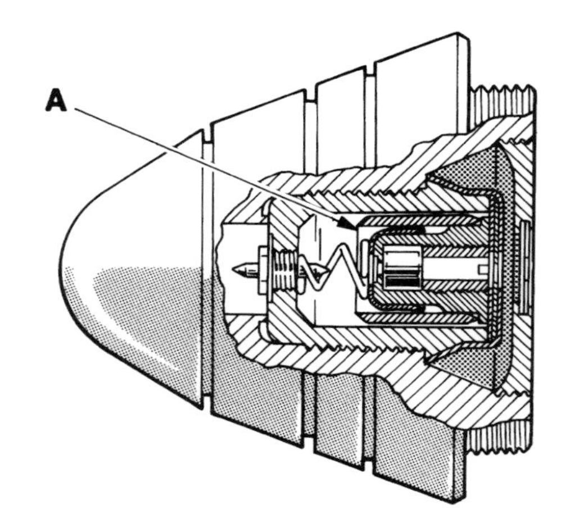

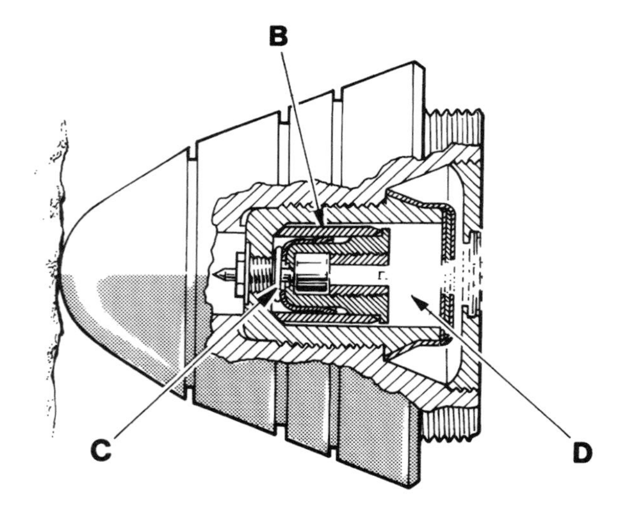

PERCUSSION FUZE OPERATION

Drill Fuze No. 80

Burnt-out service fuzes were converted to drill fuzes by being blacked all over, except for the body flange. A bright area was left on each composition ring. The setting pin was of steel and the cap was stamped with the word DRILL.

Fuze Safety Clip No. 80 Mk. I

This was a steel clip, horseshoe shaped, to fit around the No. 80 fuze and hold it in the safety condition. It had a slot to fit over the setting pin and a tongue to fit into the fixing slot. It was retained by projections which gripped the edge of the fuze body.

Fixing Key No. 17 Mk. II (Fuze Nos 80 and 83)

This was of steel, one end being ring shaped to fit over the fuze.

One edge of the ring bore was bevelled to suit the body profile of all No. 80 fuzes without covers and had a projection to fit the square notch in the fuze graduated ring. The opposite edge of the ring bore had a slot cut into it to engage with the projection on a fuze cover, when screwing the fuze into a shell.

The **Mk. I** key was without a slot and could not be used with a Mk. IV fuze with cover.

Setting Key No. 18 Mk. II (Fuze Nos 80 and 83)

This was of steel and used when the bottom time ring was too stiff to set by hand. It had a slot to engage with the projecting setting pin on the bottom time ring. The length of the key was 6.17 inches and it had a loop of white line 30 inches in length.

The **Mk. I** key was shallower in depth than the Mk. II.

Time Fuze No. 25 Mk. III (15 seconds)

This was partially similar in construction and operation to the time arrangement of the No. 80 Mk. IV fuze.

It had only one composition time ring, this being externally graduated from 0 to 44. An arrow on the time ring would coincide with a black mark on the body shoulder when set at safety. A copper safety pin passed through the top cap and detonator pellet. It was provided with a loop of red cord. This safety pin suspended the detonator pellet which was held also by a stirrup spring.

The powder magazine contained 45 grains of RFG 2 powder. External openings were waterproofed.

The weight of the fuze was 5.75 ounces.

The **Mk. II** fuze differed only in not being waterproofed.

Cartridge, primers and shells

Cartridge case

The solid drawn brass cartridge case contained a propellant charge consisting of a one pound, six and fifteen-sixteenths ounces bundle of cordite MD size 8, recessed at one end to sit over the primer and primer housing boss, the other end being in contact with the shell base.

The weight of the case, with primer, was 2 pounds 15 ounces.

Shrapnel shell

Although part of a fixed round, the shrapnel shell retained most of the features to be found on the earlier shrapnel shell projectiles used in conjunction with separate cartridges.

The **Mk. III** shell had a forged steel body with an internally recessed base to hold a tin cup containing the bursting charge. This was 2 ounces 8 drams of either RFG 2, blank FG new, SFG 2, or QFFG powder.

The shell head was formed with an external radius of two diameters. Screwed into the shell head was a two-inch brass fuze socket to receive a Time and Percussion Fuze No. 80 Mk. IV.

Fitting into the fuze socket was one end of a brass tube, the other end of which was screwed into a steel disc positioned over the bursting charge tin cup. The tube contained perforated powder pellets, which conveyed the fuze detonation flash to the bursting charge. The pellets weighed three-quarters of an ounce, this weight being included in the bursting charge total weight. The shell contained 375 mixed metal balls at 41 to the pound.

The copper driving band was secured from rotating in its groove by two waved bands. To secure the shell in its case, the case lip was pressed into the driving band groove. Shell weight, filled and fuzed, was 18 pounds 8 ounces.

The shell was painted lead grey for the purpose of identification. The weight of the complete round was twenty-two pounds, thirteen and fifteen-sixteenths ounces.

The **Mk. II** shell had a driving band slightly narrower in width to that of the Mk. III shell. It had a turned cannelure at the rear, filled with Pettman's cement, into which the cartridge case was secured with four indentations.

The **Mk. I** shell head was formed with an external radius of one and a half diameters. Early shells would take the Mk. I fuze cover only, later shells were slightly modified to take fuze covers of later Mk. numbers.

The lower portion of the shell body wall was thinner in section than that of the Mk. II or Mk. III. It contained 365 balls. The lid of the bursting charge tin cup was also of different shape.

The shell exterior was painted black.

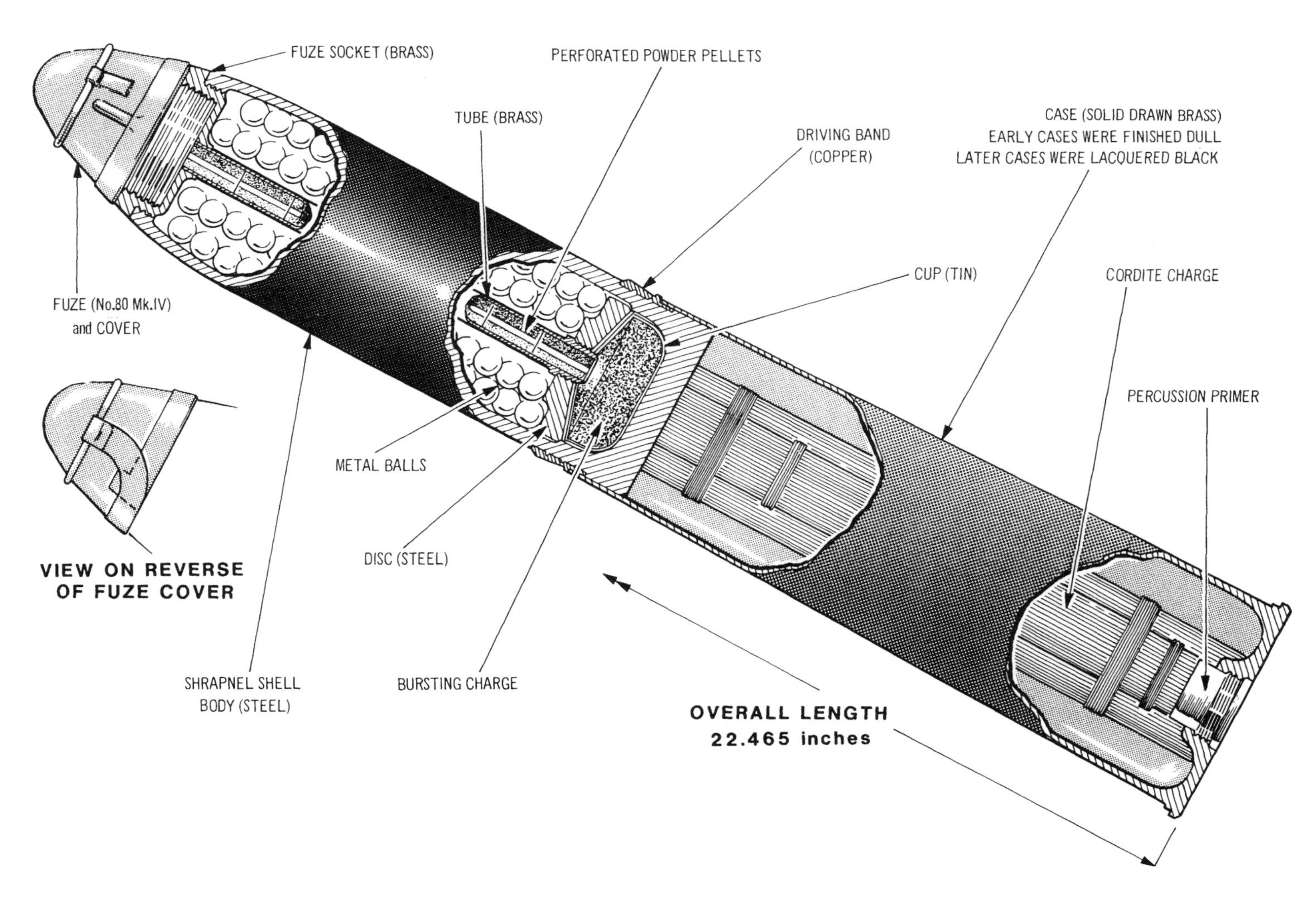

SHRAPNEL CARTRIDGE MK. I

Blank cartridge

The **Mk. II** blank cartridge consisted of a service case and percussion primer, with a 1 pound charge of LG powder in a silk cloth bag (No. 1 class), having three silk braid hoops, enclosed in a felt jacket with a lifting loop.

The cartridge mouth was closed with a split paper ring and leather-board cup, this being fitted by the use of a wood drift, supplied for the purpose.

The **Mk. I** blank cartridge had two silk braid hoops and a smaller lifting loop.

Smokeless Blank Cartridge Mk. I

This was a service case and percussion primer containing a 7 ounce charge of smokeless blank and 4 ounces 5 drams of matchwood shot.

The cartridge mouth was closed with a split paper ring and leather-board cup, this being fitted by the use of a wood drift, supplied for the purpose. Empty cartridge cases for blank use were issued in a wood box, 20 to a box. Charges were issued specifically for use in blank cartridges.

Dummy cartridge

This was used for fuze setting practice. It consisted of a service cartridge case and shell body, the latter fitted with a 2 inch fuze hole socket closed at the bottom, the body filled with a mixture of dust and lead ash. This was fitted in the normal way into the service cartridge case, which contained a wood block, recessed at one end to fit over the boss in the base, the other end butting against the shell base. A through bolt, the head of which fitted into the primer hole, passed through the wood block and screwed into the base of the shell.

For identification, four holes were bored in the case side and three in the base.

Drill cartridge case

This was an empty service case with the mouth plugged by a tightly fitting, 1 inch thick hardwood disc.

The drill primer was of the same external shape as a service primer, but bored out to house a hard rubber plug, this being held in position by a screwed plug. It was stamped, on the head, with the word DRILL.

Percussion primer No. 1

The **Mk. II** percussion primer consisted of a brass body, externally threaded to fit into the cartridge case base. It was internally bored and recessed to take the percussion cap which was secured by a screwed plug. The plug was formed with an anvil at one end, the plug body being bored to form a coned seating chamber. This

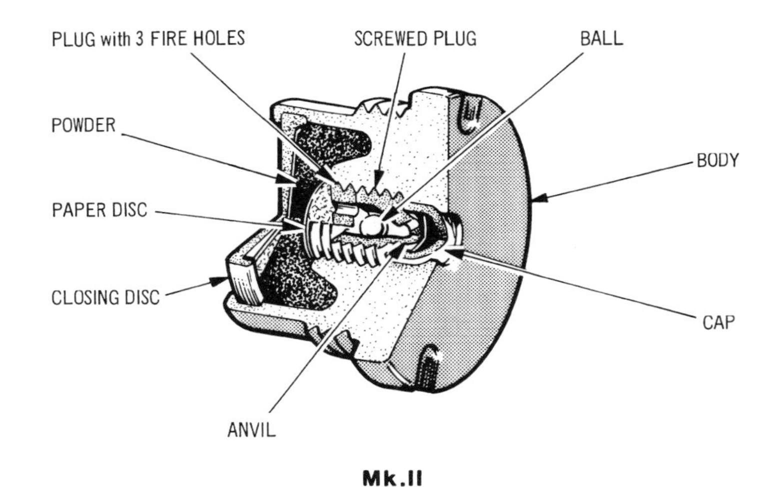

Mk.II

WHITED BROWN PAPER DISC
POWDER
PLUG with 3 FIRE HOLES
PAPER DISC
CAP
CLOSING DISC
BODY
BALL
BRASS CHAMBER

Mk.I

PERCUSSION PRIMER NO. I

contained a soft copper ball and was closed by a perforated plug. A chamber in the primer body contained RFG 2 gunpowder and was closed by a paper disc and a brass closing disc with six slits.

Upon firing, the gun firing pin crushed the percussion cap against the anvil and detonated the percussion compound. The detonation fired past the ball, through the three fire holes in the plug and ignited the RFG 2 gunpowder charge, which burst through the six slits in the brass closing disc. Gas pressure drove the soft copper ball into the coned seat of the screwed plug bore and relieved gas pressure on the cap.

The **Mk. I** primer differed from the Mk. II in the head being recessed to house a brass chamber containing the cap. The brass chamber formed the anvil and had three fire holes to enable the primer detonation to pass through the coned sealing chamber past the ball and through the fire holes in the plug to the RFG 2 gunpowder contained in the body chamber.

Primer Key No. 27

The key was used to insert or remove the percussion primer in the cartridge case. It was of steel, and had two projections to engage with the two recesses in the primer head.

The length of the key was 13.1 inches and it was fitted with a white lanyard 43 inches in length.

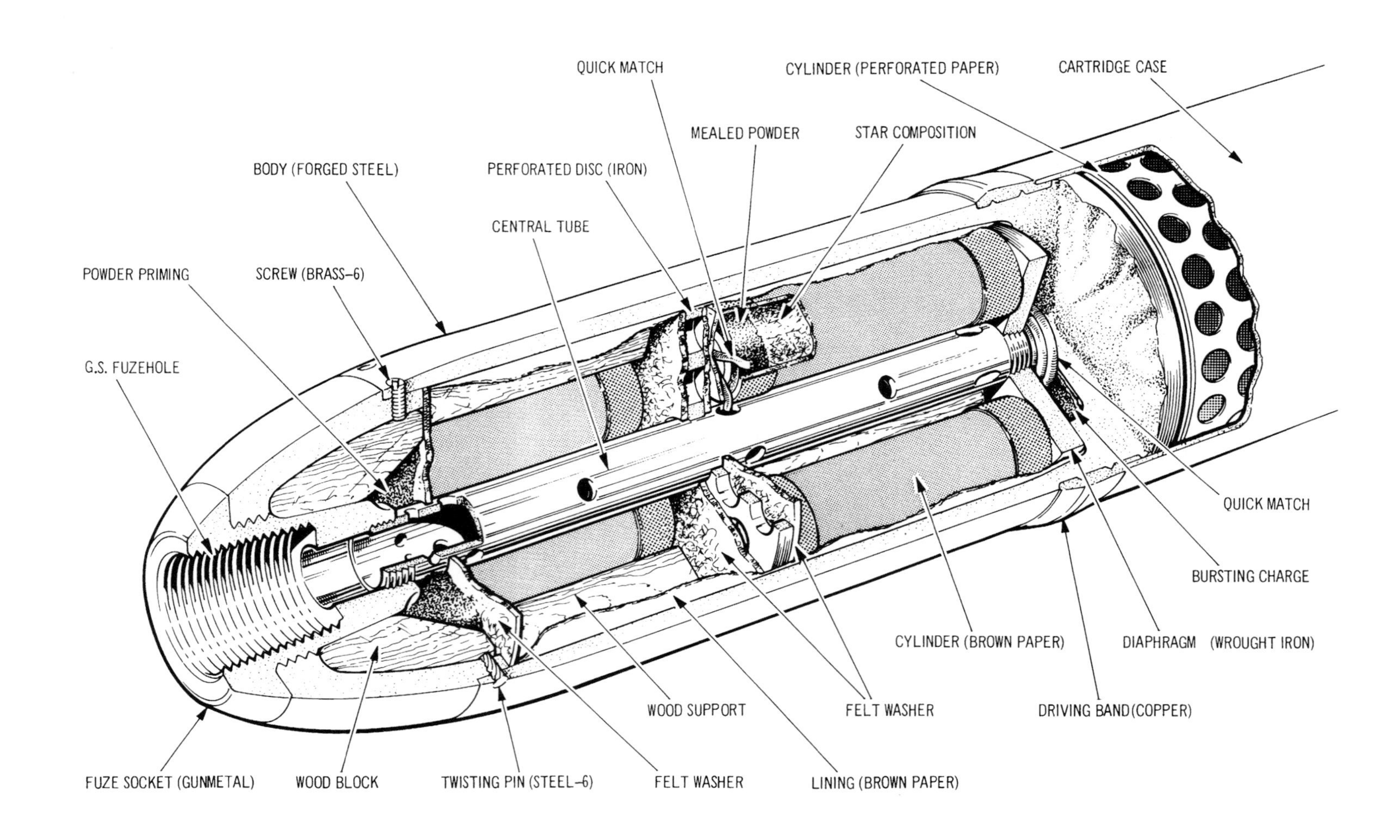

STAR SHELL CARTRIDGE MK. I

Star Shell Cartridge Mk. I

The charge, contained in a service cartridge case, consisted of 8 ounces of cordite MD, size 4¼, in a circular bundle, recessed at one end to sit over the primer boss. It was held in position in the case by a perforated paper cylinder. This had two perforated paper discs at each end, an additional unperforated disc being secured to the cylinder end which contacted the cordite charge.

The star shell had a forged steel body, recessed in the base for a bursting charge of three and one-quarter drams of RFG 2 gunpowder contained in a shalloon bag threaded with quick match.

The shell head, fitted with a gunmetal fuze socket and wood block, was secured to the body with 6 brass screws and 6 steel twisting pins. A metal tube, perforated with 12 fire holes, was screwed at one end into a wrought iron diaphragm over the bursting charge and at the other end into the fuze socket.

The shell body, lined with brown paper, contained 10 'stars', in 2 tiers of 5. A perforated iron disc, with a felt washer on either side, separated the tiers. The disc was held by wood supports placed between the stars. The ribs in the driving band groove were waved.

A Time Fuze No. 25 (15 seconds) would be used with this round, which was issued on special order only.

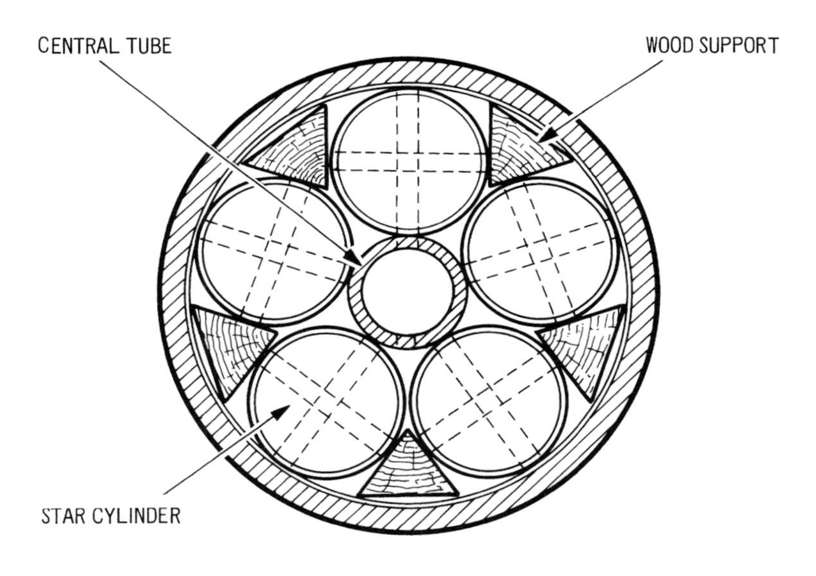

SECTION THROUGH SHELL BODY

Limber (Carriage)

The limber frame consisted of four flanged, nickel steel plate futchells, deepened where the axletree located and tapering to each end. The futchells were strengthened by corrugations on either side of the axletree location. The inner and outer futchells were connected by a nickel steel plate, semi-circular in section, riveted across their front ends. The frame was strengthened near the centre by two flanged nickel steel plate stays, riveted to the inner and outer futchells. Towards the front, the outer futchells were bent inwards and a swingletree hook was riveted to each front end. A draught pole socket was riveted between the inner futchells below the platform board and a socket to receive the draught pole end was riveted, between the inner futchells, behind the axletree. Nickel steel plate brackets were riveted to the futchell rear ends to give support to the ammunition box.

The front ends of the futchells were bent upwards to give sloping support to an elm footboard bolted across them. Between the footboard and ammunition box front was a two-piece, ash platform board, bolted across the futchells. One platform board end was recessed to give clearance for the shovel handle carried on the ammunition box side.

Half the number of limbers constructed had loops for kicking straps bolted to the footboard. Jack plates were riveted to the outer futchells beneath the axletree.

Early limber hooks were of forged steel, the bearing area being deeply hardened. Two arms of the forging overlapped the inner futchells and were riveted to them. The hook was provided with a lugged steel key, attached by a chain.

Later limbers were equipped with spring hooks, which automatically locked on engagement with the carriage trail eye. To unlimber, the catch handle would be depressed, allowing the trail eye to be lifted clear. On early pattern hooks, the steel key acted as a stop, preventing too much vertical angular movement between limber and carriage. The later spring hooks did not have this facility, and precautions had to be taken, when limbering up with the horses not hooked in, to prevent the limber from turning over backwards.

The wheels (2nd class, C pattern, No. 45), ran on a tubular steel axletree, circular in cross section. The axletree bearings were riveted to the inner futchells and bolted to the outer ones. The outer bearings had keys formed in them which engaged keyways in the axletree shoulders, these securing the axletree in position.

The wheel pipebox inner ends ran in L leather dust excluders fitted to the outer bearings.

The ammunition box was of steel plate. The front, lid, hinged steel plate and the sides were of bulletproof steel. The box top and bottom were of nickel steel plate, the bottom plate being provided with drain holes. The assembly was riveted together, the complete box being riveted to the futchells, to the futchell rear brackets and to the stay plates riveted to the outer futchells and box ends.

The box lid was hinged to the frame rear brackets and opened downwards. It was padded on the inside with felt and a leather

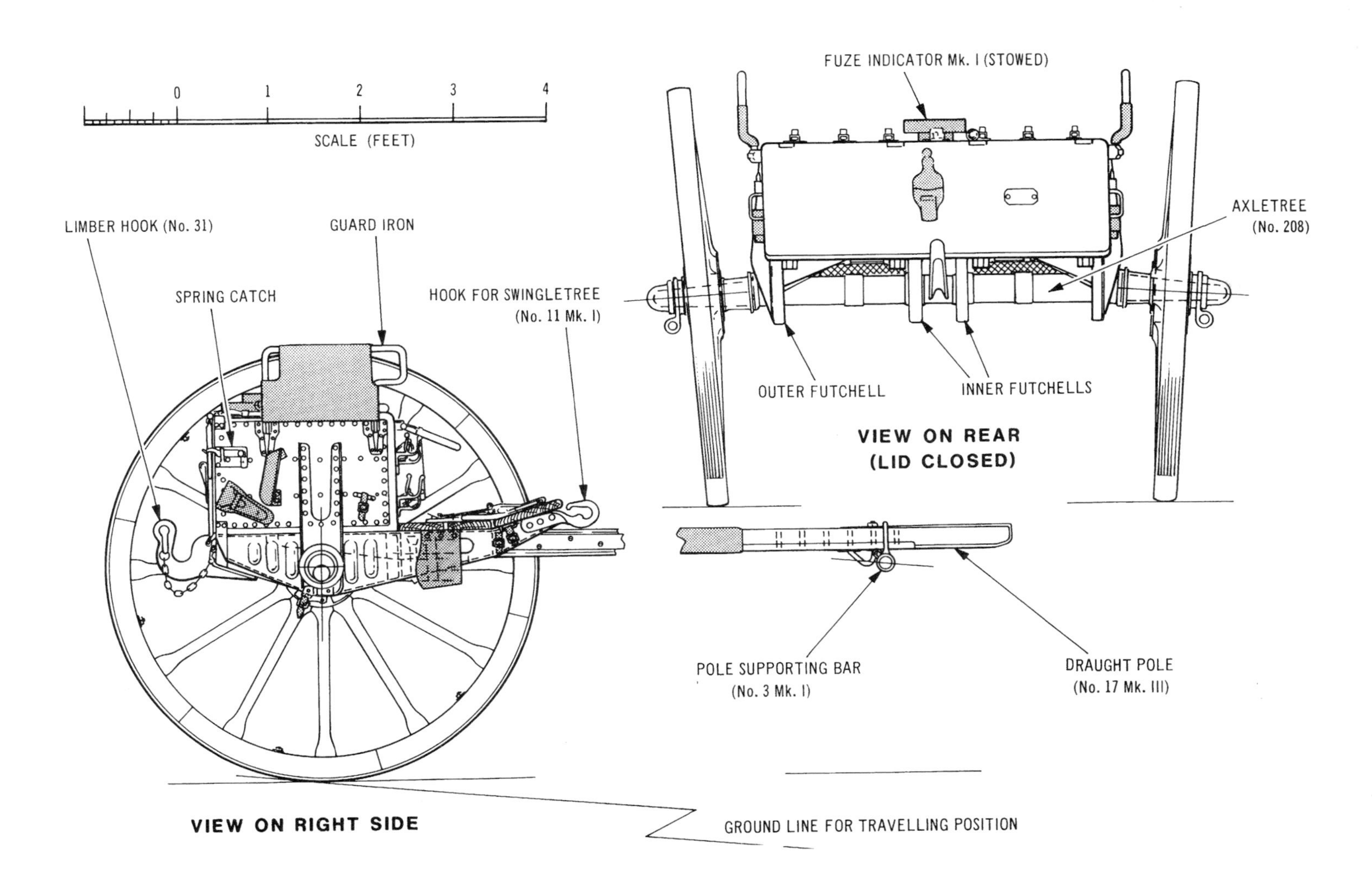

LIMBER (CARRIAGE)

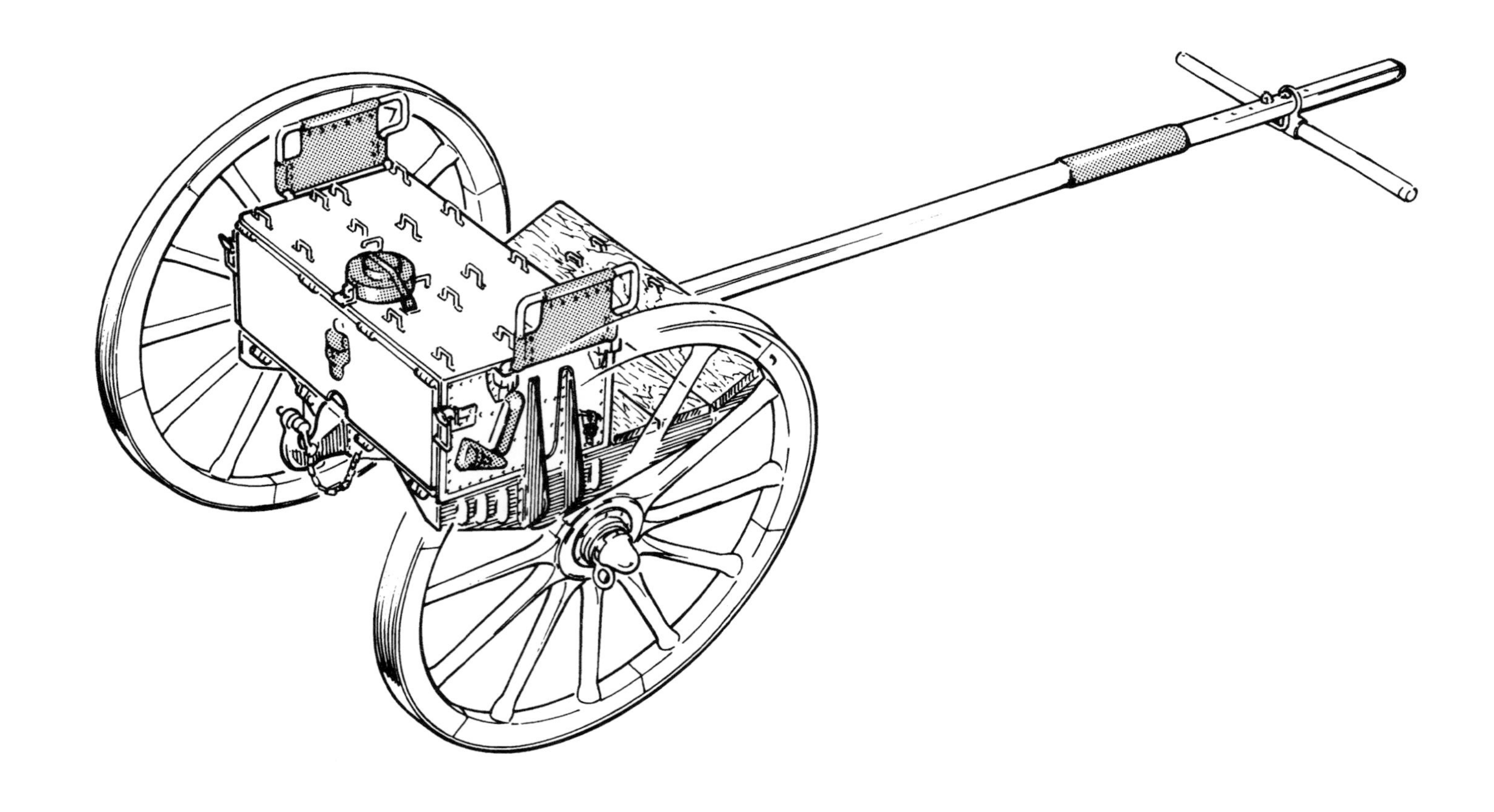

LIMBER (CARRIAGE)

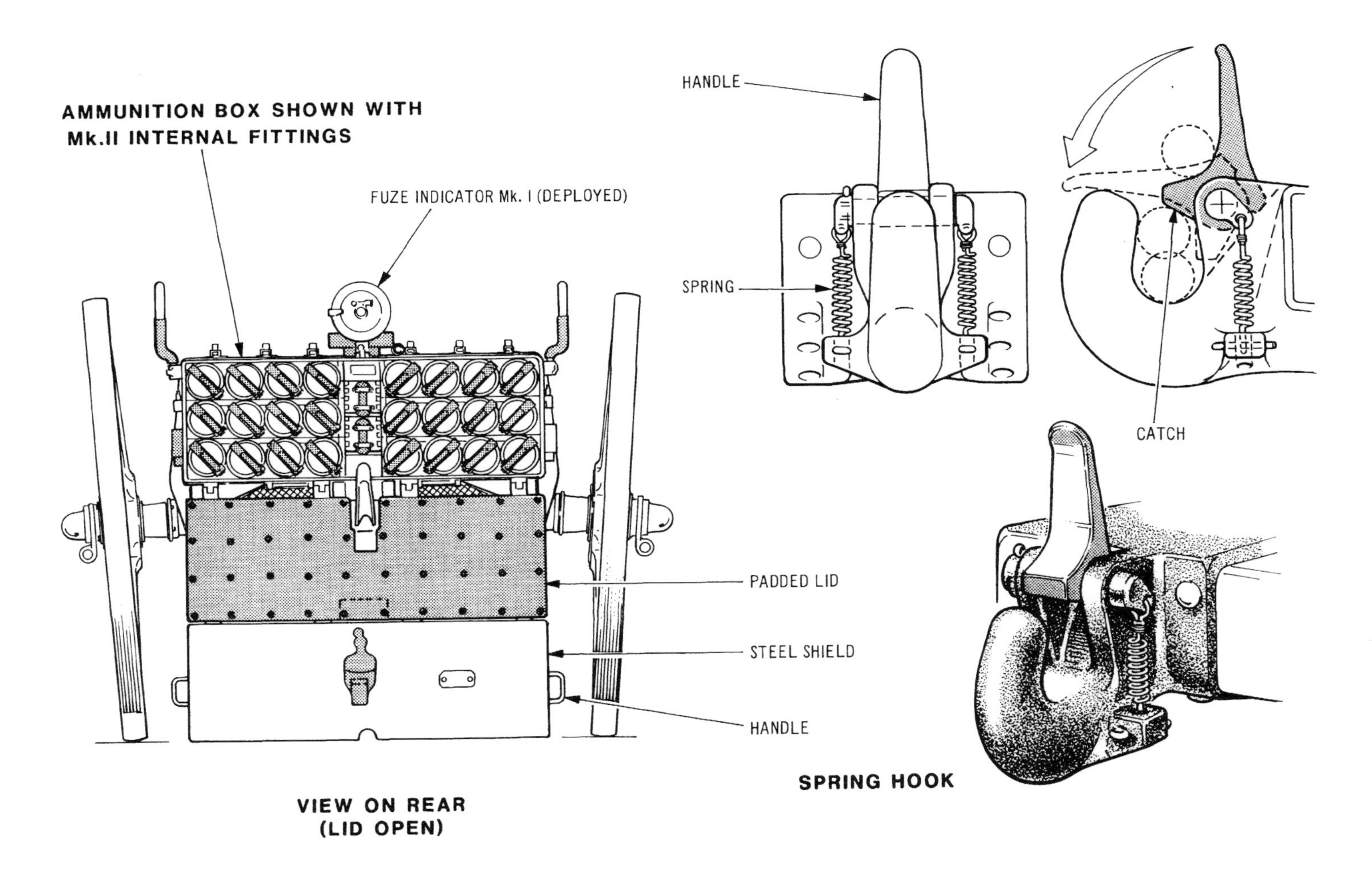

LIMBER (CARRIAGE)

cover, secured by rivets. With the lid closed, the pad acted as a steady to the cartridge ends.

A bulletproof shield plate was hinged to the lid upper edge, secured, when closed, by spring catches on the box ends engaging handles on the shield plate. The box lid was also secured by a lock and key. When opened, the shield plate, lid and box together afforded protection from small arms fire to gun crew members in the rear of the limber.

The **Mk. II** box interior (illustrated) was divided into horizontal partitions by steel shelves braced by angle steel strips, into which were wedged tubes of plaited Indian cane, each shaped to hold one round of ammunition and fitted with a quick-release strap.

The box held twenty four rounds of ammunition. Two central compartments each housed a wood tray containing small stores, secured by a spring catch.

The **Mk. I** box interior had a nickel steel vertical plate riveted inside at the rear. This had twenty-four flanged holes, each to hold the rear end of a brass tube which was shaped to conform to the contour of a cartridge. The front end of each tube had a steel stud plate riveted to it, the stud projecting through the box front plate and secured by a manganese bronze nut with split pin. The rear end of each tube was lipped and formed with a projection which engaged the cartridge clip (see page 383).

Boxes of both Mk. numbers were originally fitted with a hinge plate on the box top, at rear, for the attachment of a Fuze Indicator Mk. I.

Riveted to the top of the box sides were steel sockets, into which fitted guard irons secured by a steel screw, with leather guards. Spring clips were attached to the front of the box to carry two service rifles, in canvas covers, secured in position by quick release straps. The body underside was fitted with two wire netting receptacles, secured by spring catches and leather ties, for the carriage of various stores.

Limber (Ammunition Wagon)

This limber was similar in construction to the carriage limber, but the frame was wider to take a larger ammunition box. The box carried thirty-eight rounds of ammunition in three compartments, sixteen rounds in each outer compartment and six in the centre one. Below the centre compartment ammunition was space for a wood tray containing small stores.

Each outer compartment was fitted with a padded lid, hinged at the bottom to the rear frame brackets, with a shield hinged to it at the top.

The centre compartment lid was hinged at the top to the box and was secured by two spring catches and a lock with key. The centre lid would be closed last, as it secured the outer lids by bearing against flanges formed on them. The outer lids were also secured by spring catches, as on the carriage limber.

The outer axletree bearings were shorter than those of the carriage limber, on account of the wider frame.

The differences between the Mk. I and Mk. II carriage limbers applied also to the wagon limbers. Small fittings carried on the carriage limber applied also to the wagon limber.

Ammunition wagon

The nickel steel perch was bent in the form of a box, tapering from rear to front, overlapping and riveted on the underside. A steel plate was riveted underneath the perch at the axletree position. The centre of the perch was strengthened by steel plates riveted to each side. These plates sloped upwards to support the footboard. A hardwood block, eighteen inches long, was inserted inside the perch, near the eye, to strengthen it. The perch eye was a steel forging, the rubbing portion being hardened, secured to the perch by rivets.

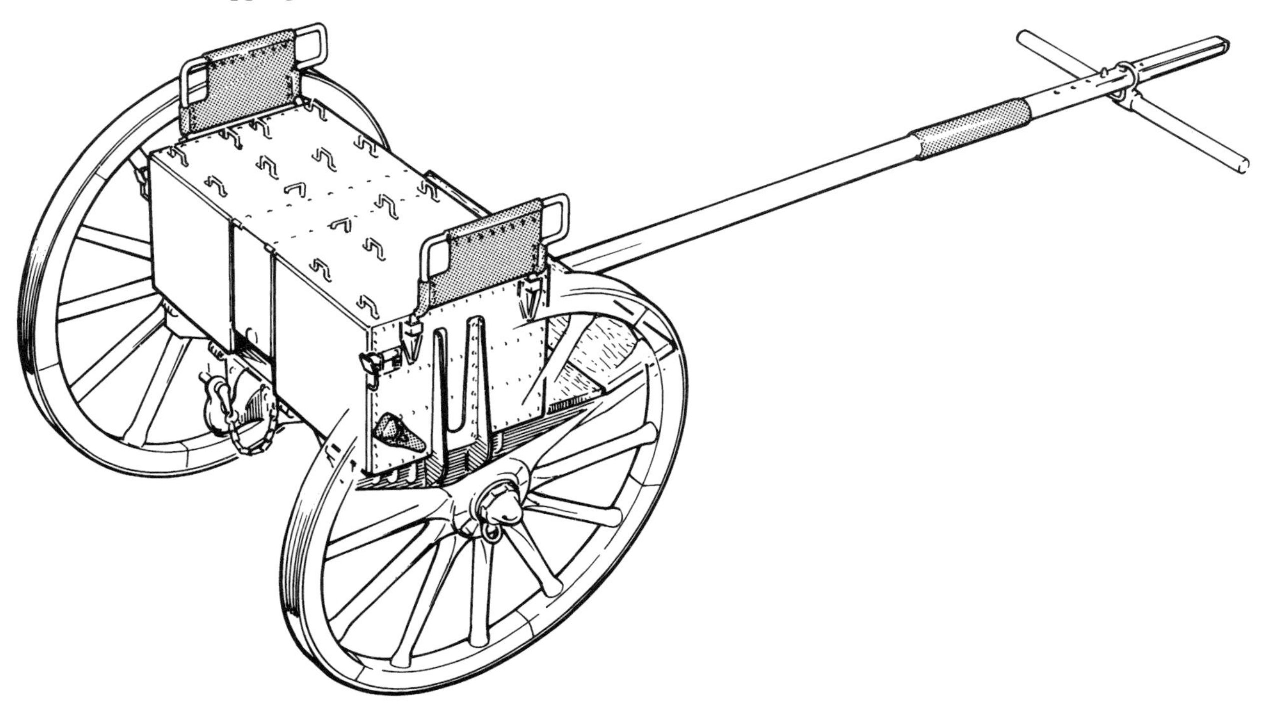

LIMBER (AMMUNITION WAGON)

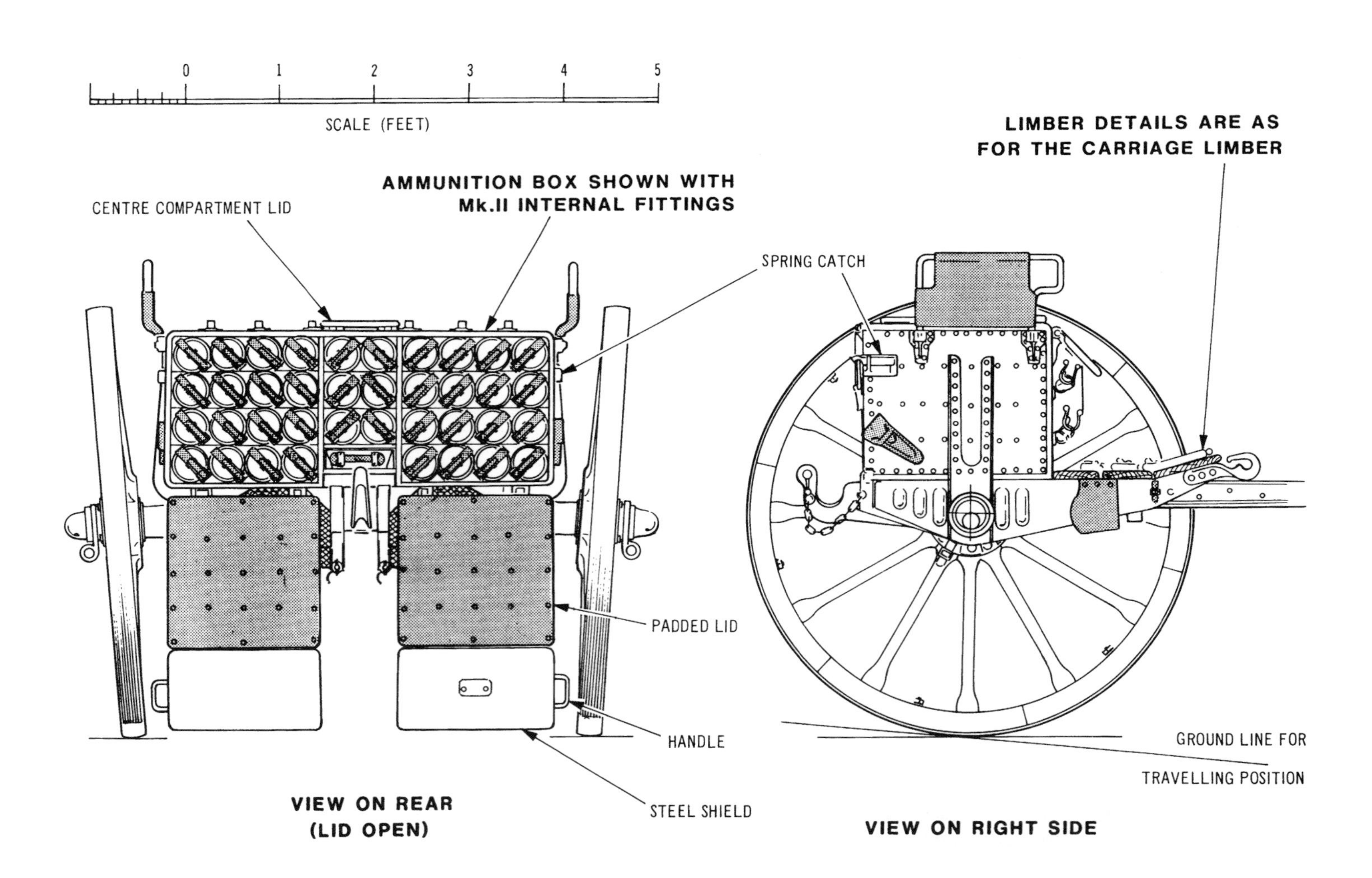

LIMBER (AMMUNITION WAGON)

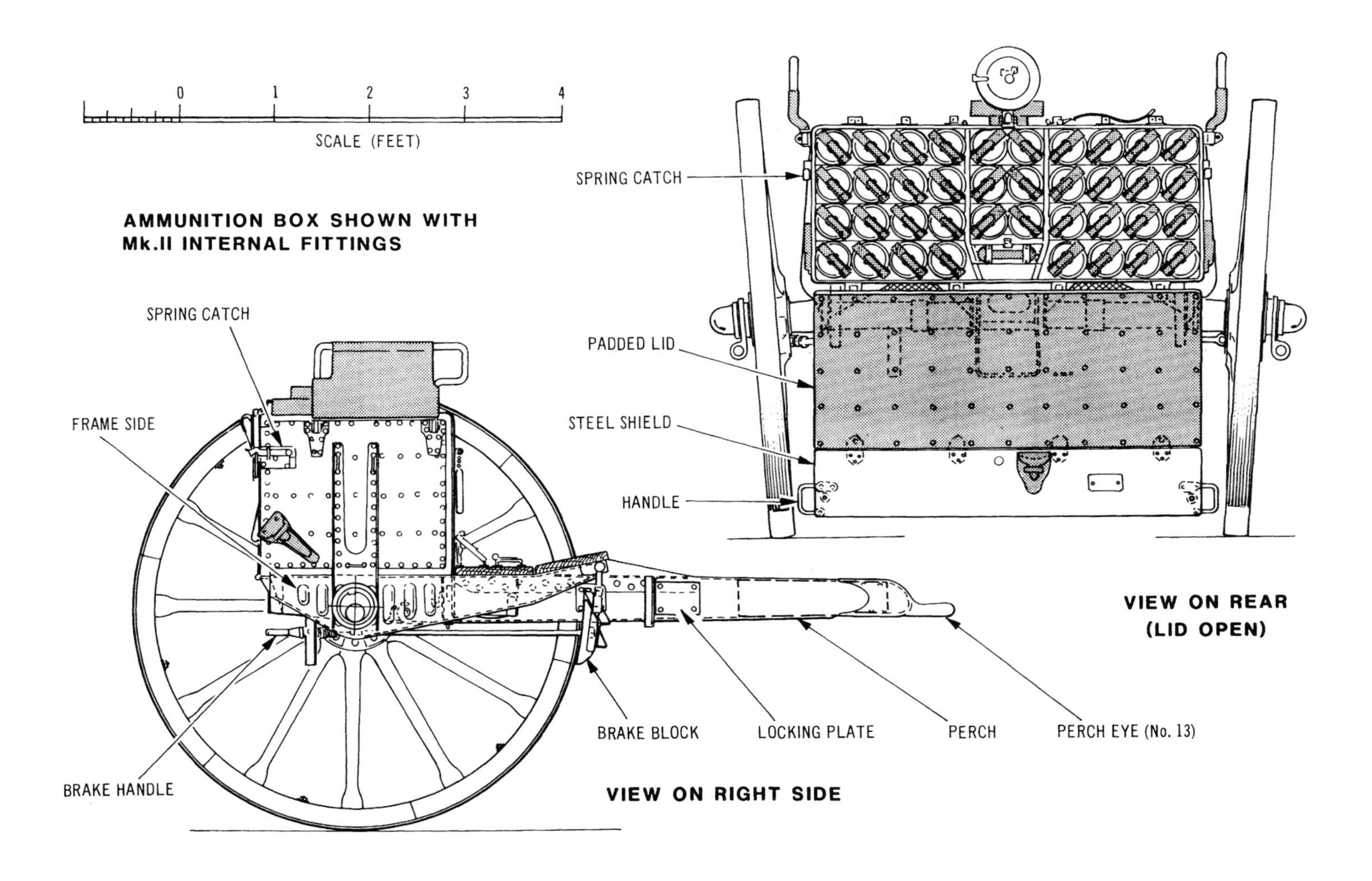

AMMUNITION WAGON

The frame sides were of flanged, nickel steel plate similar in form to the limber outer futchells. They were connected to the perch by two flanged, nickel steel stays in front of the axletree, a third stay being fitted inside the perch at this position. Brackets were attached to the rear end of the sides and perch to support the ammunition box. The frame sides sloped upwards at the front to support the footboard. The axletree and wheels were similar to that of the wagon limber, secured in the same manner.

An ash platform board, made in one piece, and an elm footboard were secured across the perch and frame sides, forward of the ammunition box. A slot was cut in each footboard supporting plate to allow handspikes to pass through when these were carried instead of a spare jointed draught pole.

The brake was actuated by a handle at the frame rear. Turning the handle caused two operating rods, linked by a bell-crank lever pivoted in a bracket bolted around the axletree, to draw the nickel steel, channel section brake bars rearwards and apply the cast iron brake blocks to the tyre.

The ammunition box was similar to that fitted to the wagon limber and carried the same number of rounds. It had only one lid, similar to that of the carriage limber.

A shelf was fitted under the platform board, on each side of the perch, each to carry a fourteen-pound grease box. There were fittings underneath the perch to carry a spare jointed draught pole or handspike, and a fitting under the footboard centre for a siege lamp box.

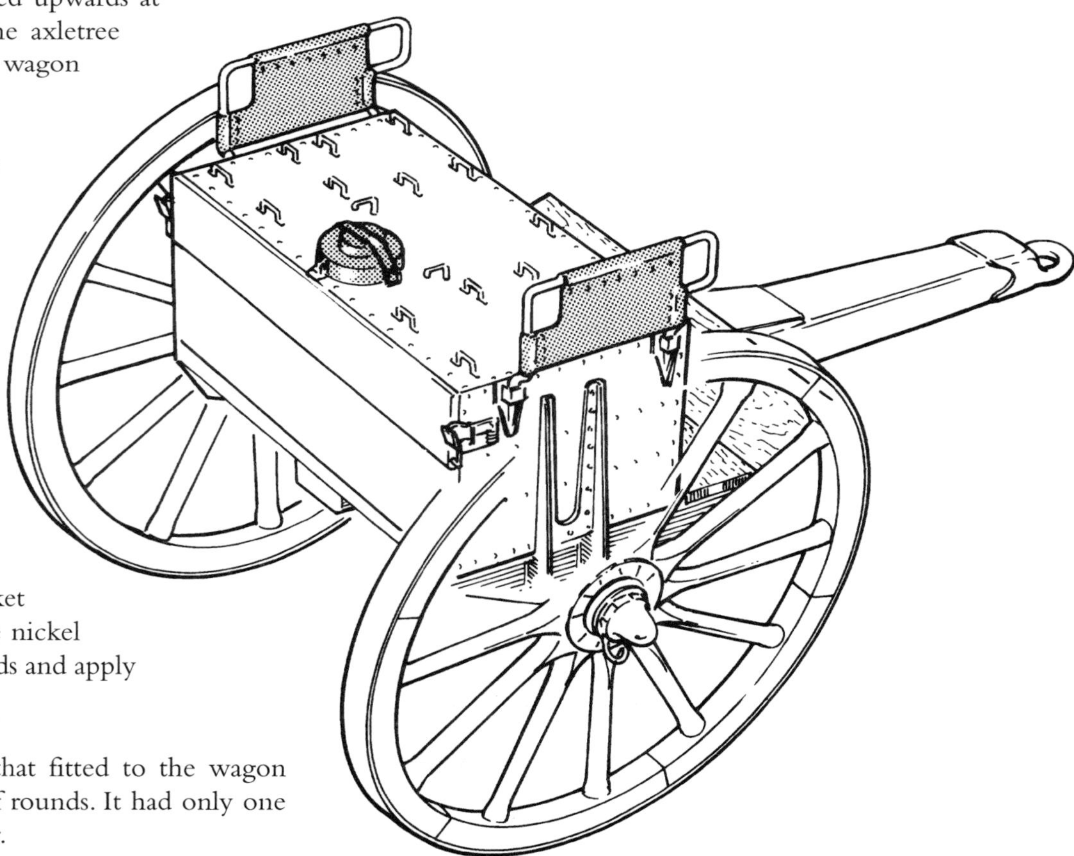

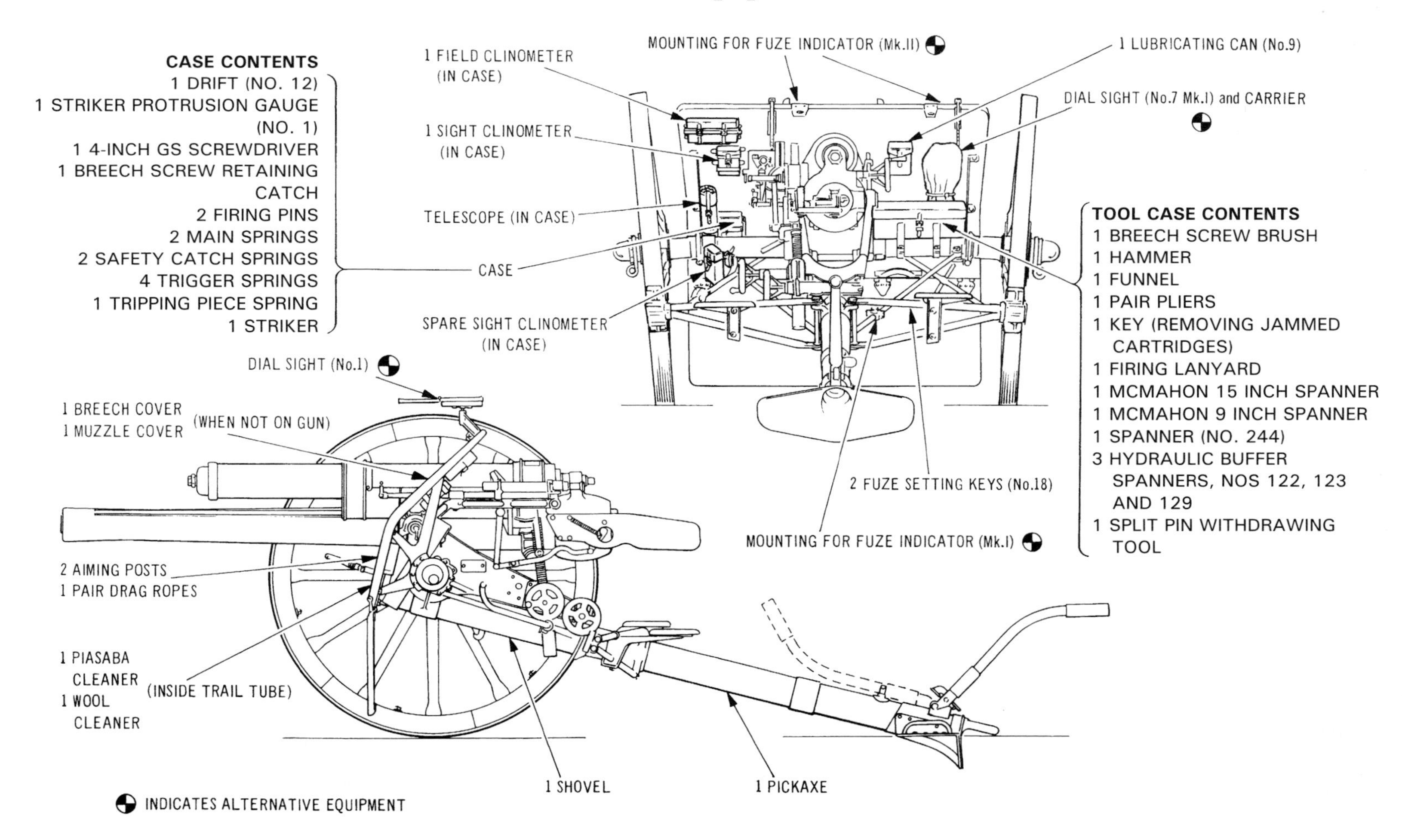

CARRIAGE – STORES AND EQUIPMENT

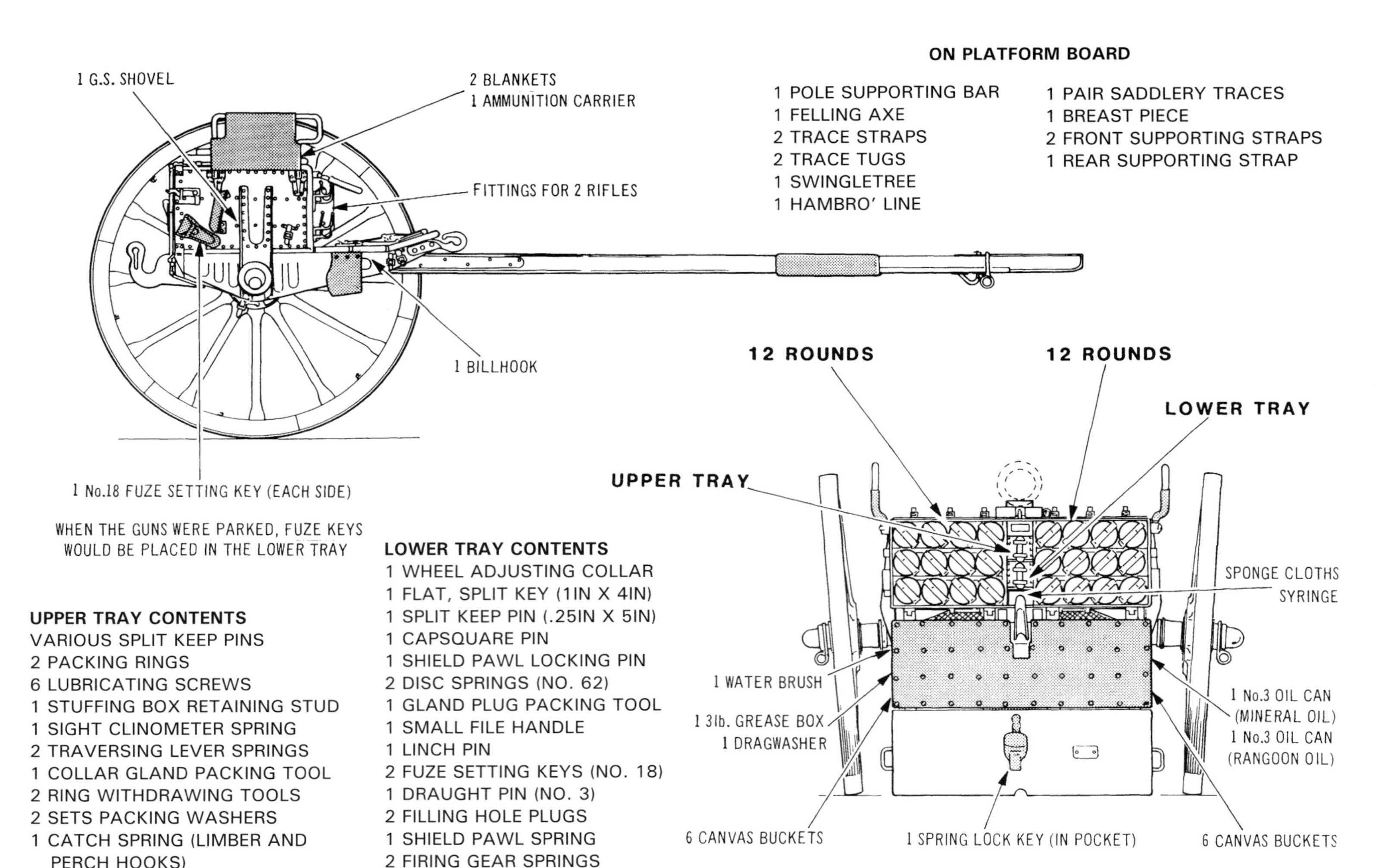

LIMBER (CARRIAGE) STORES AND EQUIPMENT

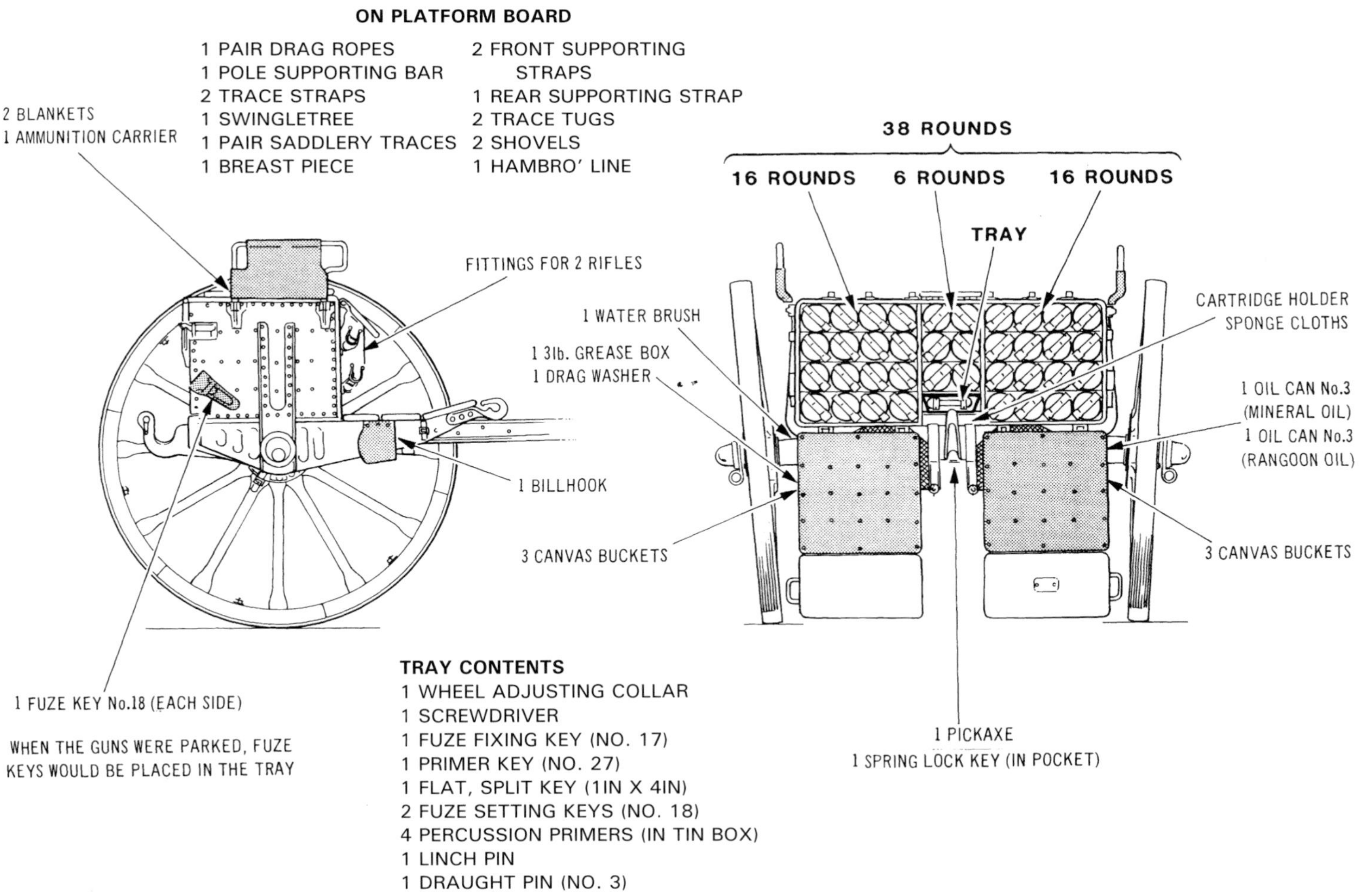

ON PLATFORM BOARD

1 PAIR DRAG ROPES
1 POLE SUPPORTING BAR
2 TRACE STRAPS
1 SWINGLETREE
1 PAIR SADDLERY TRACES
1 BREAST PIECE
2 FRONT SUPPORTING STRAPS
1 REAR SUPPORTING STRAP
2 TRACE TUGS
2 SHOVELS
1 HAMBRO' LINE

2 BLANKETS
1 AMMUNITION CARRIER

FITTINGS FOR 2 RIFLES

1 BILLHOOK

1 FUZE KEY No.18 (EACH SIDE)

WHEN THE GUNS WERE PARKED, FUZE KEYS WOULD BE PLACED IN THE TRAY

38 ROUNDS

16 ROUNDS 6 ROUNDS 16 ROUNDS

TRAY

1 WATER BRUSH

1 3lb. GREASE BOX
1 DRAG WASHER

3 CANVAS BUCKETS

CARTRIDGE HOLDER SPONGE CLOTHS

1 OIL CAN No.3 (MINERAL OIL)
1 OIL CAN No.3 (RANGOON OIL)

3 CANVAS BUCKETS

1 PICKAXE
1 SPRING LOCK KEY (IN POCKET)

TRAY CONTENTS

1 WHEEL ADJUSTING COLLAR
1 SCREWDRIVER
1 FUZE FIXING KEY (NO. 17)
1 PRIMER KEY (NO. 27)
1 FLAT, SPLIT KEY (1IN X 4IN)
2 FUZE SETTING KEYS (NO. 18)
4 PERCUSSION PRIMERS (IN TIN BOX)
1 LINCH PIN
1 DRAUGHT PIN (NO. 3)

LIMBER (AMMUNITION WAGON) STORES AND EQUIPMENT

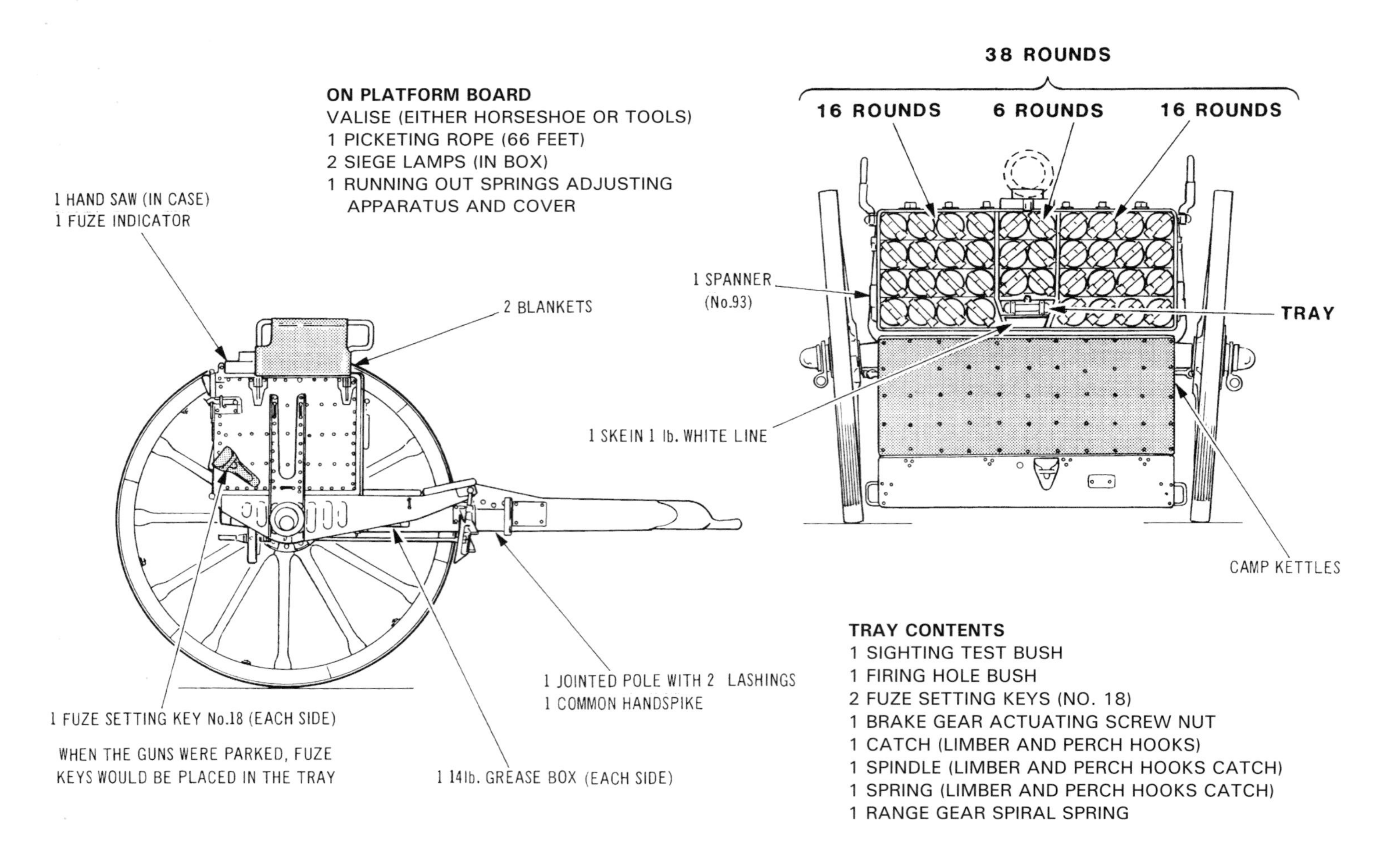

AMMUNITION WAGON STORES AND EQUIPMENT

BREECH LOADING 5 INCH HOWITZER

This breech loading howitzer is illustrated to show the early methods used in attempting some degree of control over recoil, prior to the introduction of a long recoil system.

In some cases, a 'breech pit' was excavated to prevent the breech striking the ground at high angles of elevation. The 5 inch howitzer shown here employed dragshoes to limit the amount of carriage rearward movement, in addition to the bank of hydraulic buffers and springs. Barrel recoil movement was restricted to six inches.

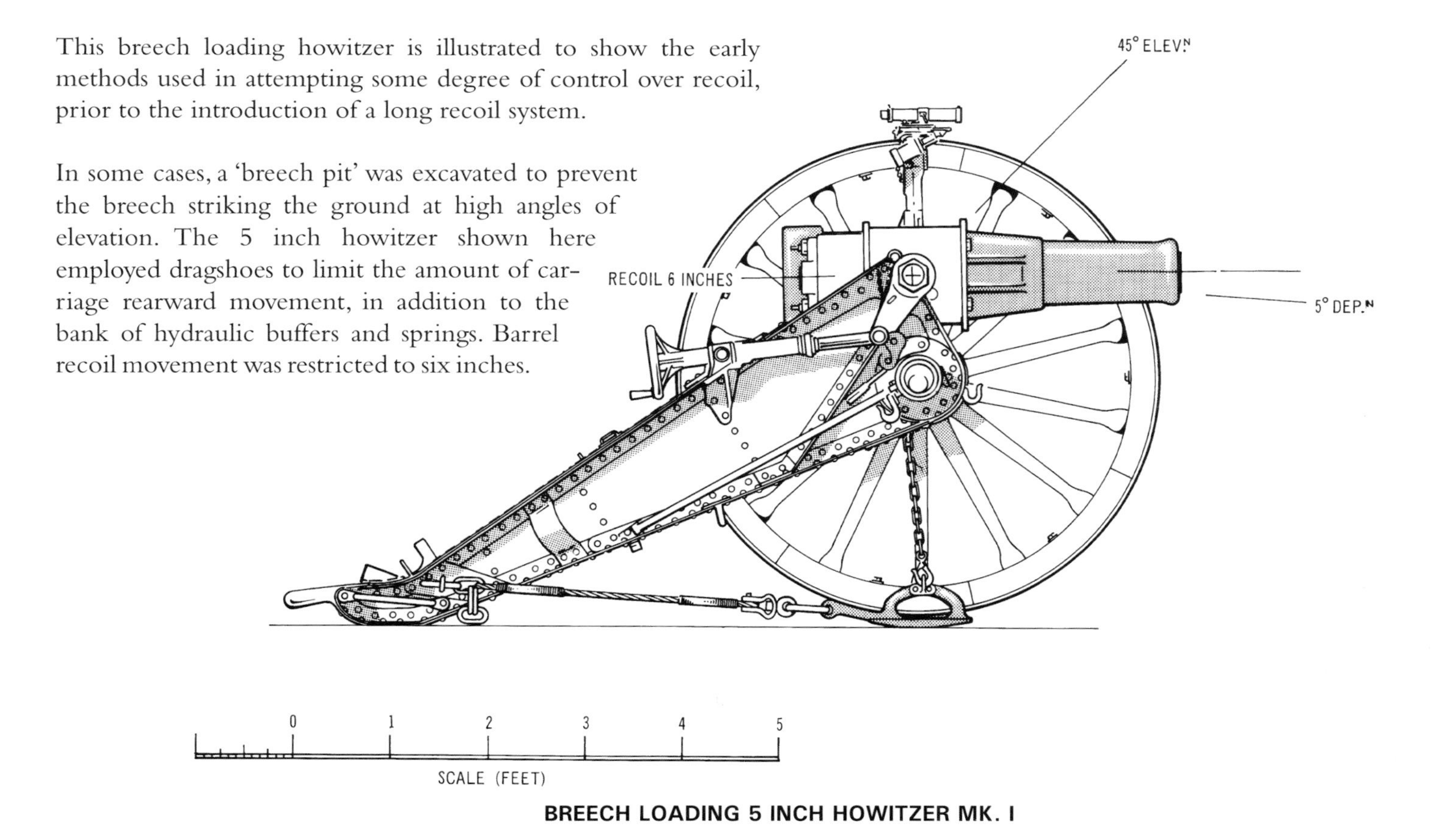

BREECH LOADING 5 INCH HOWITZER MK. I

Recoil was severe enough for removal of the sight to be necessary before firing to avoid damage. Contemporary photographs show this occurring, the sub-section sergeant holding the sight out of harm's way.

The weight of the Howitzer, with limber, as packed, was 43cwt 1qtr 8lb.

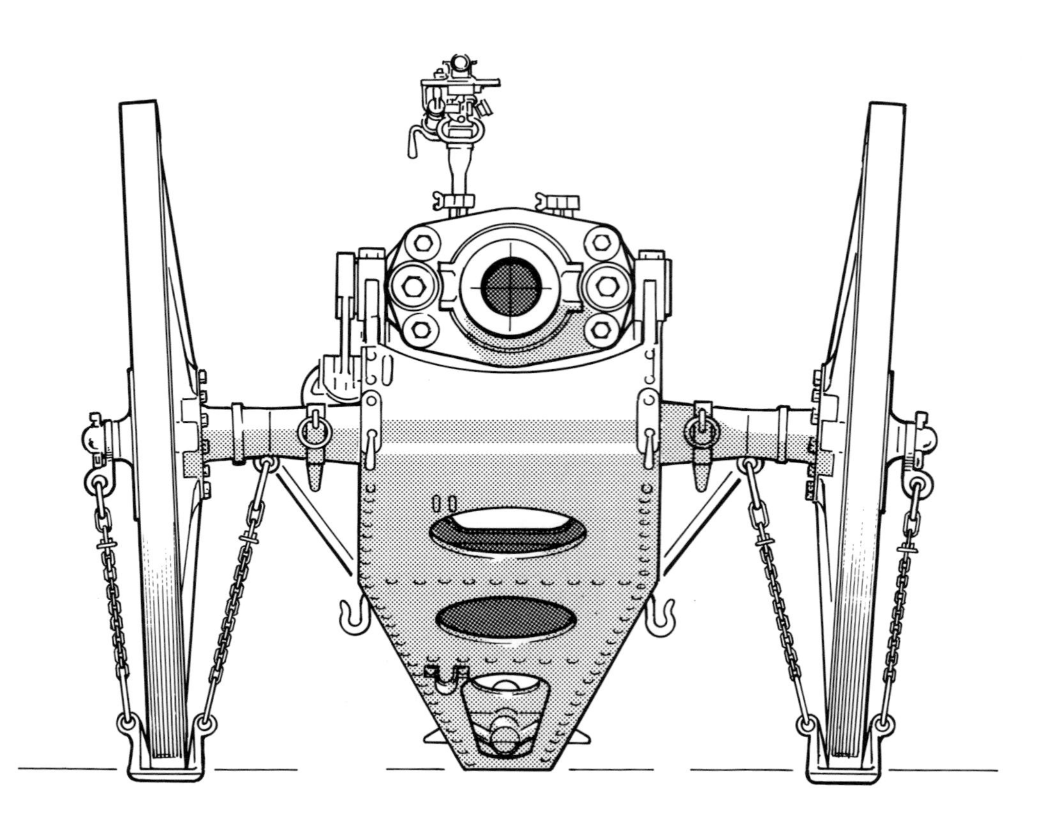

BREECH LOADING 5 INCH HOWITZER MK. I

QUICK FIRING 4.5 INCH HOWITZER MK. I

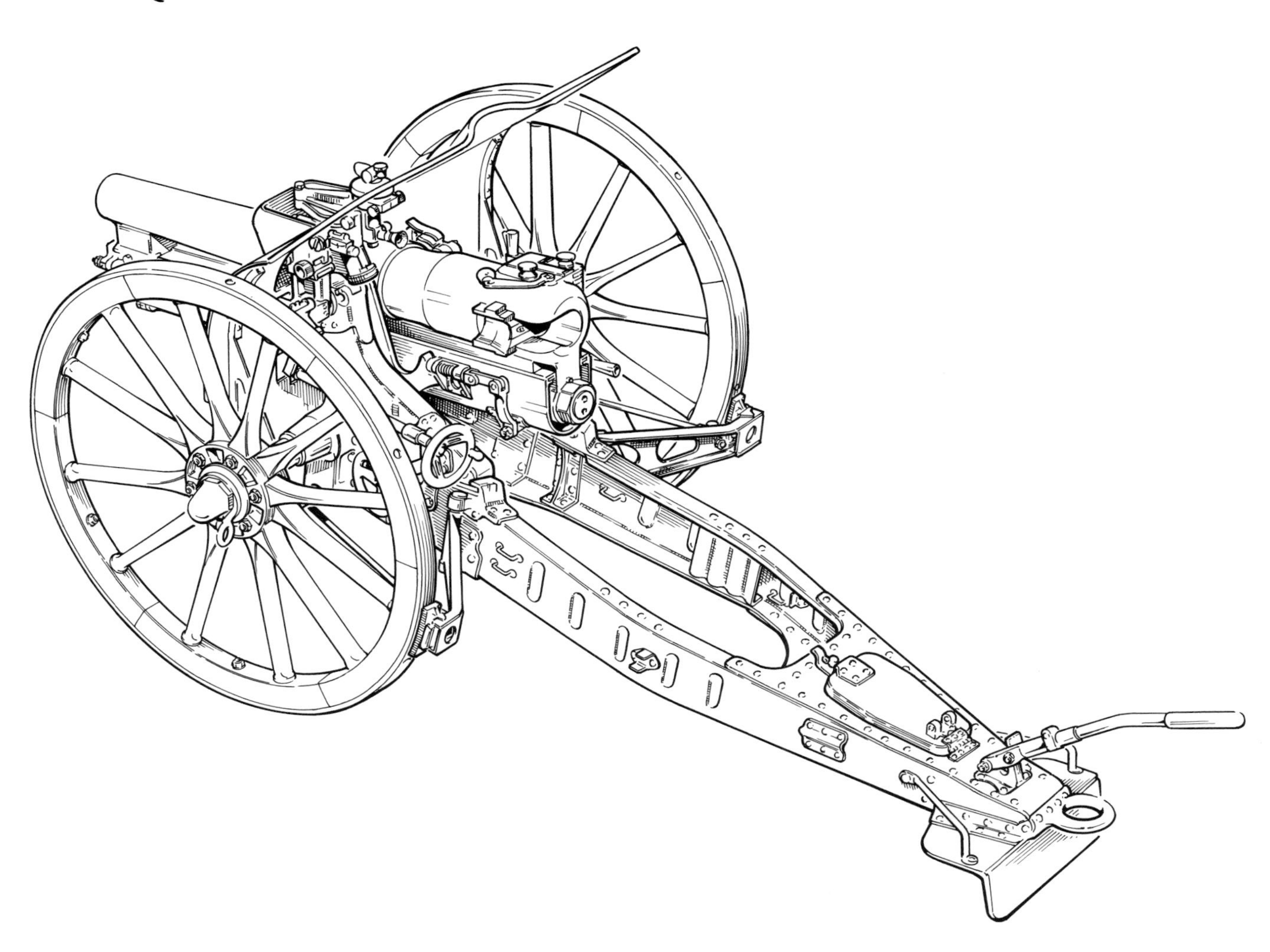

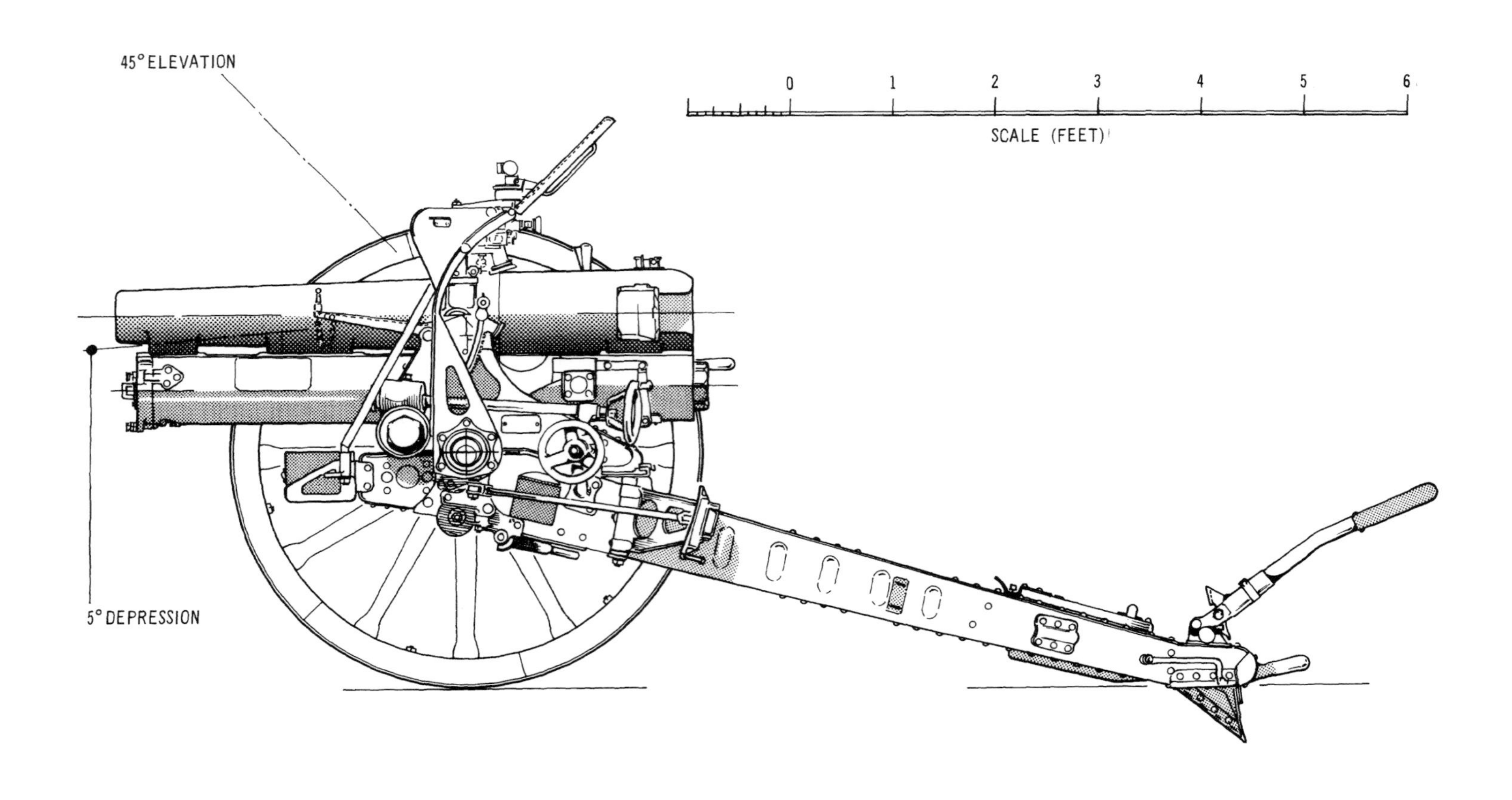

CARRIAGE – QUICK FIRING 4.5 INCH HOWITZER MK. I

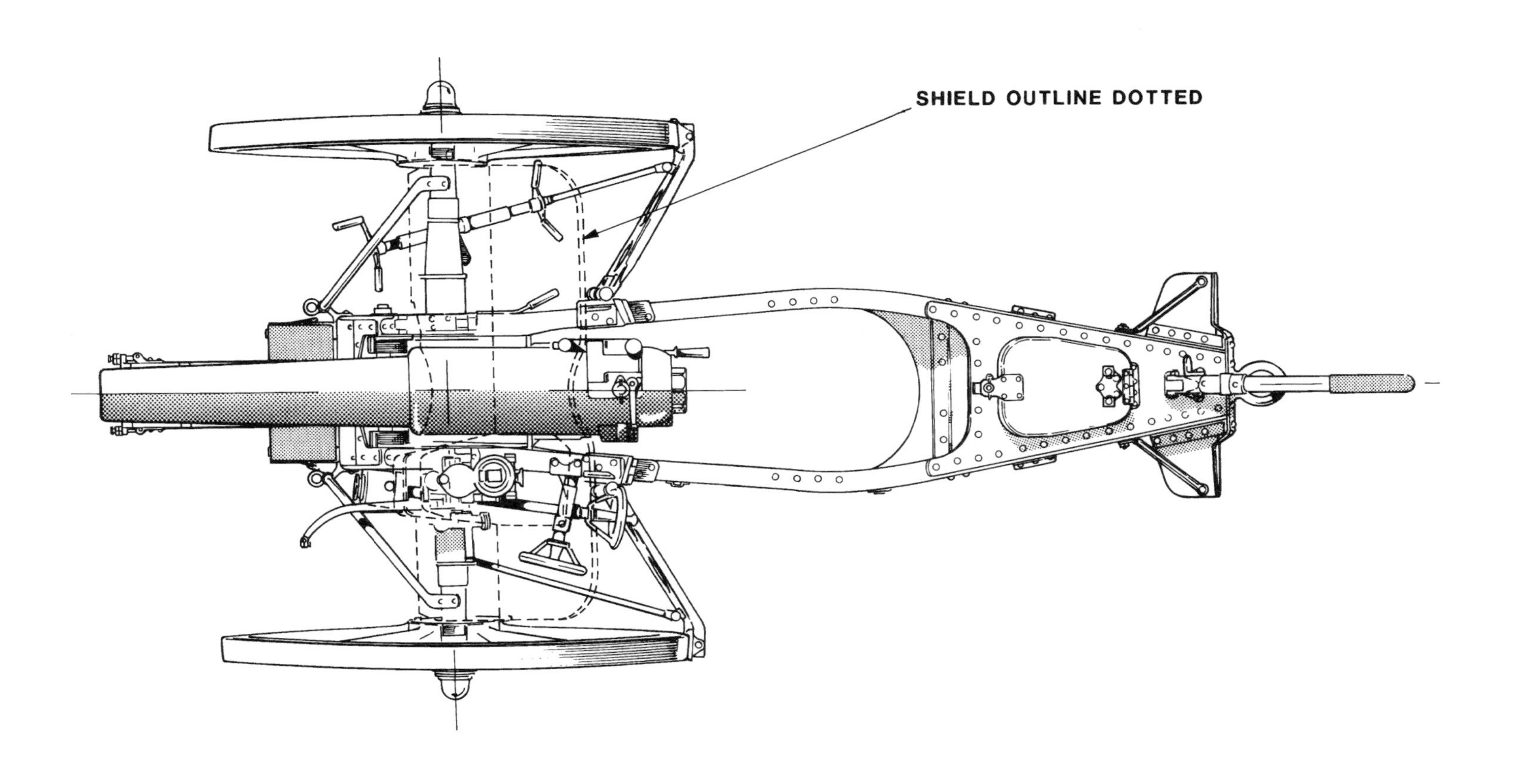

CARRIAGE – QUICK FIRING 4.5 INCH HOWITZER MK. I

QUICK FIRING 4.5 INCH HOWITZER MK. I

This gun, introduced into service in 1909, was made by the Coventry Ordnance Works. It could fire a 35 pound shell to a range of 7,300 yards.

WEIGHTS (as packed)

Carriage with howitzer	26cwt 3qtr 14lb
Carriage limber	14cwt 3qtr 14lb
Ammunition wagon	24cwt 1qtr 21lb
Wagon limber	16cwt 0qtr 14lb

Trail

The trail consisted of two flanged side brackets, of toughened nickel steel. These were connected by transoms, a top plate, a bottom plate and a front wrapping plate. Each side bracket was internally reinforced, at the axletree location, by shaped plates and, near the brake arm bearings, by steel T section stays. Two semi-circular, nickel steel bearings formed a seating for the axletree.

A forged steel bearing was riveted between the side brackets to house the carriage body pivot bolt. Anti-friction guides, of gunmetal, were attached to the top surface of the front wrapping plate. Also, gunmetal guides were attached to the trail side brackets. These allowed the carriage body to move smoothly during top traverse.

Locking plates, of forged steel, were riveted to the side brackets towards the rear to prevent damage to the trail by the limber wheels during sharp turns. The trail body, towards the rear, formed a receptacle to house the dial sight carrier. The receptacle was, in effect, a steel tank, padded and lined with leather and provided with fittings to store the carrier. It was closed by a steel, hinged cover fitted with a hasp and turnbuckle which could be padlocked.

A spade, fabricated from toughened nickel steel plates, was riveted to the trail rear end. It had, riveted to it, a trail eye of forged steel. The bearing areas of the eye and the spade bottom edge were deeply hardened. The spade had forged steel lifting handles bolted on.

A mounting bracket for the traversing lever was secured to the top plate, aft of the storage receptacle.

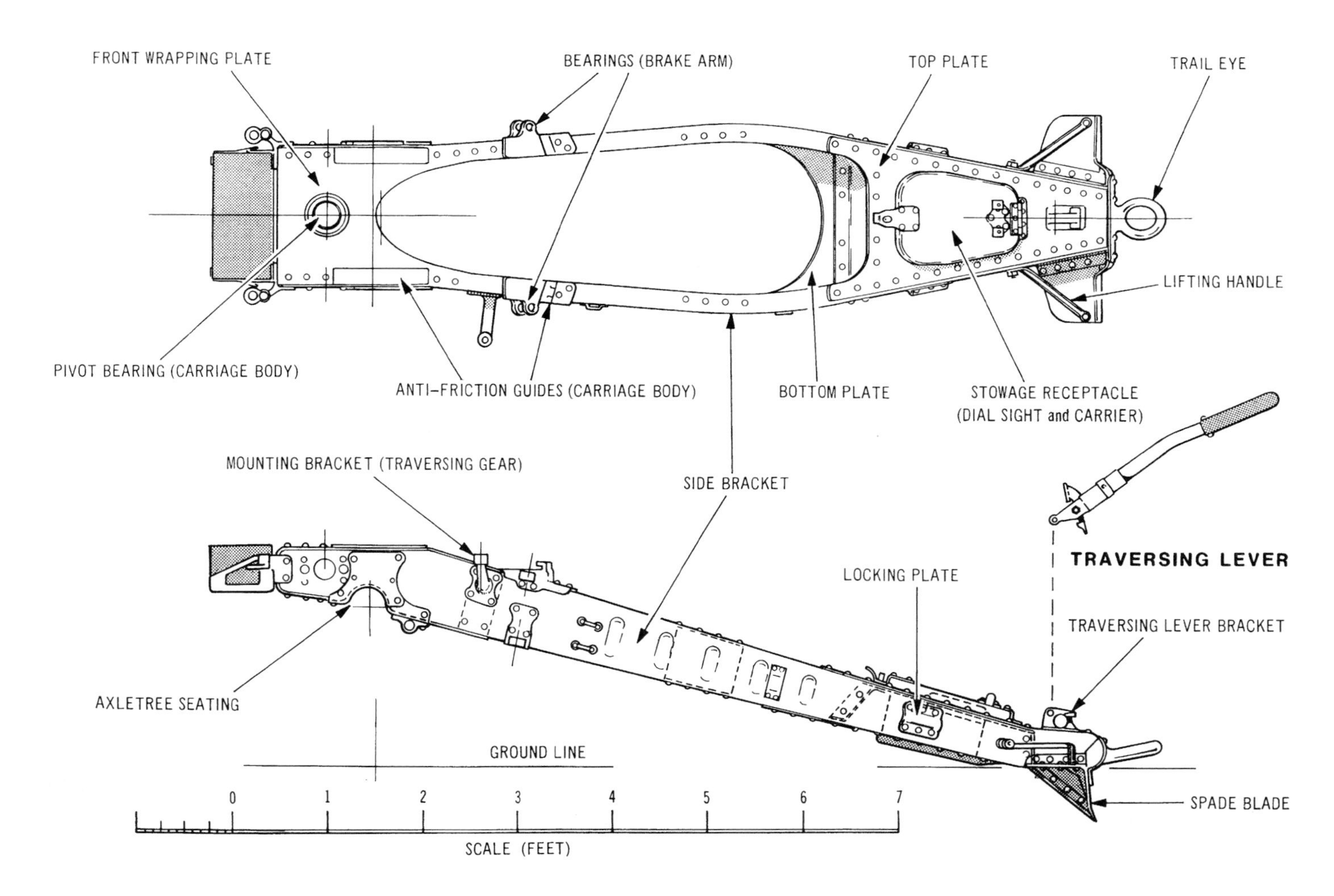
FRONT WRAPPING PLATE
BEARINGS (BRAKE ARM)
TOP PLATE
TRAIL EYE
LIFTING HANDLE
PIVOT BEARING (CARRIAGE BODY)
ANTI–FRICTION GUIDES (CARRIAGE BODY)
BOTTOM PLATE
STOWAGE RECEPTACLE
(DIAL SIGHT and CARRIER)
MOUNTING BRACKET (TRAVERSING GEAR)
SIDE BRACKET
TRAVERSING LEVER
LOCKING PLATE
TRAVERSING LEVER BRACKET
AXLETREE SEATING
GROUND LINE
SPADE BLADE
0
1
2
3
4
5
6
7
SCALE (FEET)

TRAIL

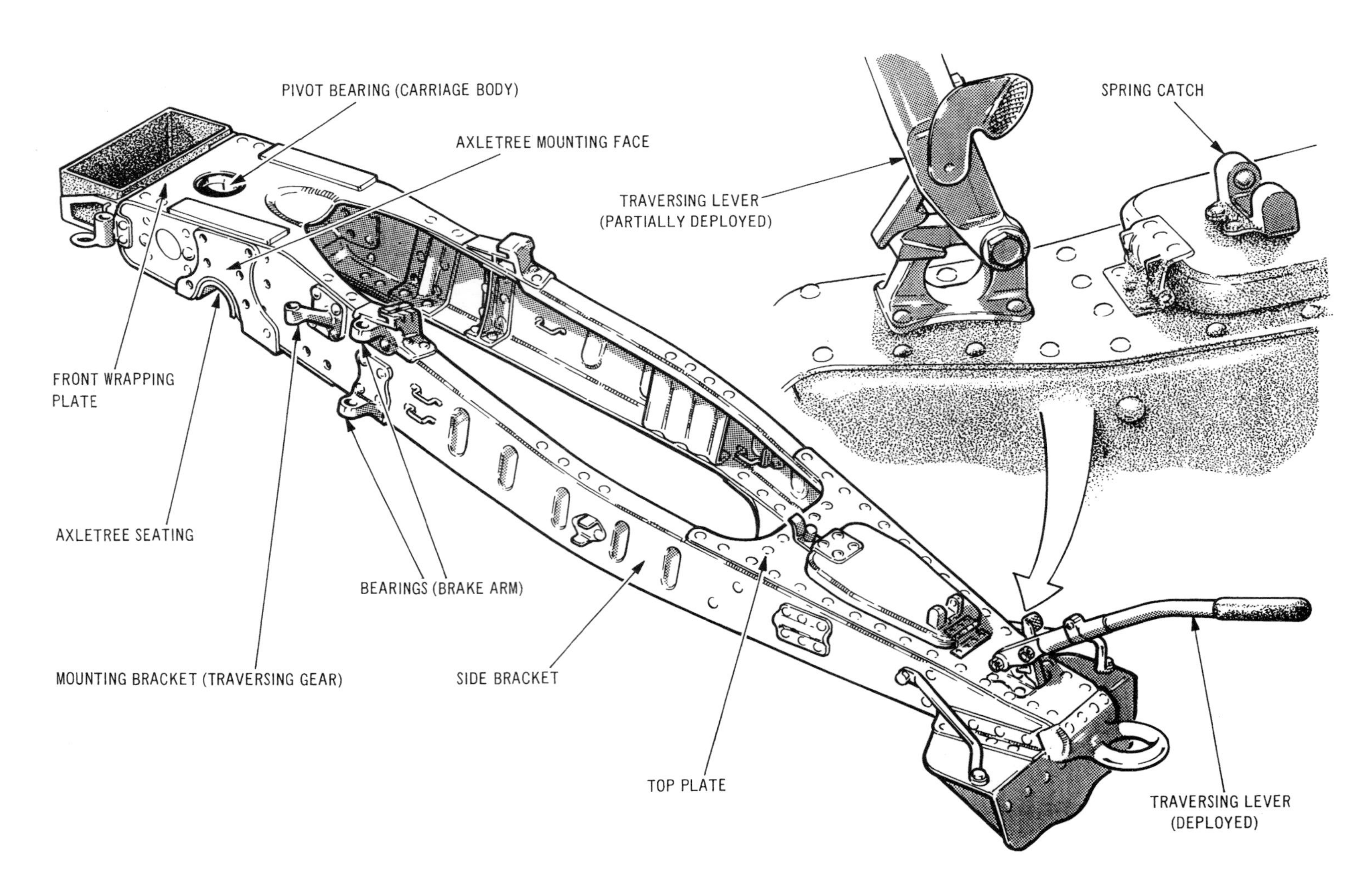
PIVOT BEARING (CARRIAGE BODY)
AXLETREE MOUNTING FACE
TRAVERSING LEVER
(PARTIALLY DEPLOYED)
SPRING CATCH
FRONT WRAPPING
PLATE
AXLETREE SEATING
BEARINGS (BRAKE ARM)
MOUNTING BRACKET (TRAVERSING GEAR)
SIDE BRACKET
TOP PLATE
TRAVERSING LEVER
(DEPLOYED)

TRAIL

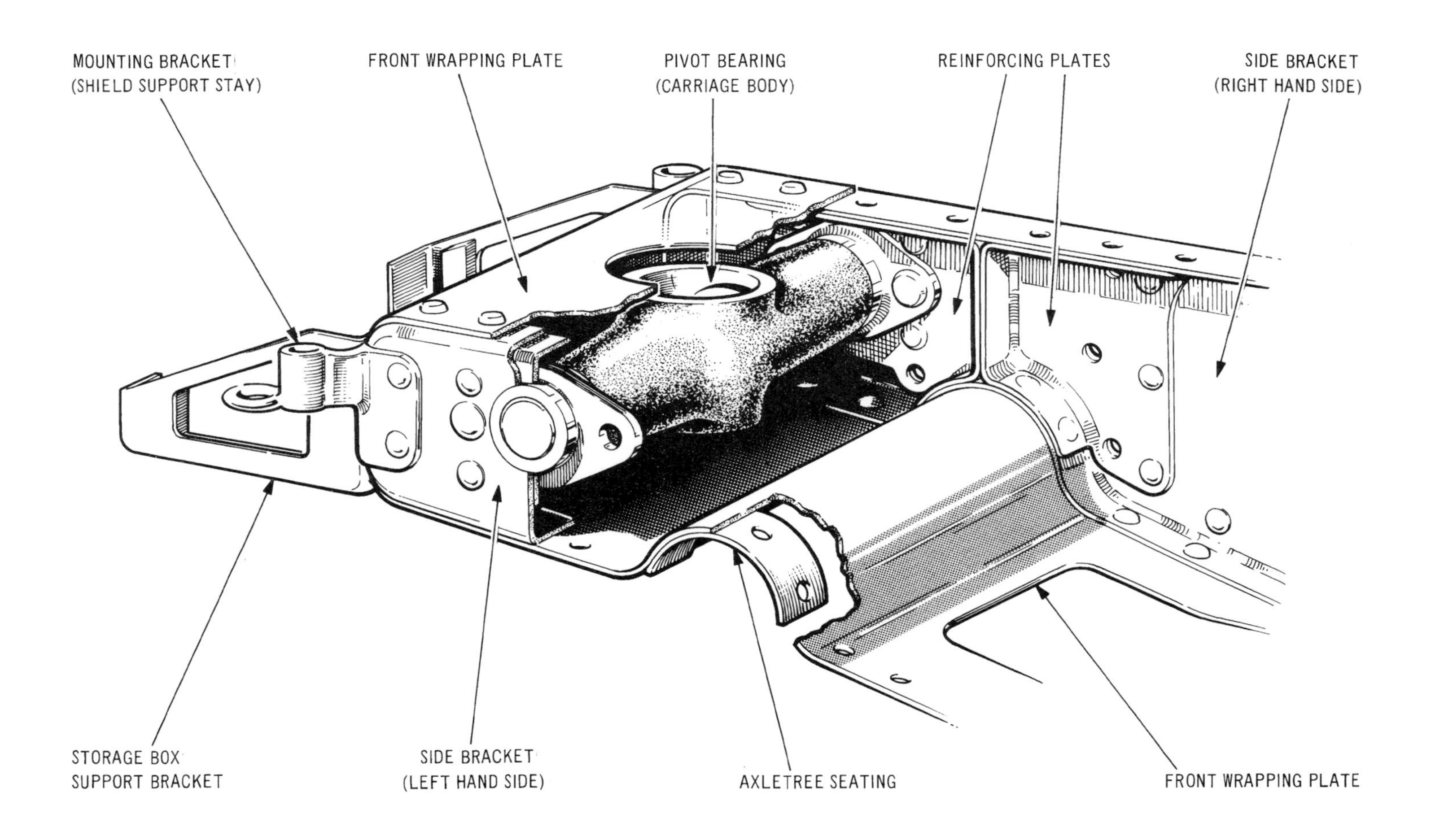

TRAIL – CONSTRUCTION DETAIL

Axletree and swinging arm brake

The axletree body, tubular in section and of nickel steel, was cranked at each end. The arms were of 2nd class C pattern, to carry 2nd class C pattern, No. 45 wheels. In an emergency, the No. 200A wheel could be used.

The axletree fitted to the trail from below, the cranked portions mating with reinforcing plates on the trail side brackets and secured with bolts and nuts. Each axletree shoulder was equipped with a forged steel bracket to house an L leather dust seal, into which fitted the wheel pipebox inner end.

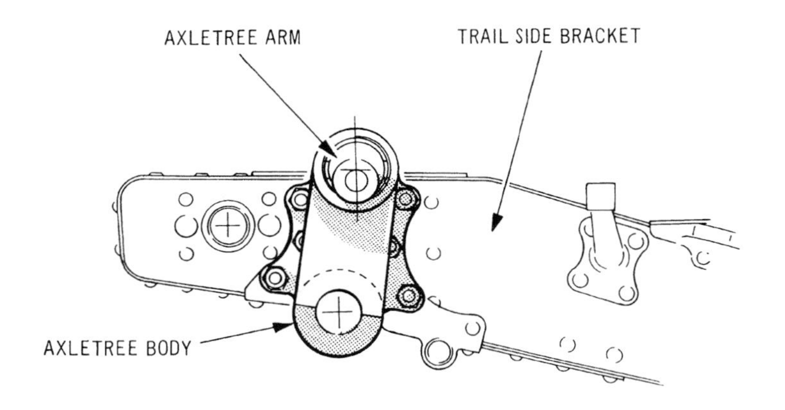

VIEW ON LEFT SIDE

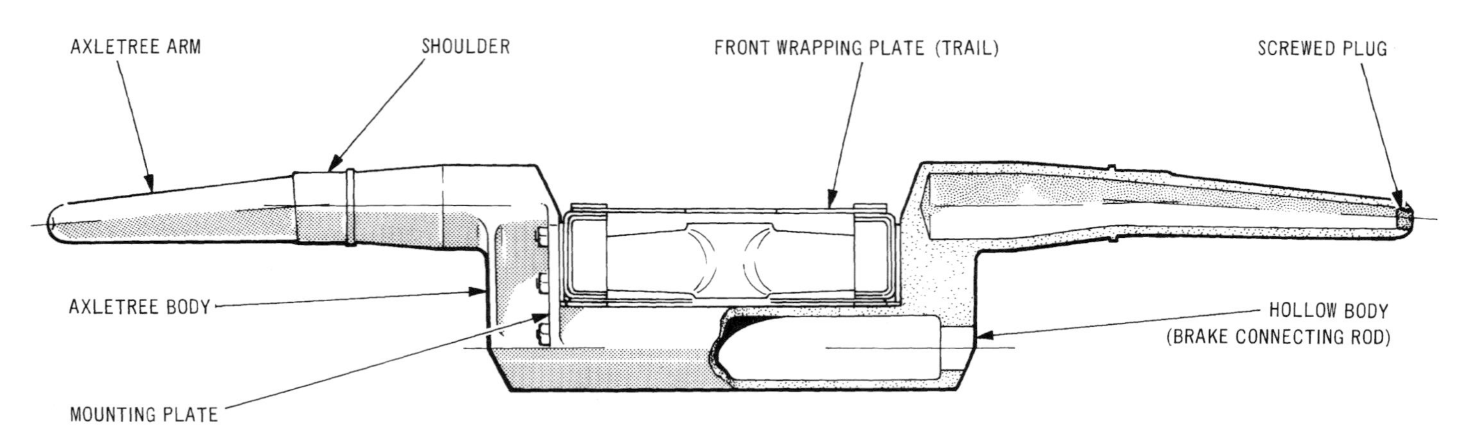

VIEW ON REAR

AXLETREE

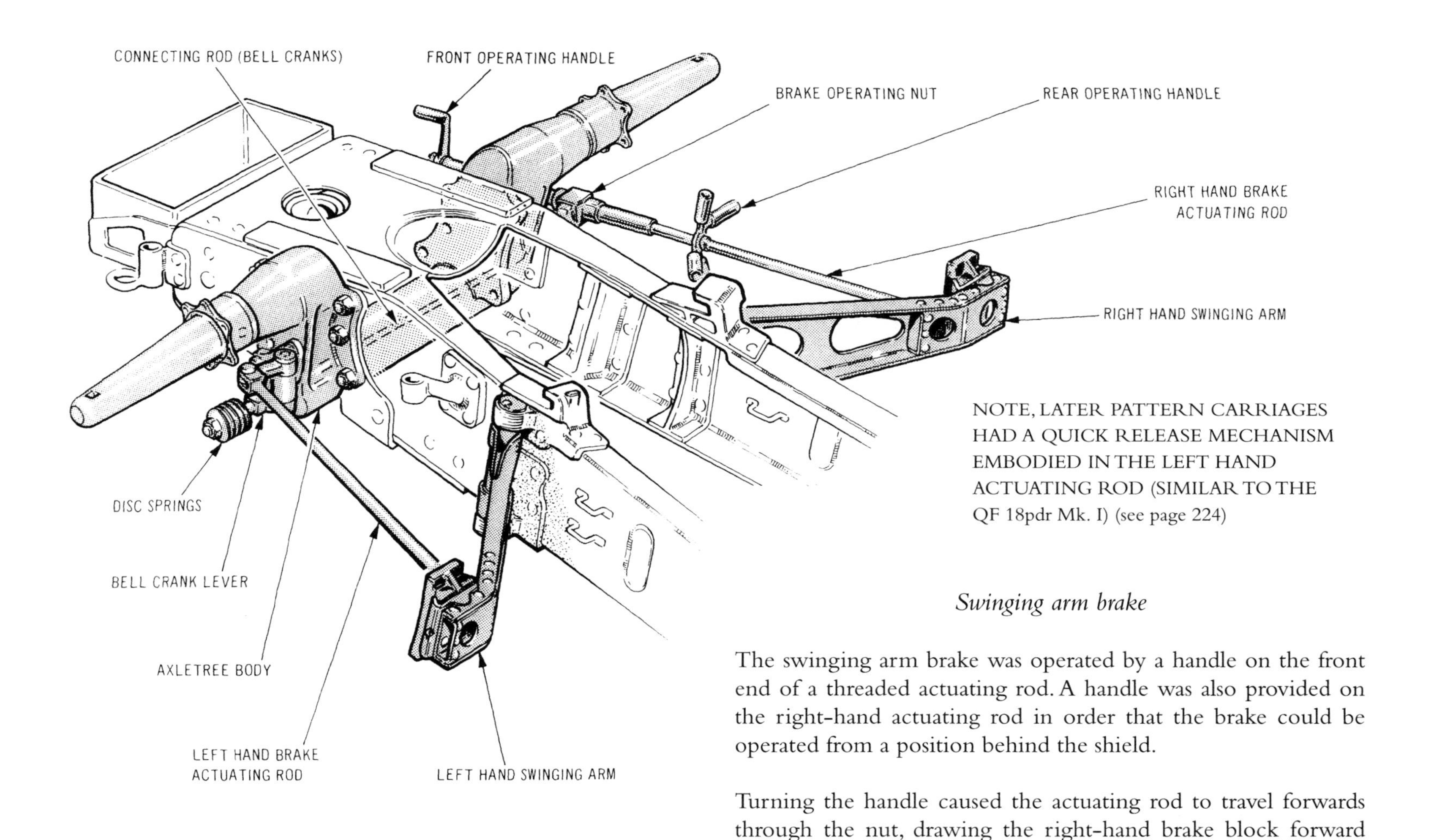

SWINGING ARM BRAKE

Swinging arm brake

The swinging arm brake was operated by a handle on the front end of a threaded actuating rod. A handle was also provided on the right-hand actuating rod in order that the brake could be operated from a position behind the shield.

Turning the handle caused the actuating rod to travel forwards through the nut, drawing the right-hand brake block forward onto the wheel. The nut then travelled rearwards, moving the connecting rods by means of the cranked levers, and drawing the left-hand brake block to contact the wheel.

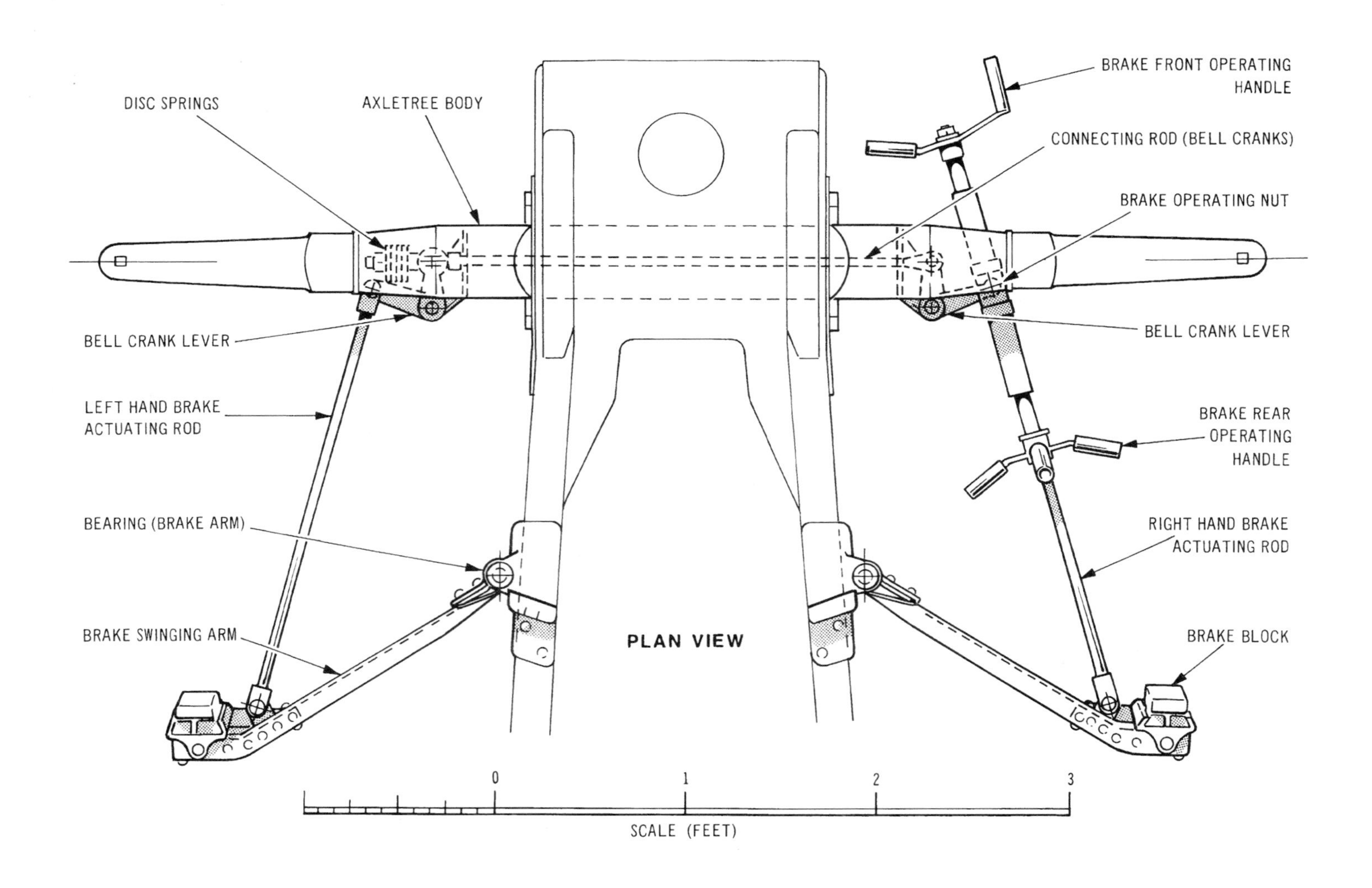

AXLETREE AND SWINGING ARM BRAKE

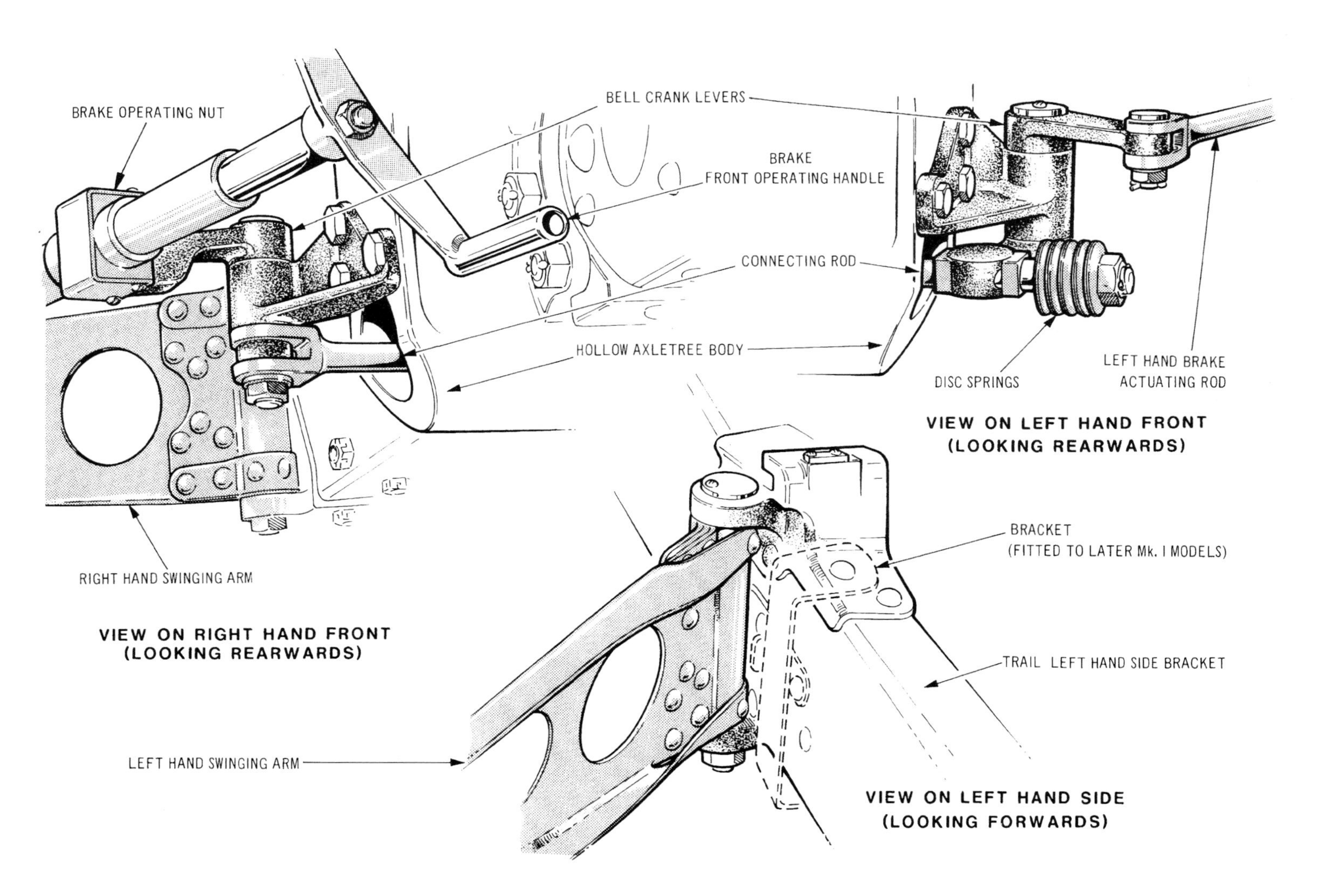

SWINGING ARM BRAKE – DETAIL

Disc springs cushioned the effect of the brake which should, however, be locked on hard before firing.

Carriage body

The carriage body consisted of two side brackets, of flanged nickel steel plate, joined by a pivot plate and a wrapping plate, both of steel, riveted on.

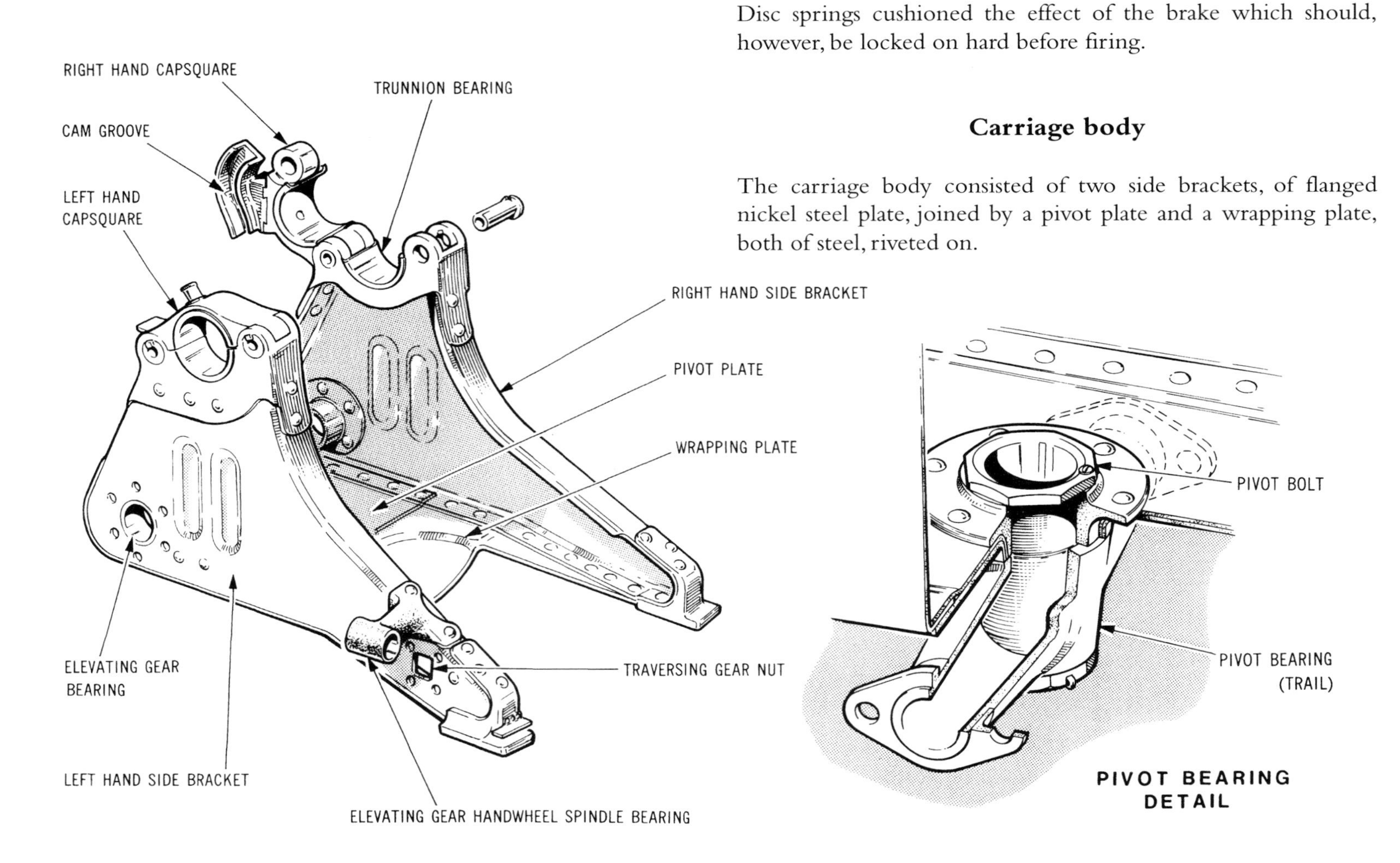

CARRIAGE BODY

The pivot plate had a manganese bronze bush, fitted centrally, which housed the pivot bolt. The pivot bolt passed vertically downwards through the trail pivot bearing and was secured by a nut and split pin.

The carriage body rested on the trail front wrapping plate anti-friction guides and was free to rotate, to three degrees either side of the centre line, for top traverse. A projecting bracket, on the rear of each side bracket, engaged the anti-friction guides which were formed as part of the trail-mounted top bearings for the brake arms.

The upper part of each carriage body side bracket was fitted with a forged steel half-bearing, fitted with a manganese bronze liner to receive the cradle trunnions. The trunnions were secured by forged steel capsquares, also lined with manganese bronze. The right-hand capsquare was fitted with a cam groove, which actuated the recoil controlling gear.

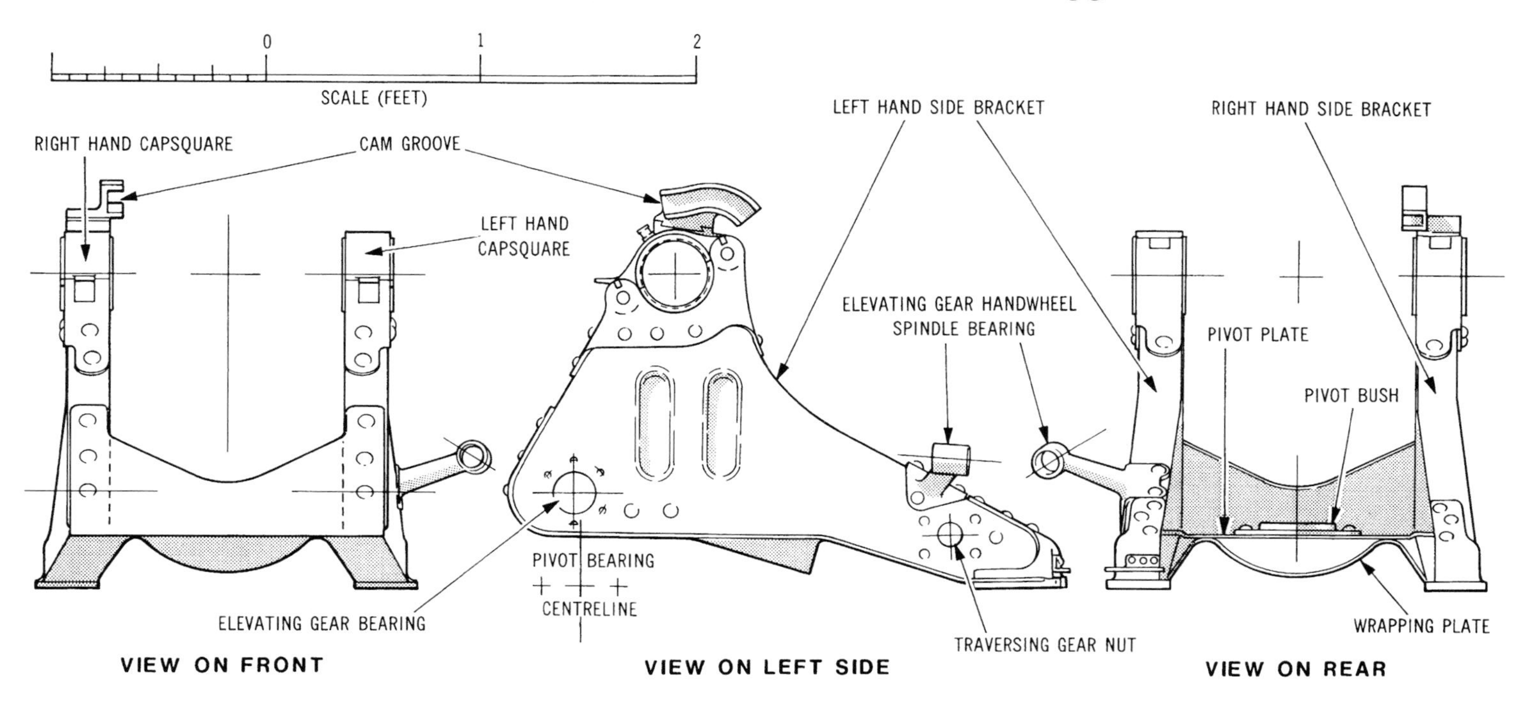

CARRIAGE BODY

A manganese bronze bearing was secured to each side bracket to house the elevating gear arc pinion spindle. The left side bracket carried a projecting bracket towards the rear, riveted on, to support the elevating gear handwheel spindle. Below this bracket was secured the traversing gear nut.

Cradle

The cradle was, in effect, the central component of the gun. It was mounted into the carriage body trunnion bearings and secured by capsquares. Mounted centrally within the cradle was the hydraulic buffer surrounded by the spring recuperator. The buffer piston rod was secured, at its forward end, to the cradle front cap by a square nut and connecting key. The recuperator springs reacted, at the rear end, against a gunmetal washer fitted into a transom riveted within the cradle body. The gunmetal washer also served as a guide for the hydraulic buffer cylinder. Within the transom was a stop for the barrel lug, consisting of a bank of leather washers.

The spring compressor had a head, at the front end, with guides to engage the ribs formed on the interior of the cradle body.

The cradle body was a drawn steel tube, basically of U section, closed at the top. Each flat side terminated at the top with flanges, these were the slides along which the barrel travelled during recoil. Internal ribs formed guides for the spring compressor head.

The cradle front cap was secured by three hinged bolts with nuts and lock nuts. In addition to securing the hydraulic buffer piston rod, the cap had, mounted on the interior face, some components of the recoil controlling gear.

Riveted around the cradle, near its centre, was a forged steel trunnion bracket. The bracket trunnion ends were threaded for nuts which retained the elevating gear arcs. The trunnion bracket right-hand side carried a vertical sliding guide bar, which operated the recoil controlling gear through a longitudinal, forged steel rod, carried within the cradle on the right-hand side.

Mounted on the cradle exterior at the rear was an operating handle and mechanism, which worked in conjunction with the elevating gear, allowing the cradle to be rapidly depressed to the loading position when firing the howitzer at angles of high elevation.

These various mechanisms are described in detail within the relevant sections which follow.

Elevating gear and quick motion mechanism (see page 316)

The elevating gear was divided into two sections: the actual elevating gear and the quick motion mechanism.

The elevating gear handwheel was connected, through a longitudinal spindle, to a worm and wormwheel, this in turn drove a cross spindle carrying two pinions. Each pinion was in gear with a toothed elevating arc, each arc free to pivot about its mounting on a carriage body trunnion.

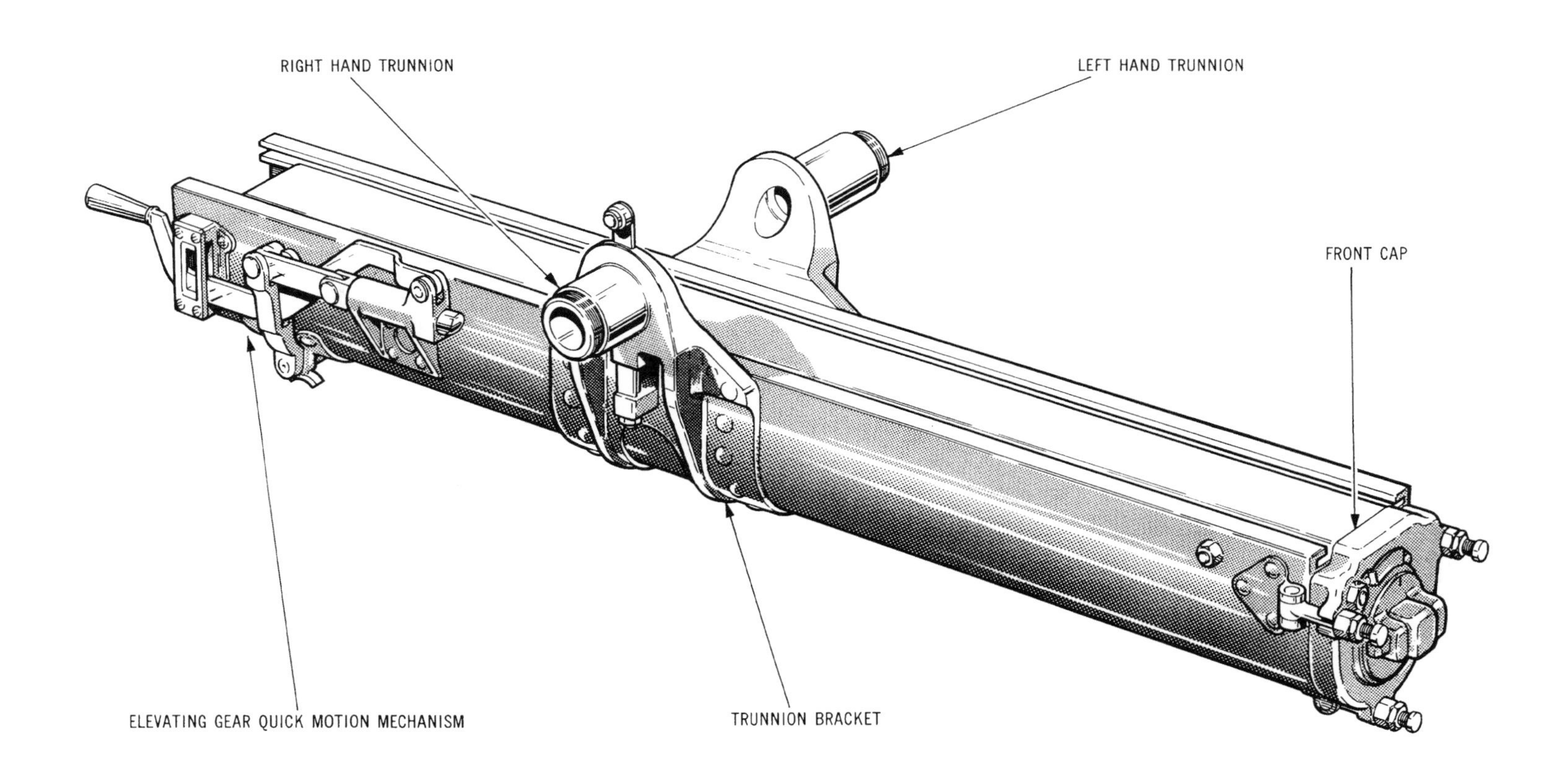
RIGHT HAND TRUNNION
LEFT HAND TRUNNION
FRONT CAP
ELEVATING GEAR QUICK MOTION MECHANISM
TRUNNION BRACKET

CRADLE

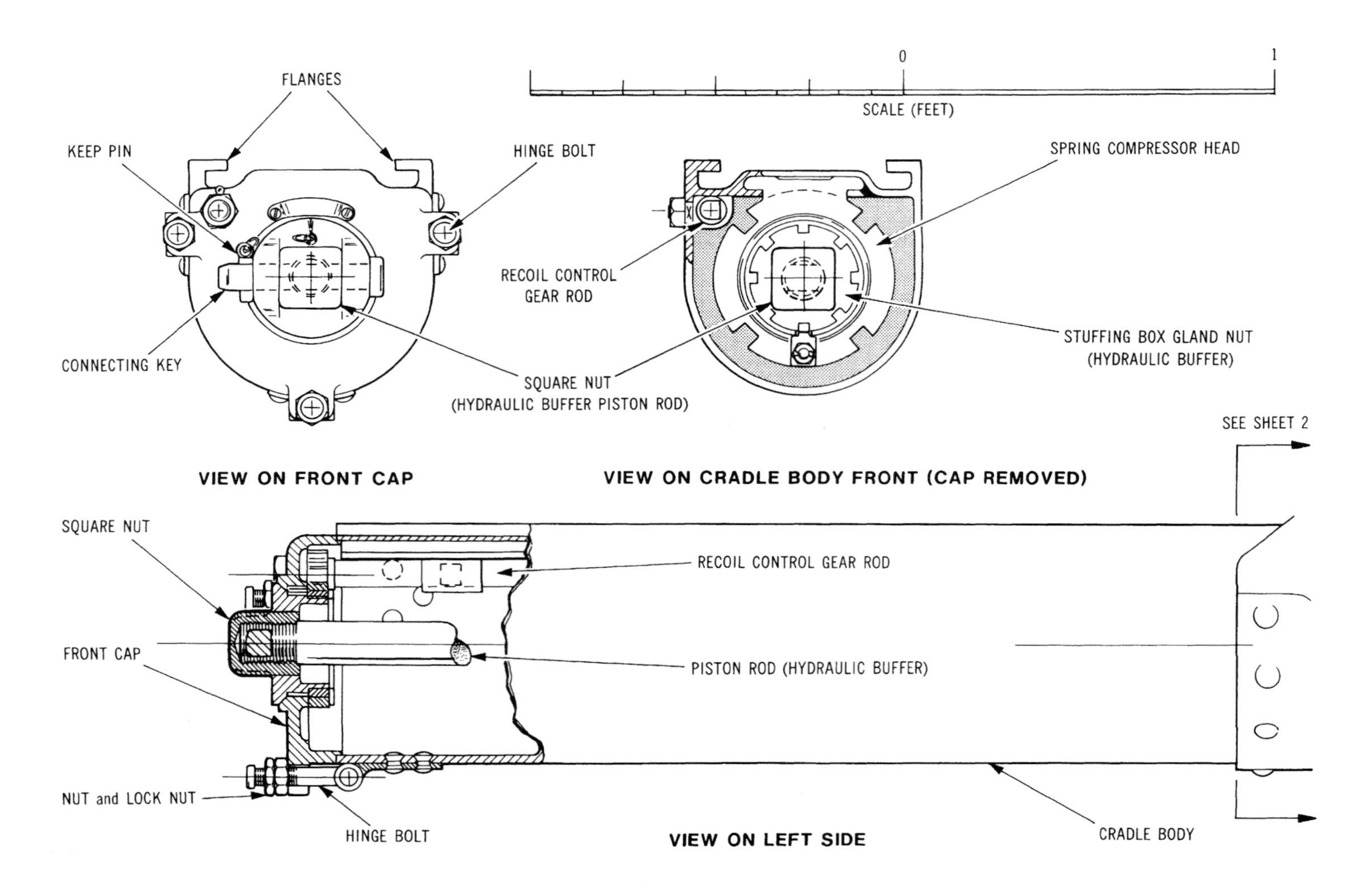

0
1
SCALE (FEET)
FLANGES
KEEP PIN
HINGE BOLT
CONNECTING KEY
SQUARE NUT
(HYDRAULIC BUFFER PISTON ROD)
SPRING COMPRESSOR HEAD
RECOIL CONTROL
GEAR ROD
STUFFING BOX GLAND NUT
(HYDRAULIC BUFFER)
SEE SHEET 2
VIEW ON FRONT CAP
VIEW ON CRADLE BODY FRONT (CAP REMOVED)
SQUARE NUT
RECOIL CONTROL GEAR ROD
FRONT CAP
PISTON ROD (HYDRAULIC BUFFER)
NUT and LOCK NUT
HINGE BOLT
VIEW ON LEFT SIDE
CRADLE BODY

CRADLE

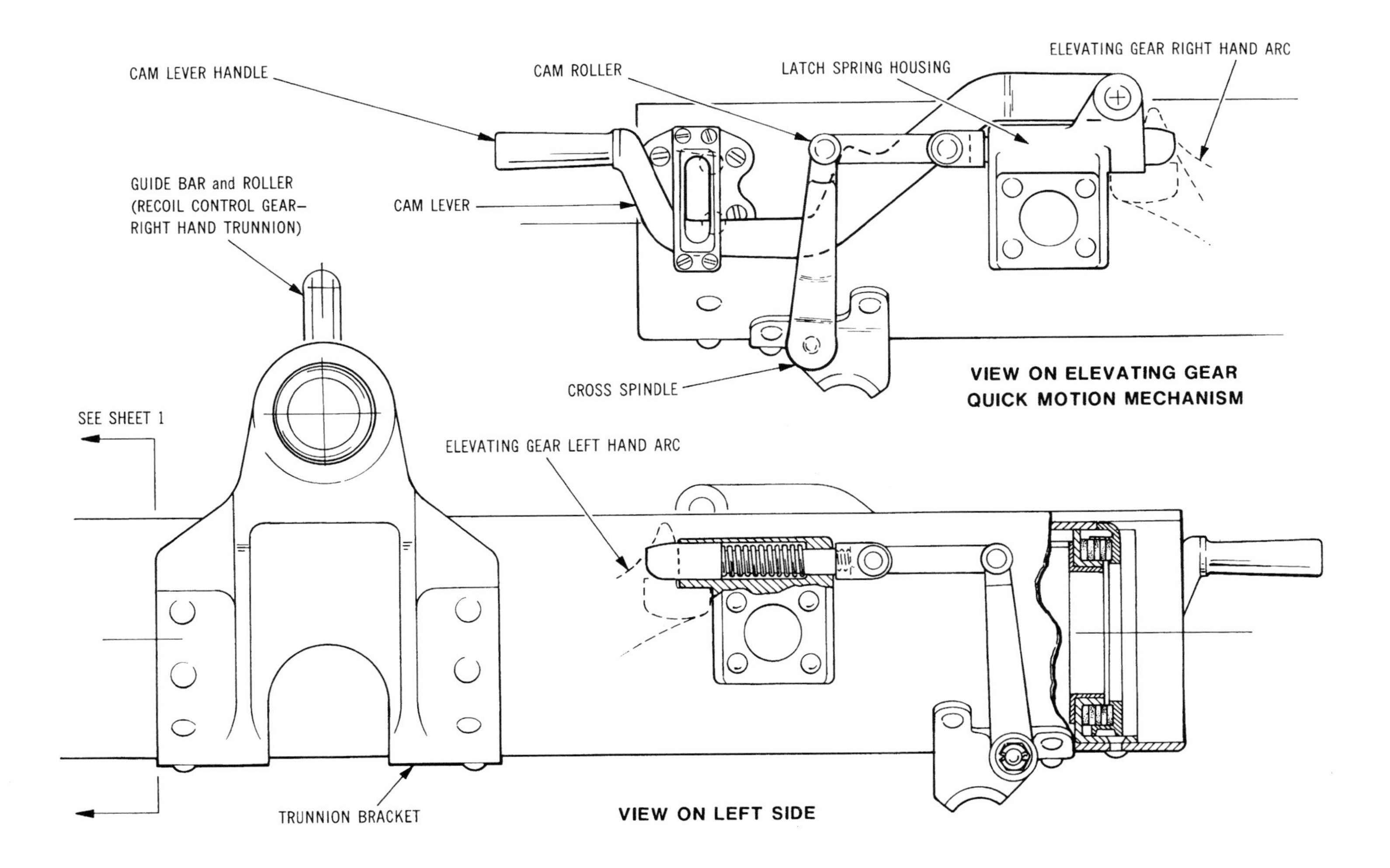

CAM LEVER HANDLE
CAM ROLLER
LATCH SPRING HOUSING
ELEVATING GEAR RIGHT HAND ARC
GUIDE BAR and ROLLER
(RECOIL CONTROL GEAR-
RIGHT HAND TRUNNION)
CAM LEVER
CROSS SPINDLE
VIEW ON ELEVATING GEAR
QUICK MOTION MECHANISM
SEE SHEET 1
ELEVATING GEAR LEFT HAND ARC
TRUNNION BRACKET
VIEW ON LEFT SIDE

CRADLE

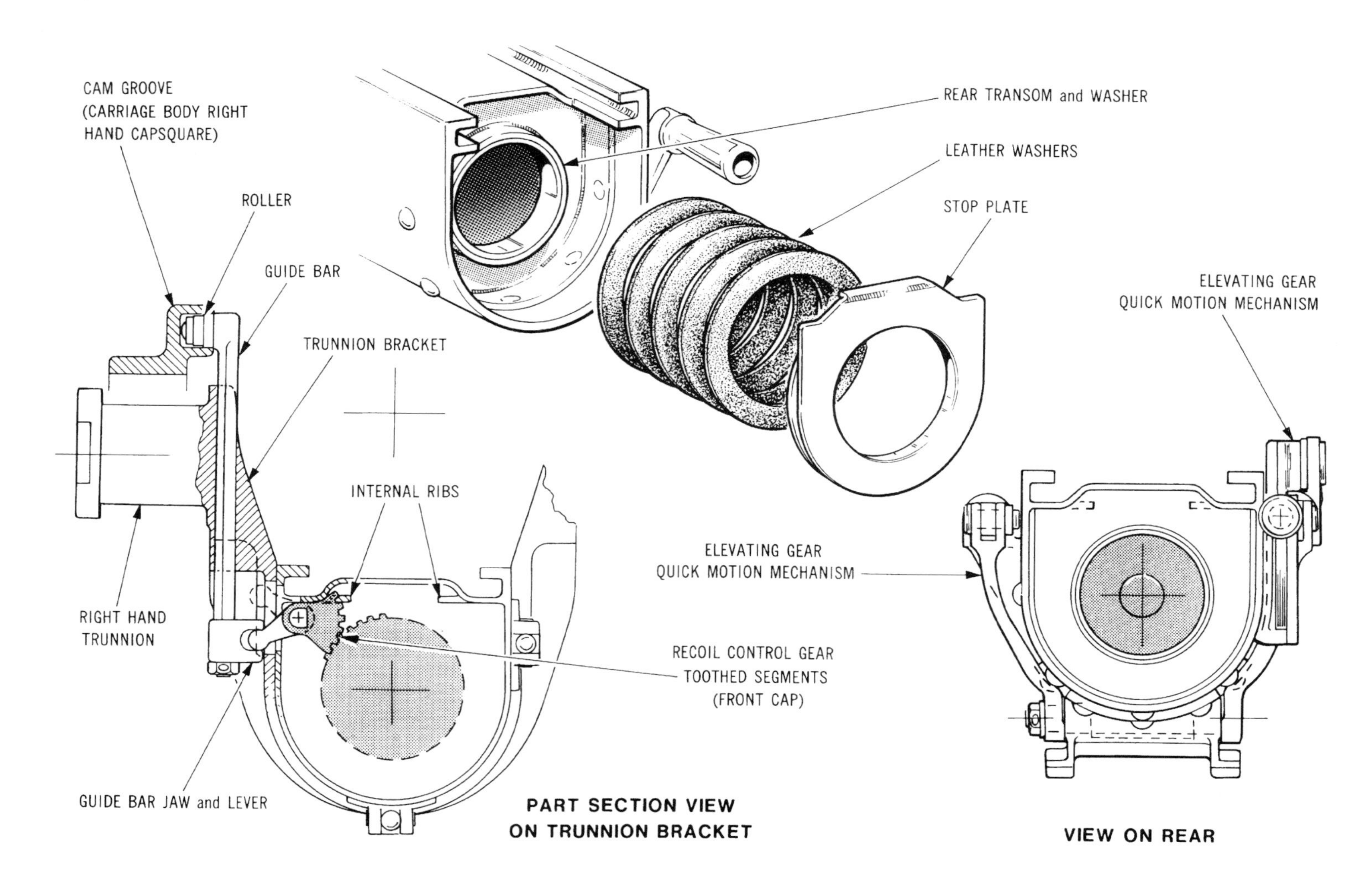

CRADLE DETAIL

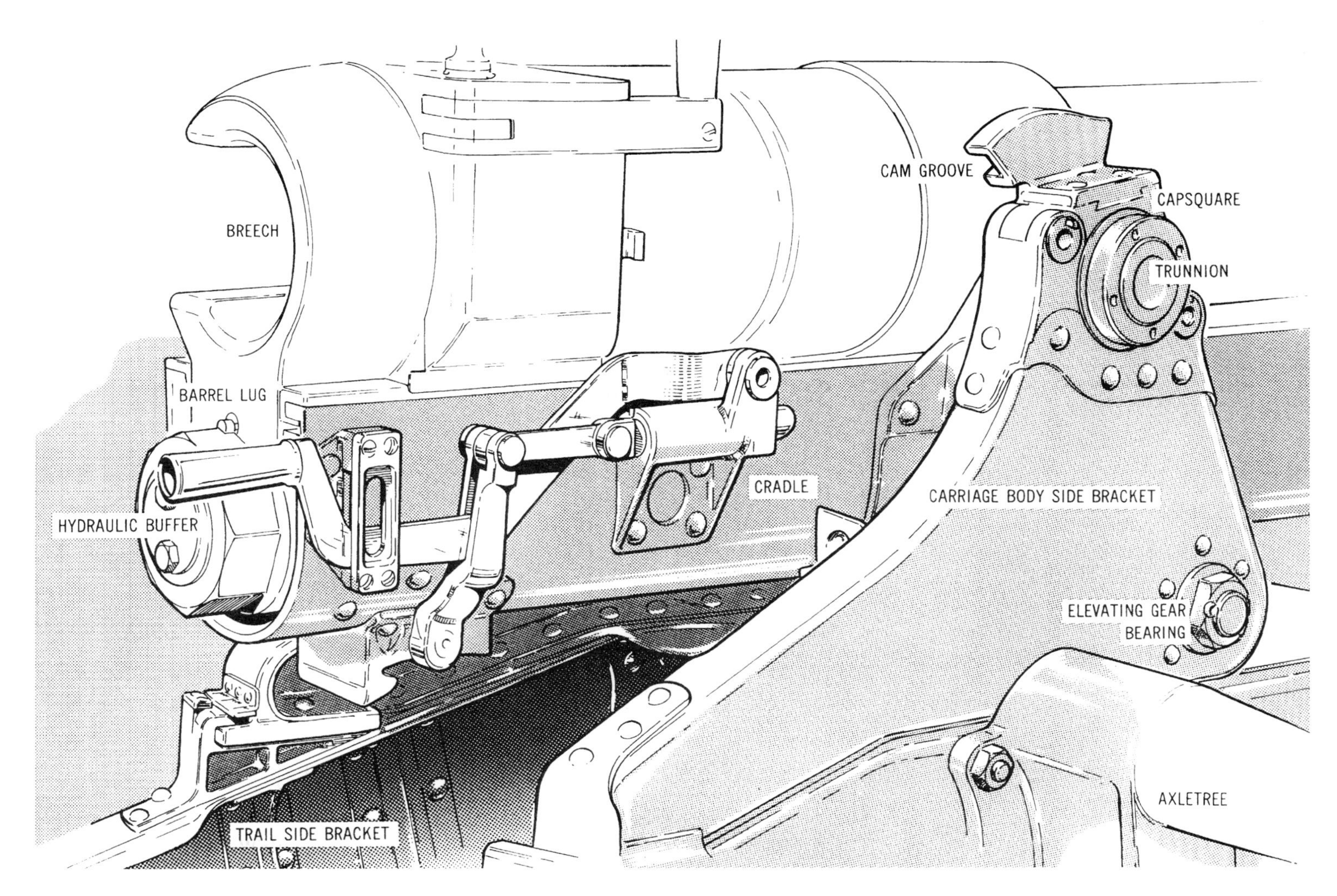

VIEW OF MAJOR ASSEMBLIES (RIGHT HAND SIDE)

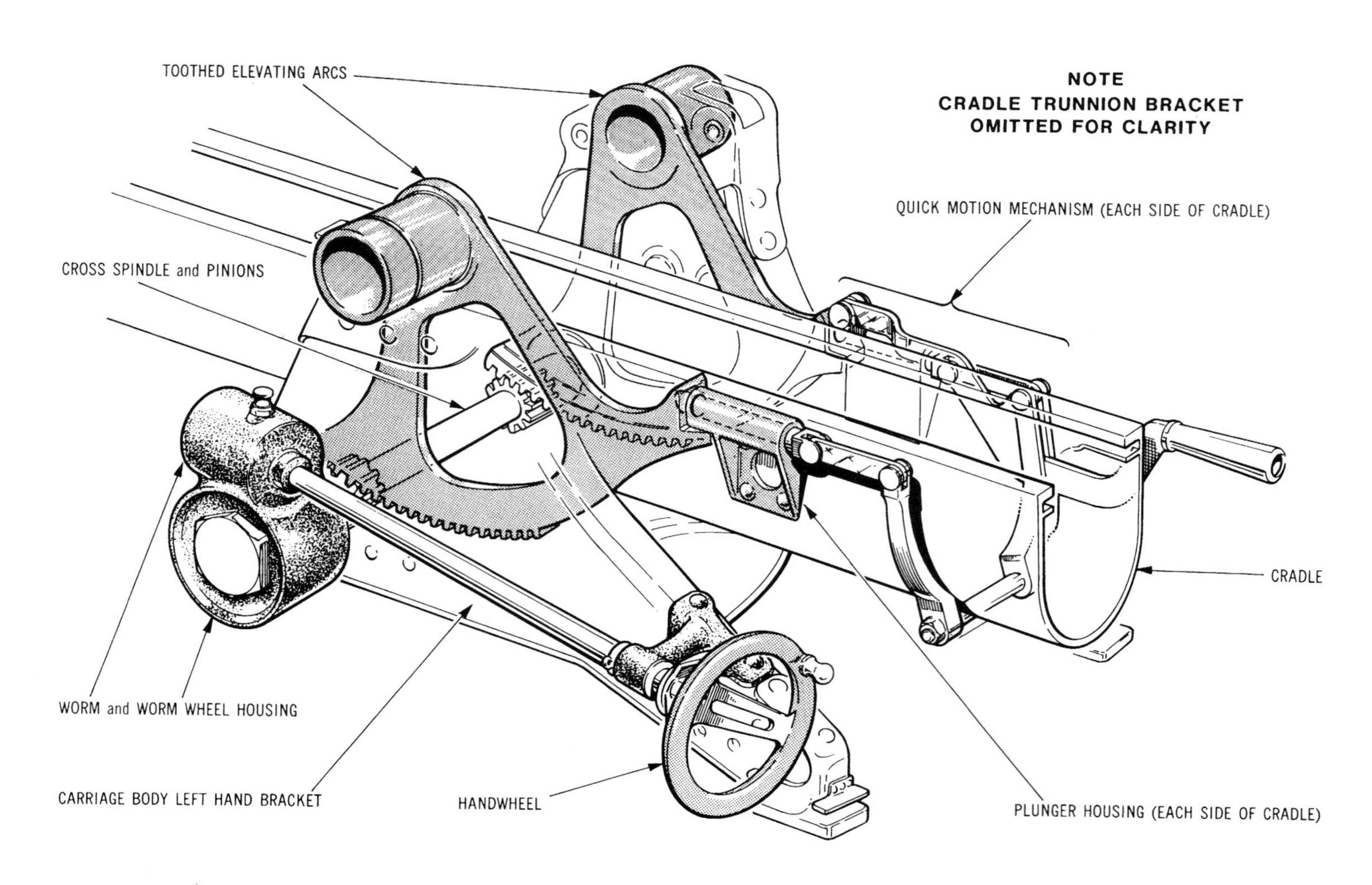

ELEVATING GEAR AND QUICK MOTION MECHANISM

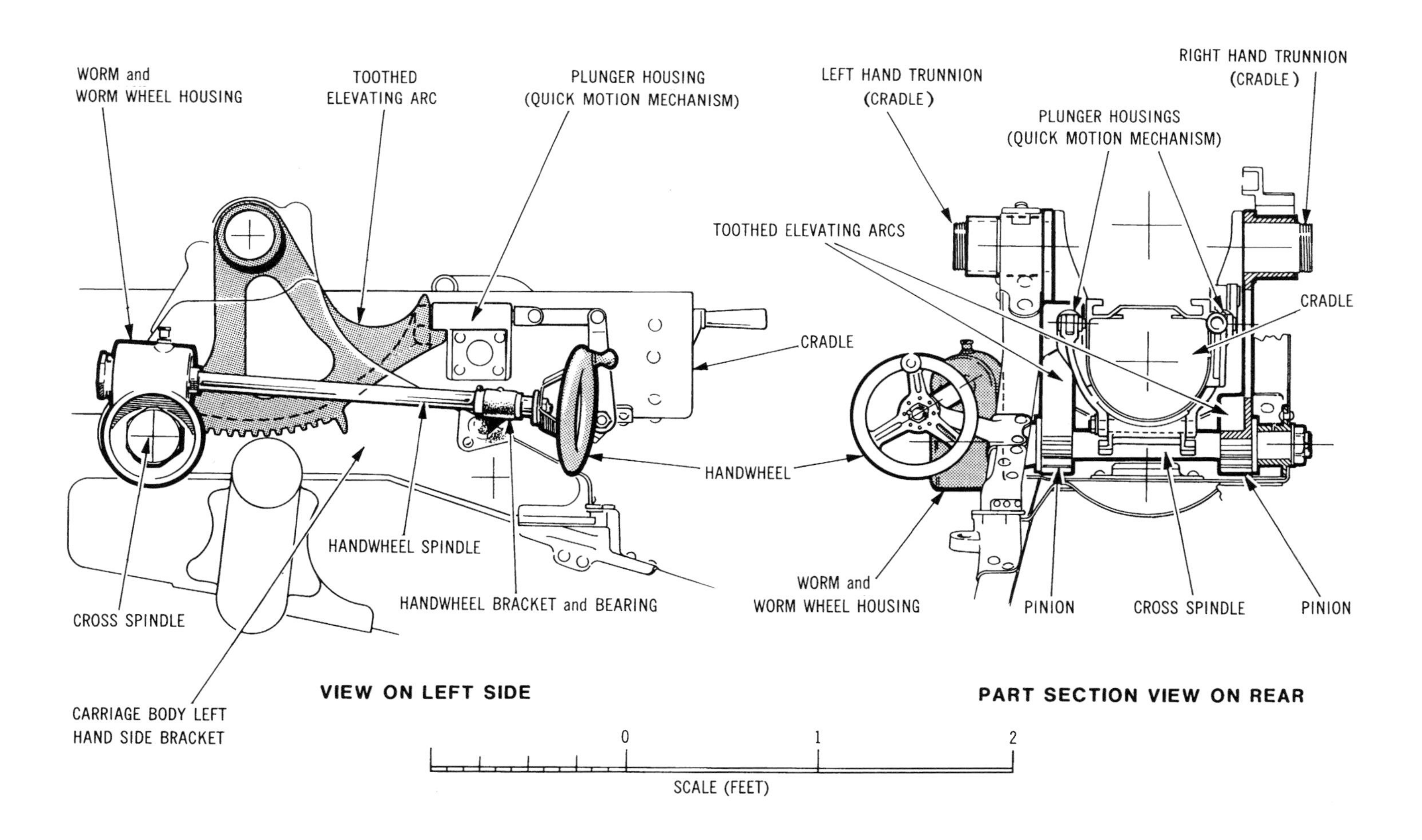

ELEVATING GEAR

The toothed elevating arcs had their rear portions extended to form stops, each stop engaging a spring plunger housing riveted to the side of the cradle. These spring plunger housings were the connecting points which conveyed the elevating gear motion to the cradle and were components of the quick motion mechanism.

The quick motion mechanism handle would be lifted (**B** to **C**), this action moving the spring-loaded latches out of engagement

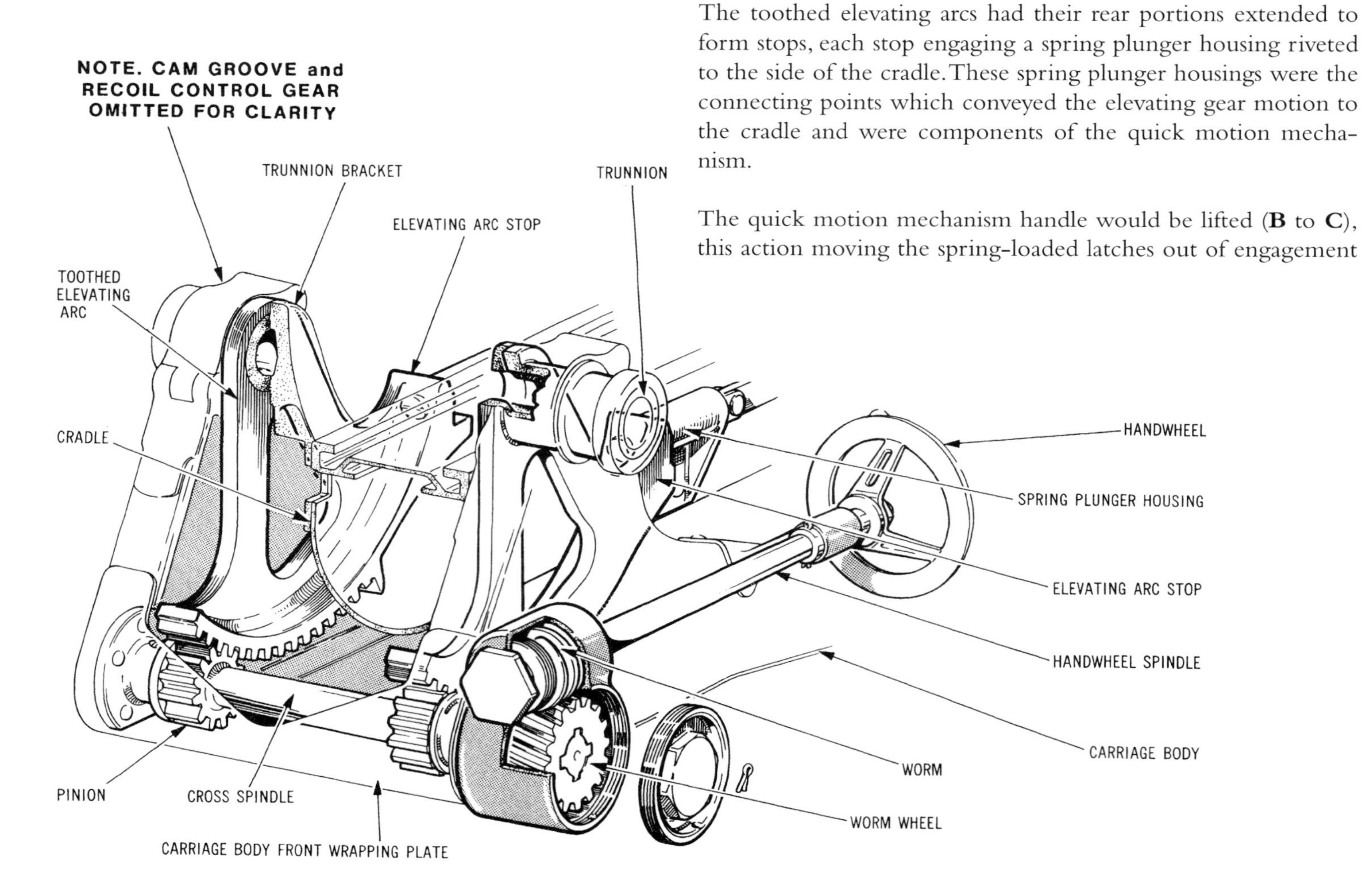

ELEVATING GEAR

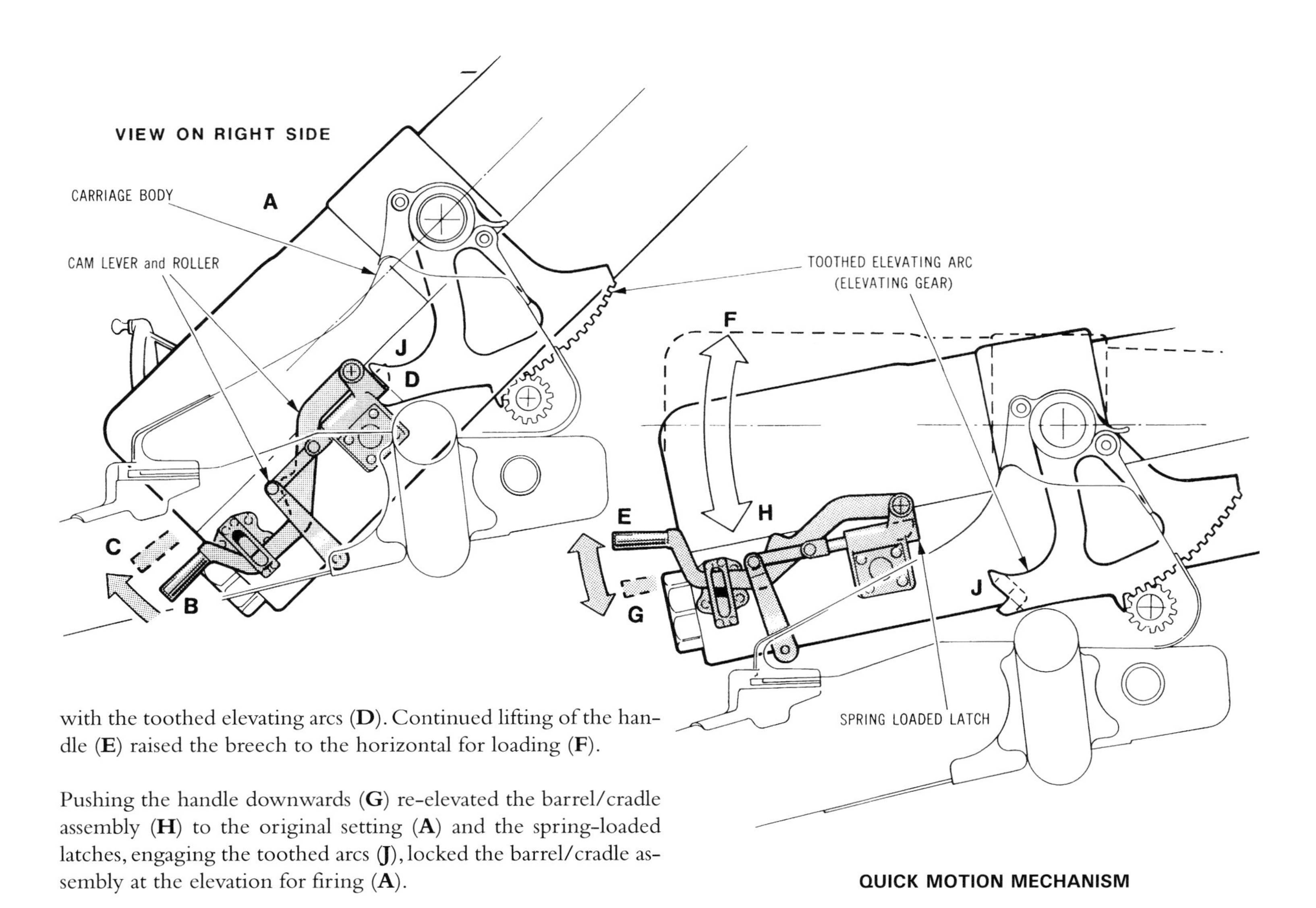

with the toothed elevating arcs (**D**). Continued lifting of the handle (**E**) raised the breech to the horizontal for loading (**F**).

Pushing the handle downwards (**G**) re-elevated the barrel/cradle assembly (**H**) to the original setting (**A**) and the spring-loaded latches, engaging the toothed arcs (**J**), locked the barrel/cradle assembly at the elevation for firing (**A**).

QUICK MOTION MECHANISM

When firing at high angles of elevation (**A**), the barrel/cradle assembly could be disengaged from the elevating gear and depressed to the horizontal for loading, without disturbing the elevating gear proper or sighting gear.

Traversing gear

The traversing gear enabled three degrees of movement either side of the trail centre line. The angle of traverse was indicated by a pointer on the trail reading against a graduated scale on the

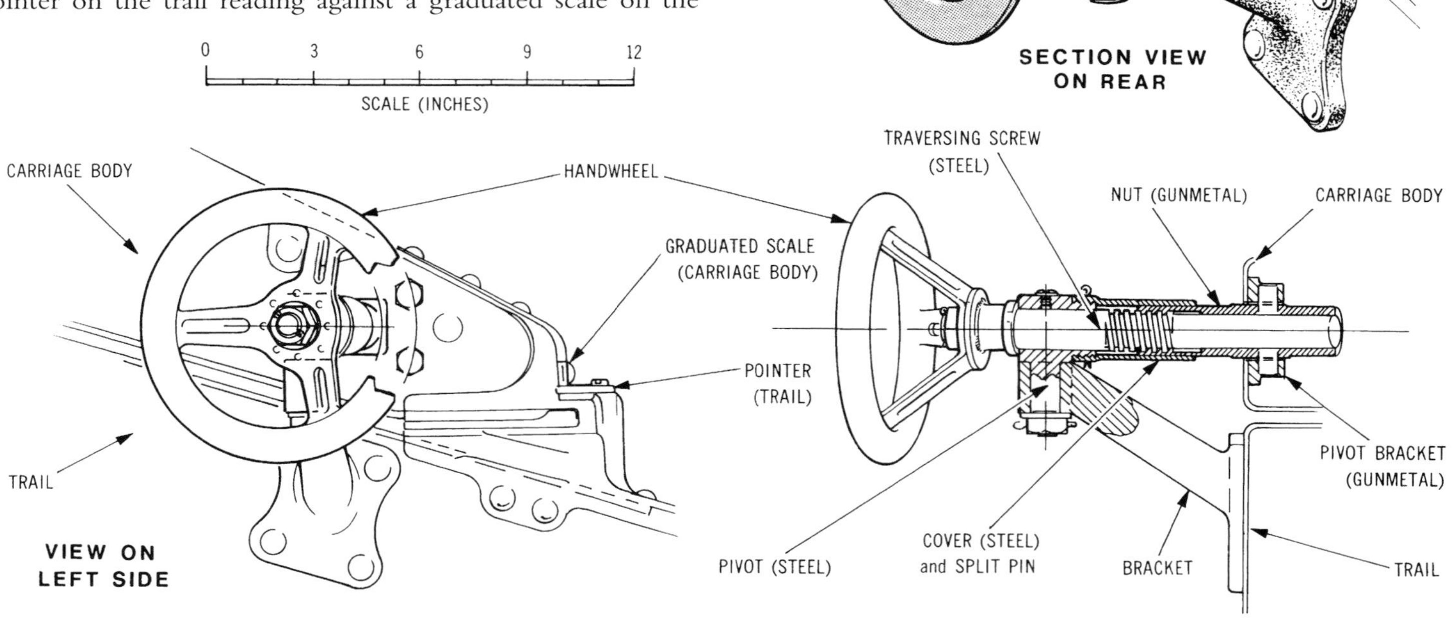

TRAVERSING GEAR

carriage body. In travelling, the carriage body would be locked to the trail with a steel pin. This prevented damage to the traversing gear by shock or vibration.

Early handwheels were built up with a steel central boss and mahogany rim, the rim covered with leather. Later handwheel rims were of gunmetal.

Cradle clamping gear

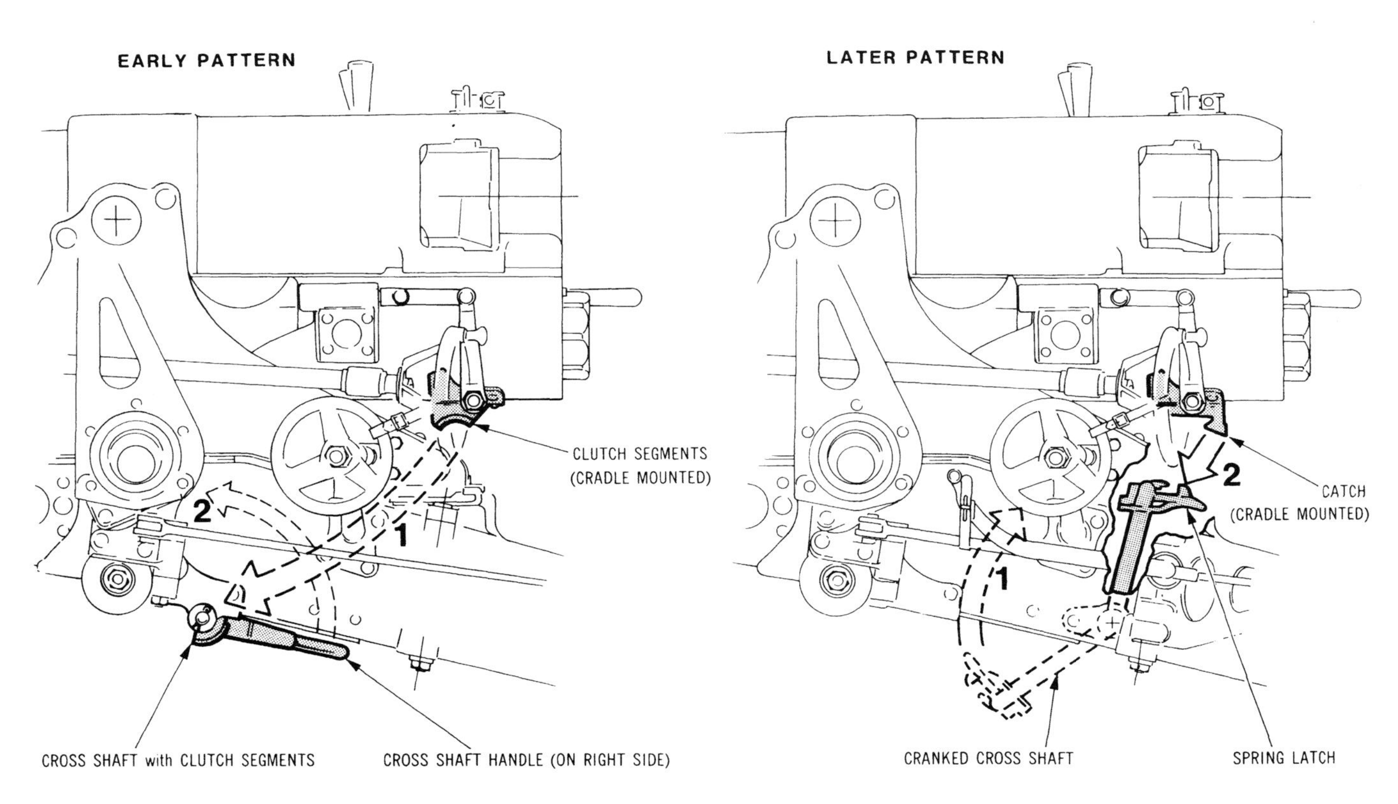

CRADLE CLAMPING GEAR (FOR TRAVELLING)

Hydraulic buffer and springs (see page 327)

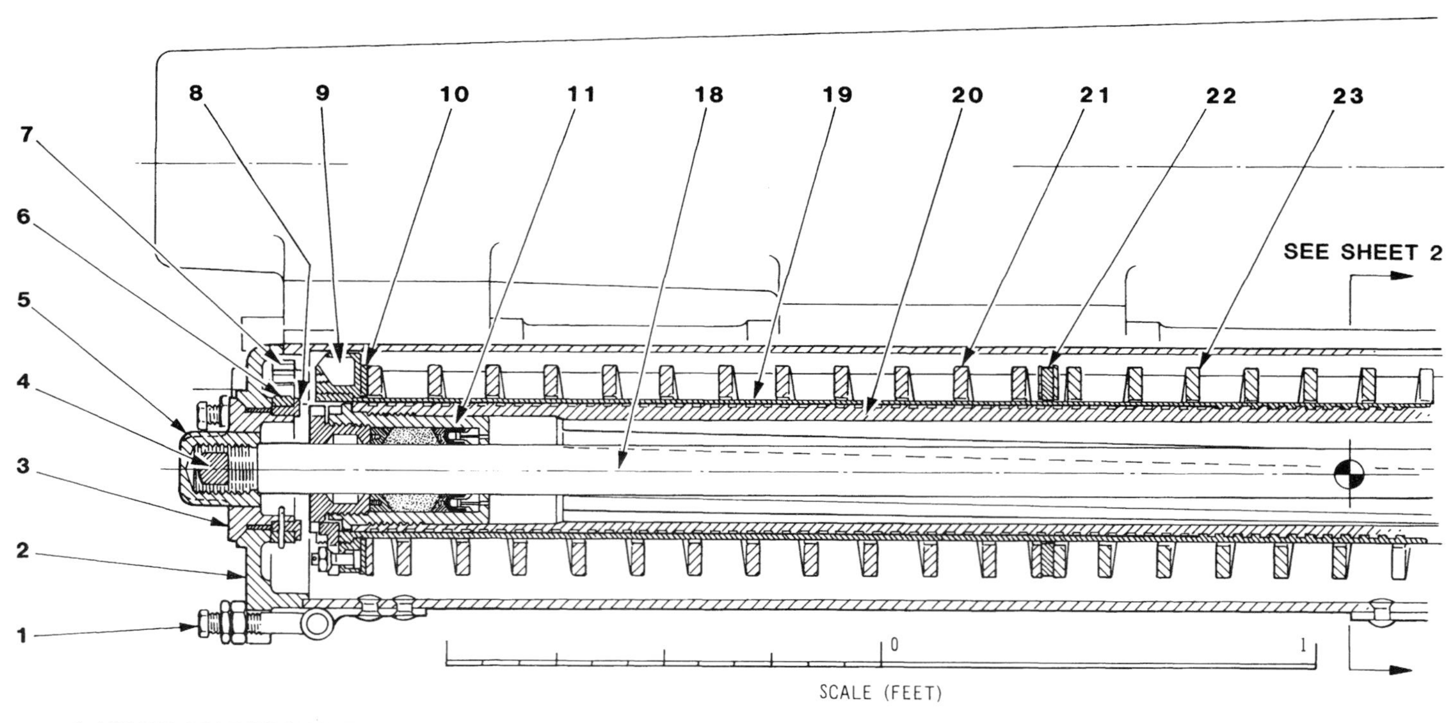

1 HINGED BOLT WITH NUT AND LOCK NUT
2 FRONT CAP (CRADLE)
3 PISTON ROD COUPLING WITH BUSH
4 COUPLING PIN
5 PISTON ROD FRONT NUT
6 TOOTHED COLLAR
7 TOOTHED ARC AND ROD (RECOIL CONTROLLING GEAR)
8 RETAINING RING
9 SPRING COMPRESSOR HEAD
10 PARTING PLATE (THIN)
11 STUFFING BOX ASSEMBLY COMPRISING 12–17
12 GLAND (PHOSPHOR BRONZE)
13 FRONT SUPPORTING RING
14 PACKING RING (ASBESTOS)
15 REAR SUPPORTING RING (BRONZE)
16 U PACKING RING (LEATHER)
17 SECURING RING (BRONZE)
18 PISTON ROD

HYDRAULIC BUFFER AND SPRINGS

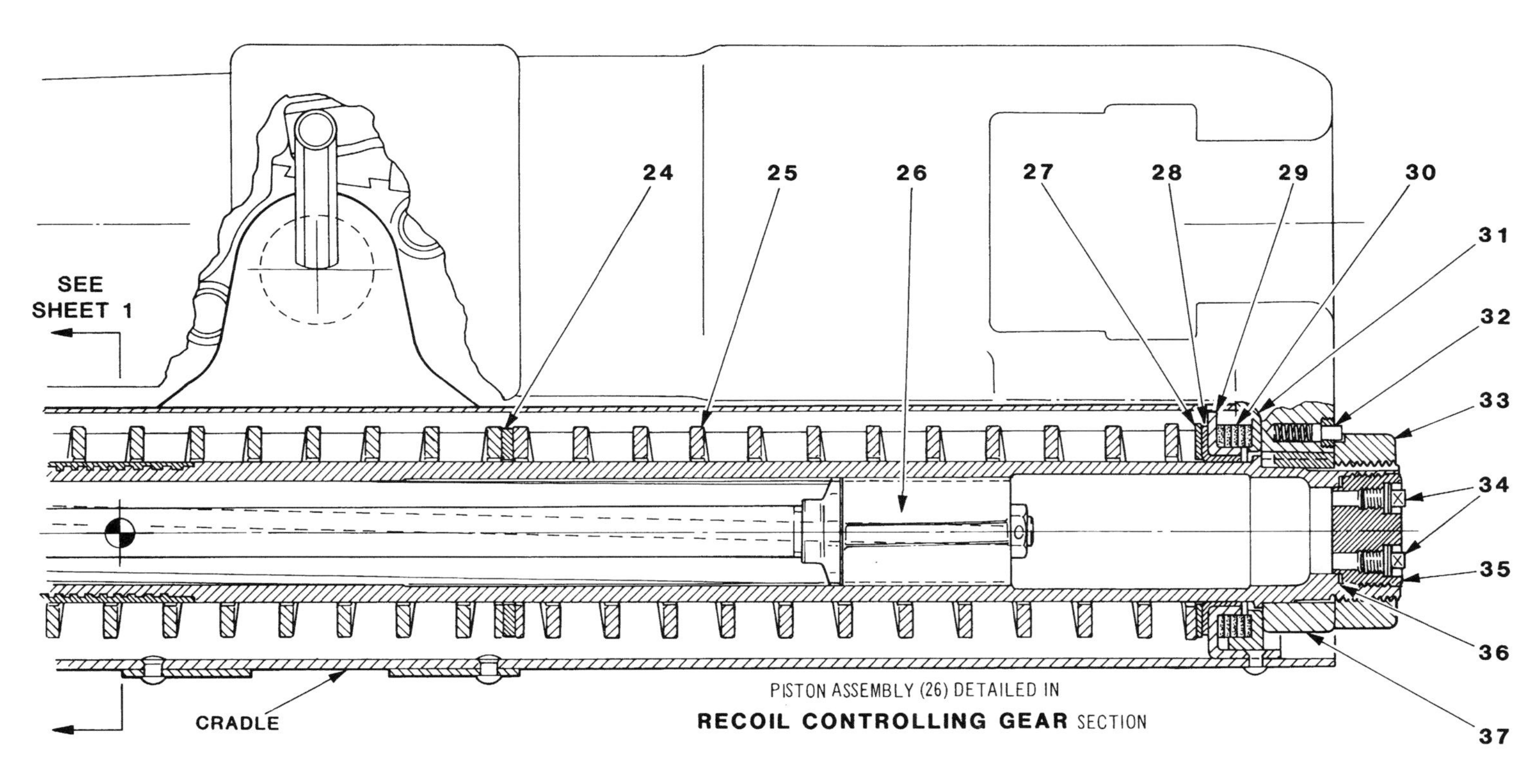

19 SPRING COMPRESSOR TUBE NUT
20 HYDRAULIC BUFFER CYLINDER (FORGED STEEL)
21 FRONT RUNNING OUT SPRING (LEFT-HAND SPIRAL)
22 PARTING PLATE (THICK)
23 CENTRE RUNNING OUT SPRING (RIGHT-HAND SPIRAL)
24 PARTING PLATE (THICK)
25 REAR RUNNING OUT SPRING (LEFT-HAND SPIRAL)
26 PISTON ASSEMBLY
27 PARTING PLATE (THIN)
28 REAR CAP BUSH
29 REAR CAP (CRADLE)
30 LEATHER STOP RINGS
31 HOWITZER STOP
32 RETAINING CATCH
33 SECURING NUT
34 PLUGS (FILLING AND VENT HOLES)
35 BUFFER CYLINDER PLUG (STEEL)
36 WASHER (TIN OR COPPER)
37 BARREL LUG (KEYED TO BUFFER CYLINDER)

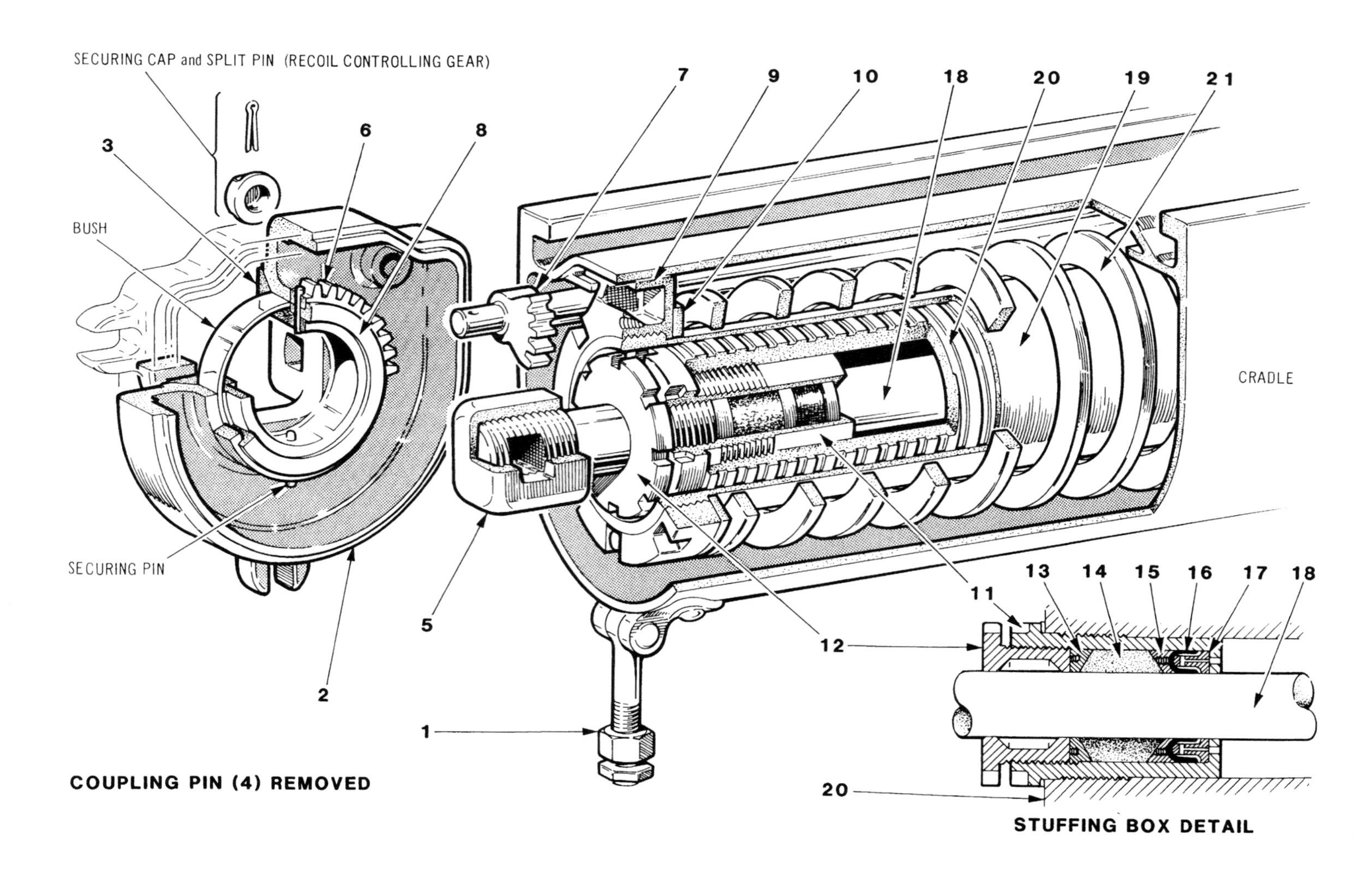

HYDRAULIC BUFFER AND SPRINGS (FRONT END DETAIL)

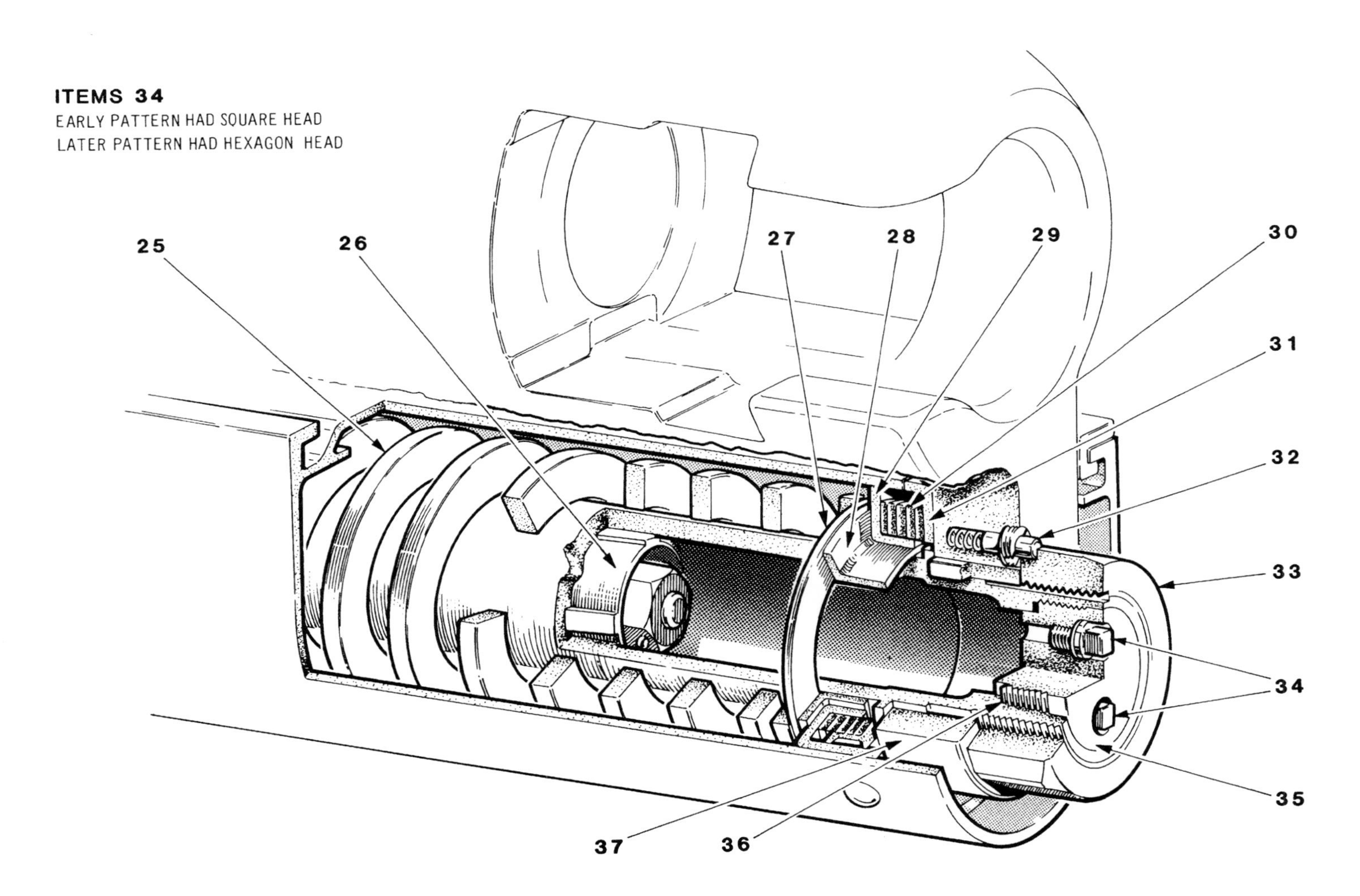

HYDRAULIC BUFFER AND SPRINGS (REAR END DETAIL)

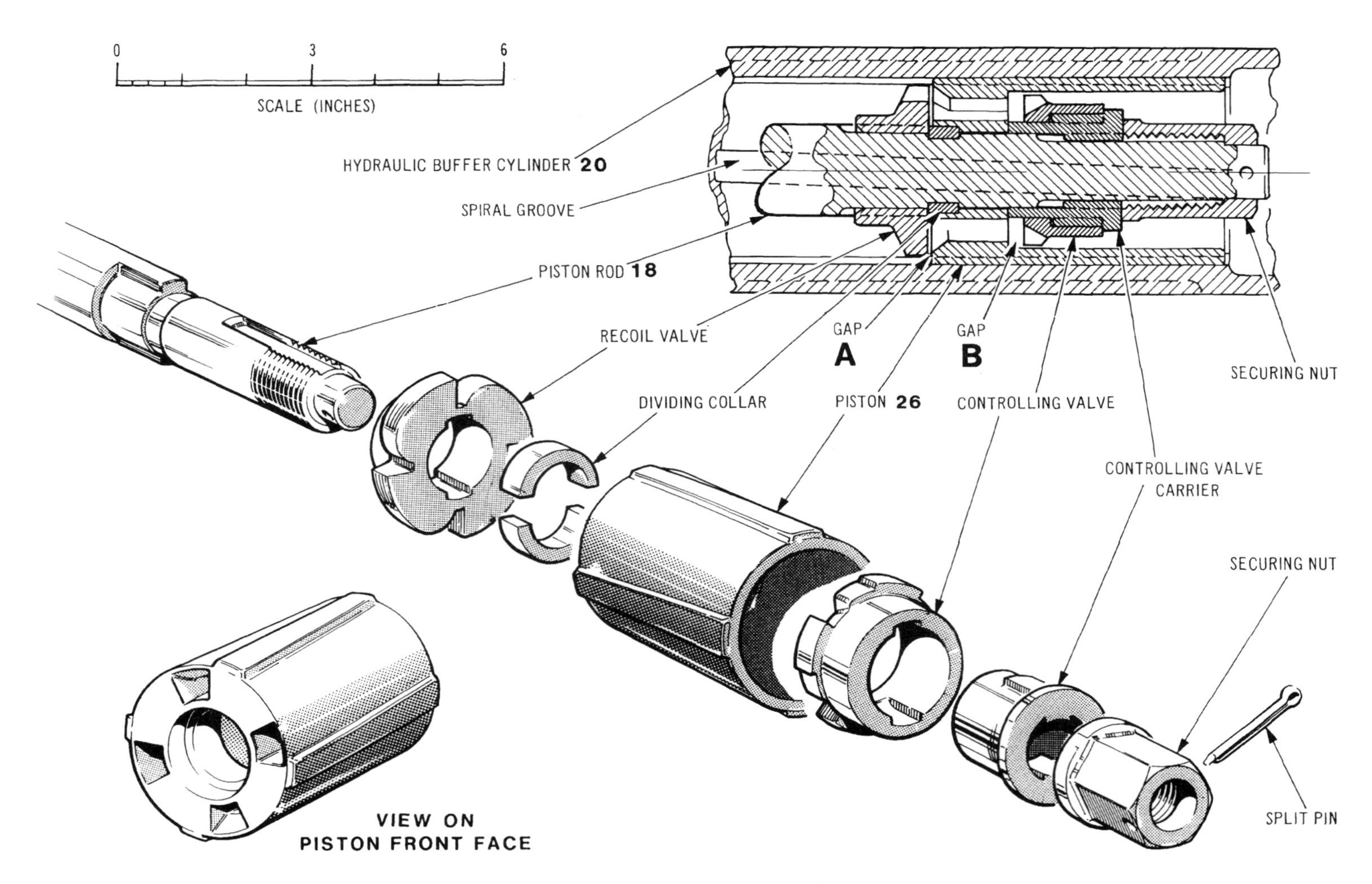

PISTON ASSEMBLY (RECOIL CONTROLLING GEAR)

Hydraulic buffer and springs

Although the hydraulic buffer and spring recuperator were basically one assembly, the simultaneous varied operations make it necessary to divide this description into separate sections, these to be read in conjunction with the relevant illustration.

The buffer cylinder bore (**20**) had four spiral grooves, equally spaced, cut into its surface for the length of maximum recoil. Into these grooves fitted raised guides on the outer surface of the piston (**26**). (See pages 322 and 323.)

The piston (**26**) was secured to the rear end of the piston rod (**18**), the rod being secured at its front end to the cradle front cap (**2** and **3**). Hydraulic leakage at the cradle front end was prevented by a stuffing box assembly (**11**) screwed into the buffer cylinder bore (**20**). (See page 324).

Hydraulic buffer contents – 9 pints of oil.

Hydraulic buffer recoiling (see opposite page)

When firing point blank, the barrel recoiled rearwards along the cradle, drawing the hydraulic buffer cylinder (**20**) over the piston (**26**), forcing the hydraulic liquid through the piston valves at **A** and **B**. The flow of liquid moved the controlling valve rearwards, opening the .10 inch gap at **B** and preventing the controlling valve effecting the flow. As the buffer cylinder continued moving rearwards, the piston body rotated in the spiral grooves and the recoil valve closed at **A**, progressively increasing the hydraulic resistance to recoil.

Spring recuperator

During recoil travel, the springs (**21**, **23** and **25**) were compressed between the spring compressor head (**9**) and the cradle-mounted rear cap (**29**). With recoil energy absorbed, the springs forced the buffer cylinder forwards. (See pages 324 and 325.)

Hydraulic buffer recuperating (see opposite page)

As the buffer cylinder (**20**) moved forwards, hydraulic liquid, passing through gap **B**, caused the controlling valve to slide forward .10 inch on its carrier, leaving only the controlling and recoil valve apertures open, through which the flow could continue. Rotation of the piston body during the buffer cylinder (**20**) forward travel, progressively closed the valve aperture, the increasing hydraulic resistance slowing the barrel speed as it neared the end of its recuperation movement. Final movement was cushioned by the controlling valve closing completely at **B**. The recoil valve would have moved forward by .10 inch and had no effect on the recuperation movement.

From this description it will be apparent that barrel recoil and recuperation caused the piston body to rotate within the buffer cylinder. The recoil and controlling valves were held against rotation by keying to the captive piston rod. When firing point blank,

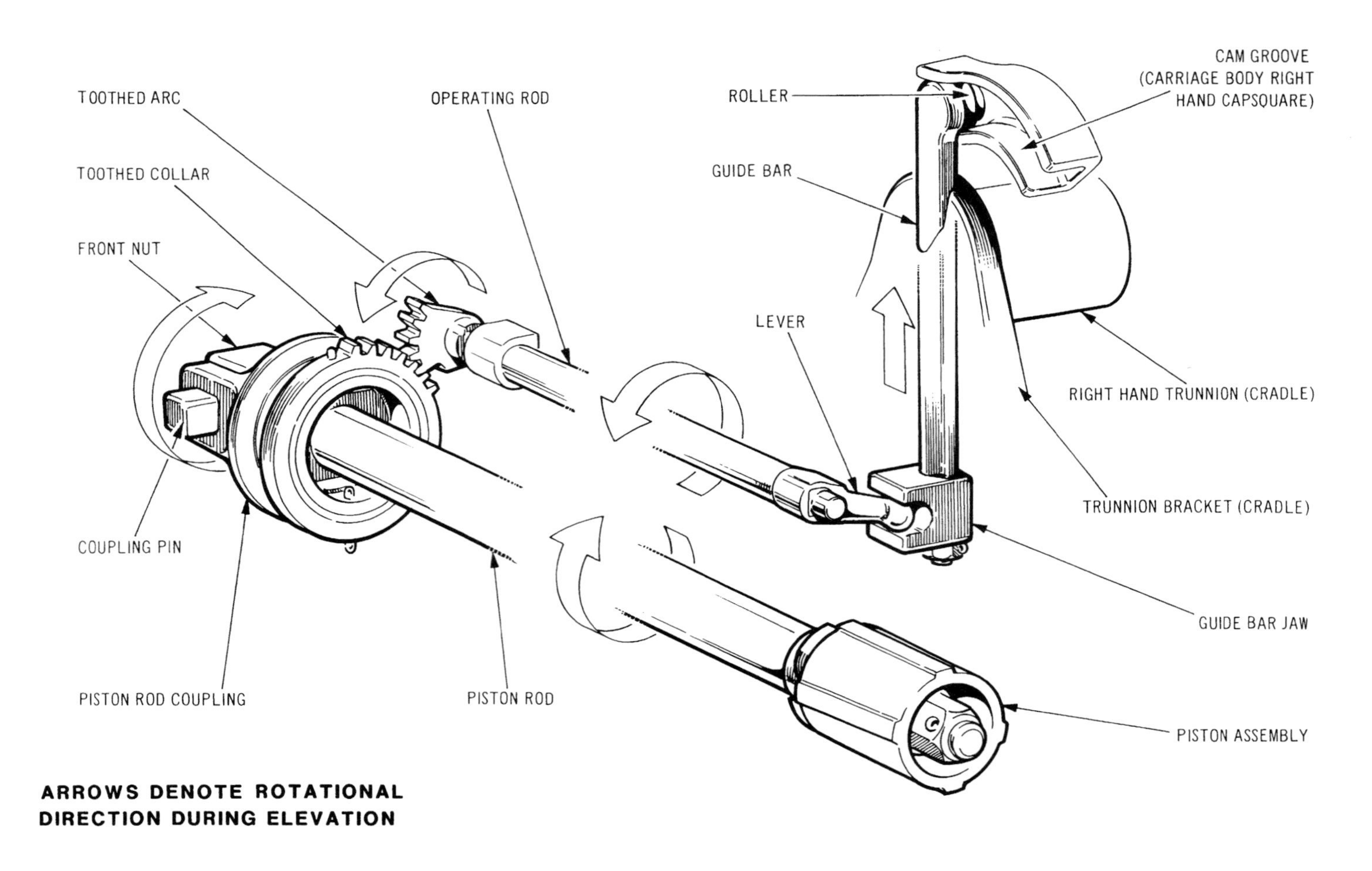

RECOIL CONTROLLING GEAR – COMPONENTS

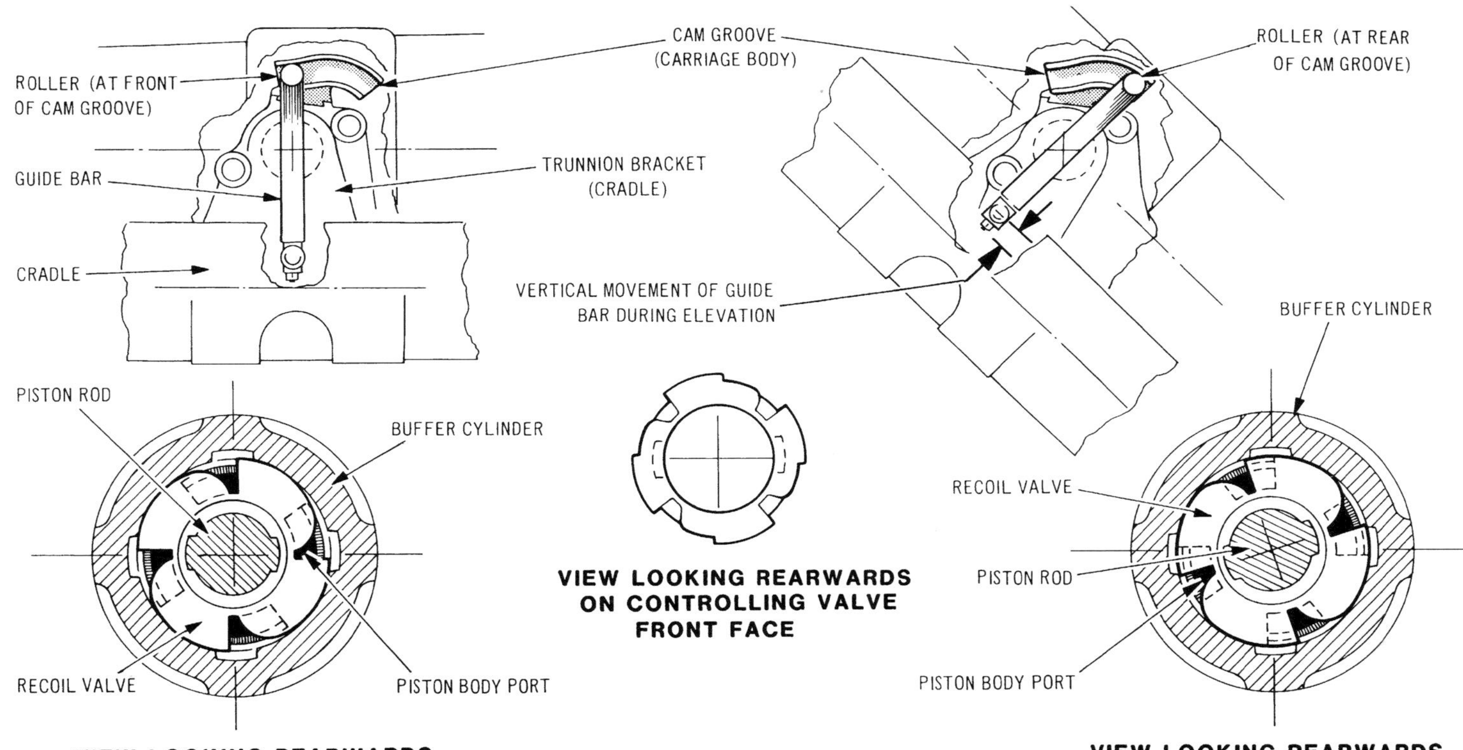

VIEW LOOKING REARWARDS ON RECOIL VALVE

(HOWITZER AT POINT BLANK)

RECOIL VALVE POSITIONED TO ALLOW FULL FLOW THROUGH PISTON BODY PORTS

FULL WORKING RECOIL – 40.5 INCHES

VIEW LOOKING REARWARDS ON RECOIL VALVE

(HOWITZER AT FULL ELEVATION)

RECOIL VALVE POSITIONED TO ALLOW PARTIAL ROTATION ONLY, RESTRICTING FLOW THROUGH PISTON BODY PORTS.

WORKING RECOIL RESTRICTED TO 20 INCHES

FOR DETAILS OF LINKAGE BETWEEN GUIDE BAR and PISTON ASSEMBLY SEE ILLUSTRATION OPPOSITE

RECOIL CONTROLLING GEAR – OPERATION

the piston valve assembly would be in the fully open condition, but able to commence closing immediately recoil movement began. Full horizontal recoil travel caused the valves to open and close to their maximum extent.

Shield

The shield was positioned in front of the axletree and secured to it by four brackets. Each outer bracket was formed with a recess to house an L section leather dust seal, secured by a steel plate, to prevent contamination of the wheel pipebox by dust or grit.

The shield was braced at the front by two stays, bolted to the shield at one end and secured into sockets, on the front of the trail, at the other end.

HINGE and SLIDING BOLT DETAIL

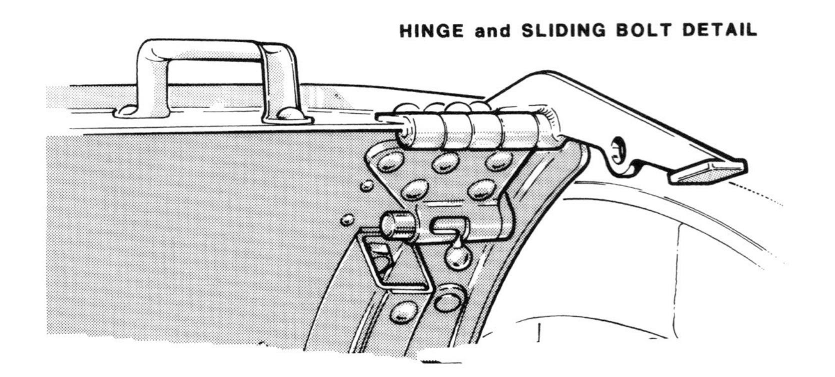

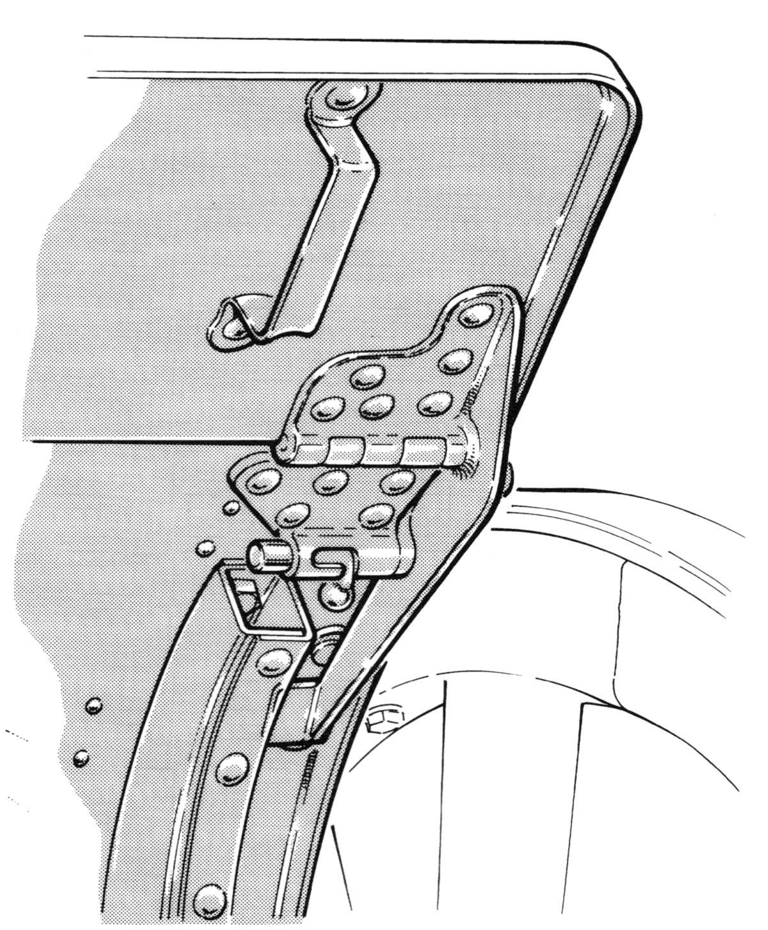

SHIELD

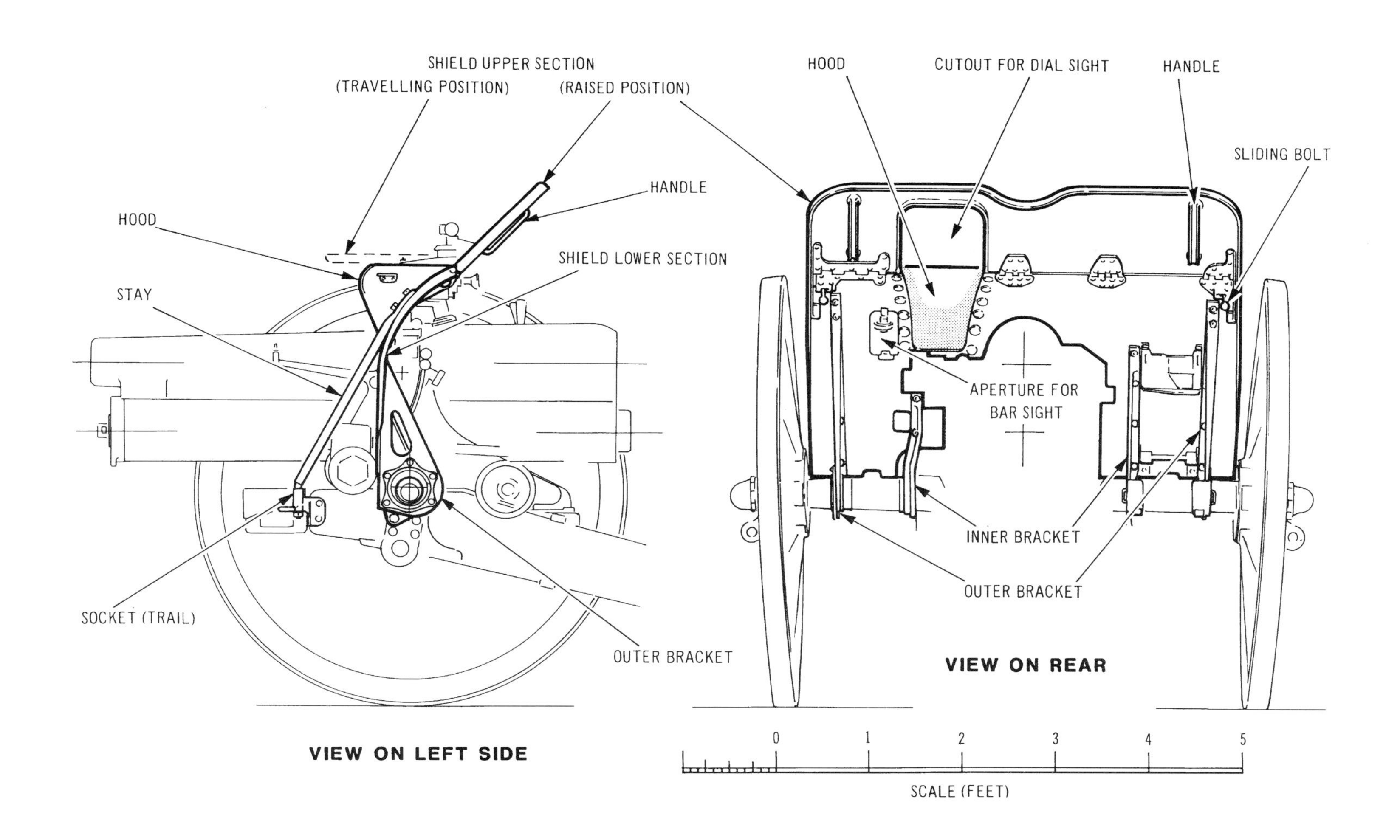
SHIELD UPPER SECTION
(TRAVELLING POSITION)
(RAISED POSITION)
HANDLE
HOOD
SHIELD LOWER SECTION
STAY
SOCKET (TRAIL)
OUTER BRACKET
VIEW ON LEFT SIDE
HOOD
CUTOUT FOR DIAL SIGHT
HANDLE
SLIDING BOLT
APERTURE FOR
BAR SIGHT
INNER BRACKET
OUTER BRACKET
VIEW ON REAR
0
1
2
3
4
5
SCALE (FEET)

SHIELD

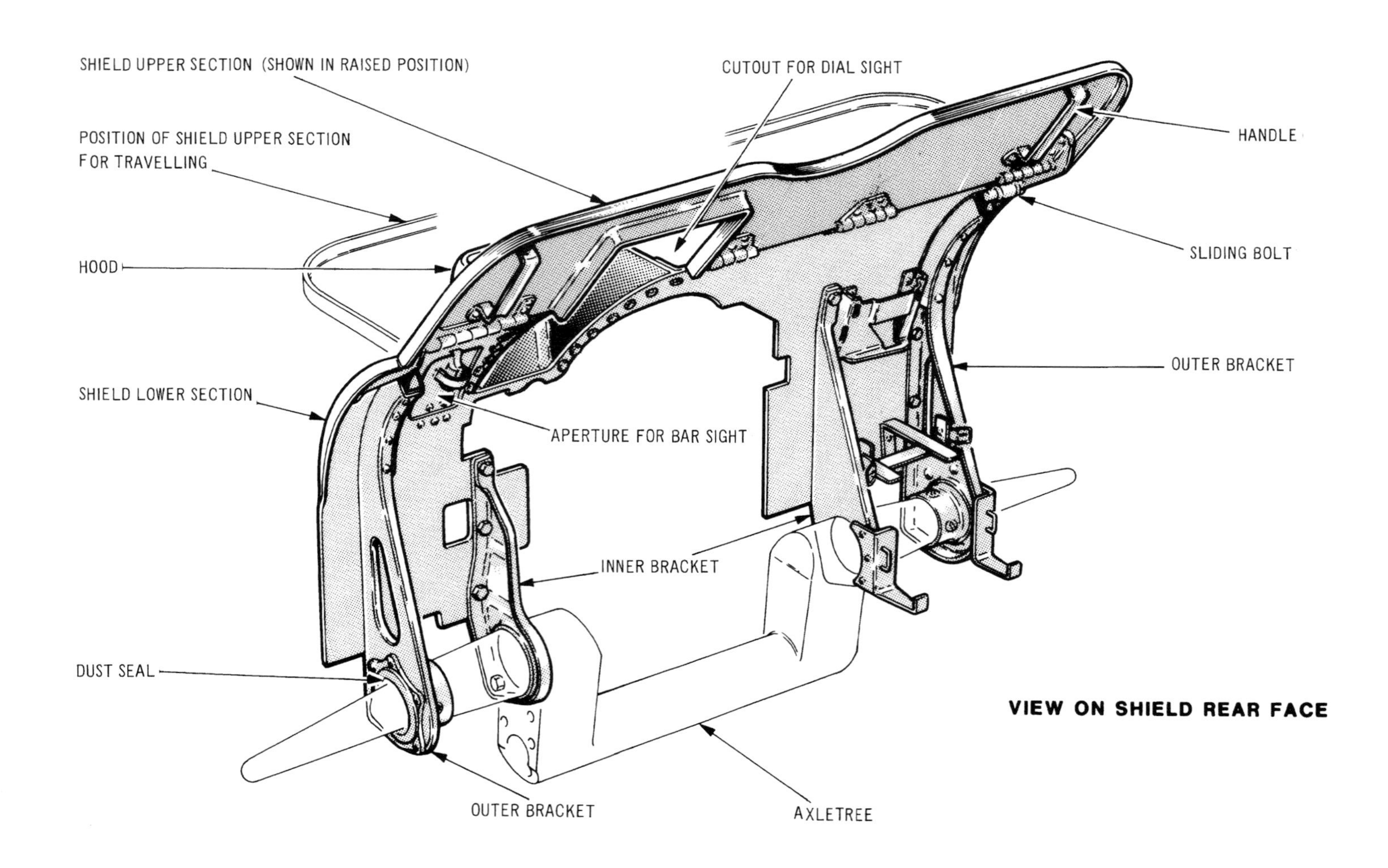
SHIELD UPPER SECTION (SHOWN IN RAISED POSITION)
CUTOUT FOR DIAL SIGHT
POSITION OF SHIELD UPPER SECTION
FOR TRAVELLING
HANDLE
HOOD
SLIDING BOLT
OUTER BRACKET
SHIELD LOWER SECTION
APERTURE FOR BAR SIGHT
INNER BRACKET
DUST SEAL
VIEW ON SHIELD REAR FACE
OUTER BRACKET
AXLETREE

SHIELD

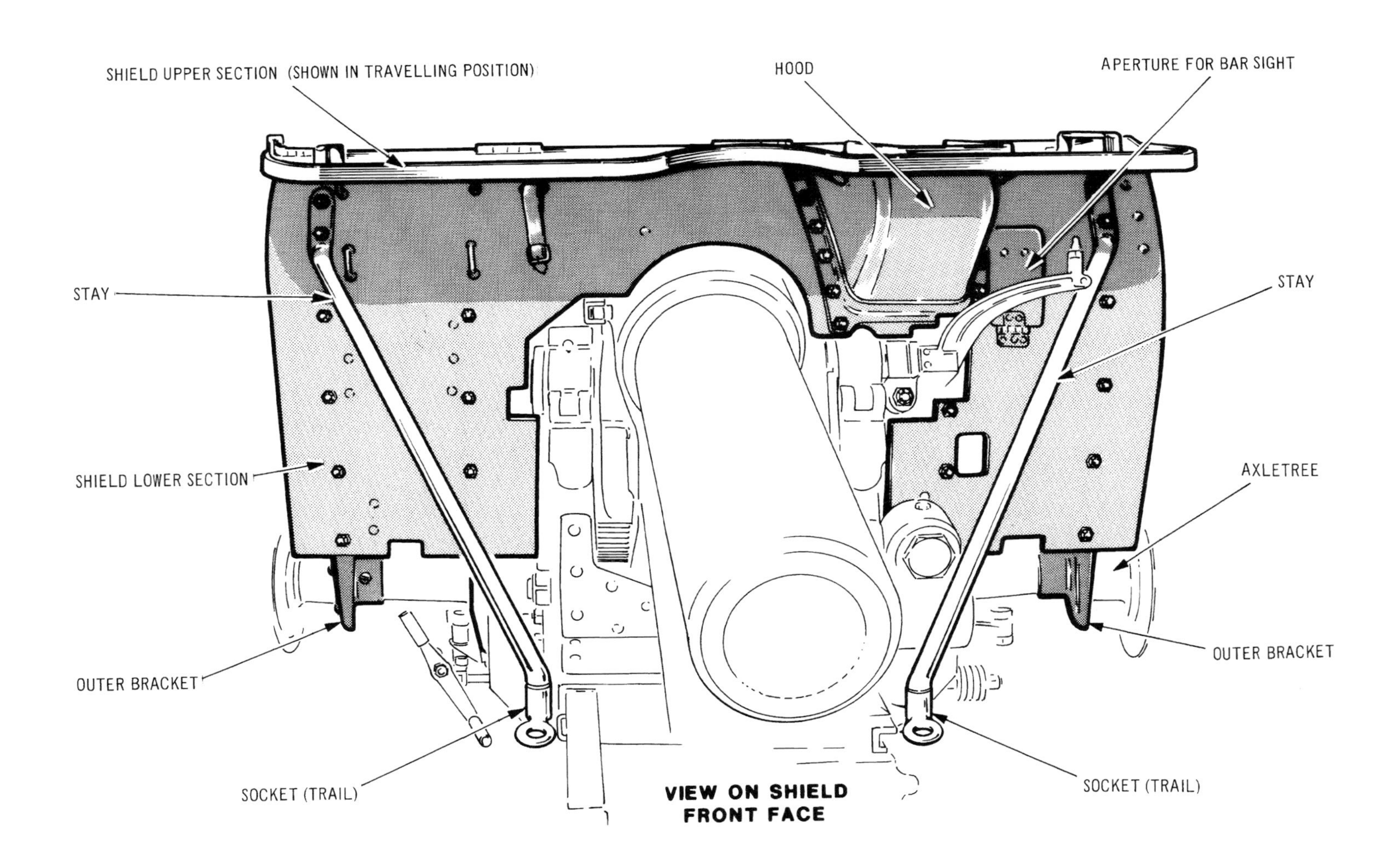
SHIELD UPPER SECTION (SHOWN IN TRAVELLING POSITION)
HOOD
APERTURE FOR BAR SIGHT
STAY
STAY
SHIELD LOWER SECTION
AXLETREE
OUTER BRACKET
OUTER BRACKET
SOCKET (TRAIL)
SOCKET (TRAIL)
VIEW ON SHIELD
FRONT FACE

SHIELD

The shield comprised two sections, hinged to each other. The lower section was secured in the manner described above. The upper section would be secured upright for action, secured by sliding bolts, or hinged forward to lie horizontal for travelling. The lower section was provided with a hood, to protect the dial sight and carrier. A hinged shutter could cover the aperture cut for the bar sight.

It was provided with fittings for the carriage of various stores and equipments.

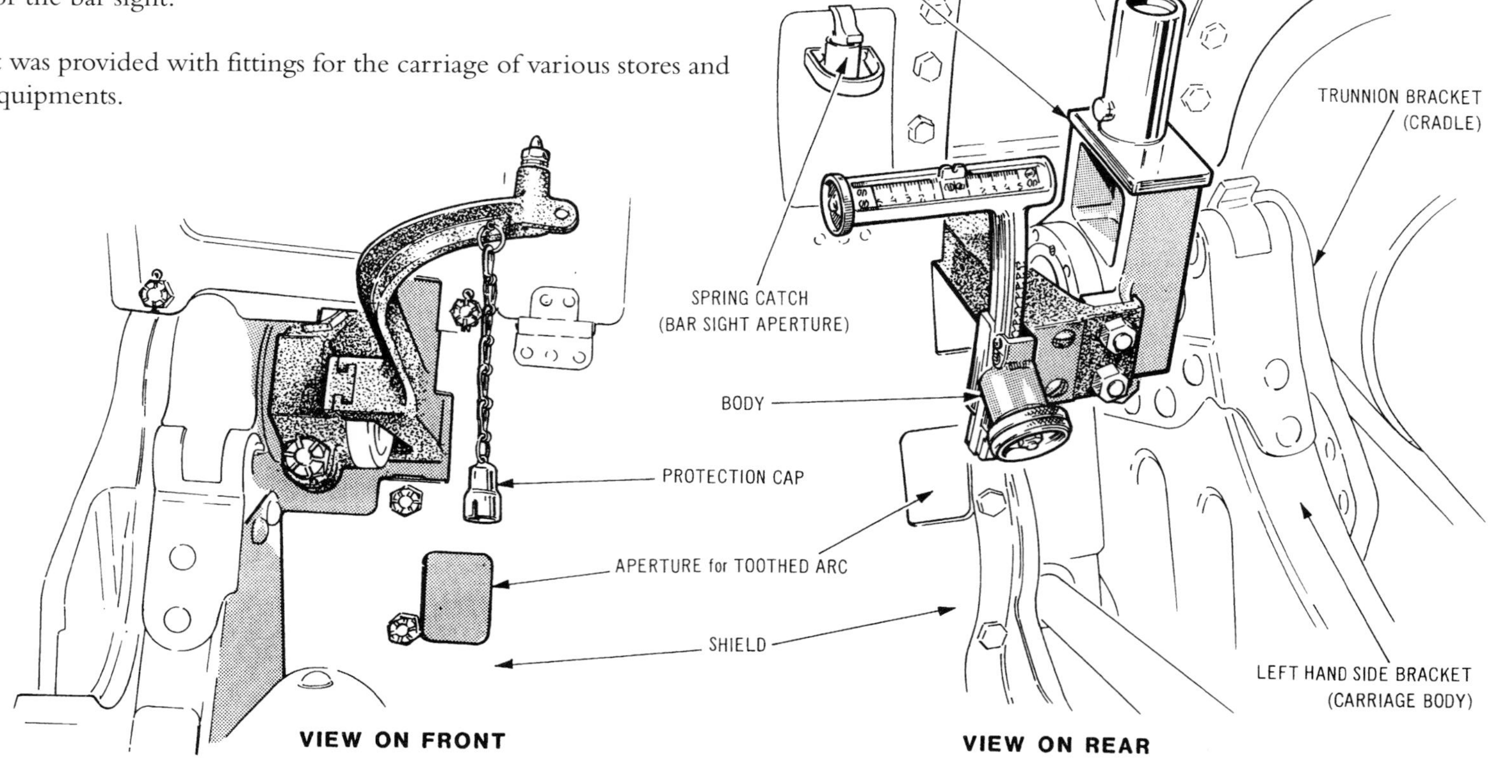

BAR SIGHT (SEE PAGE 336)

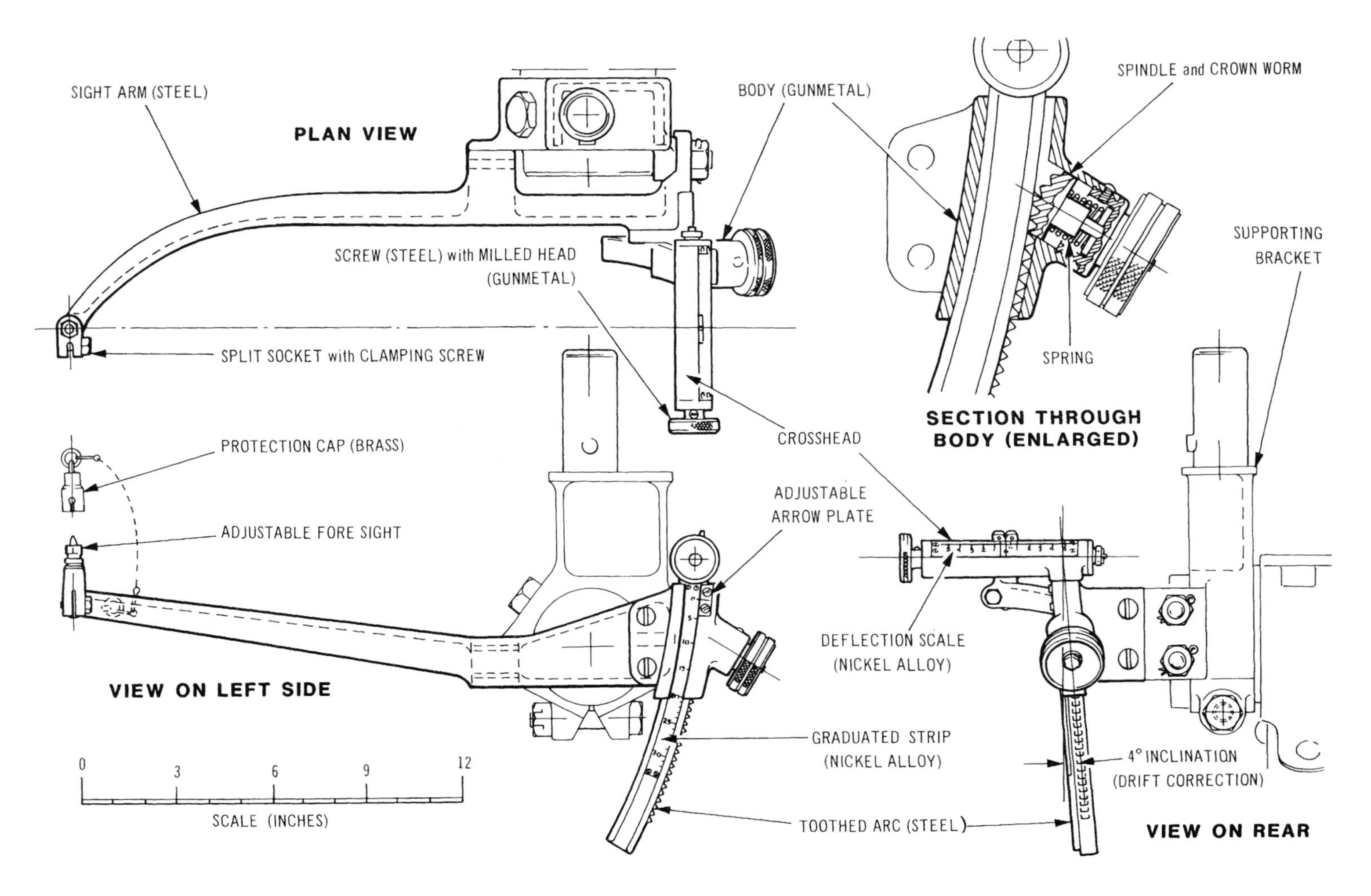
SIGHT ARM (STEEL)
PLAN VIEW
BODY (GUNMETAL)
SPINDLE and CROWN WORM
SUPPORTING BRACKET
SCREW (STEEL) with MILLED HEAD (GUNMETAL)
SPLIT SOCKET with CLAMPING SCREW
SPRING
SECTION THROUGH BODY (ENLARGED)
PROTECTION CAP (BRASS)
CROSSHEAD
ADJUSTABLE ARROW PLATE
ADJUSTABLE FORE SIGHT
DEFLECTION SCALE (NICKEL ALLOY)
VIEW ON LEFT SIDE
GRADUATED STRIP (NICKEL ALLOY)
4° INCLINATION (DRIFT CORRECTION)
0 3 6 9 12
SCALE (INCHES)
TOOTHED ARC (STEEL)
VIEW ON REAR

BAR SIGHT

Bar sight

The toothed arc had, secured to the side, a strip, graduated to 3,200 yards. The crosshead scale was graduated to five degrees, either side of the centre line, for deflection.

The crown worm was held to the toothed arc by spring pressure. This ensured that the adjuster also acted as an automatic clamp. For quick setting, the crown worm could be pulled out of engagement and the sight raised by hand, the spring re-engaging the crown worm and toothed arc when released.

Dial sight carrier No. 1 (see opposite page)

Turning the milled wheel revolved the yard scale drum and worm spindle. The worm, working along the oscillating bracket toothed arc, tilted the rocking bracket forwards or backwards about the mounting trunnion screws. As the yard scale drum revolved, the pointer ring, being held against rotation, moved up or down the drum following the spiral groove, an arrow indicating the range graduations. One-eighth of a turn of the drum represented one degree, intermediate graduations being read on the flange scale by the arrow plate mounted on the rocking bracket socket.

Turning the milled wheel (see page 340) revolved the pinion at the upper end of the spindle. This turned the bevel wheel and cam mounted on the rocking bracket top face. The friction roller, mounted in the deflection bracket and pressed against the cam by the spring plunger, caused both the deflection bracket and dial sight holder to move jointly about the front pivot bolt, thus giving automatic correction for projectile drift at all elevations. Normal deflection of five degrees, right or left, would be given by use of the deflection gear moving the dial sight holder relative to the deflection bracket.

Barrel and breech (see page 341)

Barrel construction

The barrel consisted of an **A** tube, jacket and **B** hoop, all of nickel steel. The jacket was shrunk over the **A** tube rear portion and secured by the **B** hoop, this being screwed and shrunk over portions of both the **A** tube and jacket, locked by a check screw.

The jacket was horizontally mortised through at the rear to receive the breech block and shaped to form a lug for attachment to the hydraulic buffer cylinder. A steel plunger and spiral spring were housed in the lug rear face to retain the hydraulic buffer cylinder nut. Recesses in each side of the jacket and **A** tube held the liners, which fitted over the cradle slides. Lubricators, with steel plungers and springs, were installed on each side of the **A** tube to supply oil to the liners and slides. The chamber was slightly coned throughout its length.

Vertical and horizontal lines were cut on the muzzle and breech faces and an axis line was cut, at the breech, on the left side. Barrel weight was marked on the jacket top and the royal monogram on the **A** tube top, in front of the **B** hoop. The breech exterior was marked with the type, mark number, registered number, manufacturer's initials and year of manufacture.

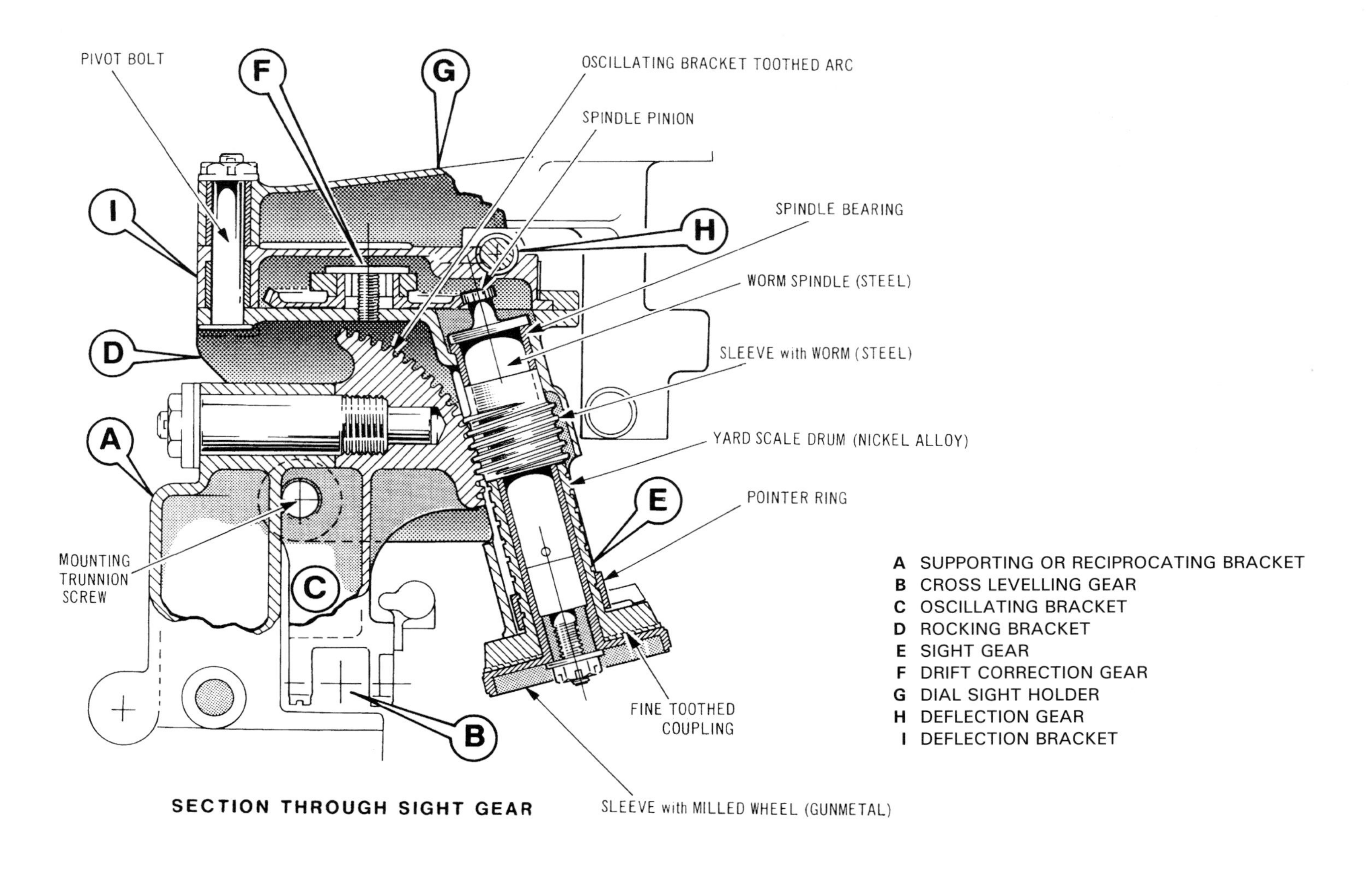

DIAL SIGHT CARRIER – NO. 1

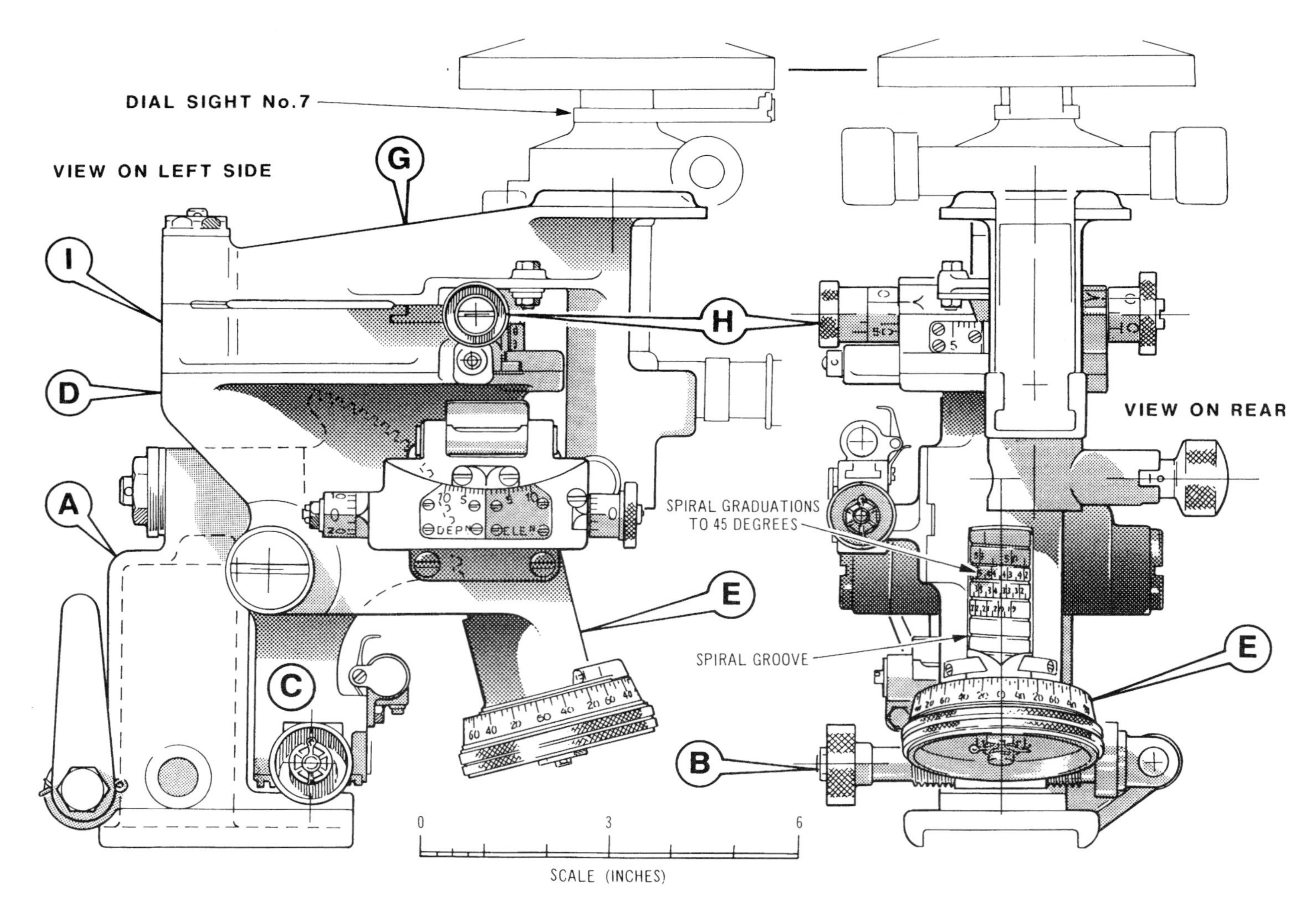

DIAL SIGHT CARRIER – NO. 1

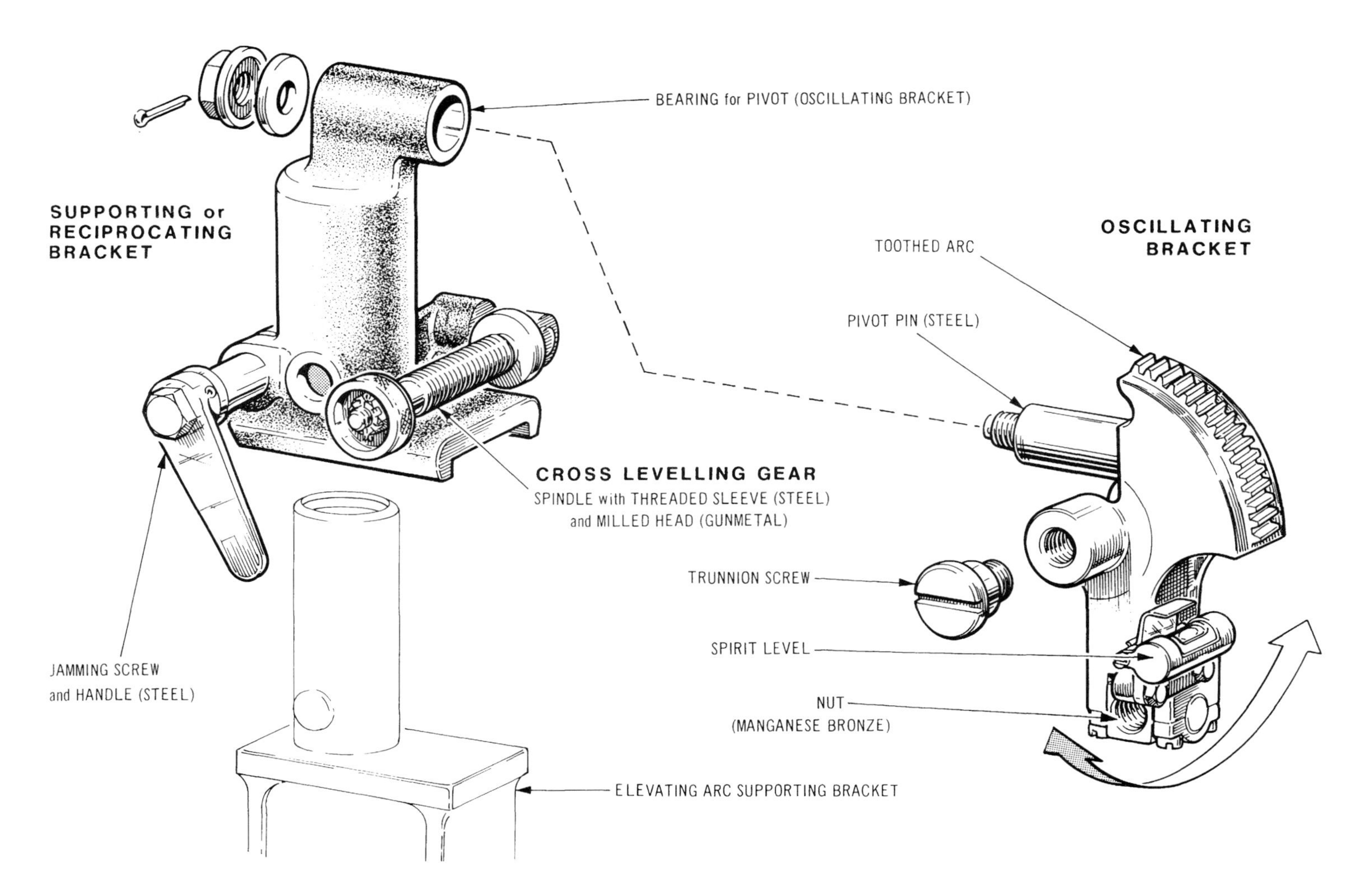

DIAL SIGHT CARRIER – NO. 1

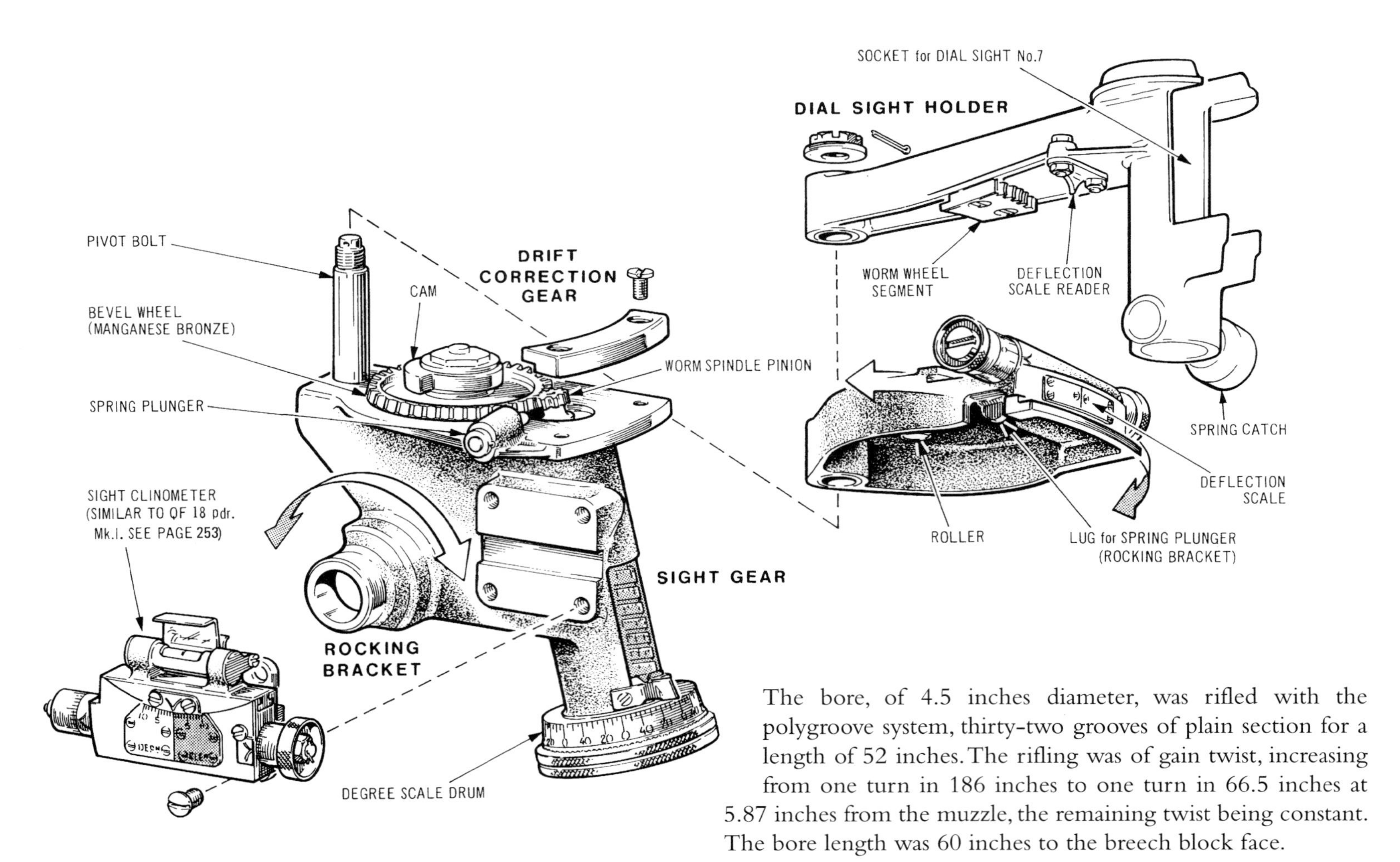

DIAL SIGHT CARRIER – NO. 1

The bore, of 4.5 inches diameter, was rifled with the polygroove system, thirty-two grooves of plain section for a length of 52 inches. The rifling was of gain twist, increasing from one turn in 186 inches to one turn in 66.5 inches at 5.87 inches from the muzzle, the remaining twist being constant. The bore length was 60 inches to the breech block face.

The barrel, without breech fittings, weighed 7cwt 3qtr 4lb. Total barrel length was 70 inches.

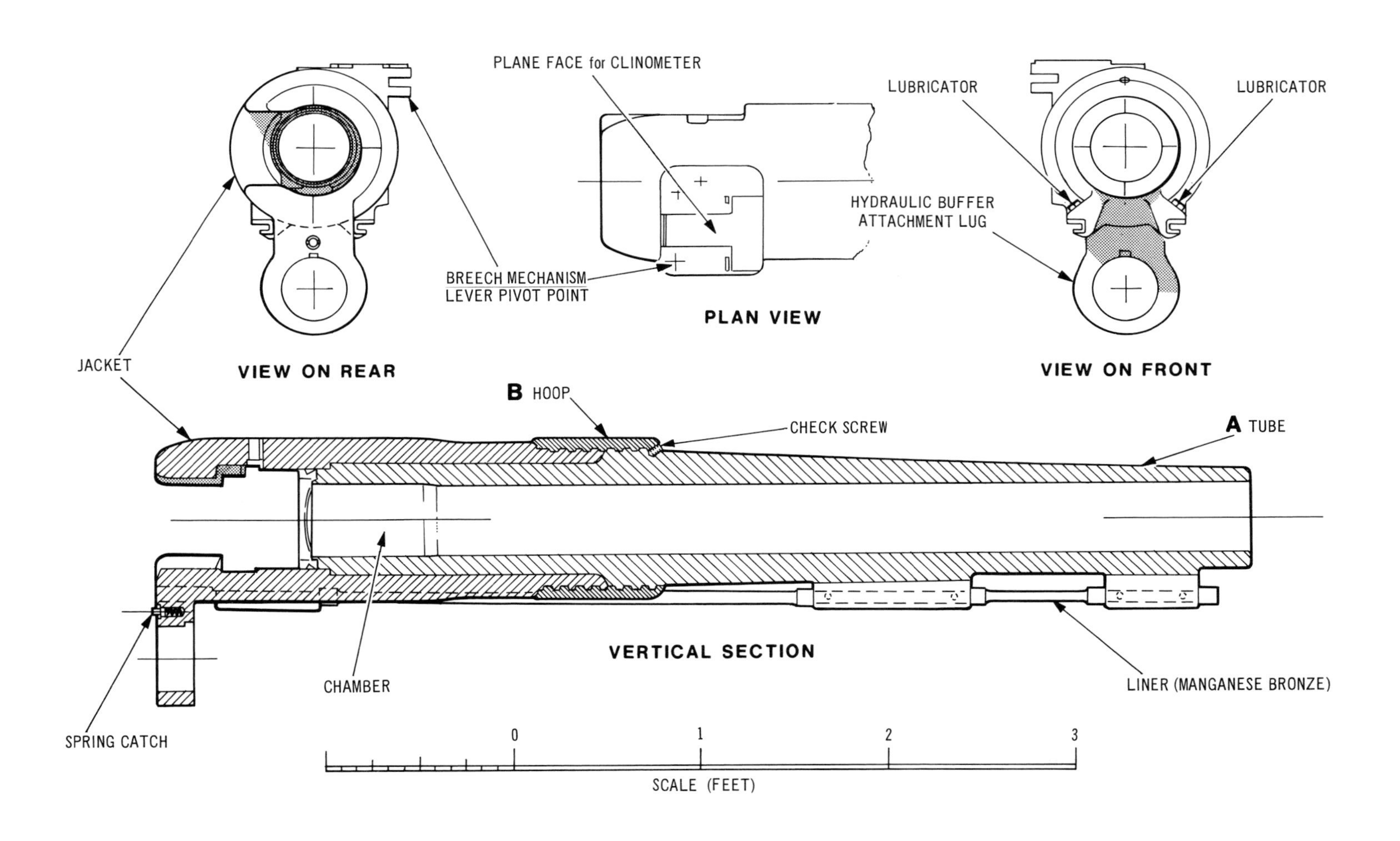

BARREL CONSTRUCTION – RIFLING DETAILS ARE DESCRIBED IN THE TEXT ON THE PAGE OPPOSITE

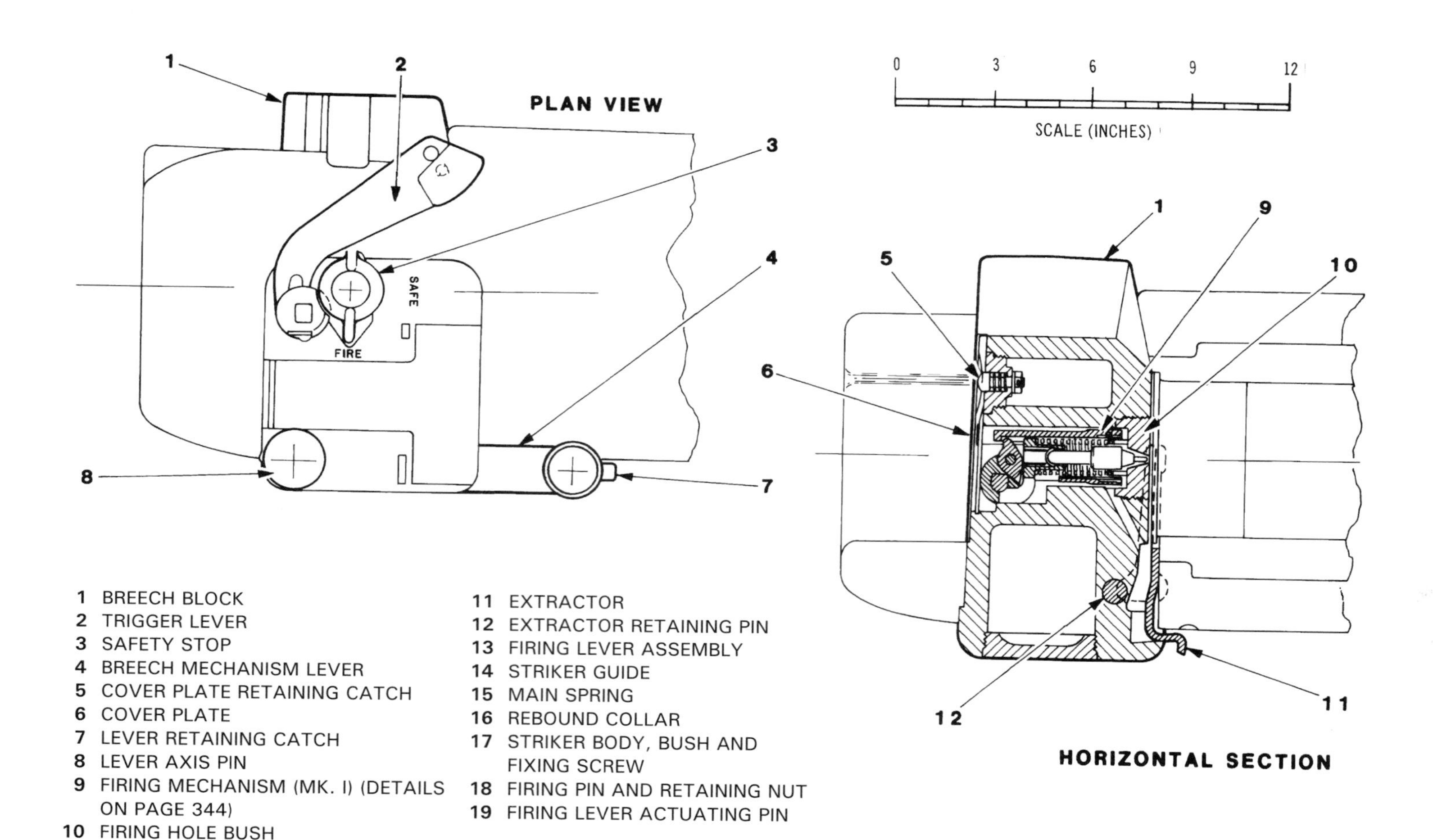
PLAN VIEW
SAFE
FIRE
SCALE (INCHES)
0 3 6 9 12
HORIZONTAL SECTION
1 BREECH BLOCK
2 TRIGGER LEVER
3 SAFETY STOP
4 BREECH MECHANISM LEVER
5 COVER PLATE RETAINING CATCH
6 COVER PLATE
7 LEVER RETAINING CATCH
8 LEVER AXIS PIN
9 FIRING MECHANISM (MK. I) (DETAILS ON PAGE 344)
10 FIRING HOLE BUSH
11 EXTRACTOR
12 EXTRACTOR RETAINING PIN
13 FIRING LEVER ASSEMBLY
14 STRIKER GUIDE
15 MAIN SPRING
16 REBOUND COLLAR
17 STRIKER BODY, BUSH AND FIXING SCREW
18 FIRING PIN AND RETAINING NUT
19 FIRING LEVER ACTUATING PIN

BREECH

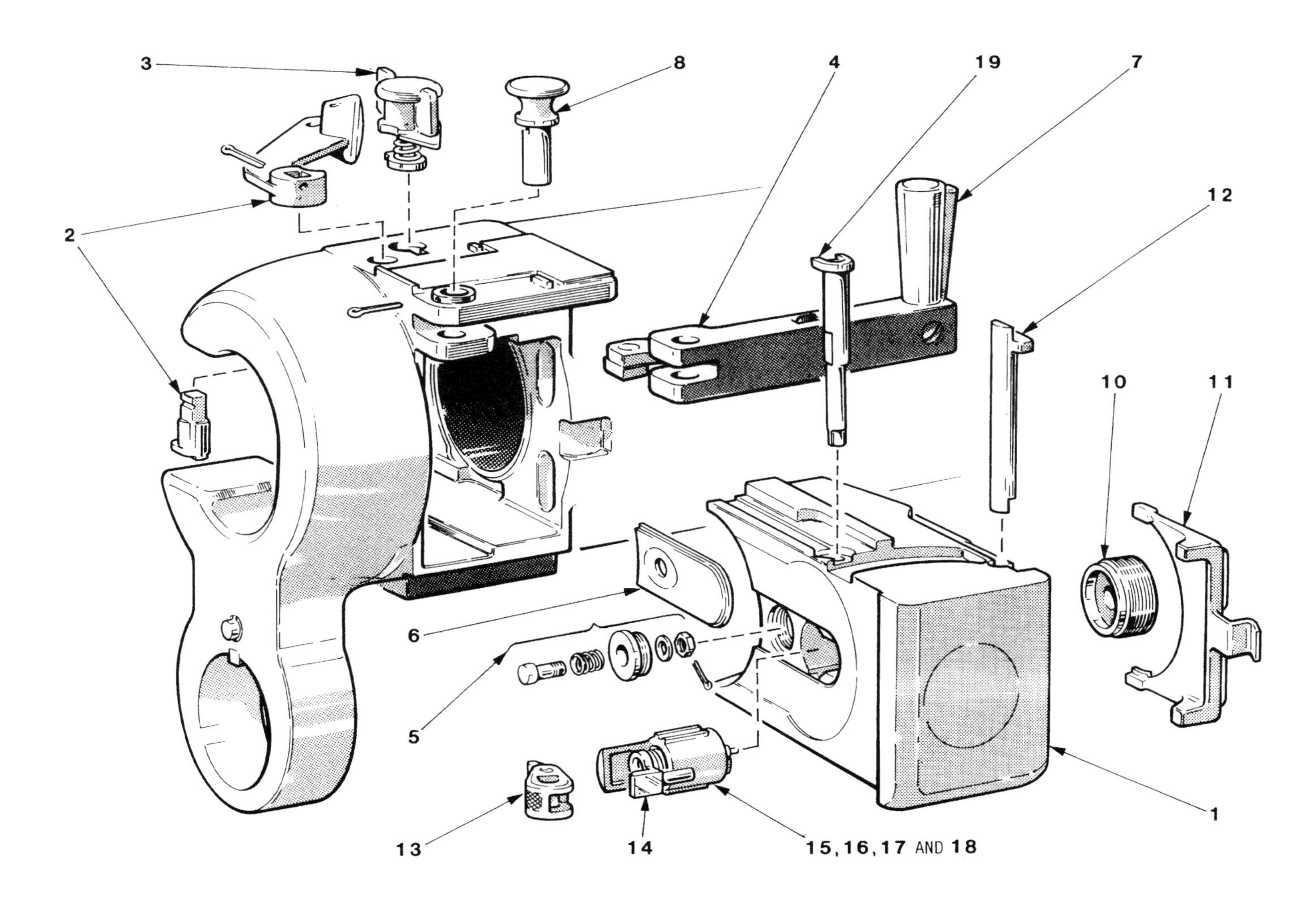

BREECH COMPONENTS

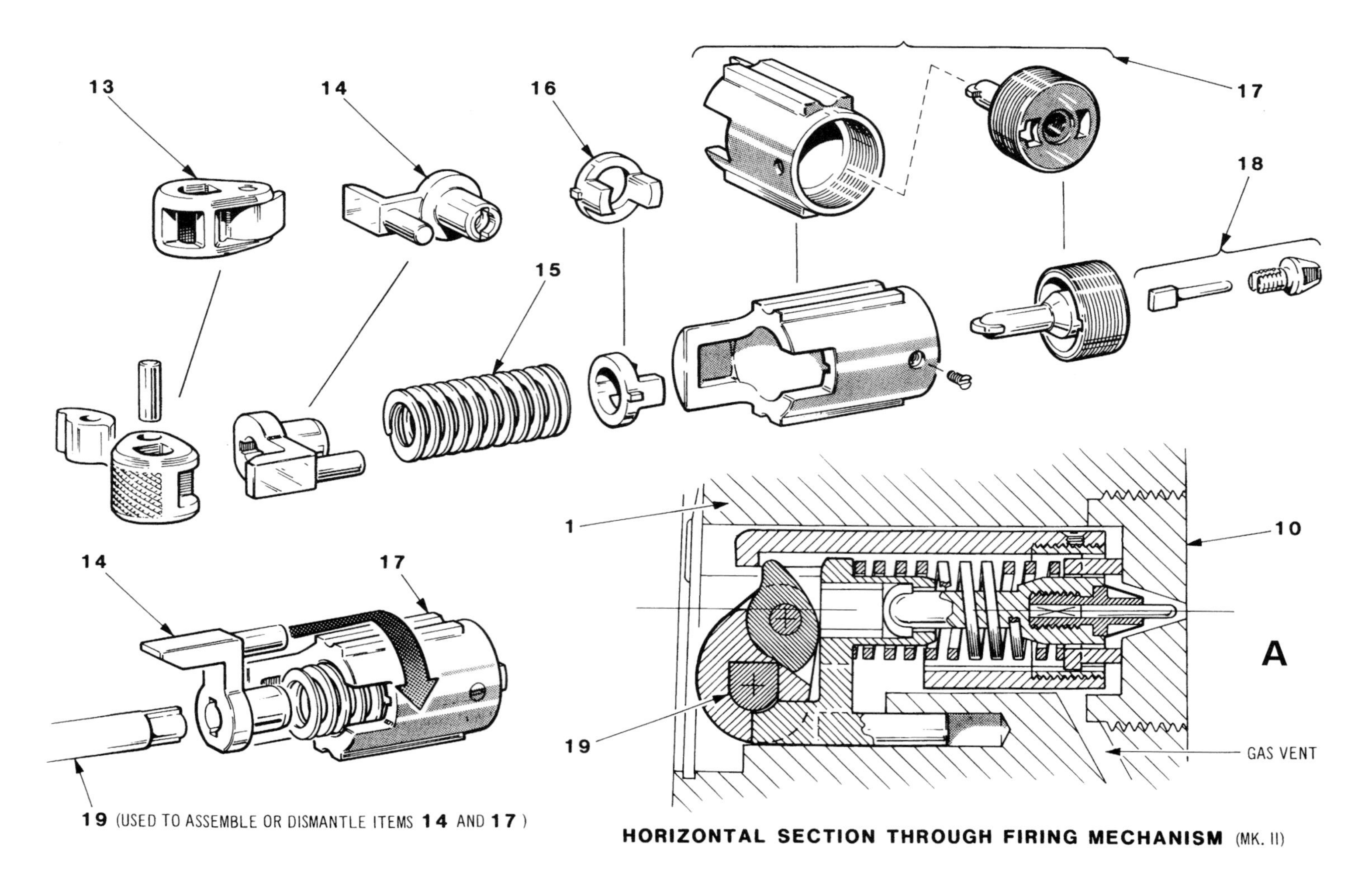

FIRING MECHANISM COMPONENTS

Firing mechanism

VIEW A This shows the Mk. II firing mechanism at rest with the breech block (**1**) closed. Note that the firing pin was withdrawn and not projecting from the firing hole bush (**10**).

VIEW B Pulling on the trigger lever (**2**) rotated the firing lever actuating pin (**19**) causing the firing lever assembly (**13**) to turn. The pawl end engaged the striker body (**17**), drawing it to the rear, while, at the same time, the firing lever (**13**) pushed the striker guide (**14**) forward, the two simultaneous actions compressing the main spring (**15**).

VIEW C Rotation of the firing lever assembly (**13**) continued until the pawl end slipped past the striker body (**17**), allowing the striker to be thrown forward under pressure of the main spring (**15**). Near the end of the striker travel (**17**), the projections of the rebound collar (**16**) stopped against the firing hole bush (**10**) inner face. The striker body (**17**) continued to travel forward far enough for the firing pin (**18**) to emerge from the firing hole bush (**10**) and detonate the cartridge percussion cap.

VIEW D Releasing the trigger lever (**2**) allowed the main spring (**15**) to return the striker guide (**14**) to the rear. A shoulder, machined within the striker guide bore (**14**), engaged projections on the striker body bush (**17**) and withdrew the firing pin (**18**) into the firing hole bush (**10**) front face. The firing lever assembly pawl (**13**) slipped past and then engaged the rear portion of the striker (**17**), this restoring the firing mechanism to the condition shown in VIEW A.

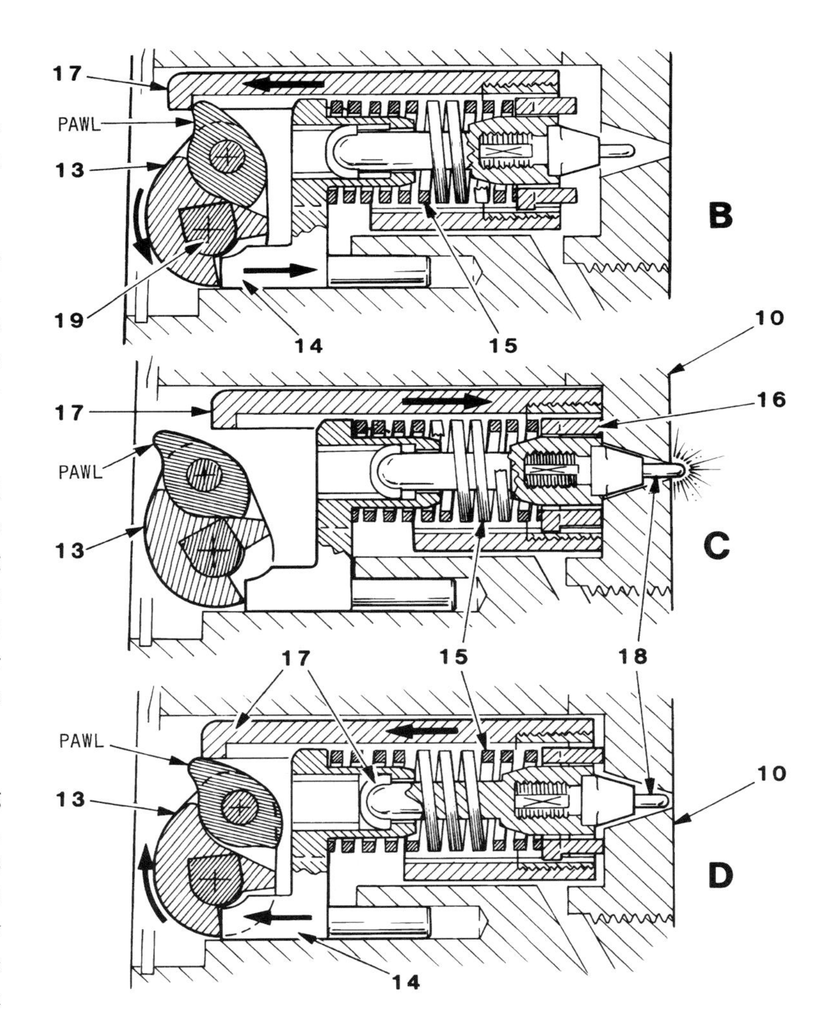

FIRING MECHANISM OPERATION

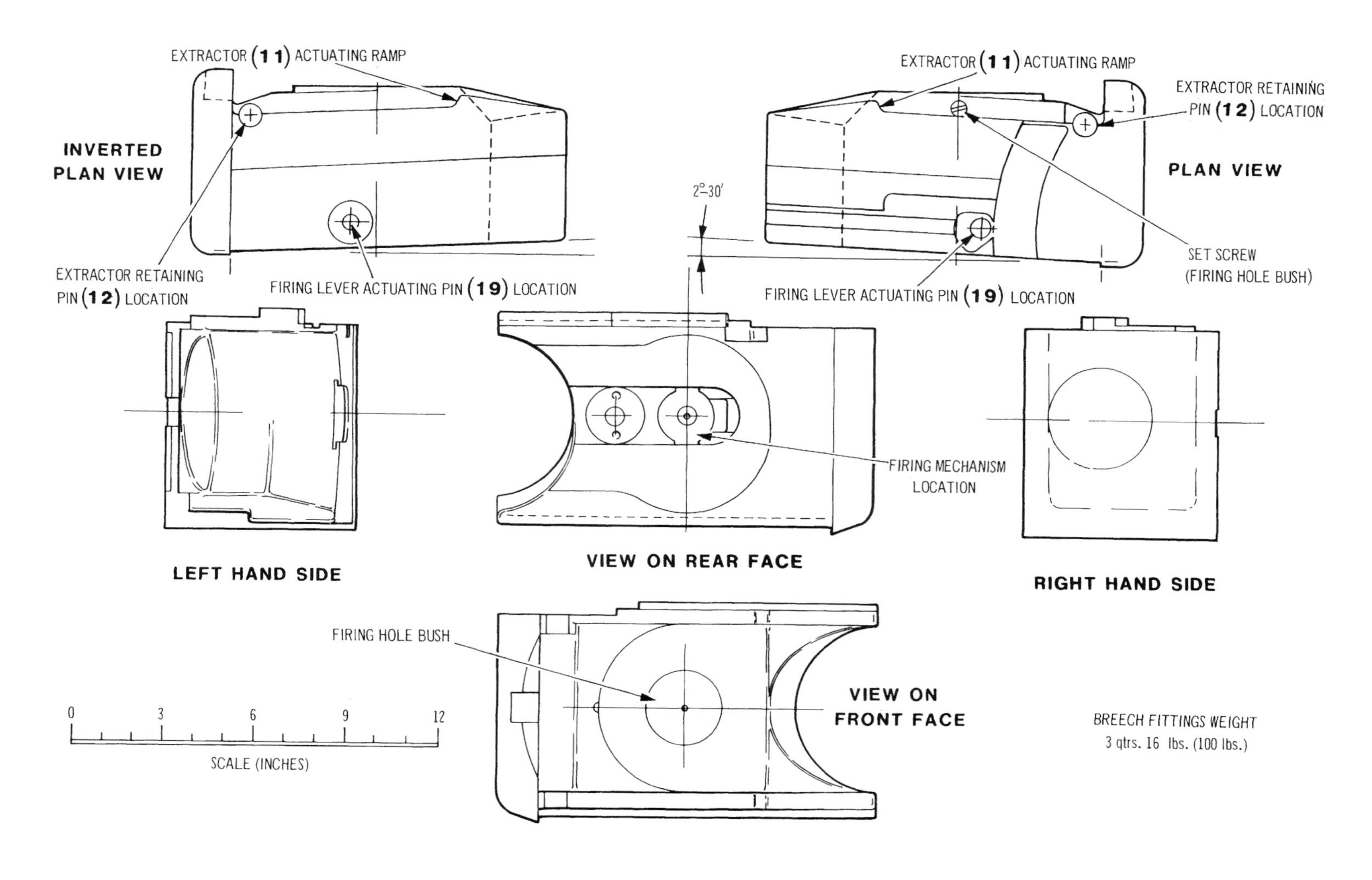

BREECH BLOCK

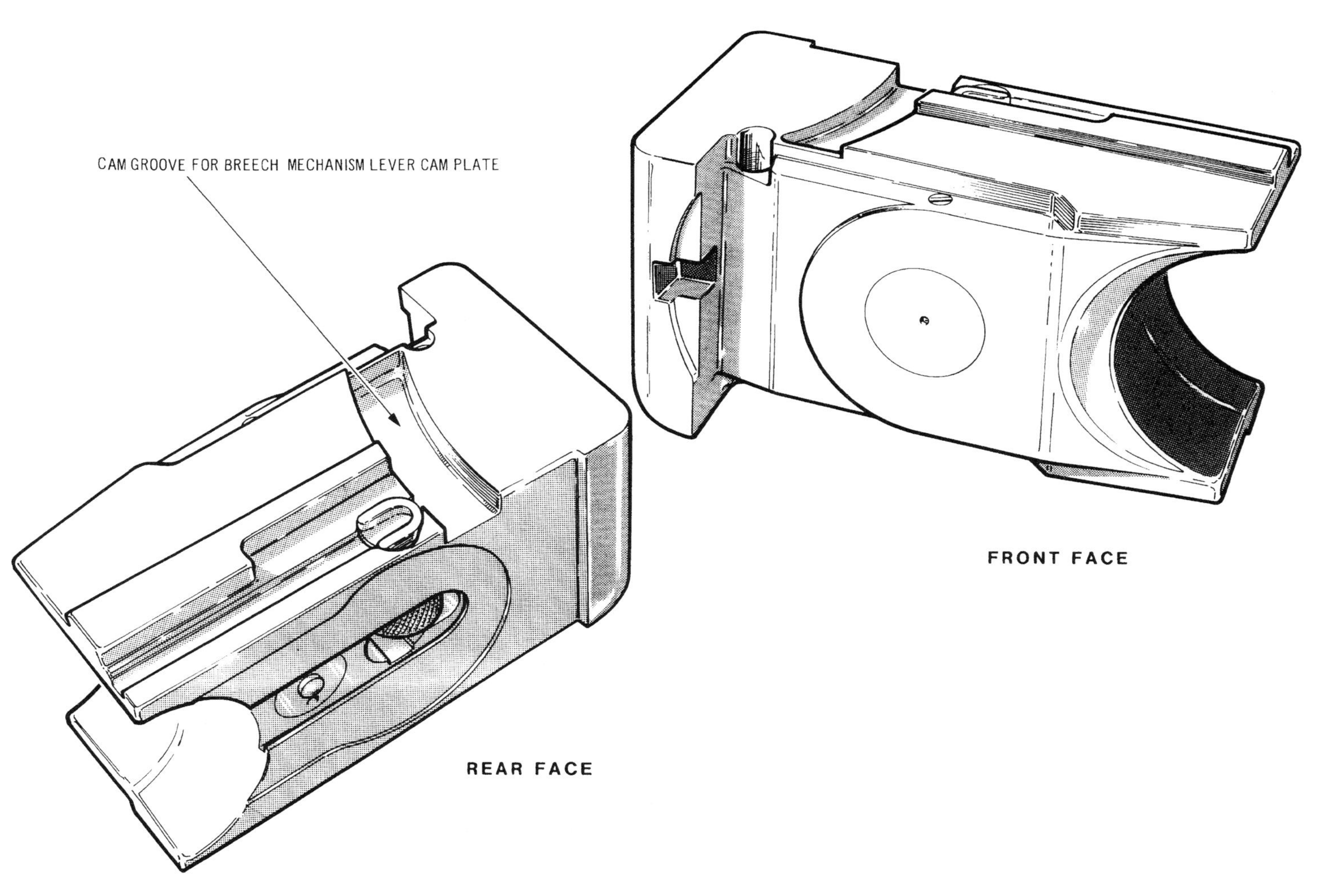

BREECH BLOCK

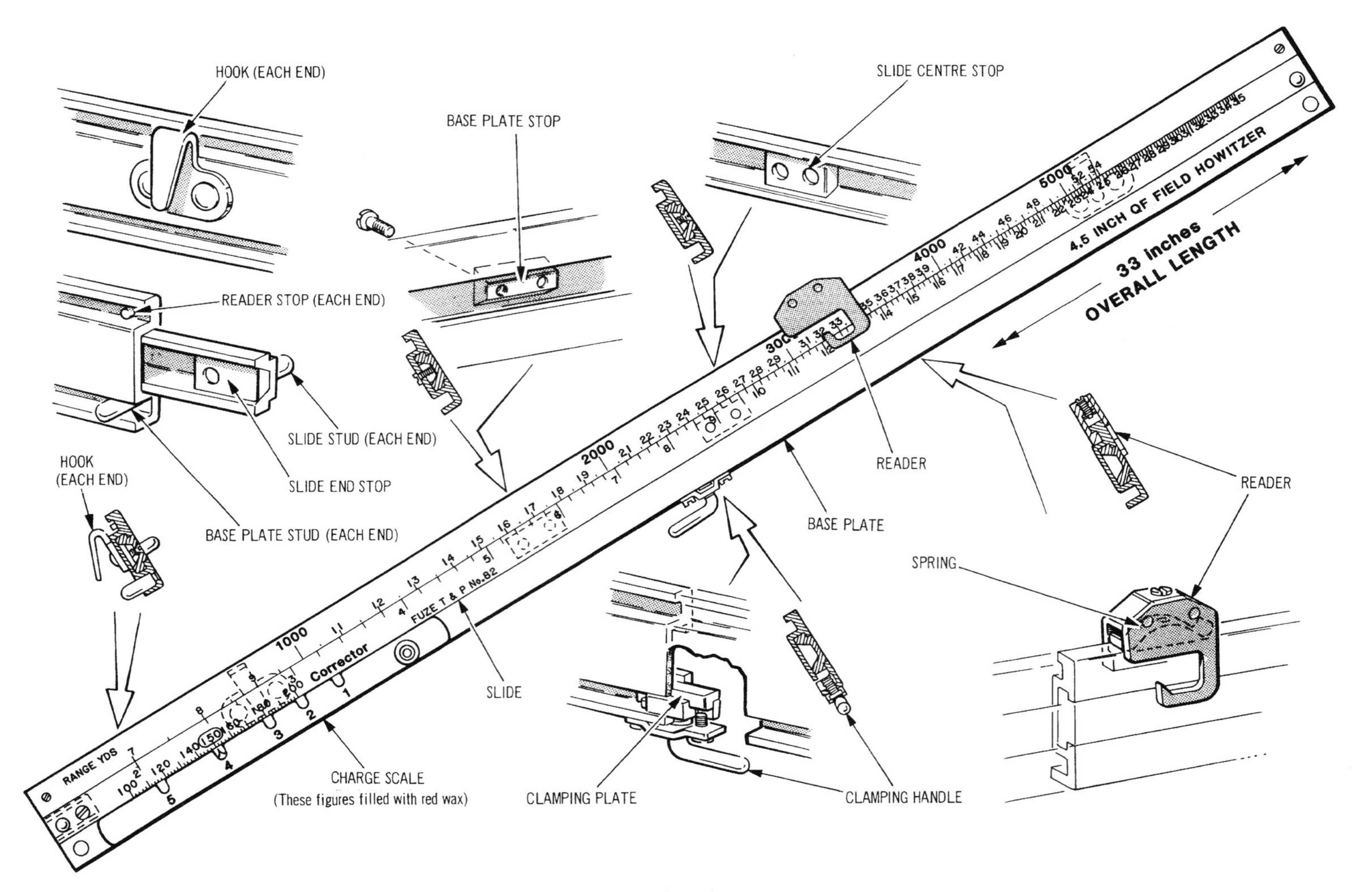

FUZE INDICATOR MK. II

Fuze indicator Mk. II

The grooved base plate was graduated on the upper portion with a range scale reading from 700 to 5,400 yards and on the lower portion with a scale for five propellant charges. A plate covered the charge scale which would only expose the arrow of the propellant charge required for a given range.

The slide, fitting into the base plate central groove, was graduated with a fuze scale, numbering from 2 to 35, on the upper edge and a corrector scale, graduated from 100 to 200, on the lower edge. An arrow, engraved on the base plate lower portion, coincided with the corrector scale 150 graduation, to indicate the normal setting.

The slide could be held at any required position by use of the clamping handle. The range and fuze scales were read by the sliding reader. The reader movement could be dampened by adjustment of the top screw tensioning the friction spring.

The fuze indicator was suspended by two hooks attached to the base plate rear face, being steadied by the two base plate studs. For travelling and in operation it was located on the rear of the ammunition wagon.

Fuze No. 82 Mk. III

Time fuze operation (see page 352)

To set the time fuze, the bottom ring (**16**) was moved around, using a No. 19 fuze key, until the graduation ordered was aligned with the setting mark.

At the moment of loading, the red TIME safety pin (**3**) would be withdrawn.

VIEW A Inertia, caused by the shock of firing, caused the safety pellet (**12**) to set back, shearing the copper suspending wire (**13**) and moving clear of the recess in the side of the retaining bolt (**10/1**).

SECTION B Centrifugal force, caused by the shell's rapid rotation, threw the retaining bolt (**10/1**) outwards, thus freeing the two remaining retaining bolts (**10/2**).

SECTION C Continued shell rotation threw the two retaining bolts (**10/2**) outwards and released the time detonator pellet (**9**). The detonator pellet (**9**) threw outwards and struck the plug needle (**8**), exploding the detonator which contained .75 grain of composition.

DIAGRAM D Flash from the detonator (**9**) fired through the powder pellet (**19/1**) into the top composition ring (**14**) which burned around until it reached the hole in the bottom ring (**16**) containing a powder pellet (**19/2**) and ignited the bottom composition ring (**16**). The time taken for the flame to reach the base powder pellet (**19/3**) varied according to the fuze setting. The flame passed through the base powder pellet (**19/3**) and ignited the fine grain powder (**23**) in the base plug, this firing through into the shell.

Maximum burning time was about forty seconds.

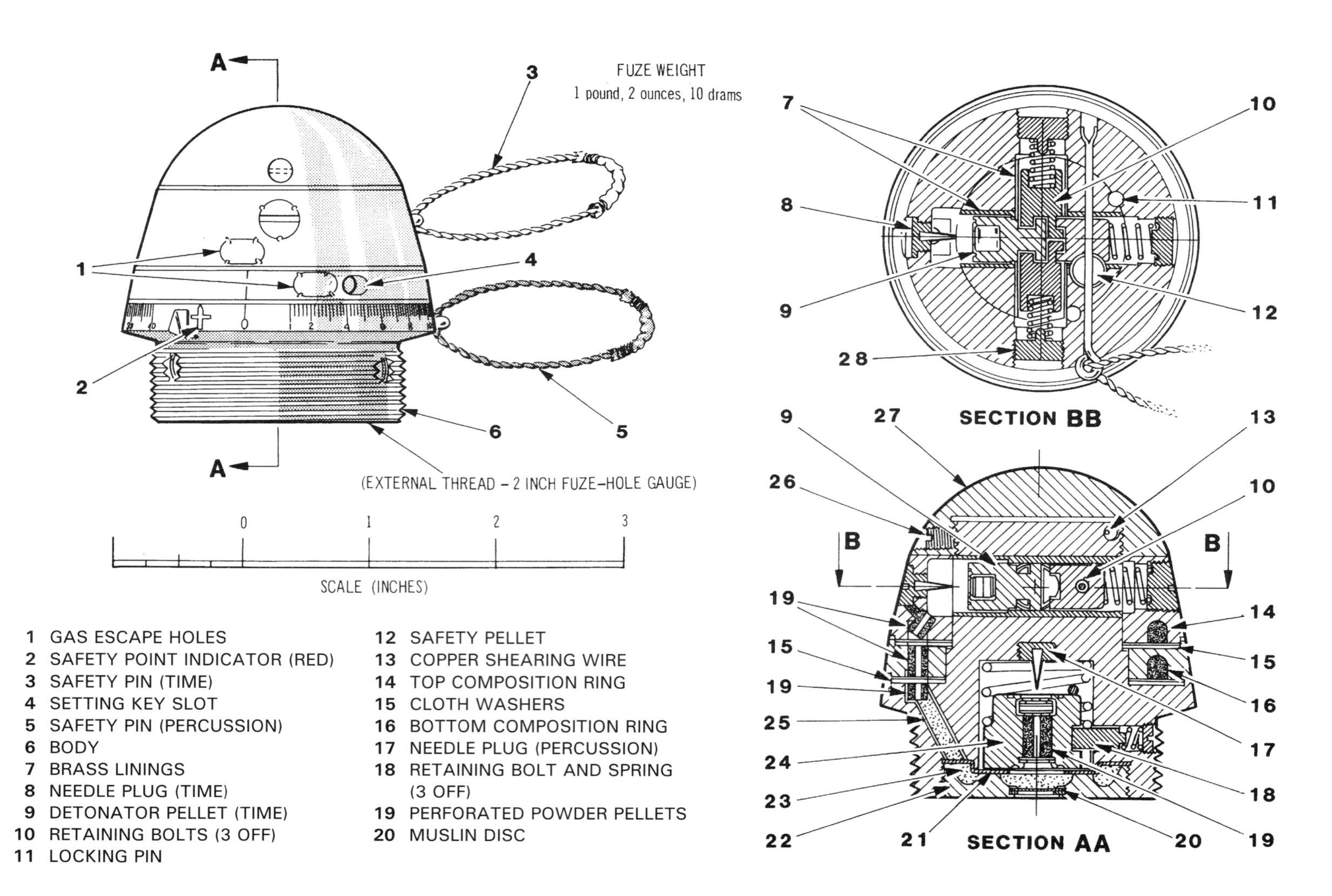

TIME AND PERCUSSION FUZE – NO. 82 MK. III

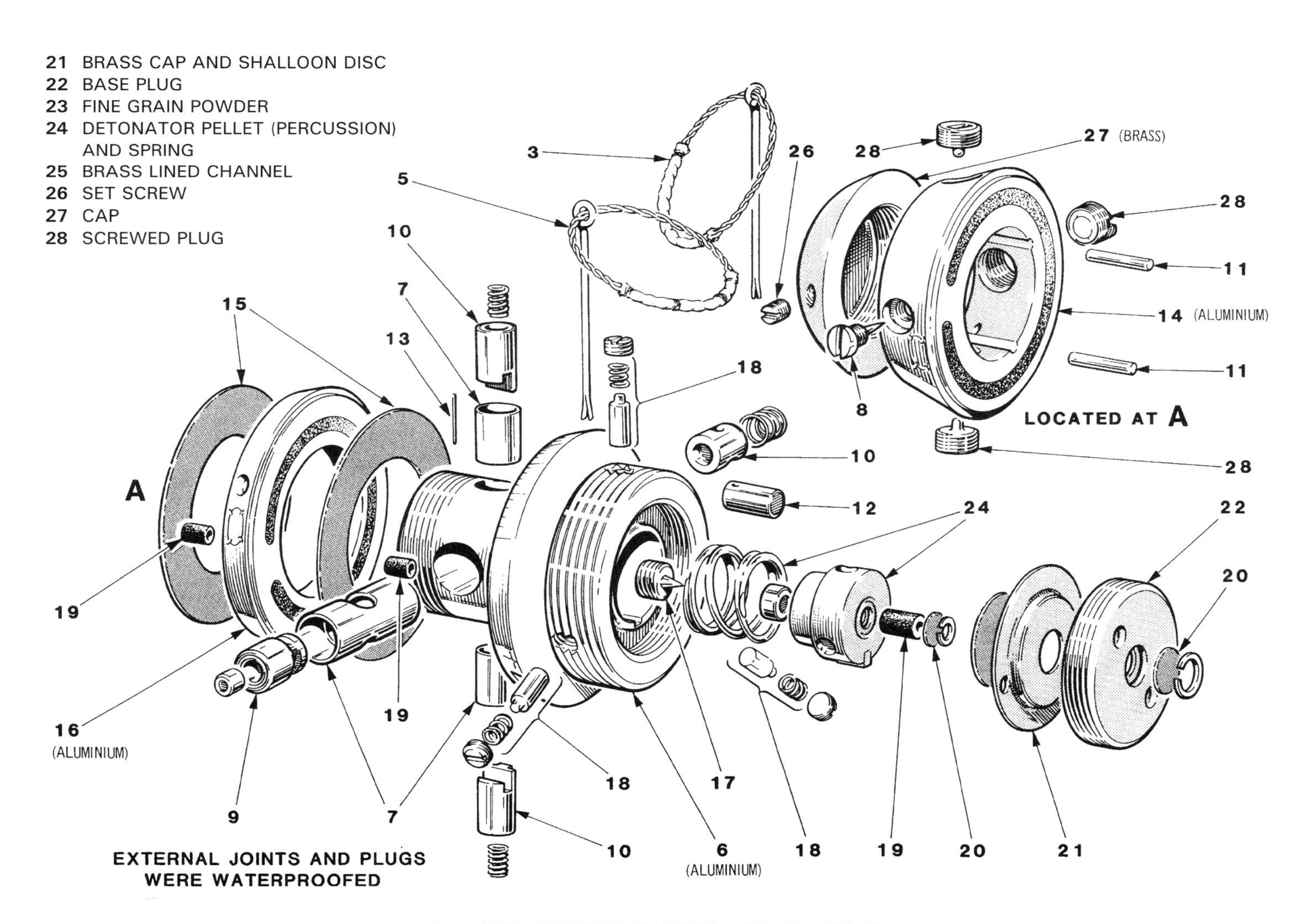

TIME AND PERCUSSION FUZE – NO. 82 MK. III

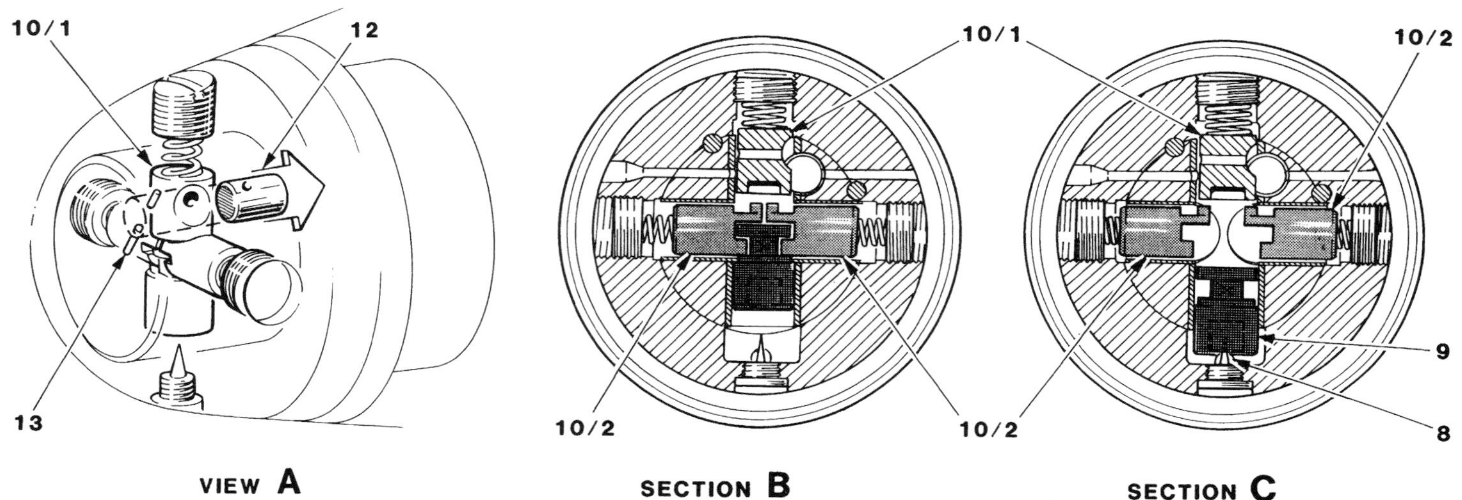

Percussion fuze operation (see page 353)

At the moment of loading the tarred black PERCUSSION safety pin (**5**) would be withdrawn.

SECTION E On firing, centrifugal force caused the three retaining bolts (**18**) to move outwards, clear of the detonator pellet (**24**). The spiral spring prevented the detonator pellet (**24**) creeping forward.

SECTION F On impact or graze, the detonator pellet (**24**) moved forward and struck the plug needle (**17**), igniting the 3 grain detonator housed within the pellet (**24**). The flash passed through the powder pellet (**19/4**) into the fine grain powder magazine contained in the base plug (**22**), this then flashed into the shell body.

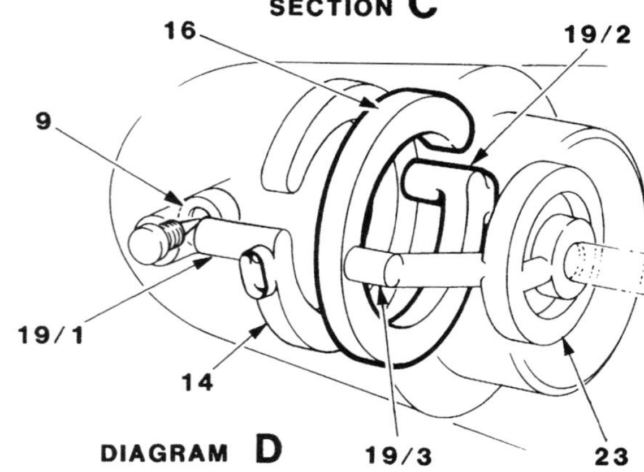

FUZE NO. 82 MK. III
TIME FUZE OPERATION

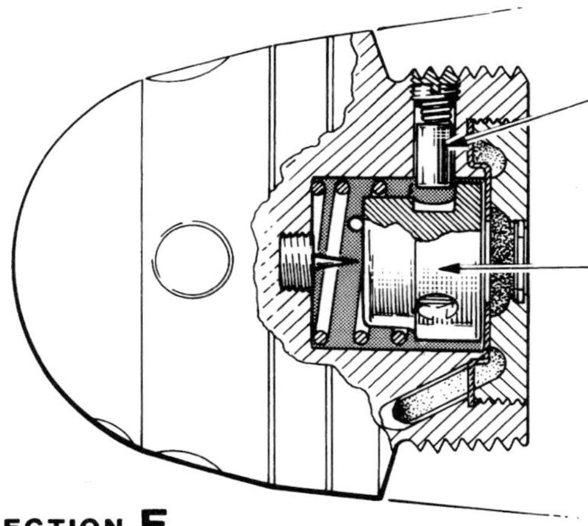

SECTION E

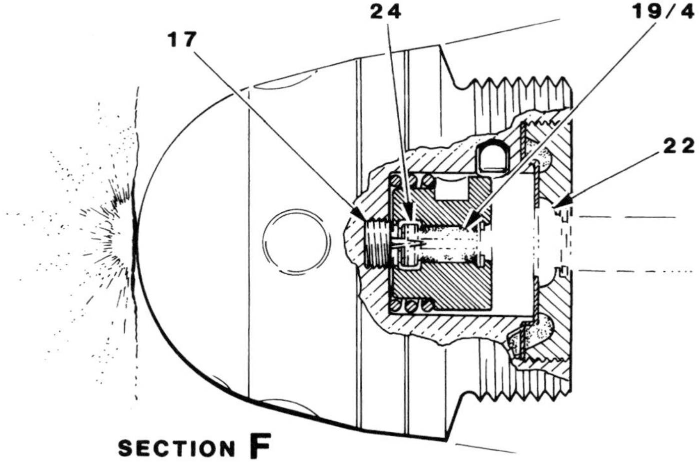

SECTION F

FUZE NO. 82 MK. III
PERCUSSION FUZE OPERATION

Fuze No. 86 (see page 354)

For operation as a TIME fuze, all three brass safety pins (**2** and **3**) were removed at the moment of loading.

Time fuze operation (see page 356)

SECTION A Shock of firing caused the detonator pellet (**10**) to move rearwards, its weight overcoming the four-winged spring (**11**), to ignite the detonator housed within the pellet (**10**), on the forward facing pellet needle (**13**). The flame fired the powder pellets (**12/1**), and the flash passed into the top composition ring (**8**).

DIAGRAM B The top composition ring (**8**) burned around until the flame reached the powder pellet (**12/2**) housed in the front face of the bottom composition ring (**7**), the position of the powder pellet (**12/2**) being governed by the fuze setting ordered. The bottom composition ring (**7**) burned around until the flame reached the powder pellets (**14**) housed within the body rear, these then transmitting the flash into the fine grain powder magazine (**20**) between the base plugs (**16** and **17**), the flash firing through into the shell body.

Removal of all three safety pins on loading ensured that, should the time fuze fail to operate correctly, the percussion fuze would detonate the shell on impact or graze.

Percussion fuze operation (see page 356)

To operate as a PERCUSSION fuze, the two percussion safety pins (**3**) would be withdrawn at the moment of loading. The time

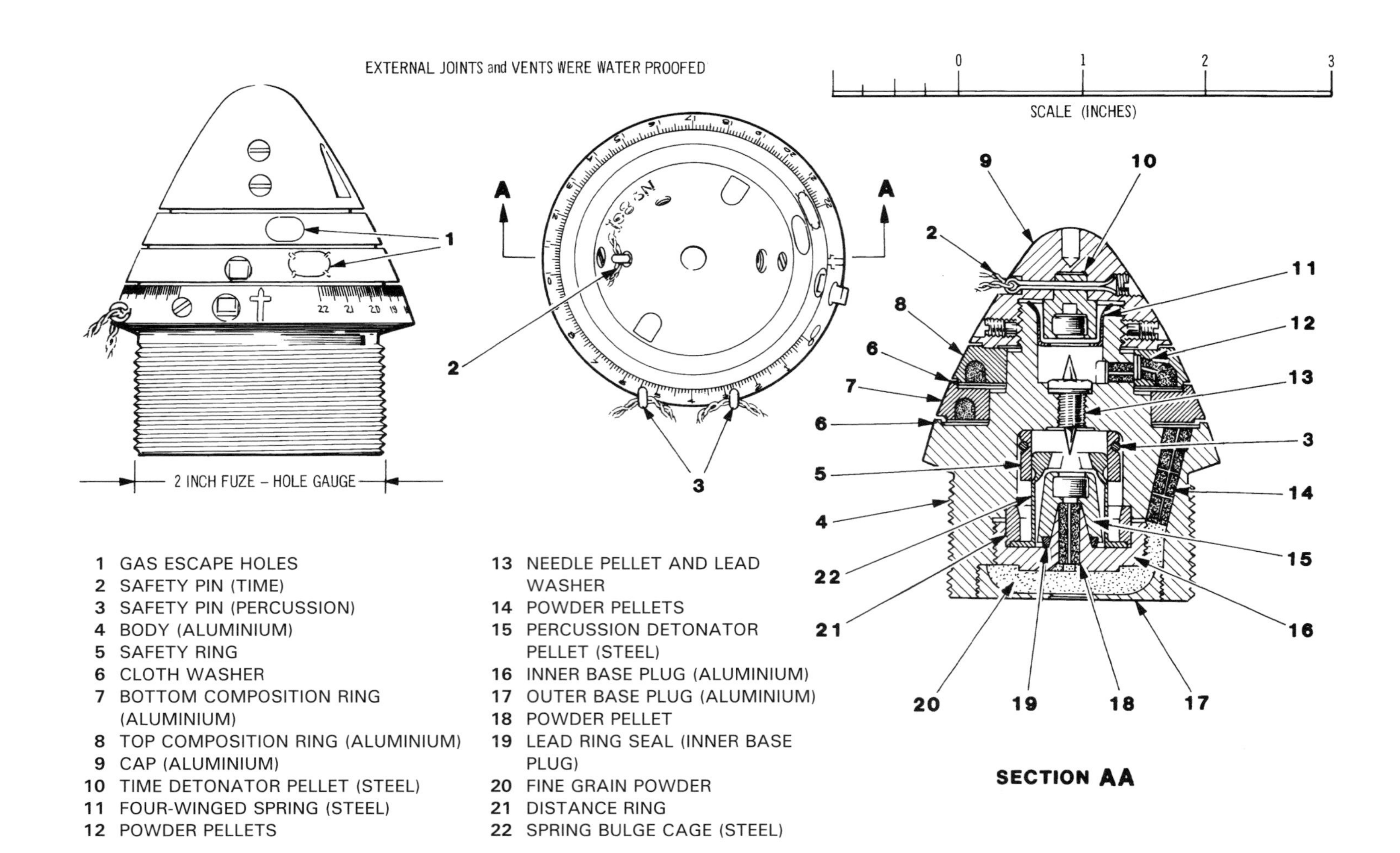

TIME AND PERCUSSION FUZE – NO. 86

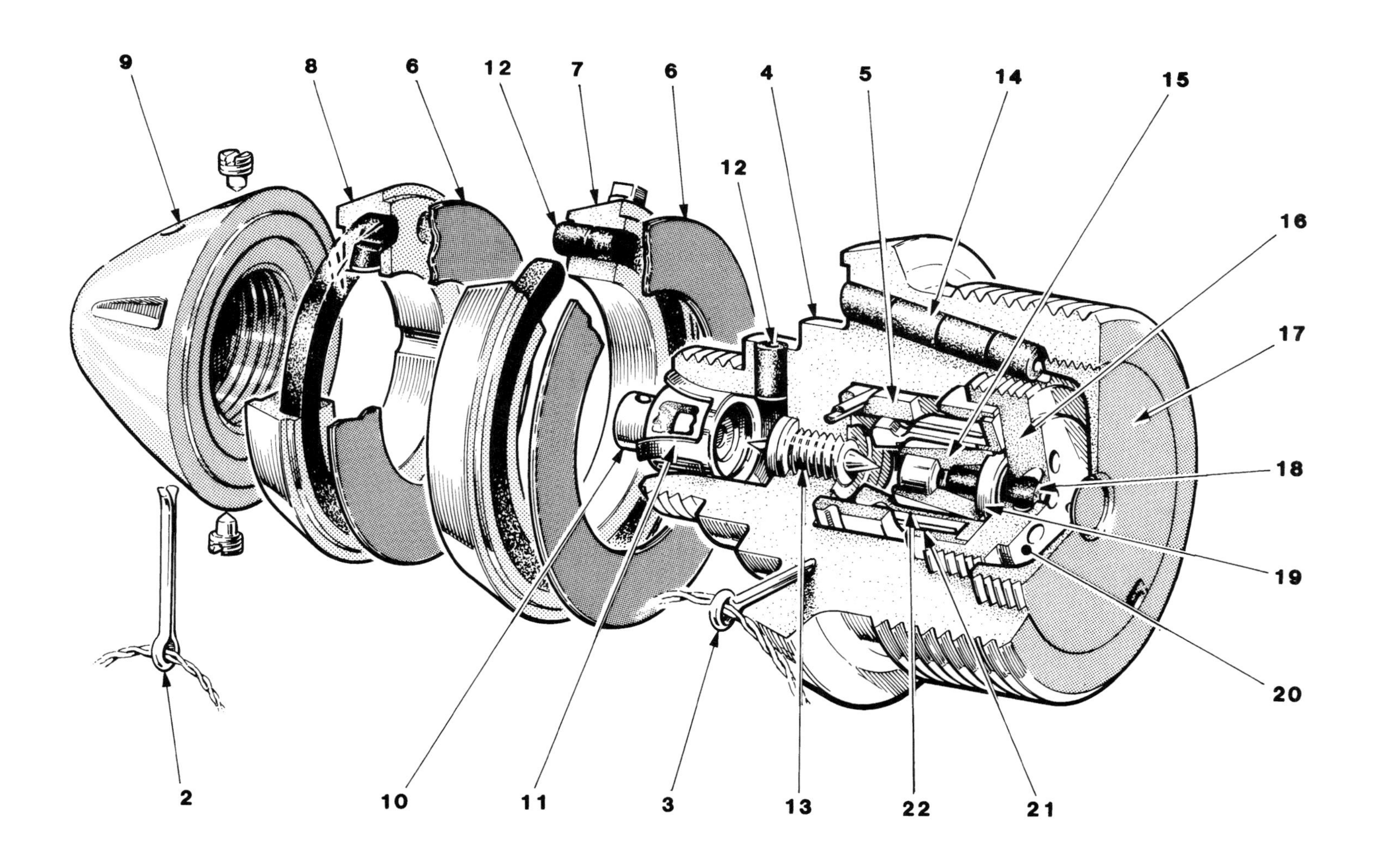

TIME AND PERCUSSION FUZE – NO. 86

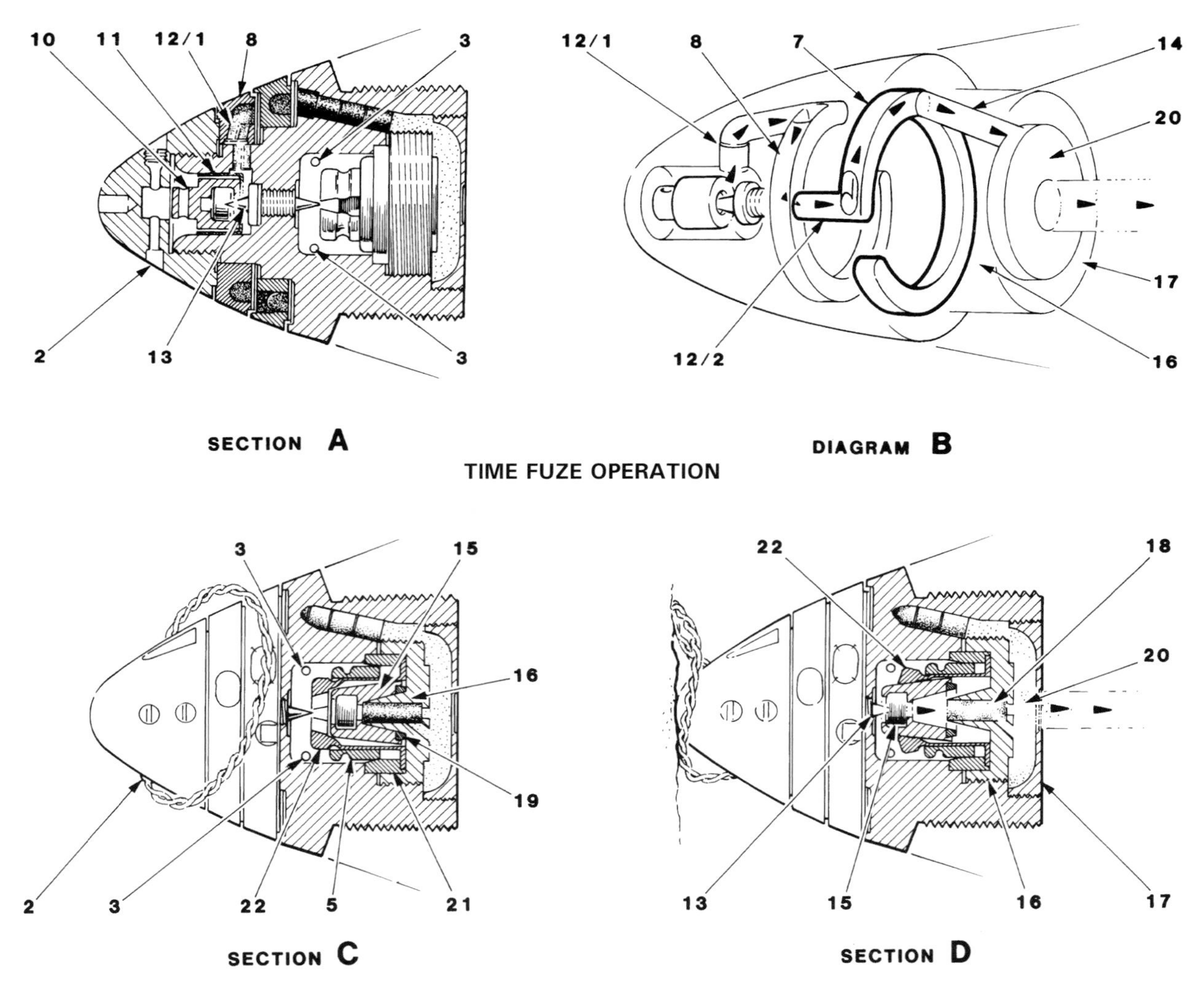
10
11
12/1
8
3
3
2
13
3
SECTION A
12/1
8
7
14
20
17
12/2
16
DIAGRAM B
TIME FUZE OPERATION
3
15
16
19
2
3
22
5
21
SECTION C
22
18
20
13
15
16
17
SECTION D
PERCUSSION FUZE OPERATION

safety pin (**2**) would be left in place and the becket looped over the fuze cap.

SECTION C Shock of firing caused the safety ring (**5**) to move back over the spring bulge cage (**22**) into the recess formed by the distance ring (**21**). The percussion detonator pellet (**15**) set back onto the lead ring seal (**19**), deformation causing it to grip the coned seating formed on the inner base plug (**16**).

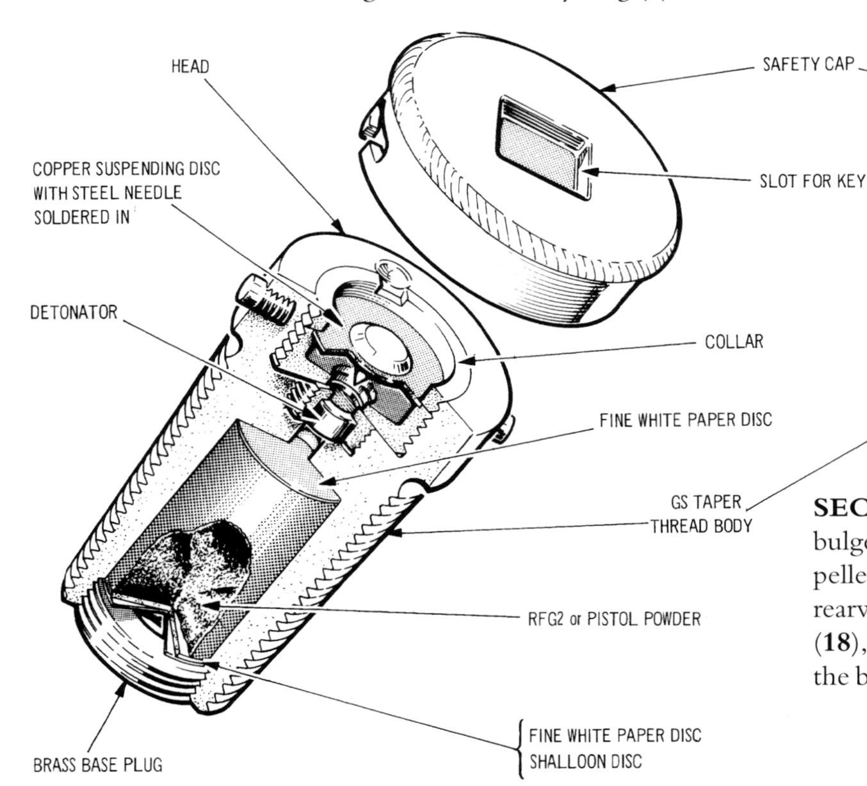

SECTIONED VIEW THROUGH TYPICAL DIRECT ACTION FUZE

DIRECT ACTION (PERCUSSION) FUZES

SECTION D On impact or graze, the spring arms of the spring bulge cage (**22**) opened outwards and the percussion detonator pellet (**15**) moved forward, the detonator being fired by striking the rearward facing pellet needle (**13**). The flash fired the powder pellet (**18**), igniting the fine grain powder (**20**) in the magazine between the base plugs (**16** and **17**) and flashing through into the shell body.

Fuze No. 17 Mk. III with cap

The gunmetal body was taper threaded externally to the GS gauge. The head had a pin on each side to engage the safety cap. A safety pin passed through the safety cap and body, the lower end of the hole being plugged with a brass screw plug.

A No. 10 key was used to install or remove the fuze as ordered. The cap and safety pin were removed at the moment of loading. The fuze weight with cap was 11 ounces and without cap, 9 ounces 3 drams.

Fuze No. 44 with cap

The fuzes were packed one in a cylinder, 50 in a wood packing case.

The weight without cap was 8 ounces, with cap and safety pins it was 10 ounces 10 drams.

Gaine No. 1 Mk. I

The gaine was a steel cylinder containing explosive. Its function was to boost the detonator flash into the shell body. It was externally threaded at one end to screw into the fuze or adaptor recess, that end being closed with a shellacked disc. The other end was internally threaded to take a screwed plug.

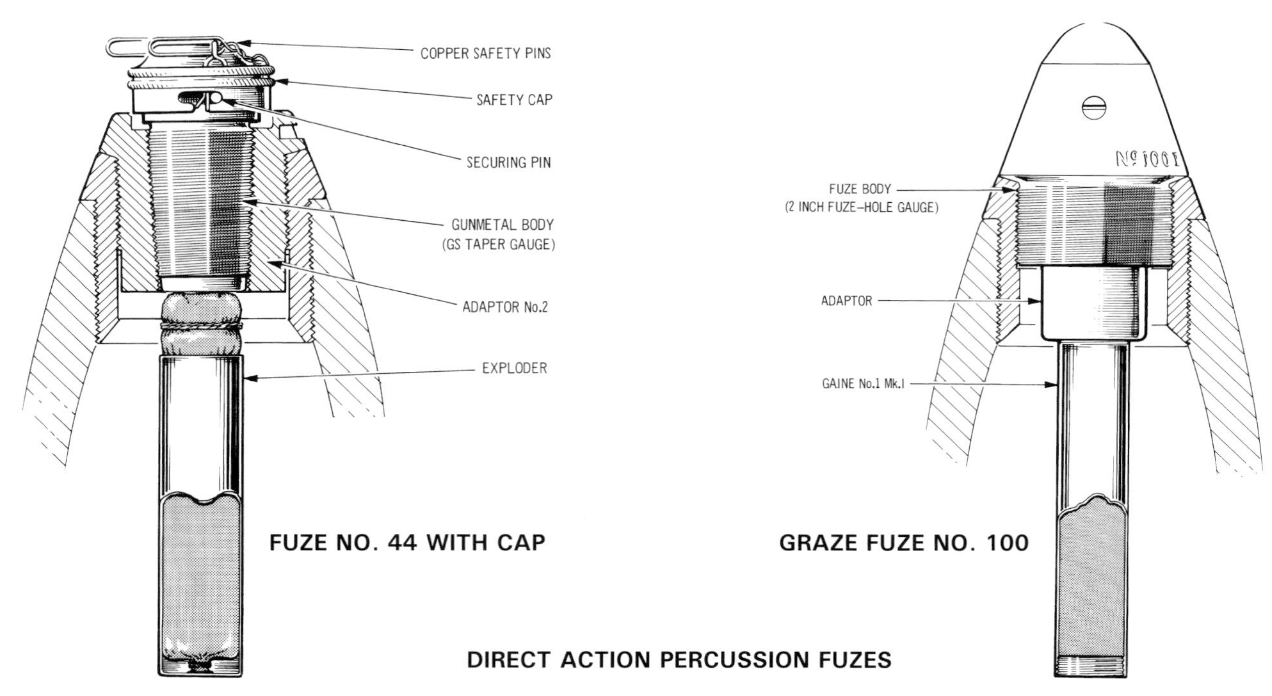

FUZE NO. 44 WITH CAP

GRAZE FUZE NO. 100

DIRECT ACTION PERCUSSION FUZES

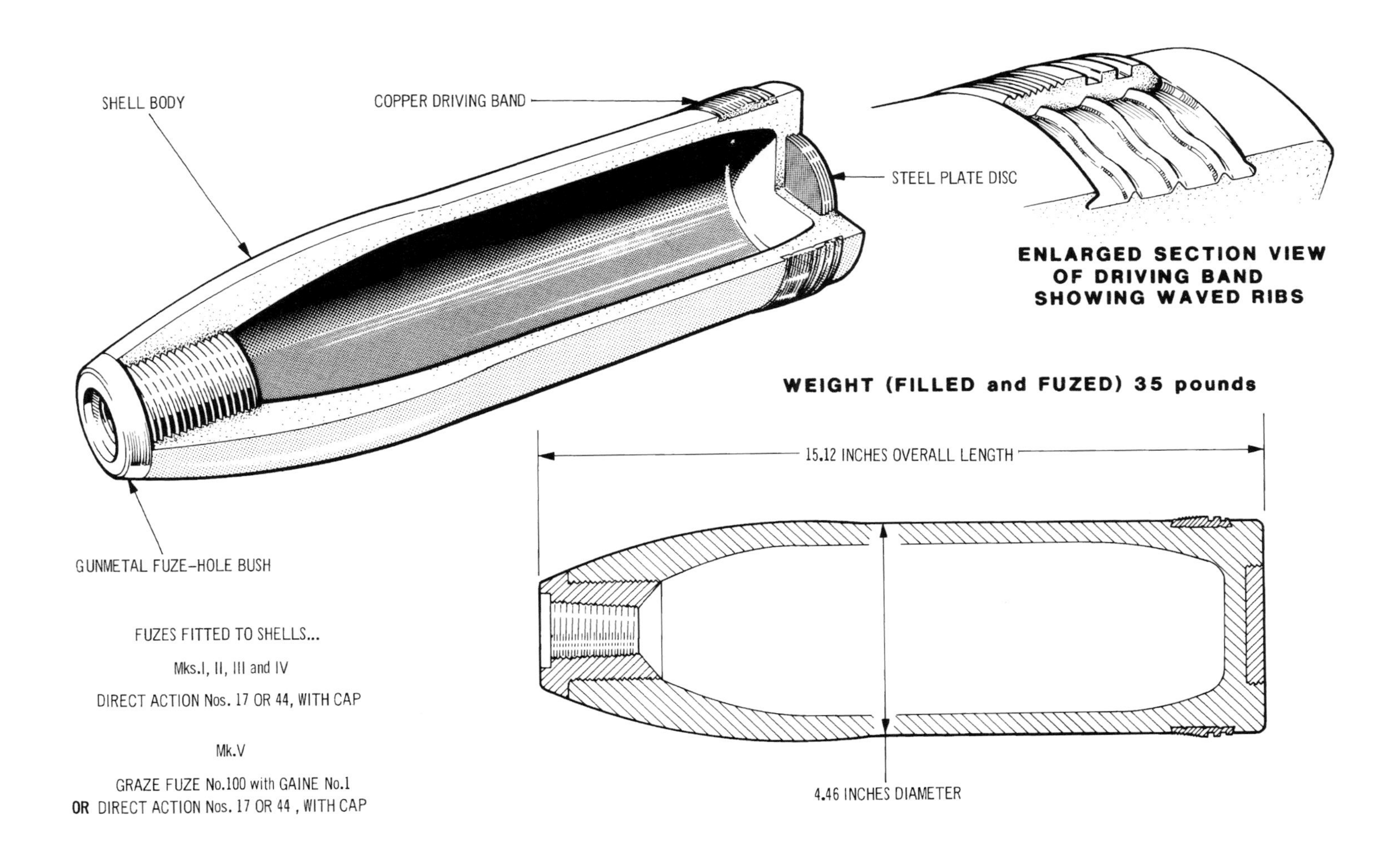

HIGH EXPLOSIVE SHELL (SEE PAGE 360)

Shells, cartridges and primers

Shell Mk. I

The forged steel body was shaped, at the head, with a radius of three diameters. The shell nose was fitted with a gunmetal bush, internally taper threaded to the GS fuze-hole gauge. A steel plate disc was screwed into the base. Forward of the shell base was an undercut groove, with three waved ribs turned in it, to house the copper driving band. The waved ribs prevented the driving band turning on the shell body. The driving band had two cannelures cut into the exterior and the front slope was serrated. The shell interior was varnished.

Shell Mk. II (illustrated on page 359)

This had a longer head and thicker walls than the Mk. I.

Shell Mk. III

This had a larger base plate than the Mk. II.

Shell Mk. IV

This had no base plate. Only a small number were manufactured.

Shell Mk.V

This was fitted with a 2 inch fuze-hole socket instead of the GS taper thread.

The shell body was filled with lyddite, a high explosive based on picric acid crystals, melted by steam and poured into the shell body.

Shrapnel shell Mk. I

The forged steel body was shaped, at the head, with a radius of three diameters. It was fitted with a gunmetal fuze-hole socket, internally threaded to the two-inch fuze-hole gauge, secured into the body with screws and twisting pins. The fuze-hole socket was fitted with a screw to secure the fuze. Near the base of the shell was an undercut groove, with three waved ribs turned in it, to house the copper driving band. The waved ribs prevented the driving band turning on the shell body. The driving band had two cannelures cut into the exterior and the front slope was serrated.

Inside the shell body, a tin cup was fitted into the base to contain the three-ounce FG powder bursting charge. Over the cup was placed a steel disc with a tube screwed into the centre, the tube passing up through the shell body and soldered into the fuze-hole socket. This tube conducted the detonator flash from the fuze into the bursting charge. The shell interior was lined with brown paper and filled with approximately 481 metal balls, these at a weight of 35 to the pound, the spaces between being filled with resin. Over the balls was a felt washer and, within the fuze-hole socket, a wood block.

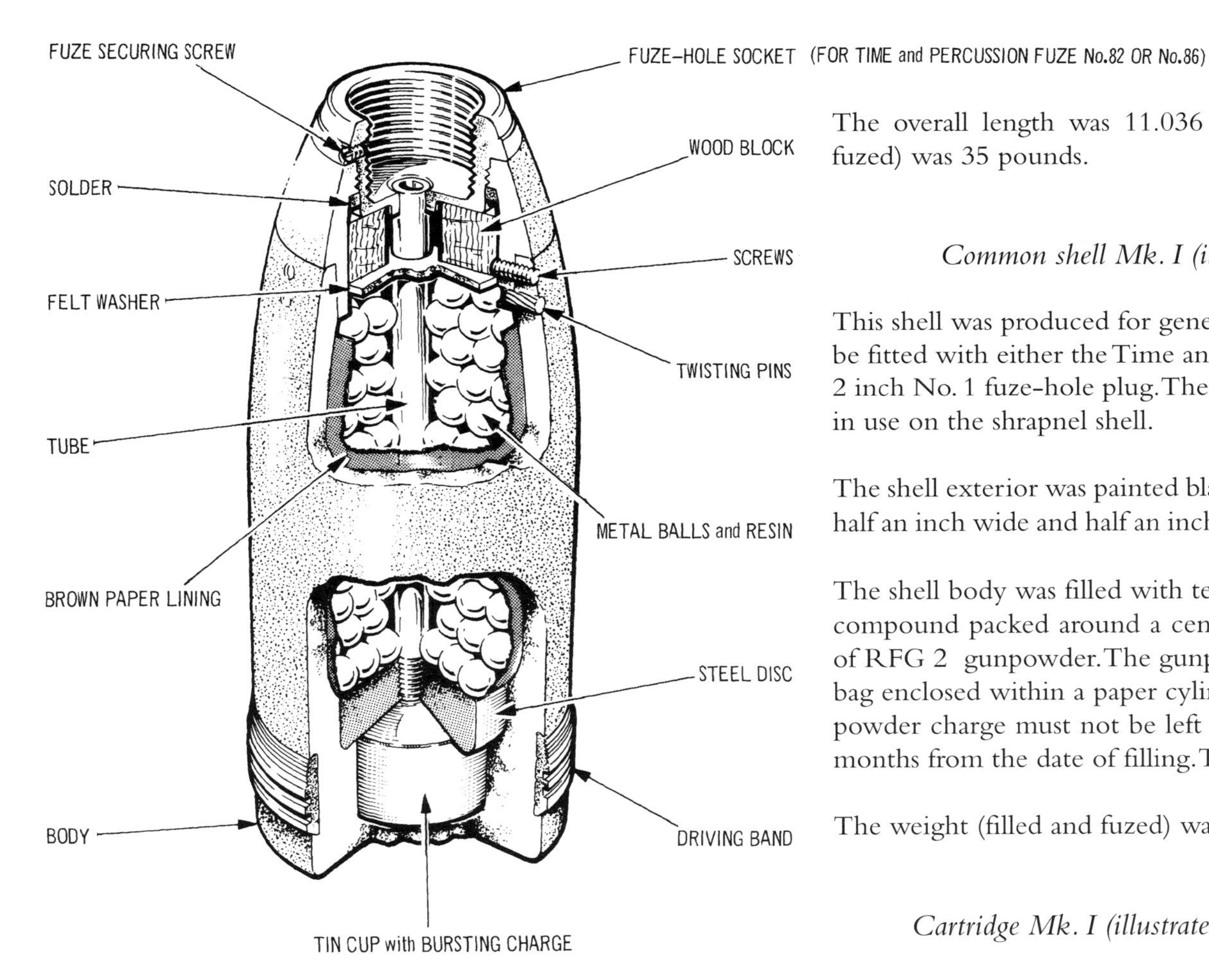

SHRAPNEL SHELL MK. I

The overall length was 11.036 inches. The weight (filled and fuzed) was 35 pounds.

Common shell Mk. I (illustrated on page 362)

This shell was produced for general use and for practice. It could be fitted with either the Time and Percussion Fuze No. 82 or the 2 inch No. 1 fuze-hole plug. The driving band was similar to that in use on the shrapnel shell.

The shell exterior was painted black, with two yellow bands, each half an inch wide and half an inch apart, painted around the body.

The shell body was filled with ten ounces of a smoke-producing compound packed around a central 3.75 ounce bursting charge of RFG 2 gunpowder. The gunpowder was contained in a cloth bag enclosed within a paper cylinder. Regulations stated that the powder charge must not be left in the shell for more than eight months from the date of filling. The shell was issued plugged.

The weight (filled and fuzed) was 35 pounds.

Cartridge Mk. I (illustrated on pages 363 and 364)

The charge was contained in a solid drawn brass cartridge case, the base designed to hold a No. 1 percussion primer. The charge consisted of 15 ounces 14 drams of MD cordite, this made up in five portions, each portion enclosed in a cambric bag and marked on the underside with the portion weight, the portion number being marked on the opposite side. The charge portions were assembled into the case with the portion numbers uppermost. The cartridge mouth was closed with a leatherboard lid fitted with a lifting band.

Early cartridge cases were sandblasted and lacquered black on the exterior, later cases were left in their natural brass finish. Cartridges were packed singly in a leatherboard lined tin box with a tear-off band in the lid.

A description of the No. 1 percussion primer is on page 279.

Cartridge Mk. I (ballistite charge) (illustrated on page 365)

This was a Mk. I cartridge case, with Percussion Primer No. 1, containing a 14 ounce 2 dram charge of ballistite, size A71, made up in five sections, each section enclosed in a cambric bag. The bags were packed in a paper ring, separated by glazed board strips into three compartments, placed inside the case. The case mouth was closed with a glazed board lid fitted with a white tape loop.

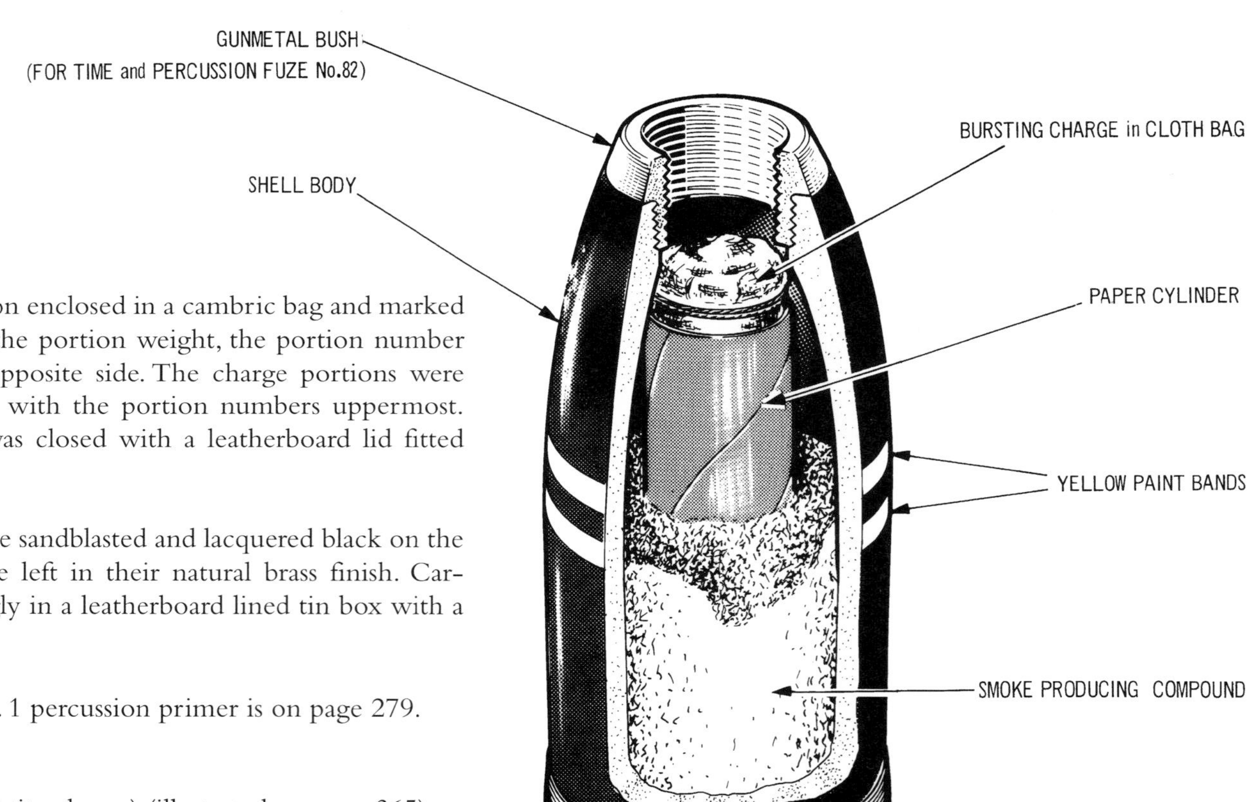

COMMON SHELL MK. I

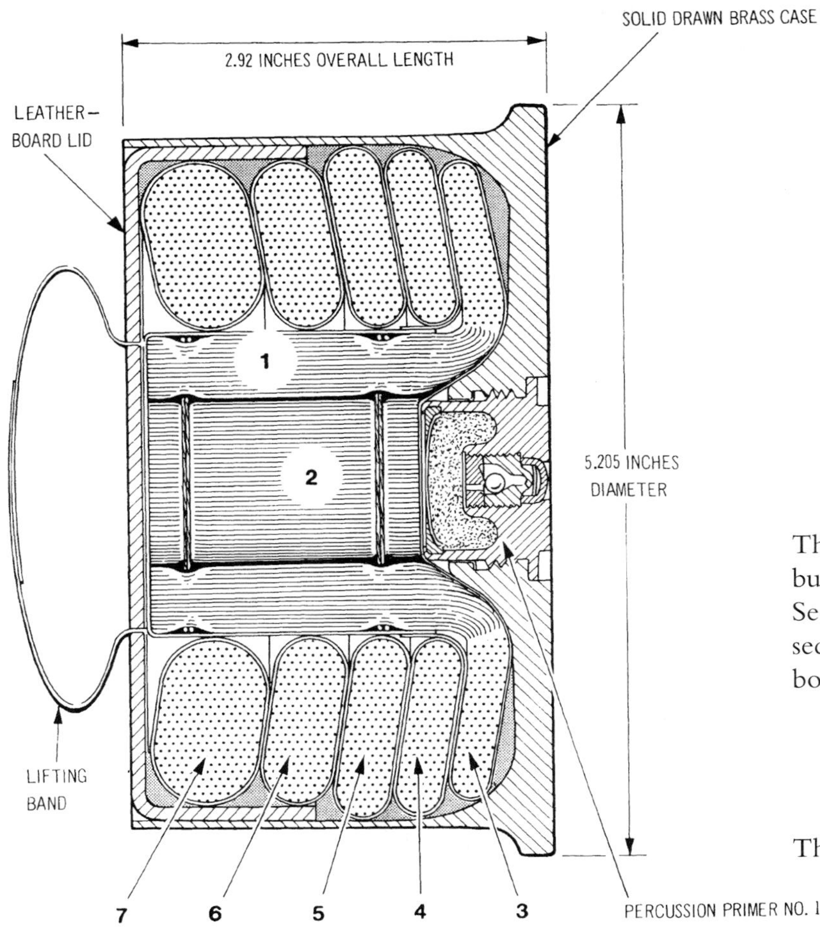

CARTRIDGE MK. I

CHARGE

1	3 ounces 4 drams CORDITE SIZE 2¼	CORE		1st. PORTION
2	1 ounce 9 drams	,,	CORE	1st. PORTION
3	1 ounce 1 dram CORDITE SIZE 4¼			1st. PORTION
4	1 ounce 5.5 drams	,,		2nd. PORTION
5	1 ounce 12 drams	,,		3rd. PORTION
6	2 ounces 9.5 drams	,,		4th. PORTION
7	4 ounces 5 drams	,,		5th. PORTION

Cartridge Mk. II (ballistite charge)

The five sections were of the same weight as the Mk. I cartridge, but had no paper ring or glazed board strips to separate them. Sections 2, 3, 4 and 5 were arranged around the end of the primer, section 1 being of case diameter and stitched inside the glazed board lid.

Cartridge Mk. I (CSP.60 charge)

This cartridge was made up in the same manner as the ballistite cartridge, except for the 1 pound 10 drams CSP.60 charge, which was made up in five sections, the weights of which were:

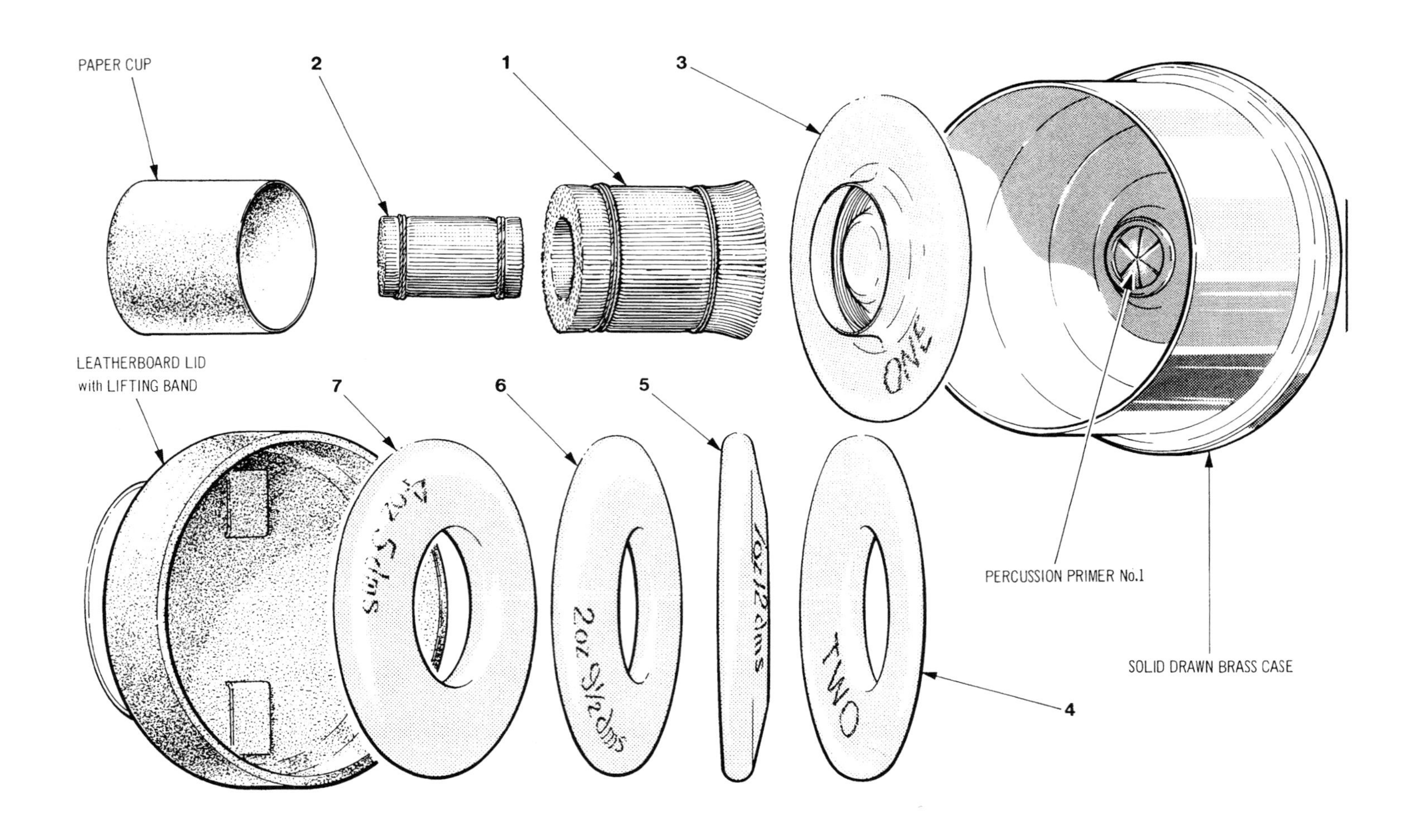

CARTRIDGE MK. I

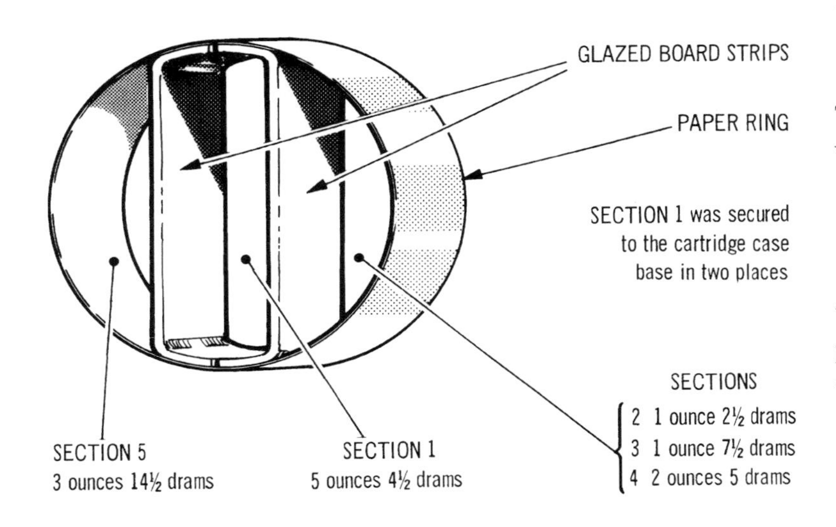

CARTRIDGE MK. 1 (BALLISTITE CHARGE)

- Section 1 – 6 ounces 8 drams
- Section 2 – 1 ounce 3 drams
- Section 3– 1 ounce 8 drams
- Section 4 – 2 ounces 11 drams
- Section 5 – 4 ounces 12 drams,
- A total of 1 pound 10 drams.

Blank Cartridge Mk. I

This consisted of 1.5 pounds RFG 2 powder, in a silk bag with a shalloon base, enclosed in a service cartridge case, the mouth closed by a leatherboard lid with lifting band.

Blank Cartridge Mk. II

This consisted of 1.25 pounds RFG 2 powder in a bag provided with a felt jacket.

Drill cartridge

This was an empty cartridge case, the mouth closed by a wood plug and stamped DRILL. Four holes were drilled in the case side and three in the base to distinguish it from a service cartridge.

Range rule

The range rule was used, by the battery commander, to decide which cartridge charge was to be used in order to attain a minimum projectile descent angle, onto the target, of twenty degrees.

The boxwood range rule operated on the principle of a normal slide rule. Used in conjunction with the dial sight carrier elevation scale drum, or with the bar sight, it enabled range setting to be done, in yards, with all cartridge charges.The rule would also display the limit of each charge.

The two scales were logarithmic. The top scale was graduated from 500 to 7000 yards and represented the true range from the howitzer to the target. The sliding central scale was graduated from 400 to 5,400 yards and was a false range to which the howitzer sights were set.The graduations were exactly the same logarithmic proportions as the top scale. On the central slide, a red

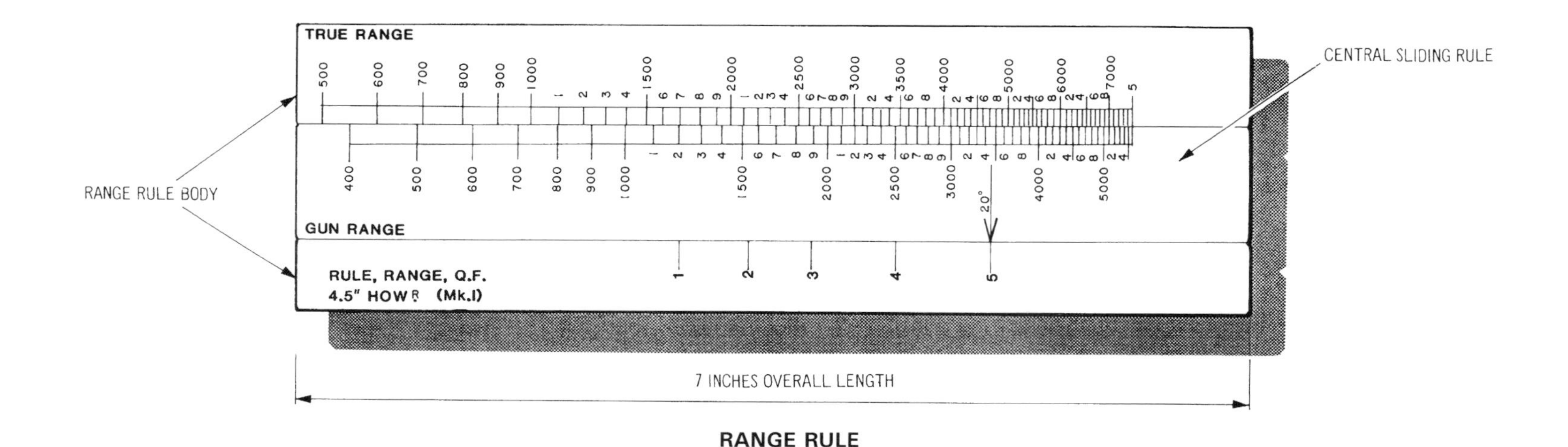

RANGE RULE

line, showing twenty degrees, was marked opposite 3,445 yards: this told which charge to use to obtain that angle of projectile descent at that range. At all elevations beyond that graduation, all descent angles would be greater than twenty degrees. The bottom scale of 1 to 5 enabled the red arrow, on the central slide, to be moved to whichever charge was to be used. If, for example, No. 5 charge was being used, the red arrow would be moved opposite 5 on the lower scale. Any particular real range on the top scale would be read against a false range on the centre scale, this false range being the one given to the howitzer. This procedure would apply to all charges except charge No. 4, for which the real range would be used.

Limber

The frame consisted of four flanged nickel steel plate futchells, made deeper towards the rear to take flanged axletree bearings. The outer futchells were connected to the inner ones by flanged nickel steel plate stays. The inner futchells were connected centrally by a draught pole socket and, at the rear, by a manganese bronze rectangular guide bracket, to house the spring limber hook. At the front, each outer futchell was fitted with a spring hook for the attachment of a swingletree.

At the axletree bearing locations, the outer futchells had nickel steel connecting plates fitted to locate the ammunition box.

Gusset stays were riveted to the futchell rear ends to give extra support to the ammunition box.

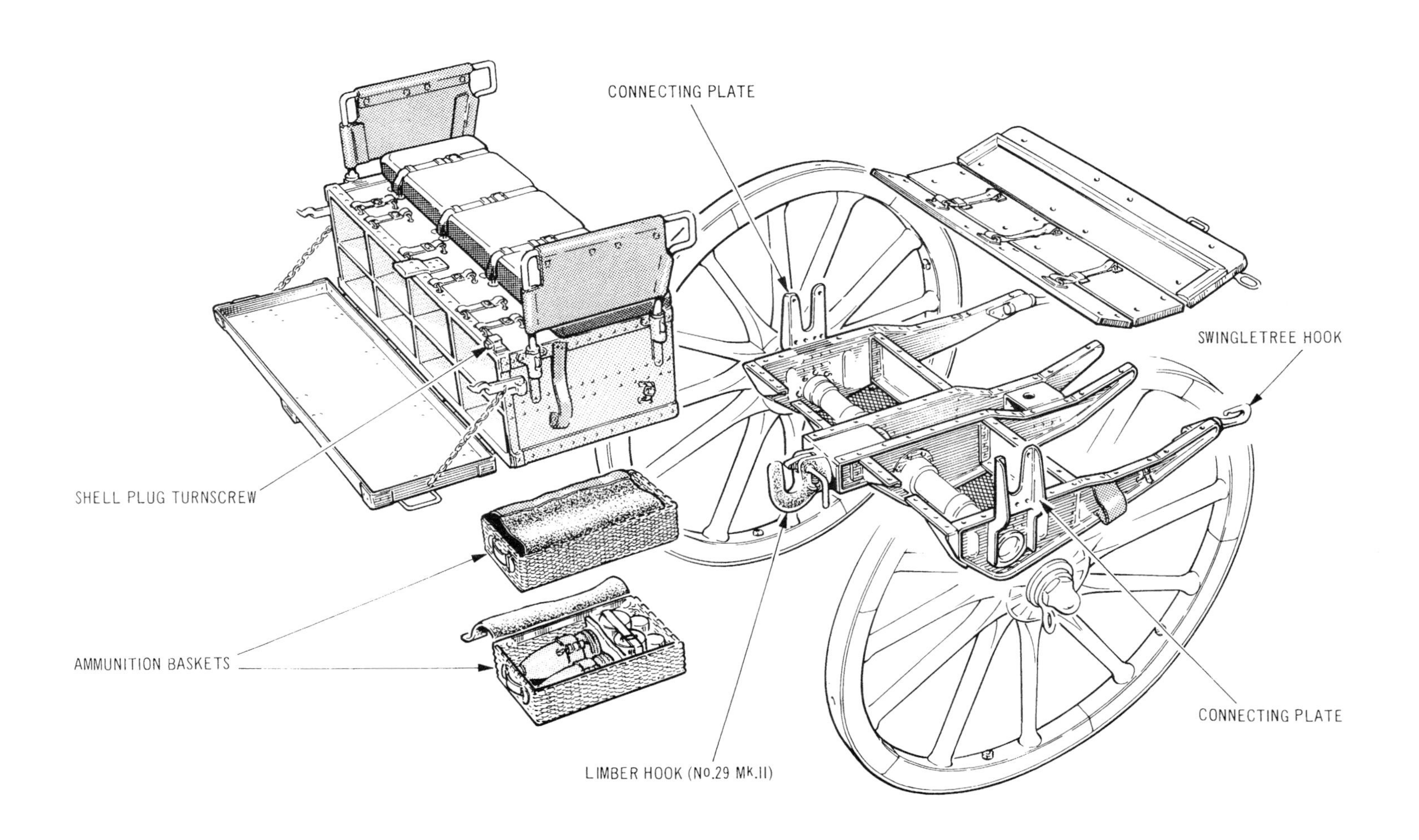
CONNECTING PLATE
SWINGLETREE HOOK
SHELL PLUG TURNSCREW
AMMUNITION BASKETS
CONNECTING PLATE
LIMBER HOOK (No.29 MK.II)

LIMBER

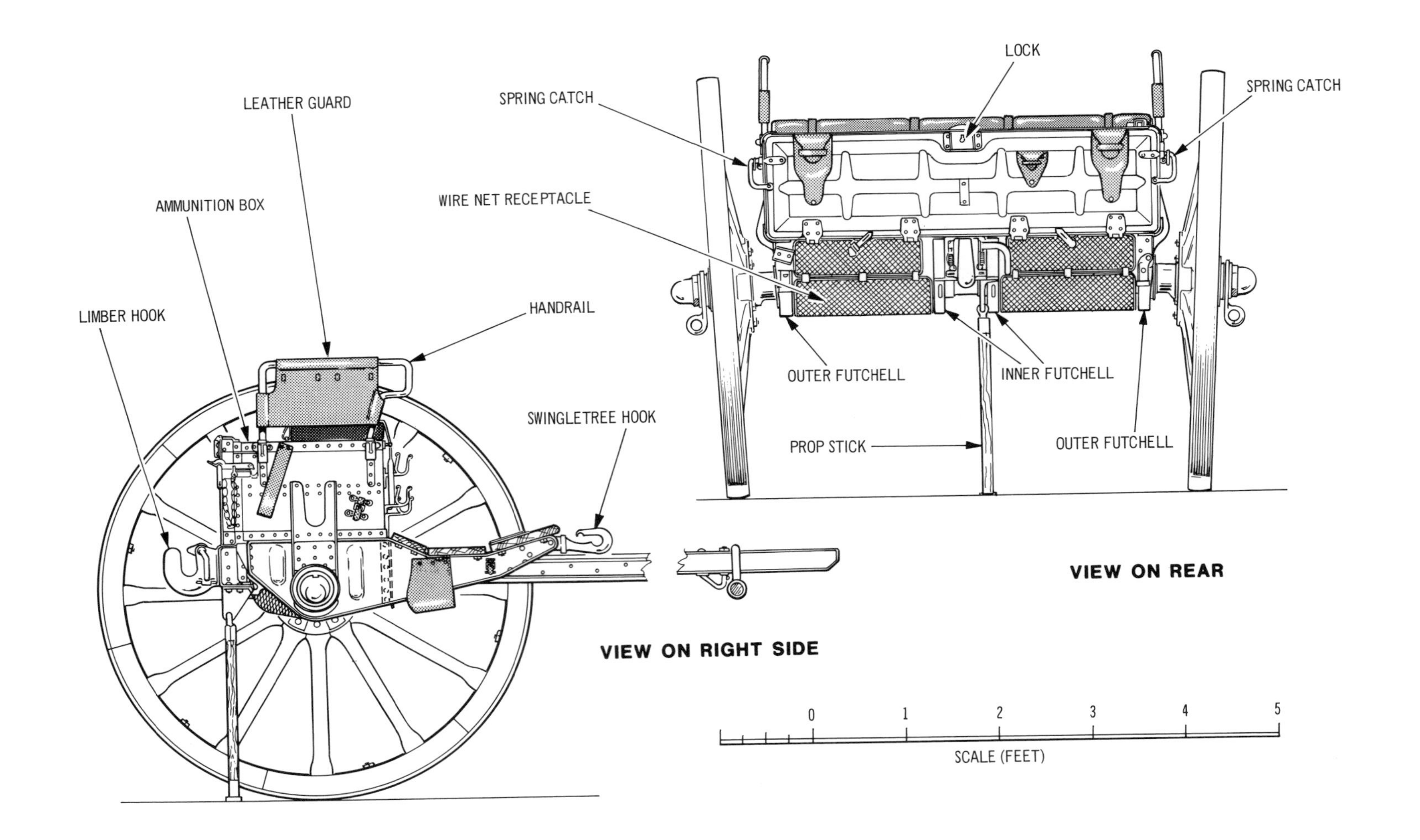
LEATHER GUARD
AMMUNITION BOX
LIMBER HOOK
HANDRAIL
SWINGLETREE HOOK
VIEW ON RIGHT SIDE
LOCK
SPRING CATCH
SPRING CATCH
WIRE NET RECEPTACLE
OUTER FUTCHELL
INNER FUTCHELL
PROP STICK
OUTER FUTCHELL
VIEW ON REAR
0
1
2
3
4
5
SCALE (FEET)

LIMBER

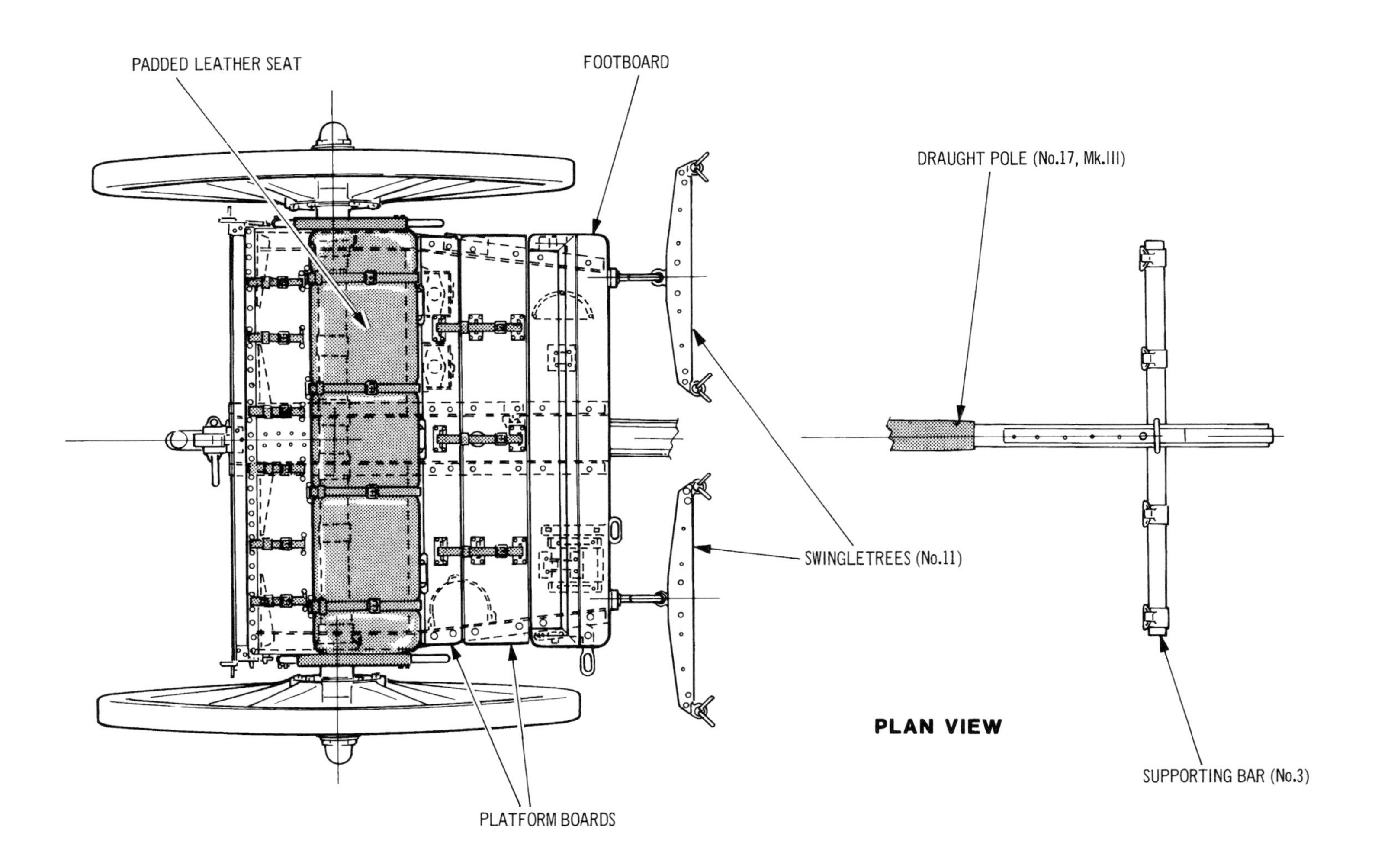
PADDED LEATHER SEAT
FOOTBOARD
DRAUGHT POLE (No.17, Mk.III)
SWINGLETREES (No.11)
PLAN VIEW
SUPPORTING BAR (No.3)
PLATFORM BOARDS

LIMBER

Both the limber hook and the swingletree hooks were fitted with springs, to ease the strain of draught on the horses, particularly when starting. The limber hook had a spring catch, similar to that fitted to the Quick Firing 18 pdr Mk. I limber, described on pages 282 and 285.

The tubular steel axletree was housed in flanged bearings attached to the futchells. Each bearing had a key to engage a keyway in the axletree and a recess to house an L section leather dust seal.

Fixed beneath the frame were two wire net receptacles, with hinged flaps secured by spring catches and leather ties, to carry twelve canvas buckets.

The ammunition box, of nickel steel, was stiffened by angle steel stays and strips and riveted to the limber frame. The interior was divided into eight compartments, to hold removable ammunition baskets. The baskets were of closely woven Palembang cane, with a leather handle secured at one end.

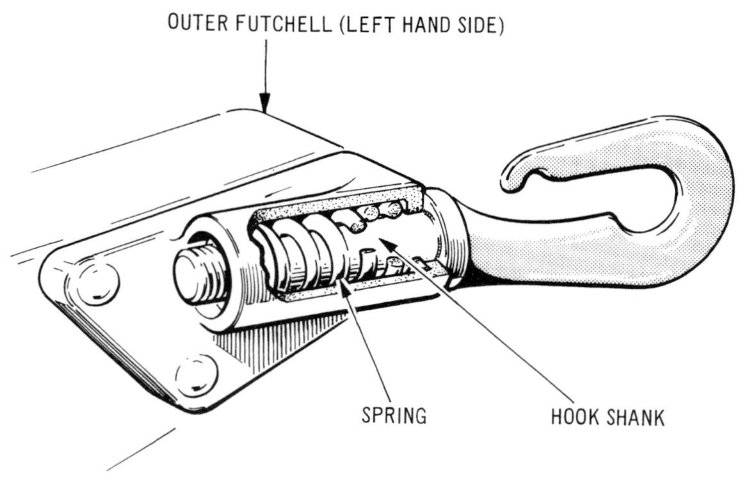

SWINGLETREE HOOK

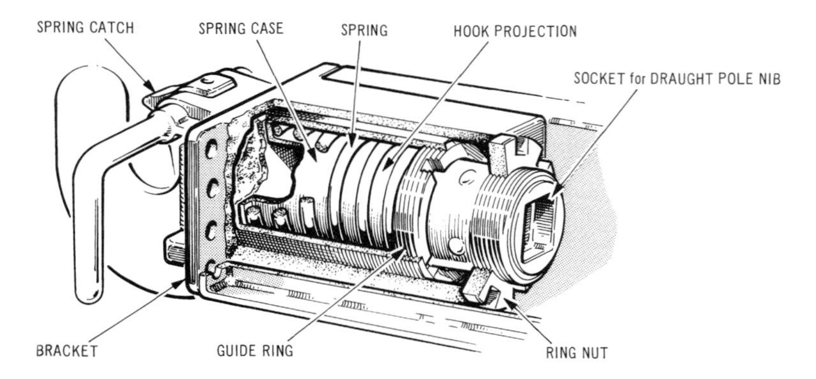

LIMBER HOOK

Carriage limbers

A carriage limber ammunition box originally held six basket carriers and a small stores tray, one compartment being left spare. Later boxes utilised this spare compartment for a second small stores tray.

Each basket carrier contained two rounds of ammunition, the projectiles resting in wood blocks and secured by leather straps, the cartridges and fuzes, carried in tins, bearing against a felt pad and supported on wood blocks, in front of the projectiles. A felt flap, with leather hinge, covered the basket contents. Baskets to carry high explosive shells were coloured yellow.

Baskets, each to carry ten blank cartridges held in wood fittings, had their ends painted blue.

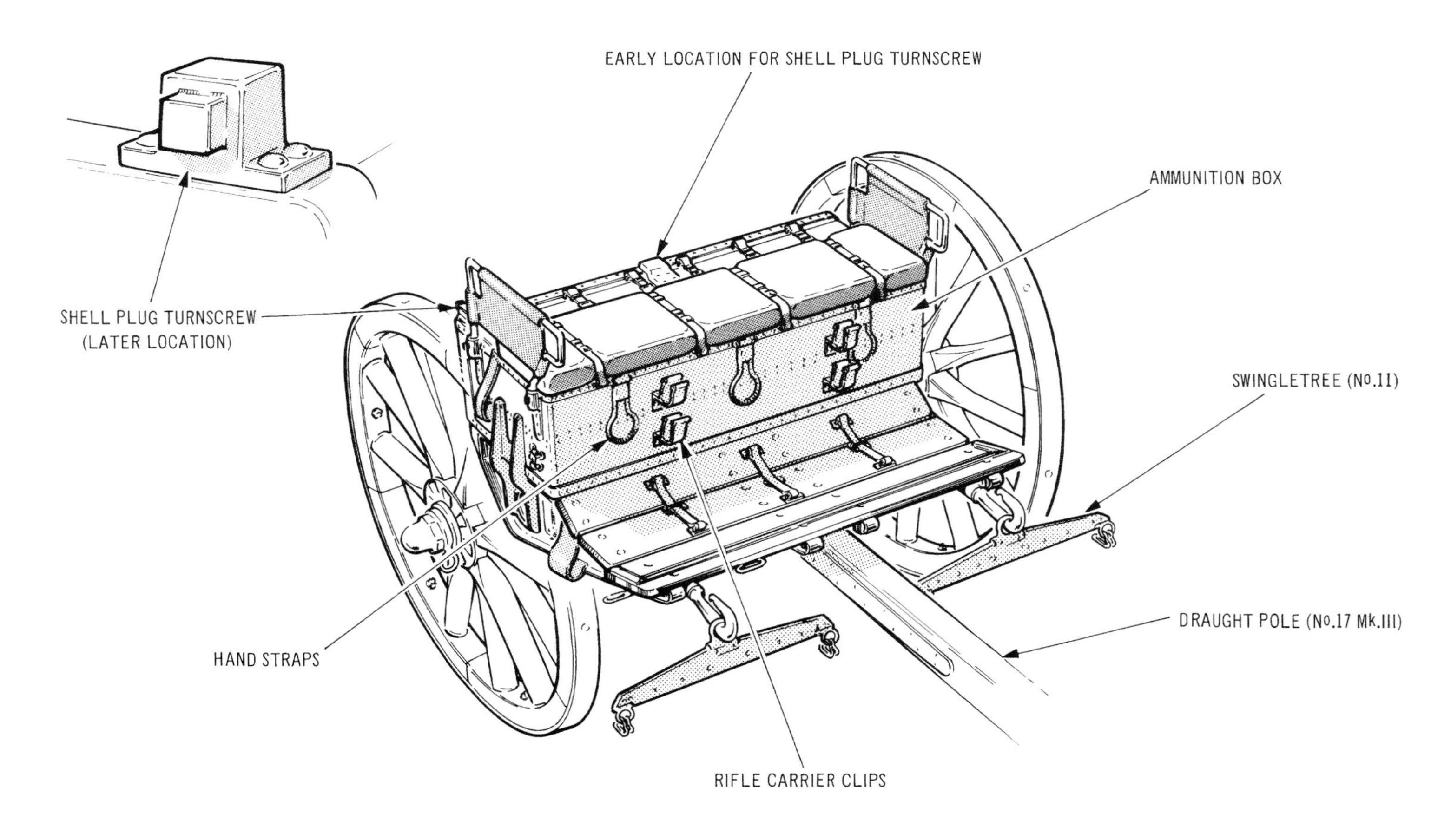

LIMBER

Ammunition wagon limbers

These limbers were similar to the carriage limbers, differing in the ammunition box being fitted with eight basket carriers and no small stores trays. Early contents were twelve shrapnel and four high explosive shells. Later contents were reversed to twelve high explosive and four shrapnel shells.

Ammunition wagon

The frame consisted of two flanged, steel plate sides, secured to a central perch of hollow section, by steel plate stays. The method of construction was basically similar to that of the limber previously described.

An unusual feature of this ammunition wagon was the provision of a perch hook, fitted to the rear, to enable two or more wagons to be coupled together. In an emergency, the wagon could double as a limber for the howitzer carriage. The arrangement of platform and footboards was similar to that already described for the limber, also the wire mesh receptacles beneath the frame.

Also beneath the frame were two brackets to carry a spare, jointed, No. 18 draught pole.

Fitted to the ammunition wagon was a tyre brake. It was operated from the wagon rear by a handle, secured to the rear end of the screwed connecting rod. Turning the handle moved the left-hand brake arm and shoe rearwards to contact the tyre. Continued turning caused the nut, mounted on the left-hand cranked lever, to move rearwards along the screwed connecting rod, this movement being transmitted, via the cross connecting rod and plain connecting rod, to the right-hand brake arm and shoe. The mechanism was cushioned by disc springs on one end of the cross connecting rod.

Ammunition box

In method of construction and attachment to the frame, the box was similar to that previously described as fitted to the limbers. It differed from the limber boxes in respect of its capacity. It was divided transversely into two main portions, each with its own lid hinged at the bottom and secured by two spring catches and a lock.

Each main portion was subdivided into eight compartments, similar to the limber boxes, each compartment to hold a removable basket containing two complete rounds of ammunition. In early ammunition boxes, the rear baskets contained shrapnel and the front baskets lyddite shells. Later ammunition boxes contained fourteen high explosive and two shrapnel shells in both the front and rear portions.

Externally, the ammunition box was similar to that of the limber boxes, being provided with a padded leather seat and hand straps for three gun crew members, plus carrying clips for rifles on the box front and various stores and equipments.

Turnscrews for shell plugs were provided, the same description applying as for the limber boxes.

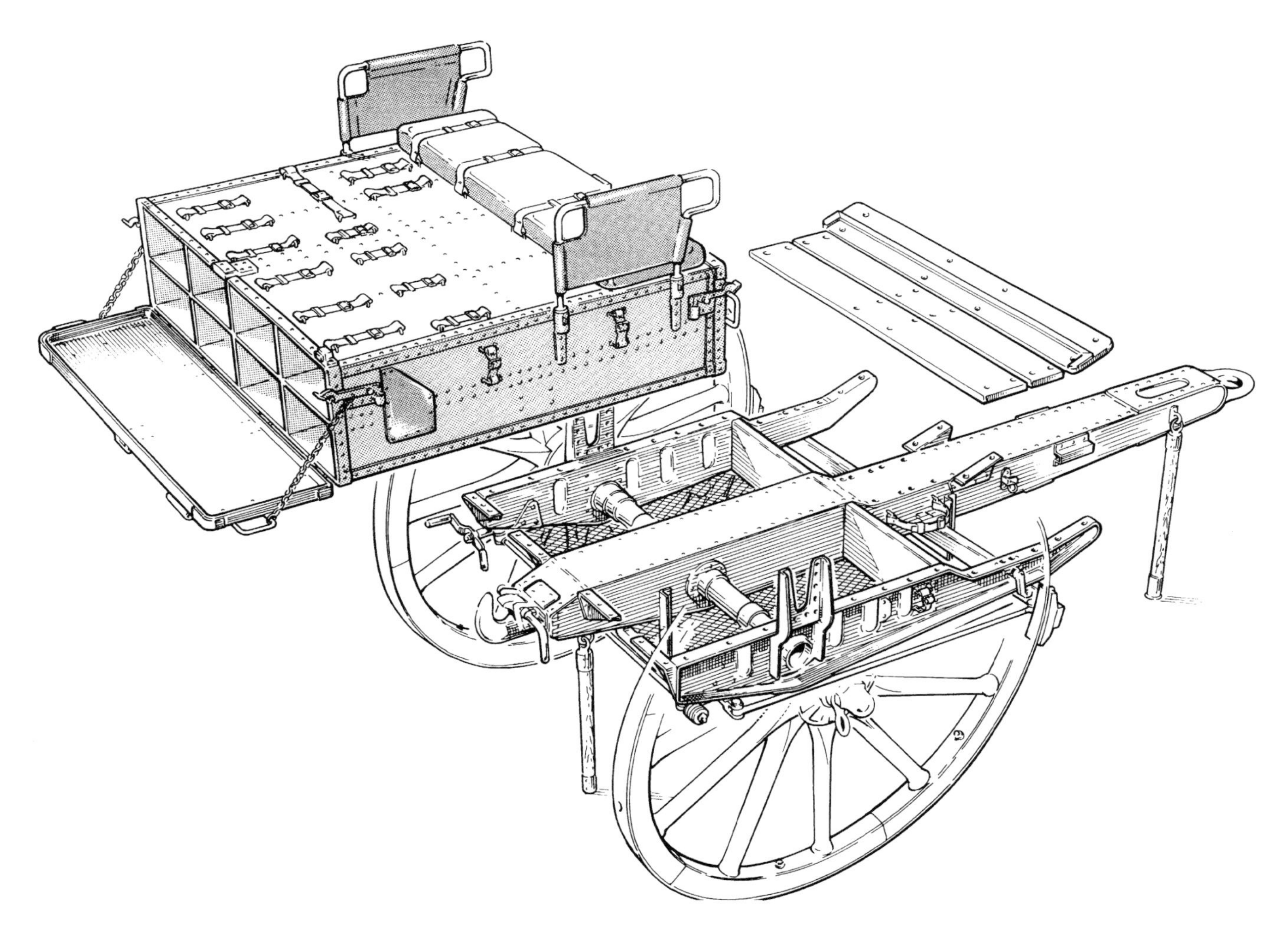

AMMUNITION WAGON

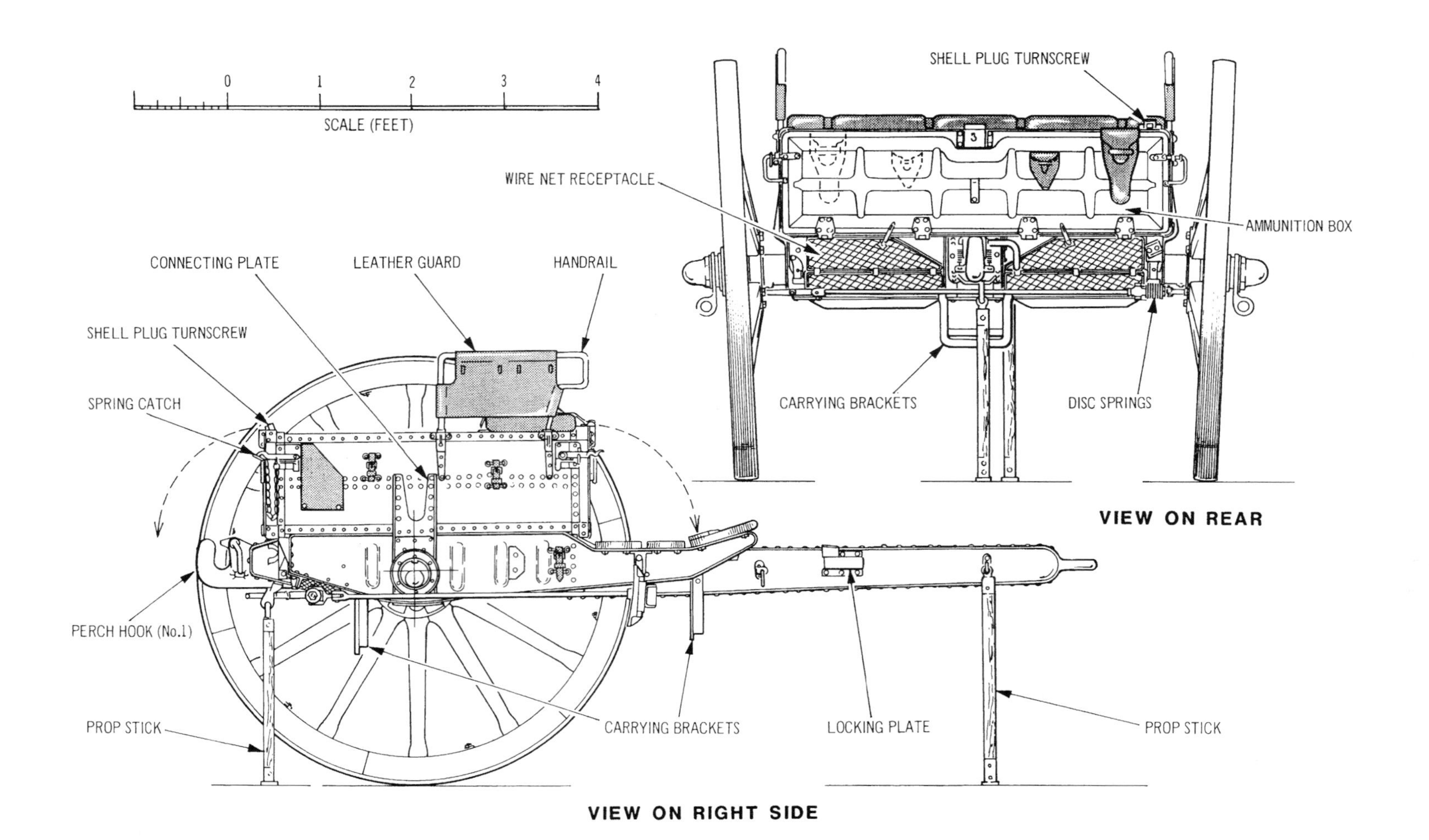

AMMUNITION WAGON

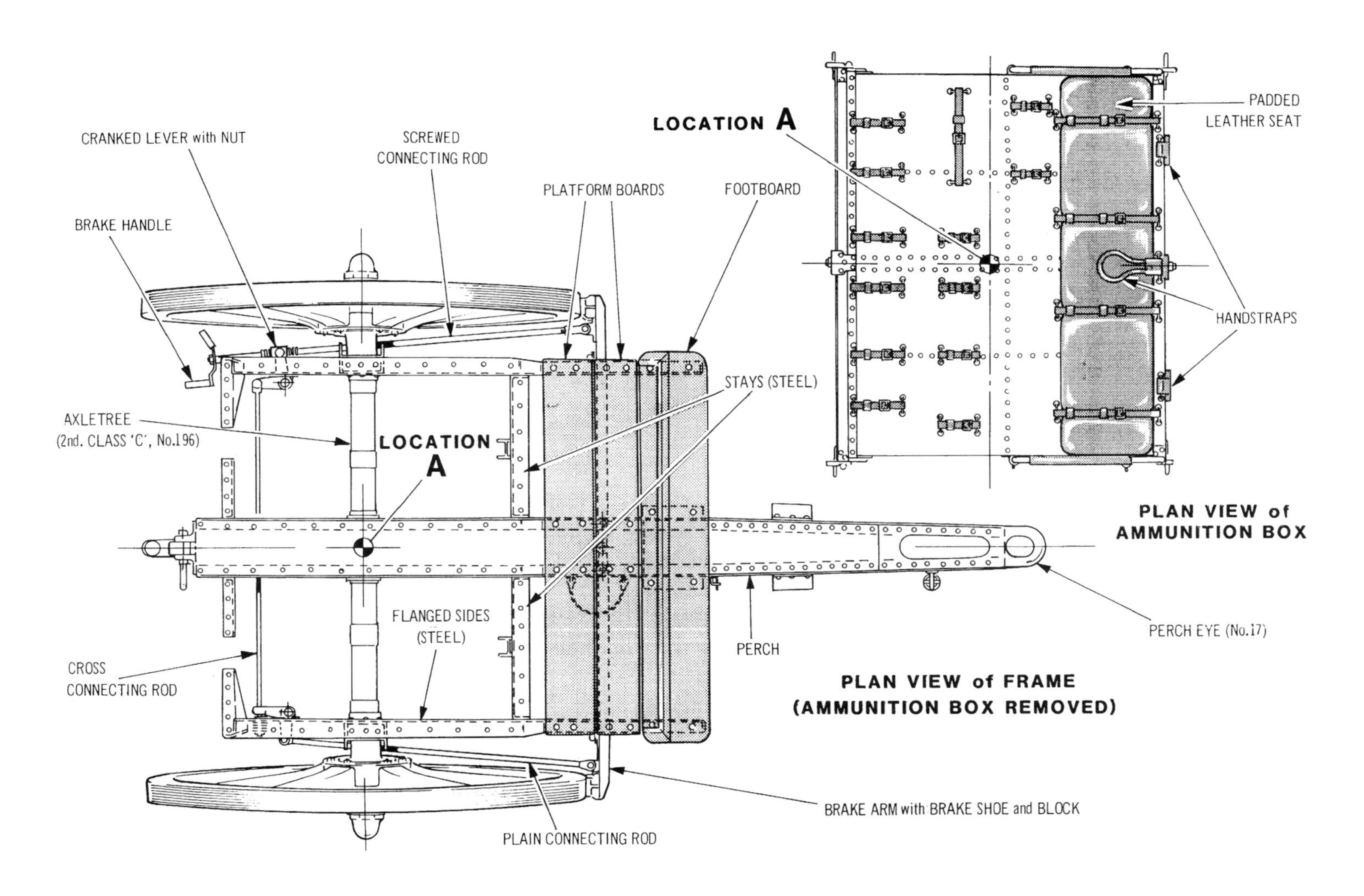

AMMUNITION WAGON

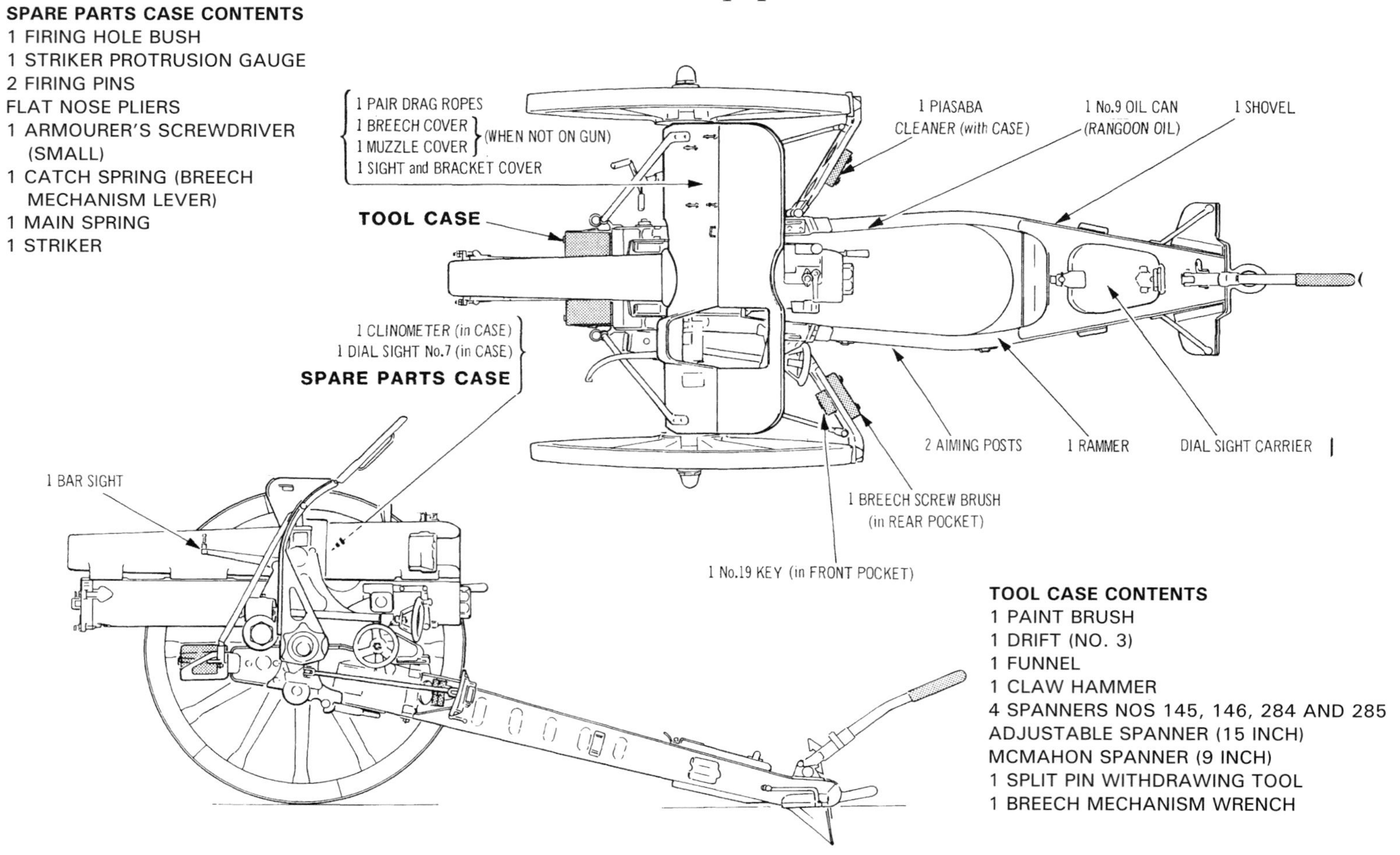

CARRIAGE – STORES AND EQUIPMENT

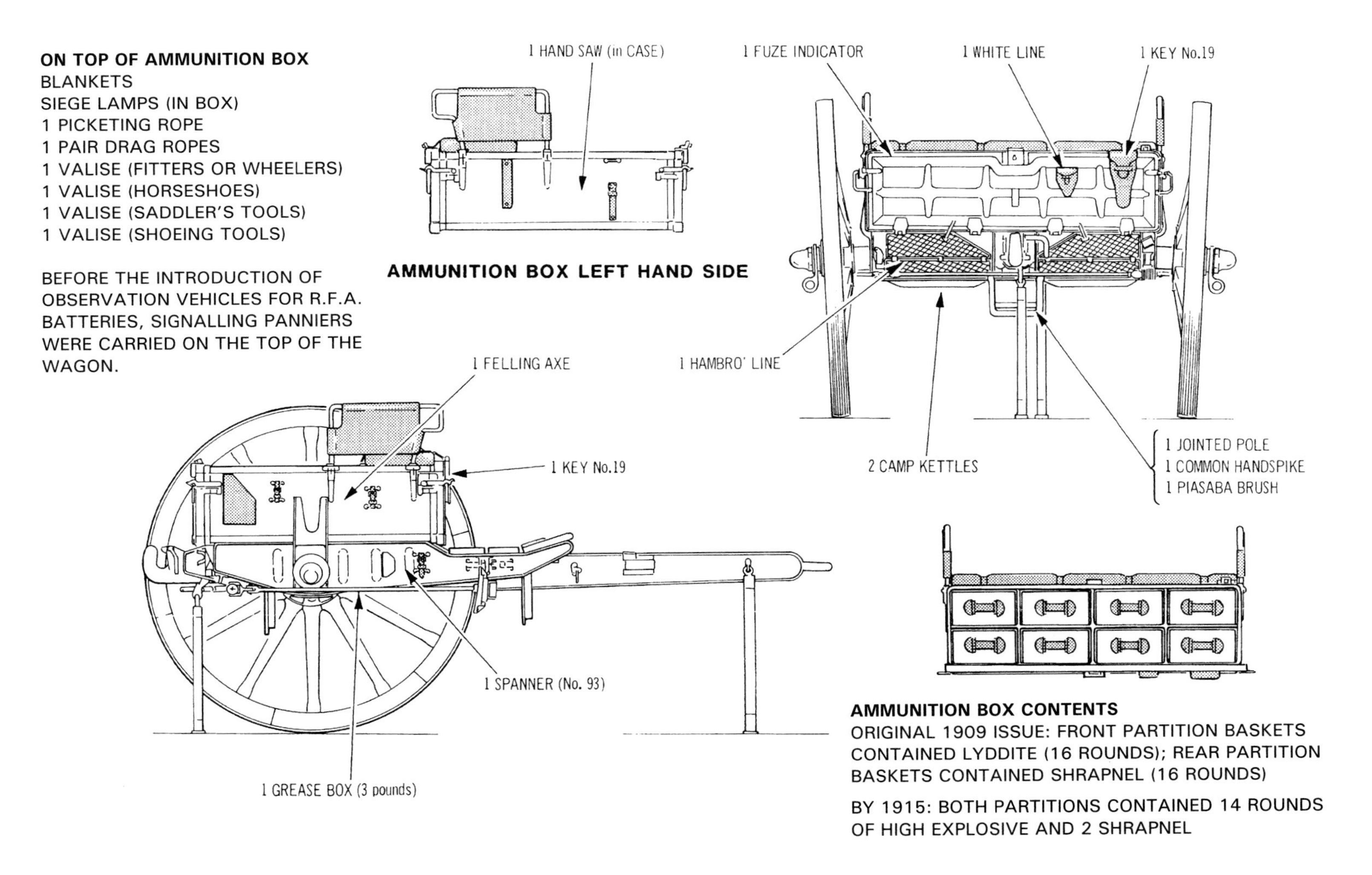

AMMUNITION WAGON – STORES AND EQUIPMENT

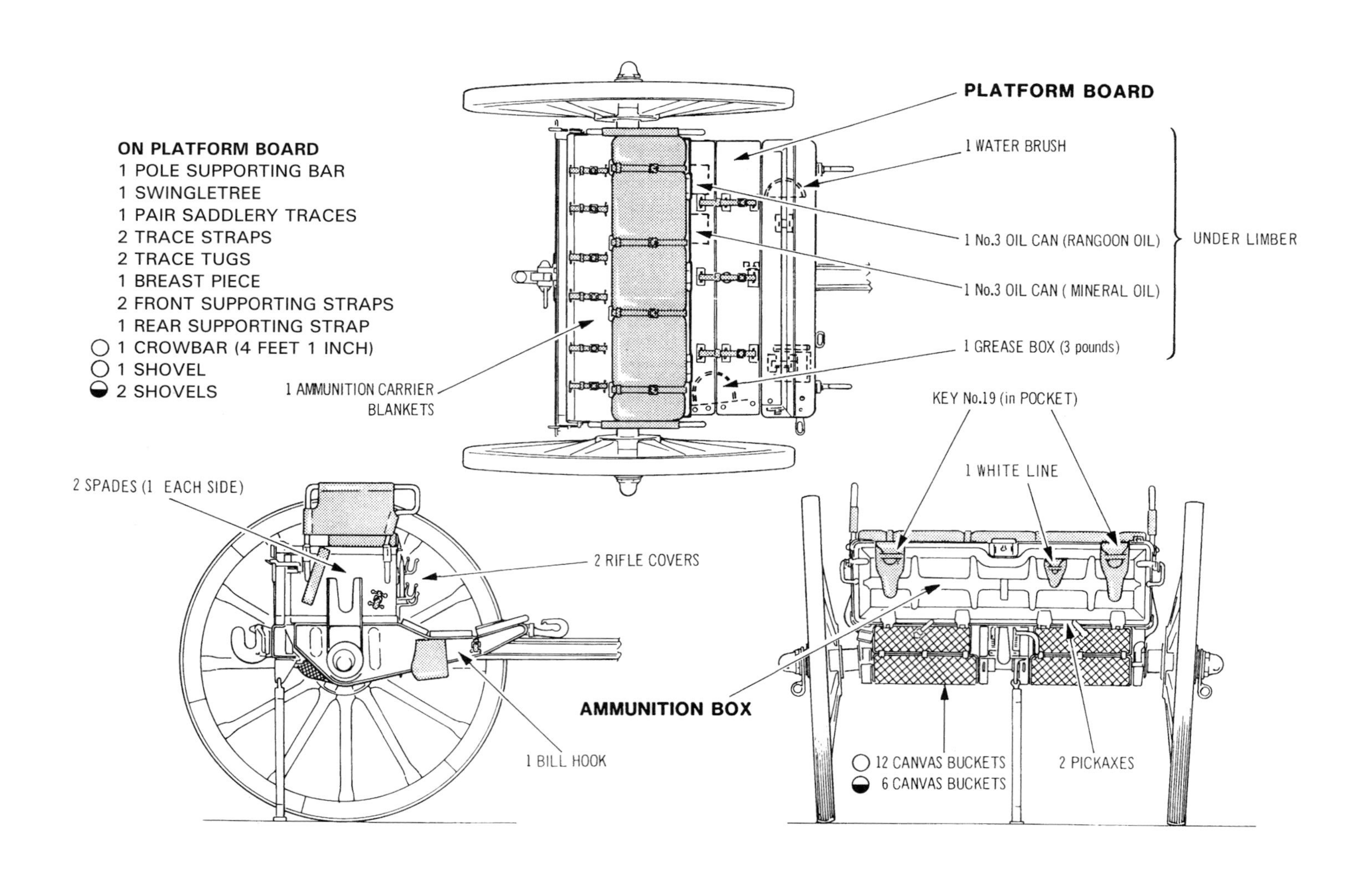

LIMBER – STORES AND EQUIPMENT

○ **SMALL STORES TRAY NO. 1 CONTENTS**

1 PISTON
1 RETARDING VALVE CARRIER
1 RETARDING VALVE
1 PISTON AND VALVE DIVIDING COLLAR
1 RECOIL VALVE
1 EXTRACTOR
1 CAM PLATE (BREECH MECHANISM LEVER)
1 FIRING LEVER ACTUATING PIN
1 TRIGGER KEEP PIN (IN TIN BOX)
PRIMERS (IN TIN BOX)
1 KEY NO. 26 (PRIMERS)
1 FILLING HOLE PLUG
2 RING WITHDRAWING TOOLS
2 ASBESTOS PACKING RINGS (IN TIN BOXES)
1 LEATHER PACKING SECURING RING
2 HYDRAULIC BUFFER PACKING WASHERS (IN TIN BOX)
1 LOCKING GEAR PLUNGER SPRING
1 CRADLE CLAMPING GEAR PAWL SPRING
1 LIMBER HOOK CATCH HANDLE
1 LIMBER HOOK CATCH (NO. 2)
1 LIMBER HOOK CATCH SPRING
1 PIPEBOX NUT FIXING SPRING
1 DRAUGHT PIN (NO. 3)
1 SPLIT KEEP PIN (.25IN X 5IN)
1 FLAT, SPLIT KEY (1IN X 4IN)
VARIOUS SPLIT KEEP PINS (IN TIN BOX)
3 FILES
1 FILE HANDLE (SMALL)
1 SCREWDRIVER (6 INCH)
1 DIAL SIGHT CARRIER ADJUSTING WRENCH
CHALK

TIN BOX CONTAINING

3 LUBRICATING HOLE SCREWS
1 COVER PLATE CATCH SPRING
1 CYLINDER NUT CATCH SPRING
1 SAFETY STOP SPRING
1 SIGHT SUPPORTING BRACKET SPRING
1 TRAVERSING LEVER SPRING
1 TRAVERSING LEVER SECURING CLIP SPRING
1 AUTOMATIC CLAMP SPIRAL SPRING
1 CAPSQUARE PIN SPRING
1 SHIELD SHUTTER SPRING

○ **SMALL STORES TRAY NO. 2 CONTENTS**

1 TRIGGER
1 DIAL SIGHT CARRIER TESTING DISC
10 SPONGE CLOTHS
1 WHEEL ADJUSTING COLLAR
1 WHEEL LINCH PIN
1 WHEEL DRAG WASHER
1 WHEEL DUST CAP

○ ON CARRIAGE LIMBERS ONLY

◒ ON AMMUNITION WAGON LIMBERS ONLY

UNMARKED ITEMS WERE COMMON TO BOTH LIMBERS

○ **SMALL STORES TRAY No.2** ○ **SMALL STORES TRAY No.1**

AMMUNITION BOX CONTENTS – CARRIAGE LIMBER

ORIGINAL 1909 ISSUE: 6 BASKETS AND 1 SMALL STORES TRAY (ONE COMPARTMENT LEFT EMPTY): 4 BASKETS CONTAINED SHRAPNEL (8 ROUNDS); 2 BASKETS CONTAINED LYDDITE (4 ROUNDS)

BY 1915 (ILLUSTRATED): 6 BASKETS AND 2 SMALL STORES TRAYS: 5 BASKETS CONTAINED HIGH EXPLOSIVE (10 ROUNDS); 1 BASKET CONTAINED SHRAPNEL (2 ROUNDS)

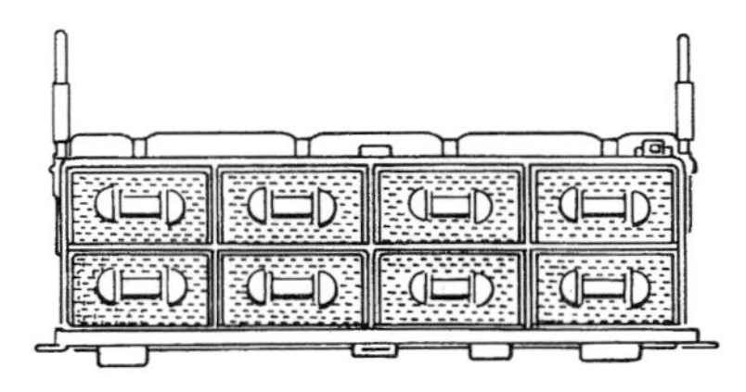

AMMUNITION BOX CONTENTS – WAGON LIMBER

ORIGINAL 1909 ISSUE: 8 BASKETS: 6 BASKETS CONTAINED SHRAPNEL (12 ROUNDS); 2 BASKETS CONTAINED LYDDITE (4 ROUNDS)

BY 1915: 8 BASKETS: 2 BASKETS CONTAINED SHRAPNEL (4 ROUNDS); 6 BASKETS CONTAINED HIGH EXPLOSIVE (12 ROUNDS)

LIMBER – STORES AND EQUIPMENT

MISCELLANEOUS STORES

This section lists some of the stores carried by the various artillery described earlier in the book.

Only items have been included where research has yielded sufficient accurate information, contemporary lists often tending to provide a rather bland description, with no dimensions or materials quoted.

Despite extensive research, some of the following descriptions are not as comprehensive as one would wish, the available information produced here being considered preferable to no information at all. Some items have been included in this section if they were issued for use on more than one type of equipment, this to avoid repetition in the relevant portions of the book.

Adjusting apparatus for running out springs

(Use: BL (Conv) 15 pdr, QF 13 pdr and QF 18 pdr)

The adjuster was carried on the limber footboard and protected by a waterproof canvas cover, shaped to suit. To use the adjuster, the locating thread was screwed into the control plunger and clamped by the lock nut. The fork was positioned over the screw thread until the studs located into the holes in the outer spring case rear.

For use on the BL (Conv) 15 pdr, the fork stops would locate against the inner spring case. The actuating nut was then turned along the operating screw thread until coming up against the fork end face. Further rotation of the actuating nut compressed the recuperator running out springs.

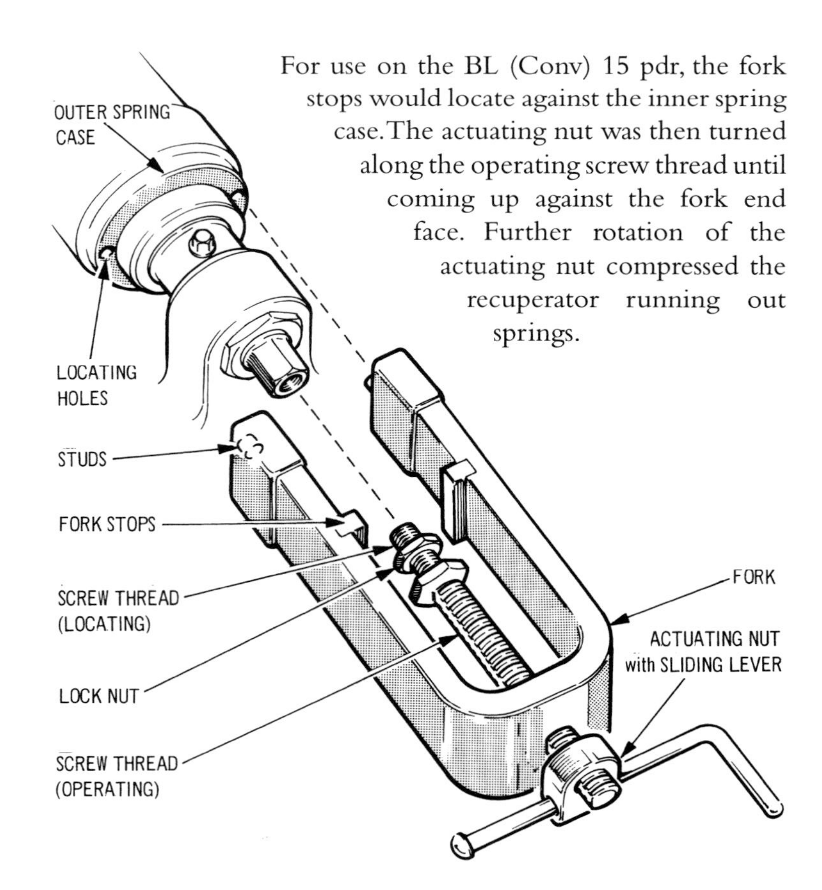

Aiming posts

(Use: auxiliary aiming points by field guns when the target could not be seen from the battery)

An aiming post was of tubular steel with a projection, located towards the lower end, in order that it could be forced into the ground by pressure of the foot.

AIMING POSTS

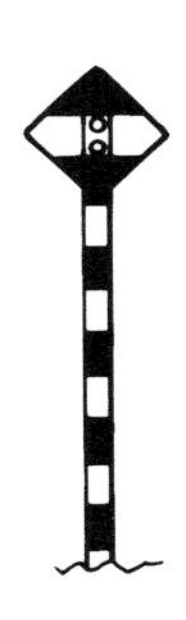

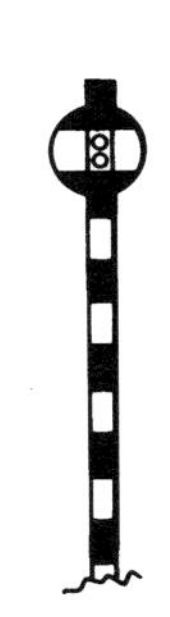

The post top was fitted with a shaped plate of iron or steel, usually square or diamond shaped. The post was painted for its whole length with alternate black and white bands, one and a half inches long. Overall length was four feet.

Ammunition carrier

(Use: QF 13 pdr and QF 18 pdr)

This carrier enabled one man to bring four complete rounds of ammunition to the gun. It was made of waterproof canvas, fastened at the front with a strap and buckle. On each side were two pockets, each to carry one round. Two lifting handles, secured to each side, catered for men of different heights.

AMMUNITION CARRIER

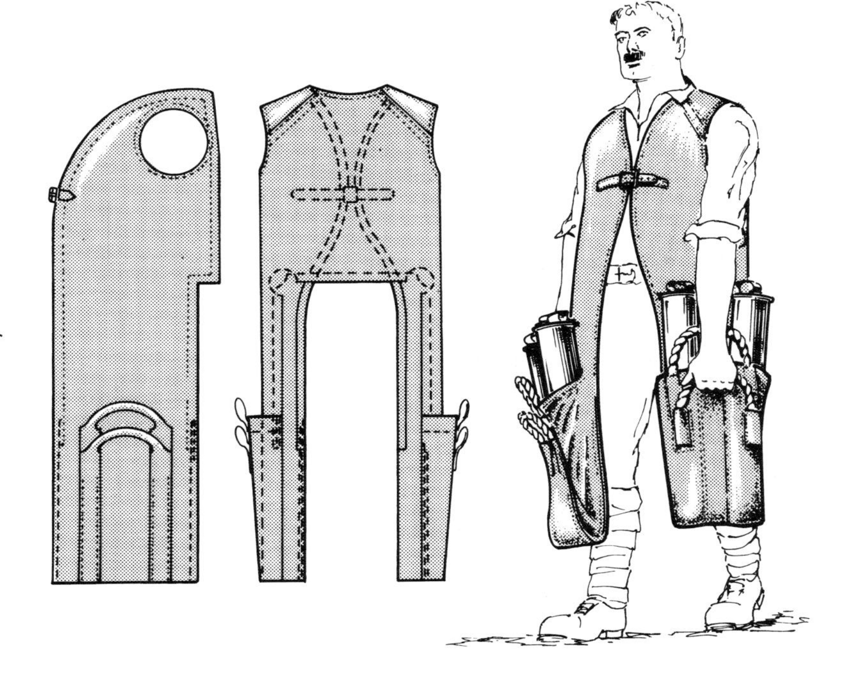

Bar to support draught pole

(Use: to support the front end of Draught Poles
Nos 14, 17, 18 and 20)

BAR No. 2 This was a circular ash stave, two inches in diameter, thirty-eight and a half inches long, fitted at each end with a steel socket with loop. It was riveted to the draught pole by means of the forged steel socket riveted at the centre.

BAR No. 3, Mk. II This was a circular ash stave, two inches in diameter, forty-five and a half inches long. A forged steel pole socket, with an eye, was riveted at the centre, the eye fitting over the end of the draught pole. Four sockets, with triangular links, were positioned along the bar for attachment of the rapid release harness breast collar straps.

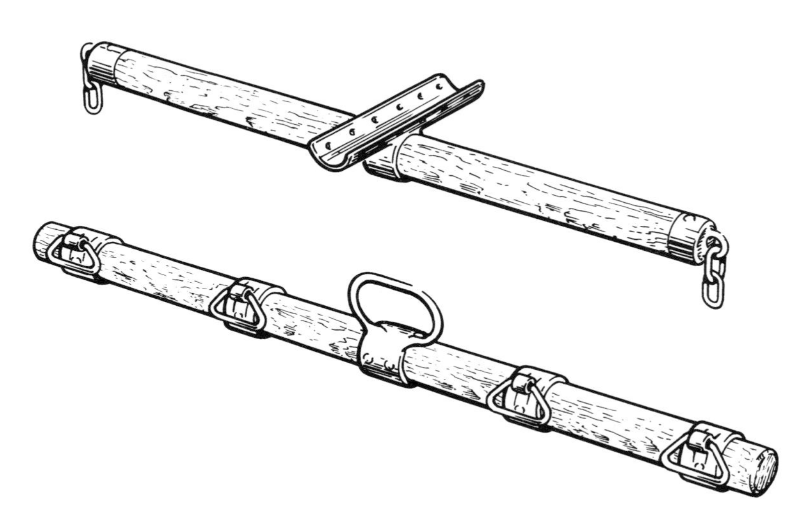

Boxes

STORES BOX No. 10 Mk. I Used with the QF 13 pdr and QF 18 pdr batteries and ammunition columns. It was of deal, with elm ends, each end provided with a rope loop handle. The hinged lid, canvas covered, was secured closed by a hasp and turnbuckle. The box was fitted internally with wood blocks and a tray for spare parts of the gun and carriage.

BOXES FOR FUZES These were of tin, made in a variety of sizes to hold time and percussion and direct action fuzes. They were generally fitted with a wood block which was bored out to hold the fuzes perpendicular to the bottom of the box. The lids, fastened with clips, were lined on the inside with leather covered cork. A gunmetal lifting loop was attached to the box end.

GREASE BOXES There were two types of tin box for containing grease, listed as **magazine** and **half round**. The magazine was a rectangular box, with a hinged lid secured by a hook on the lid and a loop on the box side. There were two sizes, one containing seven pounds of grease, the other, fourteen pounds. The half round grease tin, used for field service, held three pounds.

SIEGE LAMP BOX The box held two lamps for use in night firing. It was of deal, with elm ends. The lid, clamped with ash, was canvas covered and secured closed by a hasp and turnbuckle. The lid interior and box bottom were fitted with lining pieces to hold the lamps in position. Near the box bottom were loops to hold twenty-four spare candles.

TELESCOPIC SIGHT BOX Used with some BL 15 pdrs to hold the Scott's sights. It was a rectangular, steel plate box, with a hinged lid secured by a spring catch and secured to the limber platform board by straps.

TOOL BOX Used on howitzer carriages. It was a rectangular leather box, with a lid secured closed by a strap and buckle. The interior was divided to hold the tools. It was secured to the carriage by screws.

Cartridge clip

(Use: QF 13 pdr and QF 18 pdr)

The brass clip engaged with the rim of the cartridge case. The longer arm, which was painted red, was shaped to spring over the rim and lock the clip in position. A canvas loop served as a handle to insert or withdraw the cartridge from the ammunition box basket or tube. The clip also served to protect the percussion primer. The parts of the clip not painted red were sandblasted and lacquered black.

To insert a cartridge into an ammunition box tube, the cartridge was pushed in fully, so that the red clip arm was inside the tube extended rim, then partially turned to bring the arm inside the rim, locking the cartridge in position.

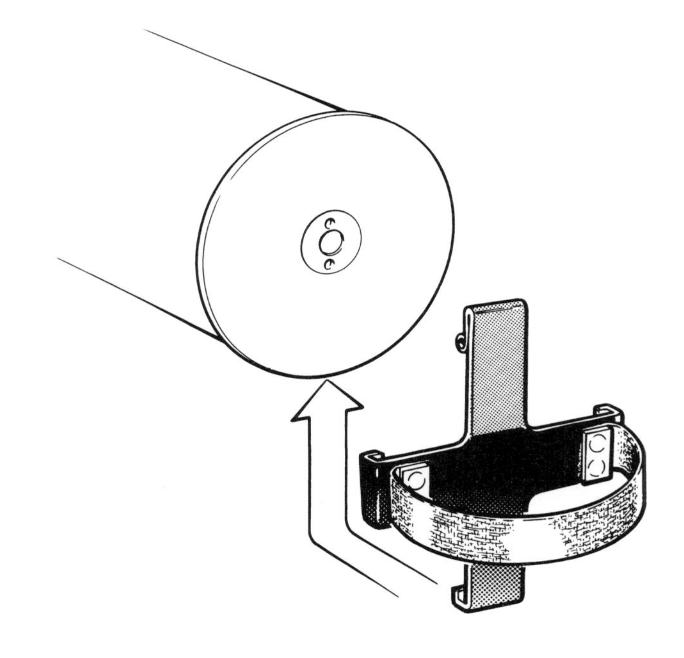

Draught poles

No. 17 Mk. I

Made of ash, twelve feet seven inches in length. At the front was a loop, to which were attached links for the rapid release harness. The early issues of this draught pole proved to be weak in service, later issues were strengthened by steel plates added to the sides at the rear.

This became the No. 17 Mk. II.

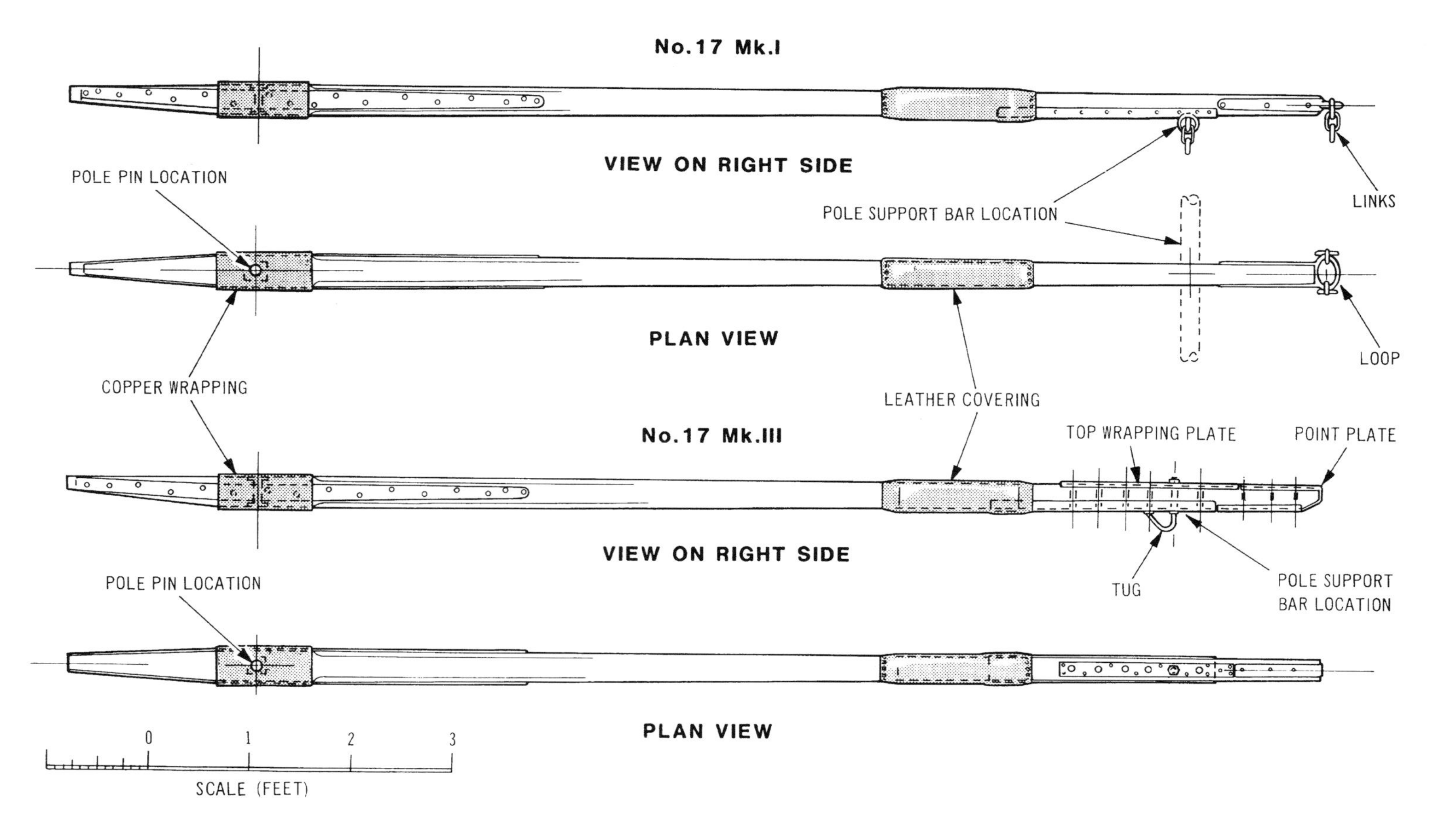

MISCELLANEOUS STORES

No. 17 Mk. III

This pole was used for all field limbers, also for limbered wagons. Made of ash, it was twelve feet, four and a half inches in length. It was steel shod on both sides at the rear end. At the front, where the pole support bar rested, it was plated with steel. A steel top wrapping plate and a point plate were also fitted. The portion which rested in the limber pole staple was wrapped with copper. Near the front end was a tug, for attachment of the rapid release harness.

For use with the BL (Conv) 15 pdr or BL 5 inch howitzers, some of these poles were fitted with a draught pole point clip loop.

No. 18 (spare pole)

Used as the No. 17 Mk. II but made in two pieces, connected centrally by a hinged joint. It was carried as a spare pole under the ammunition wagons.

No. 18 Mk. II (spare pole)

Used as the No. 17 Mk. III, also made in two pieces, connected centrally by a hinged joint and carried as a spare pole under the ammunition wagons.

Cases

These were generally made of leather, shaped to suit the item which they contained. Cases for the billhook, dragwasher and felling axe were of leather, doubled and sewn along one or more sides, secured to the limber with screws.

Cases for lubricating oil cans, clinometers, fuzes and tubes, water brushes and tools were of leather. A lid, where fitted, was secured by a strap and buckle. The case body was generally fitted with a strap and buckle, which attached through staples to whichever vehicle was applicable.

The leather tool cases supplied with the BL (Conv.) 15 pdr, QF 13 pdr and QF 18 pdr were secured to the axletree, on supporting brackets, with bolts.

The case for a piasaba cleaner was of waterproof canvas, shaped to hold the cleaner and lead ball. Attached to the case centre was a leather strap to secure it to the carriage.

Covers for breech and muzzle

These were made of khaki-coloured waterproof canvas, tailored to suit the guns to which they were applicable, secured in position by a strap and buckle.

Drag ropes

These were of two classes, **heavy** and **light**.

Both classes had similar terminal fittings; at one end was a black painted iron hook, at the other end was a leather lined eye-splice. The **heavy** drag rope hook had a slot, to take a tie attached to the shank. The drag was a three inch white rope, thirty feet in length. It was issued to all siege guns and howitzers.

The **light** drag was a two inch white rope, fifteen feet six inches in length. It was issued to BL 12 pdr and BL 15 pdr guns and BL 5 inch howitzers.

Funnels

(Use: BL (Conv) 15 pdr, QF 13 pdr and QF 18 pdr)
This funnel (right) was a Mk. II pattern, used for filling the hydraulic buffer. It was of leather, made to fold flat for storage when not in use.

(Use: QF 4.5 inch howitzer)
This funnel (left) was used for filling the hydraulic buffer. It had a leather cone, secured into a gunmetal socket by a nut, shaped to suit. The upper portion of the nut held a copper strainer, secured by a ring nut. The lower end of the socket fitted into a bent tin spout.

Lifting jack

The lever was supported by a movable pin in the fork, enabling the height to be varied for use on the axletrees of various carriages and limbers. The pawl, pivoted to the lever, would engage the rack teeth on the fork rear face and keep the lever in position when weight was applied to it.

The jack could lift up to half a ton.

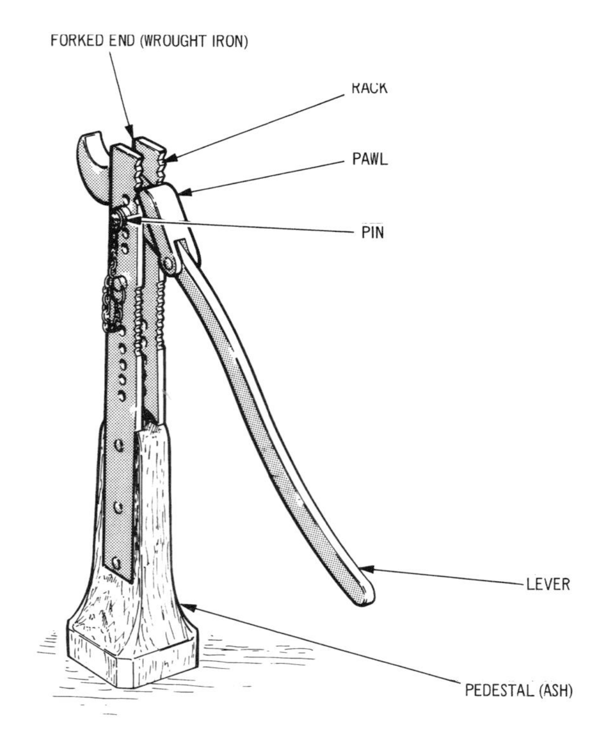

Lubricating oil cans

Oil Can No. 3

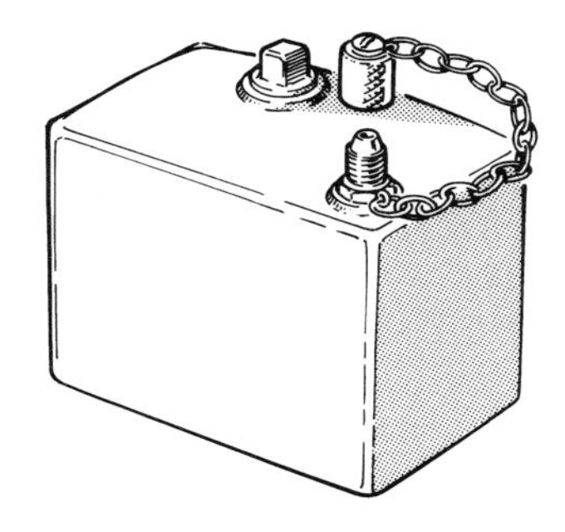

(Use: BL and BL (Conv) 15 pdrs, QF 13 pdr, QF 18 pdr and QF 4.5 inch howitzer)

Oil Can No. 9

This can was used for general service. It was fitted with a removable spout and spring valve to control the flow, this operated by an external knob near the handle. The spout was fitted with a flanged disc, a V-shaped aperture in the flange controlling the flow of oil.

McMahon spanner

This spanner, issued for general field use, was termed the McMahon 15 inch. The movable claw was controlled by rotation of the thumbscrew in the toothed rack opening or closing the jaws.

Piasaba brush and cleaner (illustrated on page 388)

(Use: QF 4.5 inch howitzer and BL and BL (Conv) 15 pdrs, QF 13, 15 and 18 pdrs)

These brushes and cleaners were assembled in a manner which enabled a worn or damaged section to be replaced without the need to scrap the whole brush.

Early patterns had the piasaba grass glued into place. Later patterns had the grass secured with copper wire.

Pockets

Breech brush pocket (use: BL 15 pdr)

This was of leather, with a flap closed by two straps and buckles. Two straps, attached to the rear, secured the pocket to the carriage.

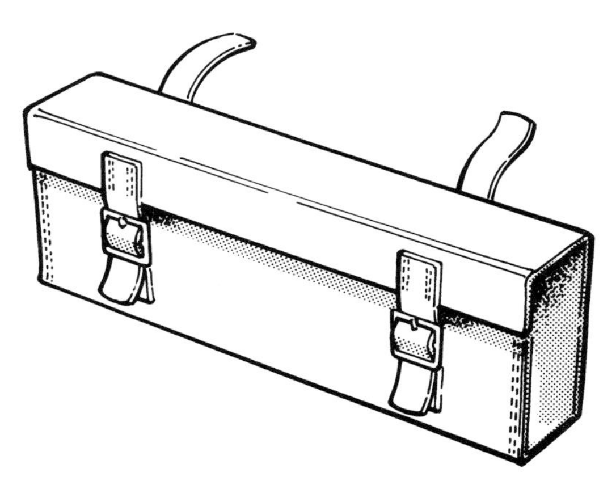

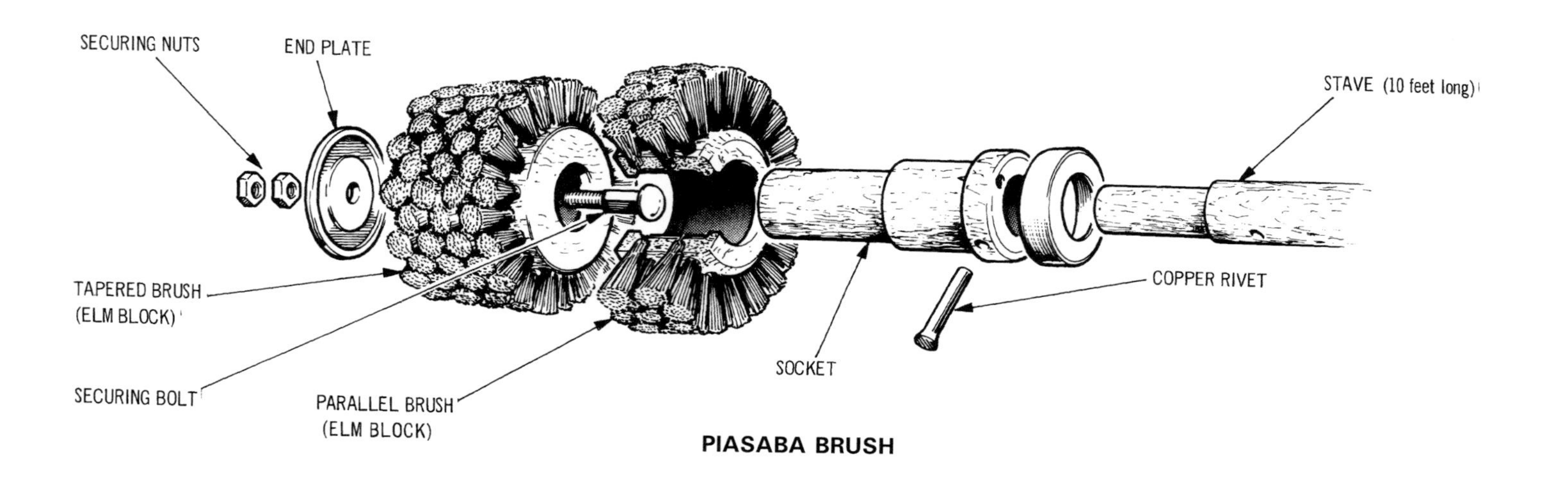

PIASABA BRUSH

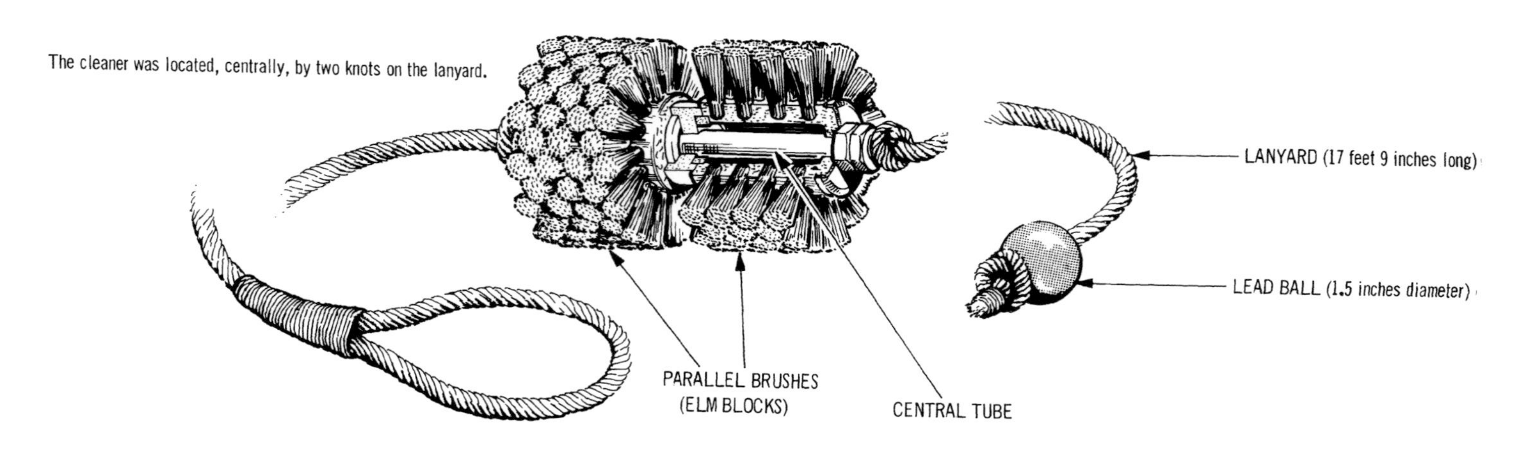

PIASABA CLEANER

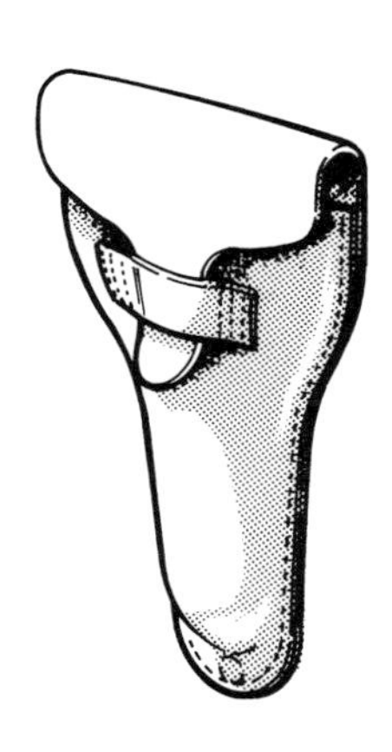

Fuze key pocket

There were two patterns of this pocket, both of leather, shaped to hold the fuze key with lanyard. A flap served as a lid, secured closed by a loop.

The pattern for use on a gun carriage was provided with two straps on the rear for attachment. The pattern for use on a limber or ammunition wagon had no straps and was attached by screws.

Spring lock key pocket

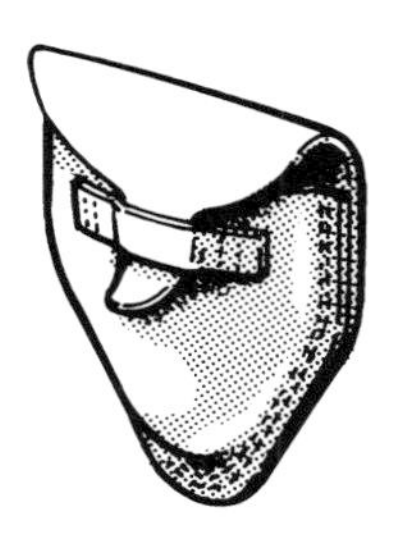

This was of leather, secured to the rear of ammunition boxes by screws.

T-friction Tube Pocket Mk. III

(Use: BL 15 pdr)

This pocket was of brown leather, made to hold 47 T-friction tubes. Two receptacles were provided for lanyards. Two straps were riveted to the pocket rear for attachment.

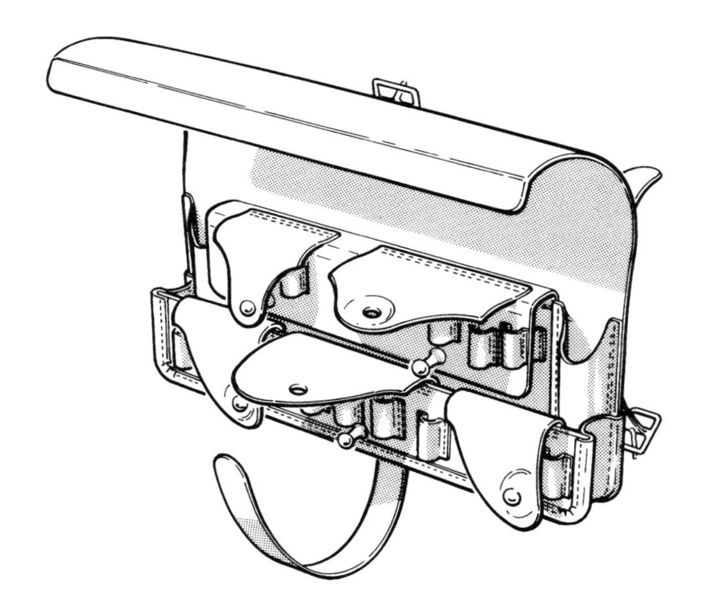

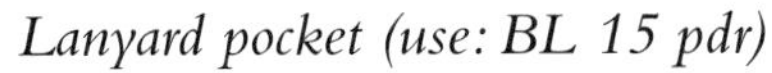

Lanyard pocket (use: BL 15 pdr)

Linch pin pocket

This consisted of two pieces of leather, sewn together, open at both ends. A strap, sewn on, secured the spare linch pin in place. The pocket was attached to the limber underside by screws.

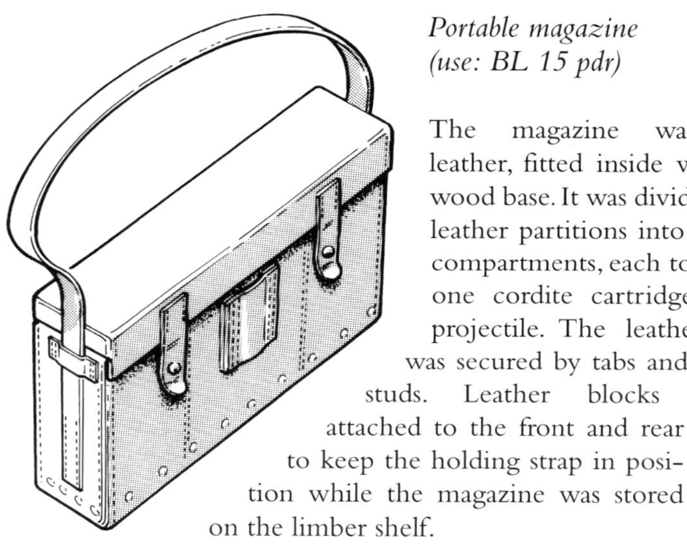

Portable magazine
(use: BL 15 pdr)

The magazine was of leather, fitted inside with a wood base. It was divided by leather partitions into three compartments, each to hold one cordite cartridge and projectile. The leather lid was secured by tabs and brass studs. Leather blocks were attached to the front and rear to keep the holding strap in position while the magazine was stored on the limber shelf.

Rammer

(Use: BL and QF 15 pdrs)
The rammer was of wood with a copper band, secured by three nuts, at one end.

Removal tool for outer spring case

(Use: BL (Conv) 15 pdr)
The hydraulic buffer and springs having been removed, this tool was passed through the outer spring case from the front, until the flange studs engaged their locating holes in the spring case rear inner face. The loose collar was then screwed up against the spring case rear outer face, clamping the tool in position. The rod was then turned to remove the spring case from the cradle.

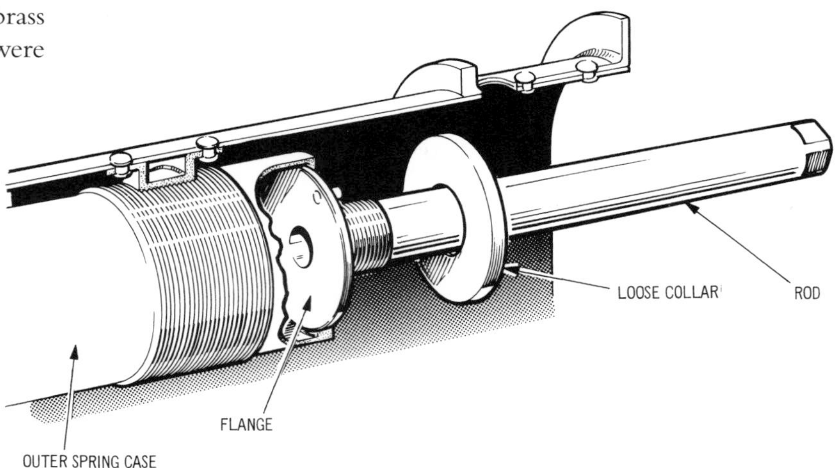

Sponge

(Use: BL and BL (Conv) 15pdrs, QF 15 and 18 pdrs)
The sponge head was of elm, covered with fleecy hosiery which was glued on and tied by a cord. It was attached to an ash stave, ten feet long, secured by copper rivets.

Sponge bucket

This bucket was similar to a water bucket. It also was made of leather, but covered with a teak lid. The lid had a hole to admit the sponge, closed, when not in use, with a plug. The bucket was painted lead colour.

Sponge cap

This was made of waterproof canvas, fitted with a cord to secure it over the sponge head.

Swingletrees

The **No. 7** was used for BL 15 pdr and 5 inch howitzer limbers and some wagons. It was an ash bar, twenty-eight inches in length, with a central steel socket and a steel socket, with loop, at each end. It was replaced by the No. 10.

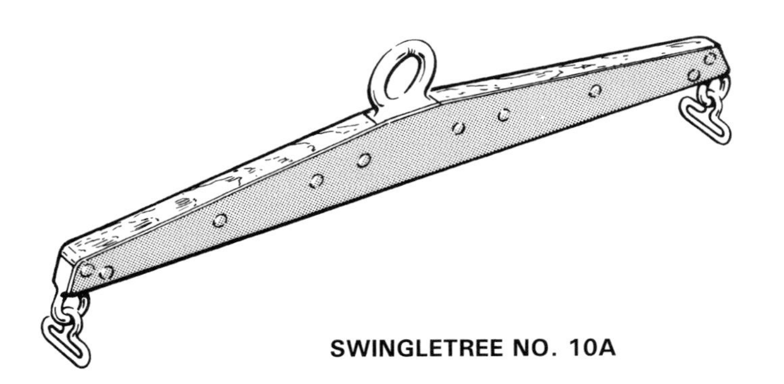

SWINGLETREE NO. 10A

The **No.7A** differed in having links for the rapid release harness at each end.

The **No. 10** replaced the No. 7 for all field vehicles fitted with pole draught. It was of trough-shaped steel plate, filled in with yellow deal, twenty-eight inches long. It had a central steel loop and a steel loop at each end.

The **No. 10A** (illustrated below left) was fitted with links for the rapid release harness and replaced the No. 10.

The **No. 11** replaced the No. 10A. It was similar except for the end fittings.

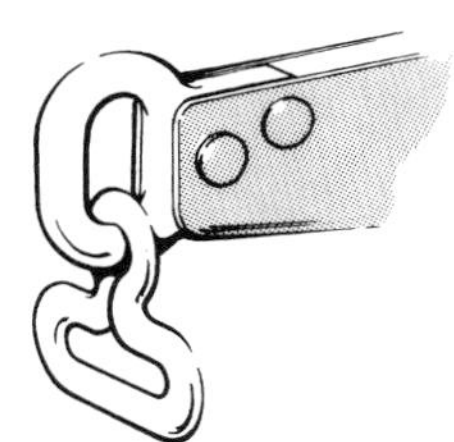

Syringe

(Use: QF 18 pdr)

The syringe body and spout were of tin. The steel plunger was packed with cotton wool soaked in tallow. The syringe capacity was one-tenth of a pint, that being the quantity of liquid to be withdrawn from the hydraulic buffer after filling.

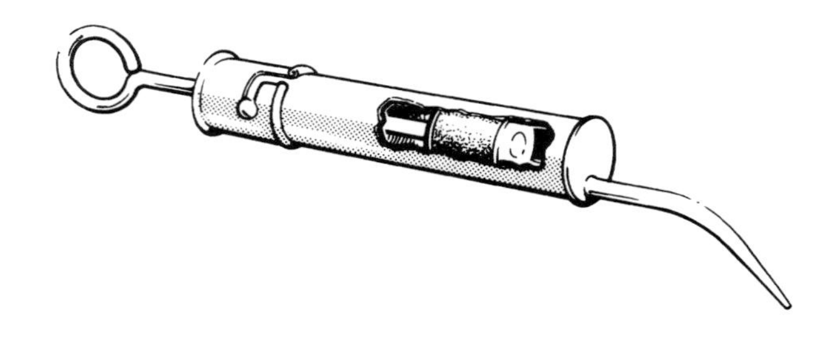

Ties

A tie was made from a strip of leather five inches long. To make a tie, one end of the leather strip was doubled over for one-quarter of an inch and a piece of thicker leather placed in the fold. A hole was then pierced through the three thicknesses and the other end of the strip passed through the hole and pulled tight. This formed a button at one end of the tie. A suitable size button hole was then cut at the other end.

Trace couple

This was used as a temporary replacement for a broken link. The links adjoining a broken one would be hooked onto the couple and prevented from coming off by use of a tie, passed through the couple eyes. A couple for field artillery service was made from a length of round iron, three-eighths of an inch in diameter, six inches long before forming.

Wool cleaner

(Use: BL and BL (Conv) 15 pdr and QF 18 pdr)

The cleaner was located, centrally by two knots on the lanyard.

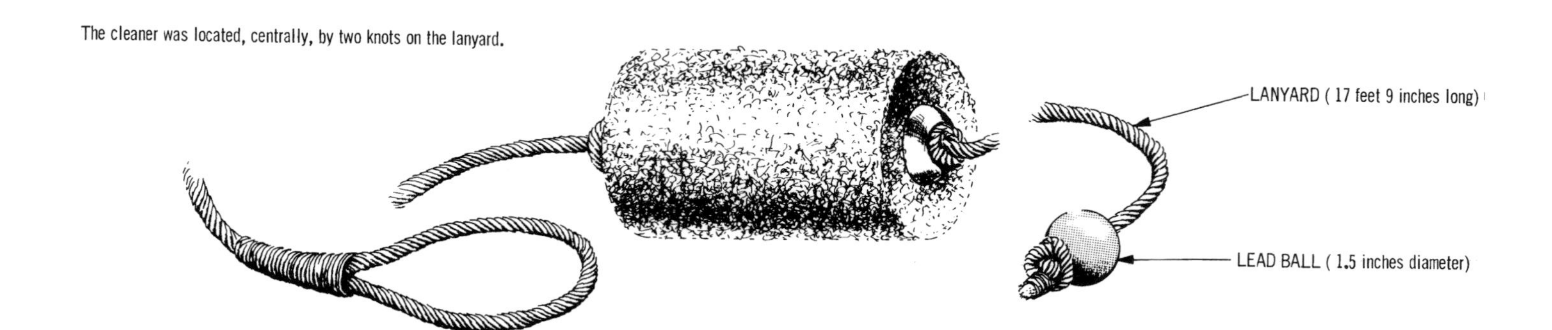

The cleaner was located, centrally, by two knots on the lanyard.

HARNESS

The draught system employed with light artillery during the period with which we are concerned, was the pole draught system. Early artillery was drawn by animals coupled to their task by shafts, but in 1895 this was changed, for a variety of reasons, to pole draught.

During this period, changes were also made to the harness used to connect a team of horses to a limber. The main difference was in the adoption of the breast harness in place of the neck collar. The neck collar, as incorporated in the Army Service Corps harness introduced in 1890, was actually a more suitable method of draught, due to the horse being able to exert all its effort and weight to pull a load. The disadvantage was in the need for a neck collar to be a good fit. During active service, or over a period of sustained heavy work, a horse could rapidly lose condition. This would cause the collar to become a poor fit, resulting in severe collar galls.

The advantages of a breast collar were that it would adapt itself to a horse's changing condition and could be easily adjusted to avoid any areas which showed signs of galling.

The Royal Artillery Draught Pole Breast Harness was introduced in February 1904. The modified pattern described here was introduced in 1911, reducing the number of components, to simplify its use in the field.

Quick release (see page 396)

To join the harness, the bent link was passed through the shackle, then the strap passed through that portion of the bent link protruding beyond the shackle, the strap preventing the link and shackle pulling out of engagement.

To disengage the harness, the strap was simply pulled from the bent link, this allowing the link and shackle to drop apart.

The wheel (rear) pair of horses, in addition to pulling, could provide a braking effort by means of the harness breeching. They also carried the draught pole support bar by means of the neck pieces coupled through their breast collar backing rings (see page 397).

Harnesses for the centre and lead pairs were similar to each other, but differed considerably from that of the wheel pair, needing to provide a pulling effort only. Tractive effort passed from their breast collar D-rings, by means of the tugs and wire traces, directly to the swingletrees (see page 398).

The unused draught tug chain links of the lead pair were secured, by leather ties, to the breast collar backing rings.

The team of six horses was controlled by three drivers, riding

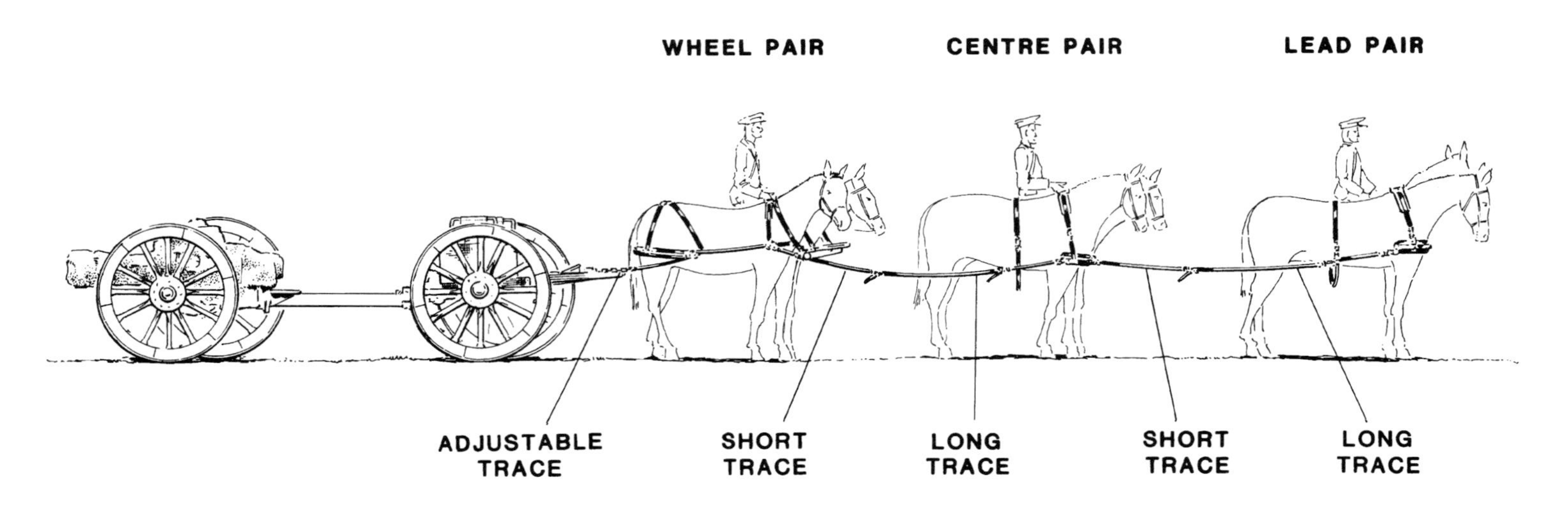

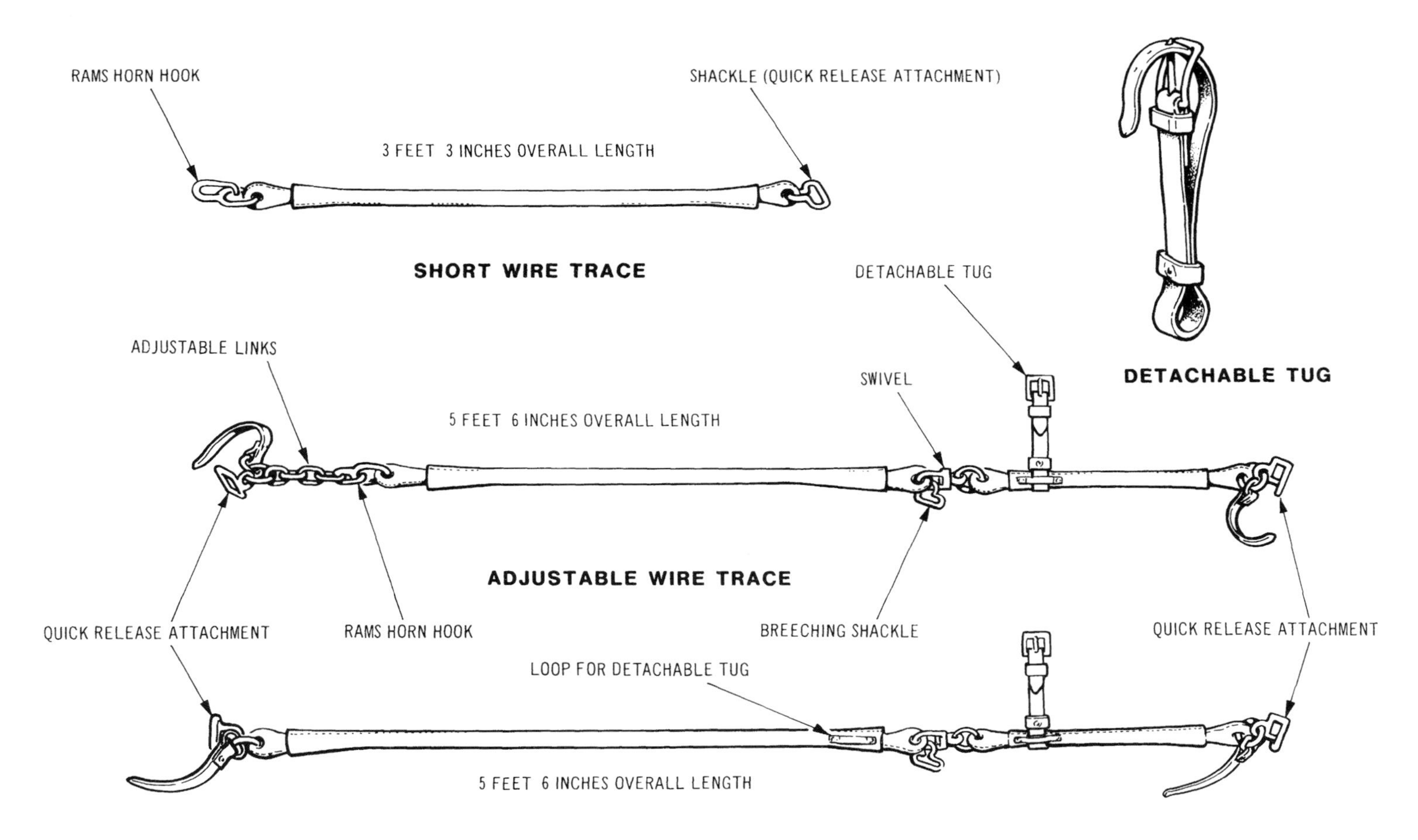
RAMS HORN HOOK
SHACKLE (QUICK RELEASE ATTACHMENT)
3 FEET 3 INCHES OVERALL LENGTH
SHORT WIRE TRACE
DETACHABLE TUG
DETACHABLE TUG
ADJUSTABLE LINKS
SWIVEL
5 FEET 6 INCHES OVERALL LENGTH
ADJUSTABLE WIRE TRACE
QUICK RELEASE ATTACHMENT
RAMS HORN HOOK
BREECHING SHACKLE
QUICK RELEASE ATTACHMENT
LOOP FOR DETACHABLE TUG
5 FEET 6 INCHES OVERALL LENGTH
LONG WIRE TRACE

HARNESS

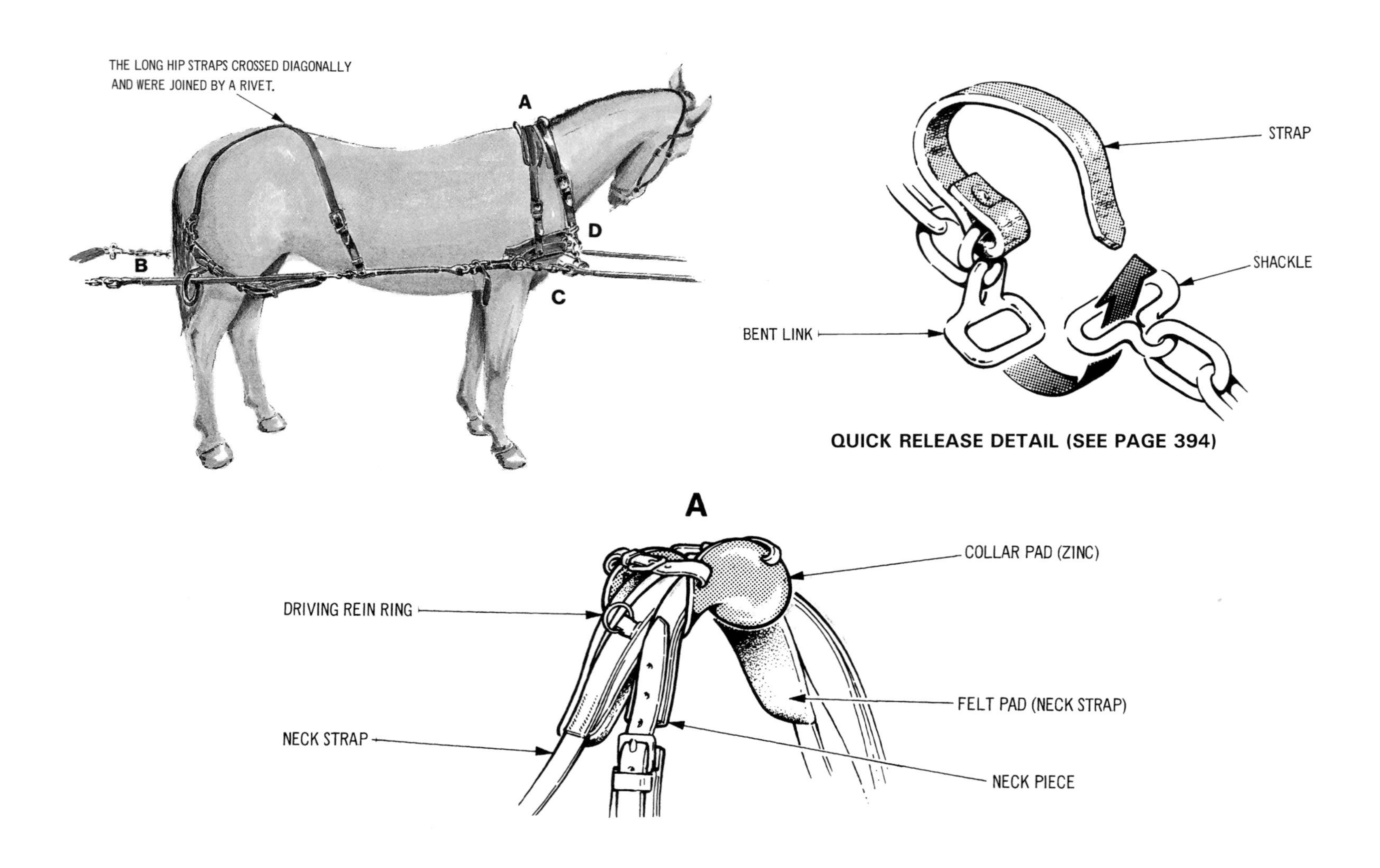

THIS HARNESS SET WAS FOR THE WHEEL (REAR) PAIR ONLY.

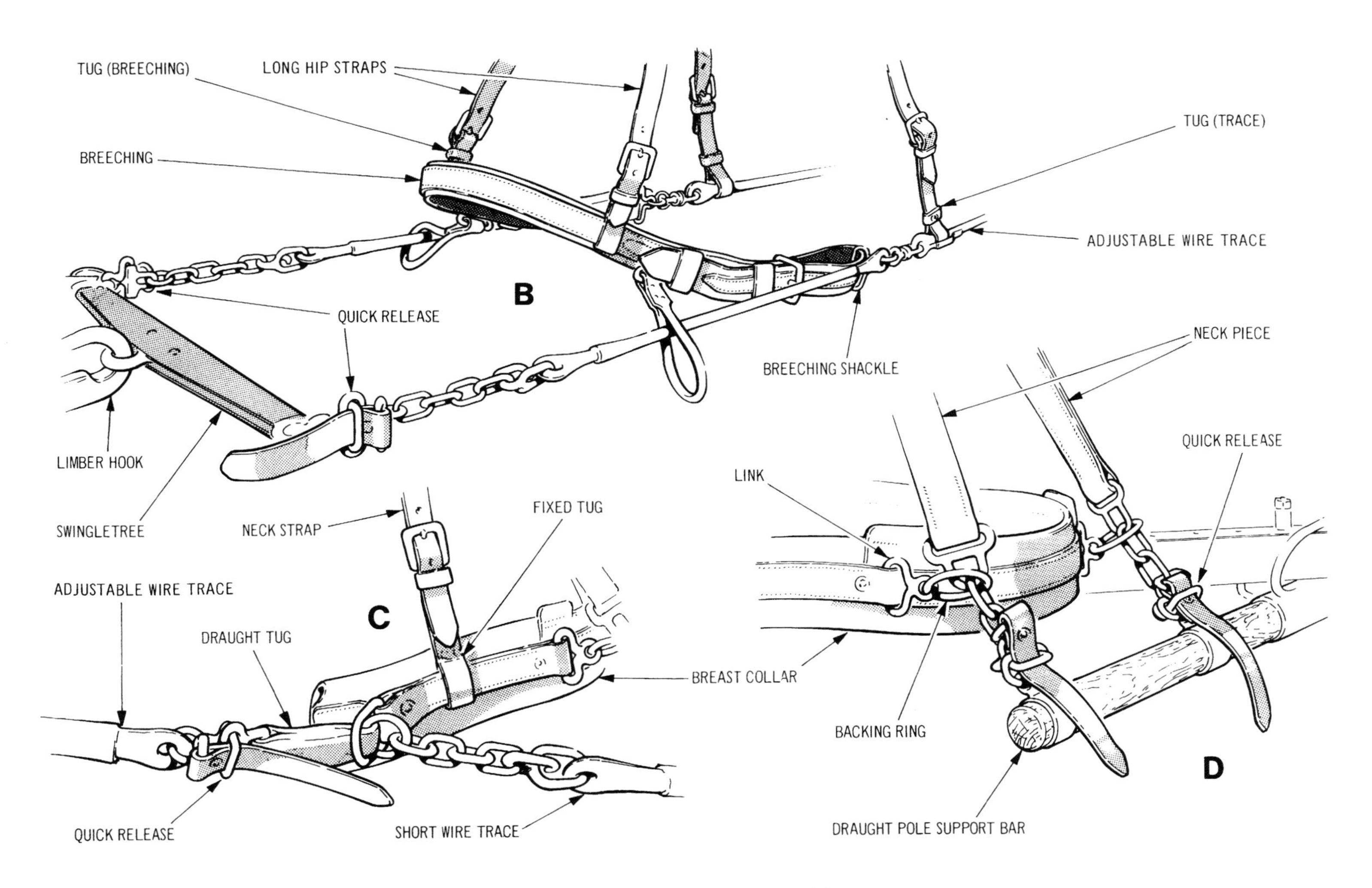

WHEEL (REAR) PAIR HARNESS

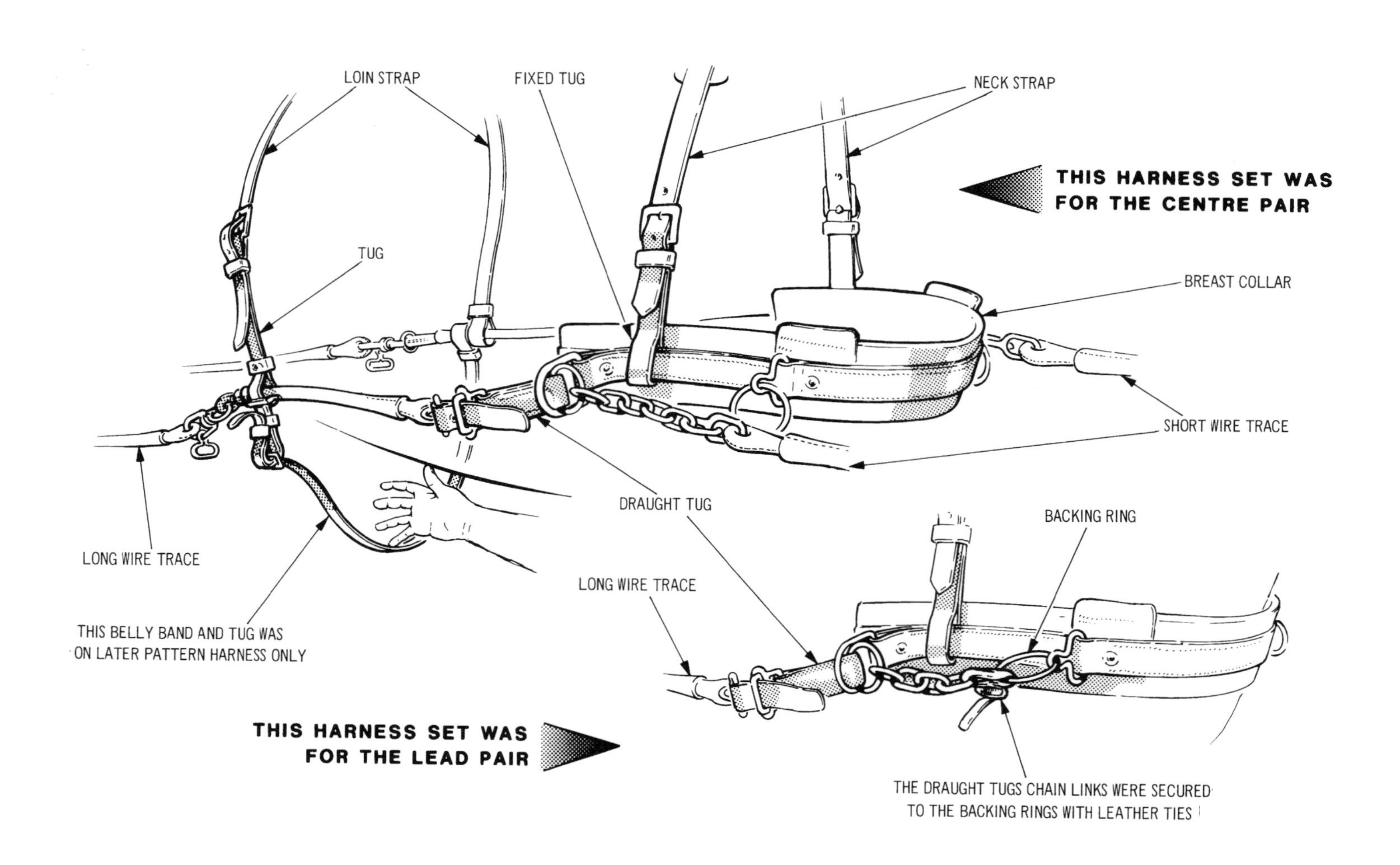
LOIN STRAP
FIXED TUG
NECK STRAP
THIS HARNESS SET WAS FOR THE CENTRE PAIR
TUG
BREAST COLLAR
SHORT WIRE TRACE
DRAUGHT TUG
BACKING RING
LONG WIRE TRACE
LONG WIRE TRACE
THIS BELLY BAND AND TUG WAS ON LATER PATTERN HARNESS ONLY
THIS HARNESS SET WAS FOR THE LEAD PAIR
THE DRAUGHT TUGS CHAIN LINKS WERE SECURED TO THE BACKING RINGS WITH LEATHER TIES

HARNESS

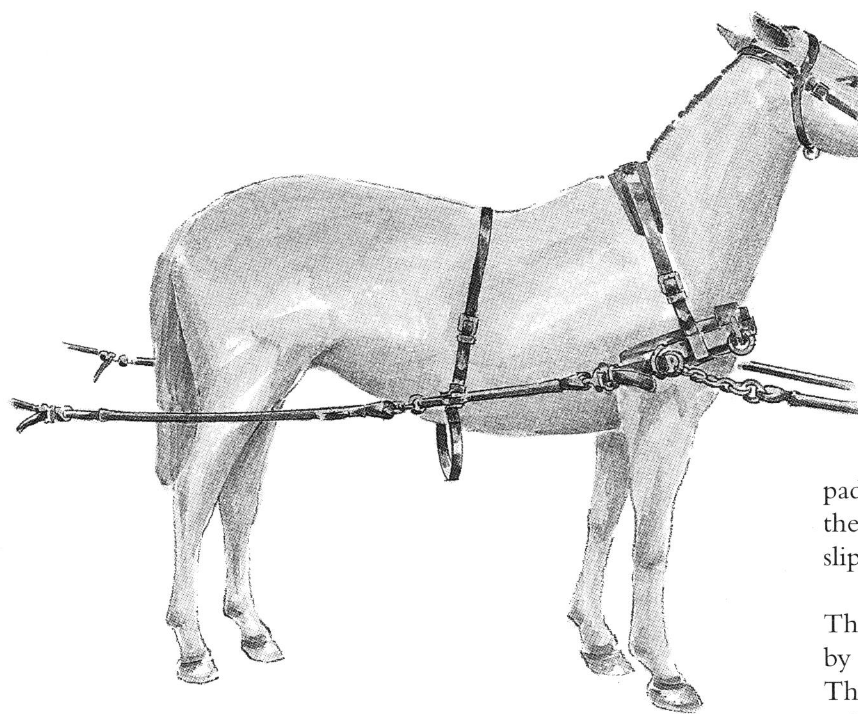

postilion, on the near (left) side. Their saddles, known as the Universal Pattern, 1902, were independent of the draught harness (see page 400).

Saddle (illustrated on pages 400 and 401)

The basic saddle component was the frame, or tree, comprising two side bars (**3**) of wood, generally beech, joined by two arches (**1** and **4**). These arches, the pommel or front arch (**1**) and the cantle or rear arch (**4**), were both made of steel. A webbing sling joined the two arches and supported the leather seat (**2**).

To the side bars (**3**) were attached the leather flaps (**7**), the top tabs of the V-attachments (**8**) and the staples or links to carry the stirrup leathers (**11**).

The side bars (**3**) were fitted with numnah pannels (**5**). These were of felt, with leather pockets, the side bars fitting into the leather pockets at the side bar rear (fan)(**6**) and front (burr)(**13**), the latter having a securing strap. The purpose of the numnah pannels was to give padding without filling the channel below the seat, also to protect the side bars and to provide a surface to grip the blanket, avoiding slipping of the saddle.

The V-attachment (**8**) connected the girth (**9**) to the side bars (**3**) by way of the girth straps (**16**), sweat flaps (**15**) and V-straps (**14**). The girth (**9**) was of leather or cord, with split openings and two pairs of buckles with which to attach the girth straps (**16**). Near to each end was sewn a leather loop, through which was passed the surcingle (**12**).

The surcingle (**12**) was a plain leather strap, passed over the seat (**2**) and through the girth loops, the ends being buckled together below the girth.

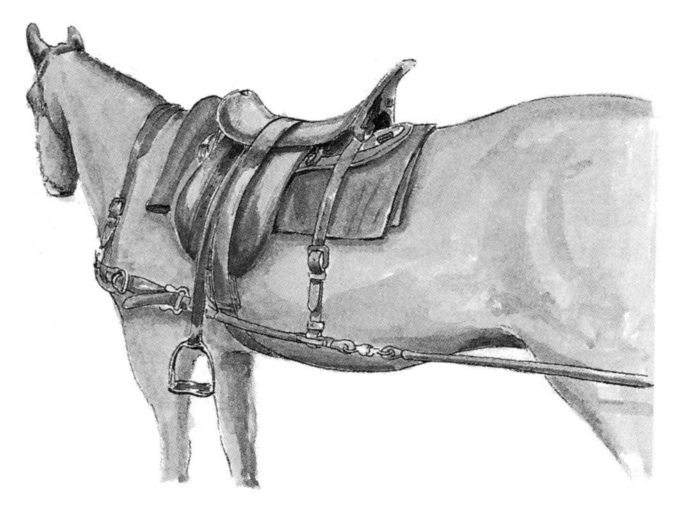

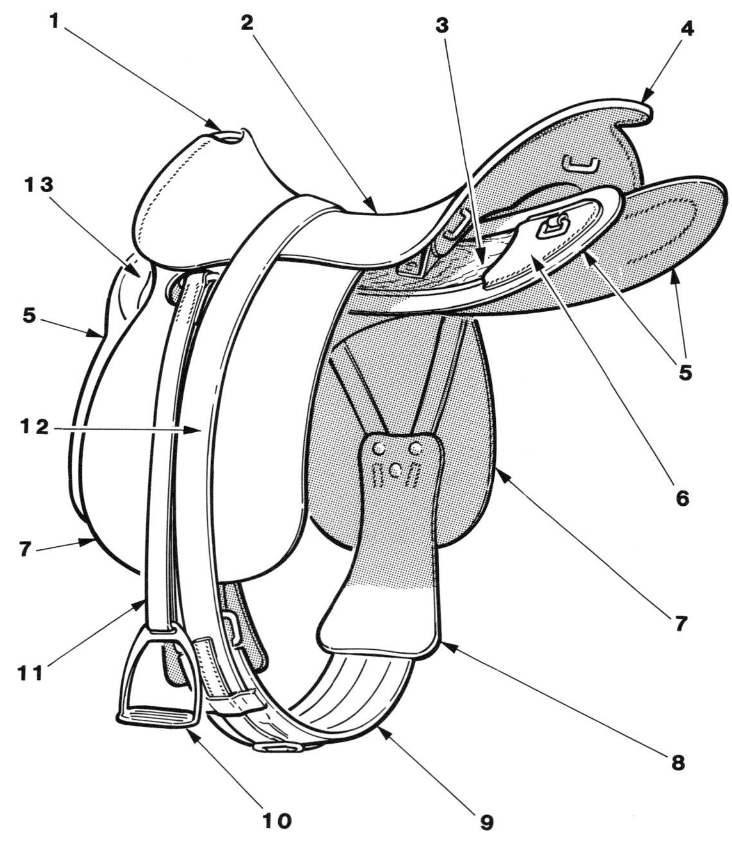

1 POMMEL (FRONT ARCH)
2 SEAT
3 SIDE BAR
4 CANTLE (REAR ARCH)
5 NUMNAH PANNEL
6 FAN
7 FLAP
8 V ATTACHMENT
9 GIRTH (CORD OR LEATHER)
10 STIRRUP IRON
11 STIRRUP LEATHER
12 SURCINGLE
13 BURR
14 V STRAP
15 SWEAT FLAP
16 GIRTH STRAP

SADDLE

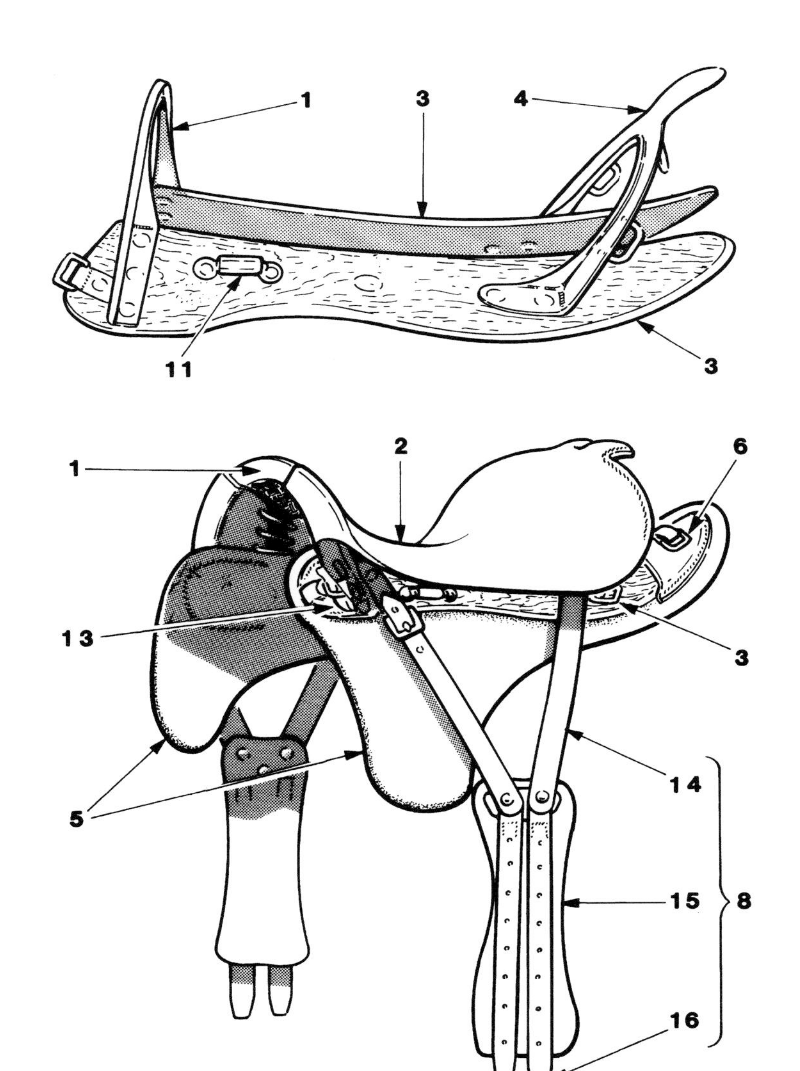

Head collar, bit and bridlehead

The Service Head Collar was designed to be capable of use either as a bridle, or as a head collar in the stable or on the picket line.

As with the saddle, it was essential that the head collar was carefully fitted to the horse. Great care was necessary to ensure that the bit (**9**) was of the correct size. A narrow bit would pinch the horse's lips and a wide one could move sideways and cause bruising.

A straight barred bit placed more pressure on the tongue, a bit with a port (**21**) put more pressure on the bars, the tongue fitting into the port. Which of these was used would depend on such factors as the horse's training and temperament, also the skill and experience of the rider. The use of a bit with a very narrow or high port would only be allowed in exceptional circumstances and used by a particularly good horseman.

Length of the reins was such that, when held centrally in the left hand, they would just touch the rider's waist with a light feel of the horse's mouth.

A head rope could be fitted by securing it through the jowl piece lower ring (**5**).

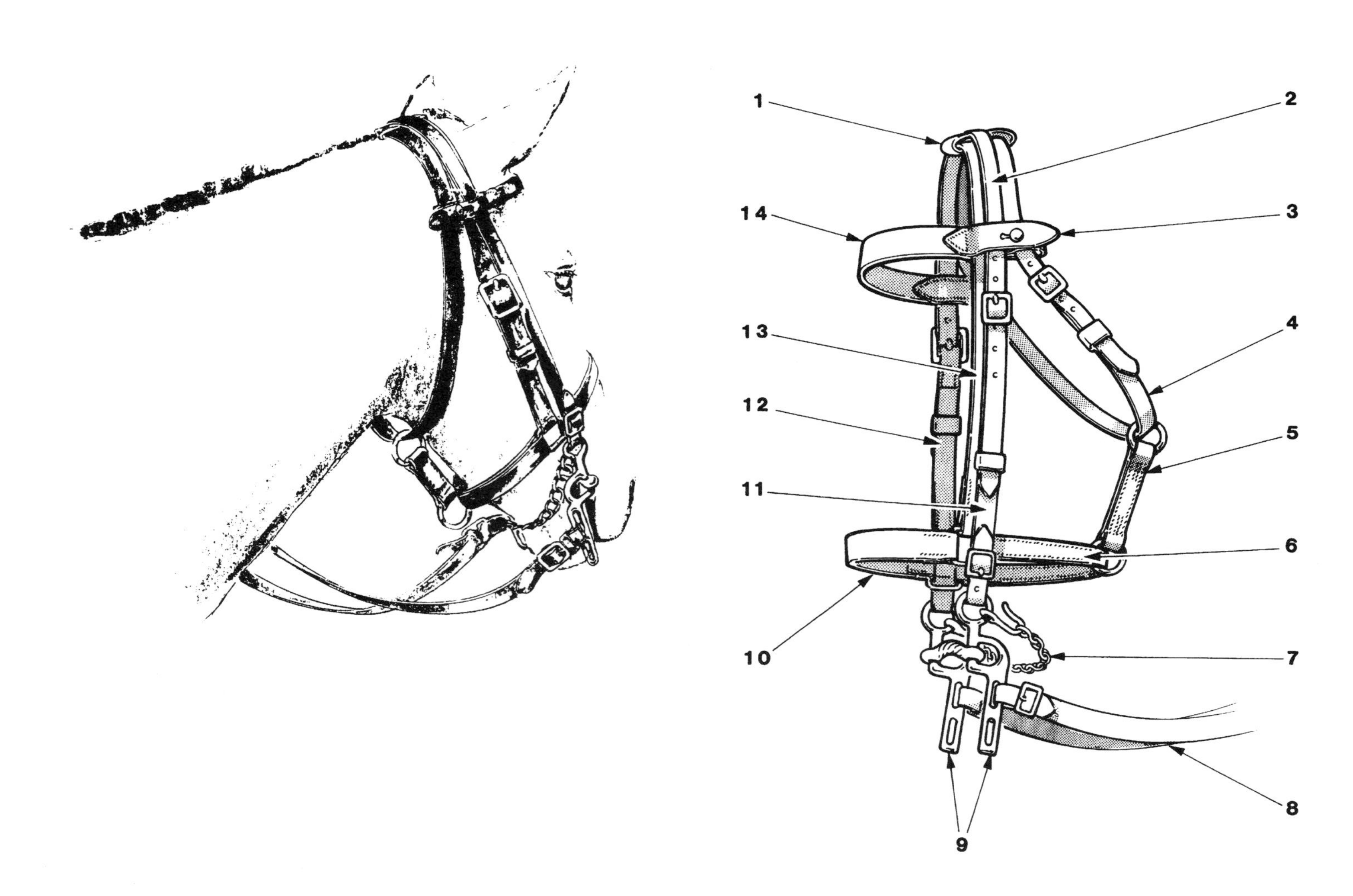

HEAD COLLAR, BIT AND BRIDLEHEAD

1 CROWN LOOP
2 BRIDLEHEAD LONG PIECE
3 BROW BAND TAB
4 THROAT LASH
5 JOWL PIECE
6 BACK STAY
7 CURB CHAIN
8 REIN
9 BIT
10 NOSE BAND
11 BRIDLEHEAD SHORT PIECE
12 BUCKLING PIECE
13 CHEEK PIECE
14 BROW BAND
15 BIT – CHEEK
16 BIT – EYE
17 BIT – UPPER BAR
18 BIT – CENTRE BAR
19 BIT – LOWER BAR
20 CURB CHAIN HOOK
21 MOUTHPIECE – PORT MOUTH
22 MOUTHPIECE – CANONS

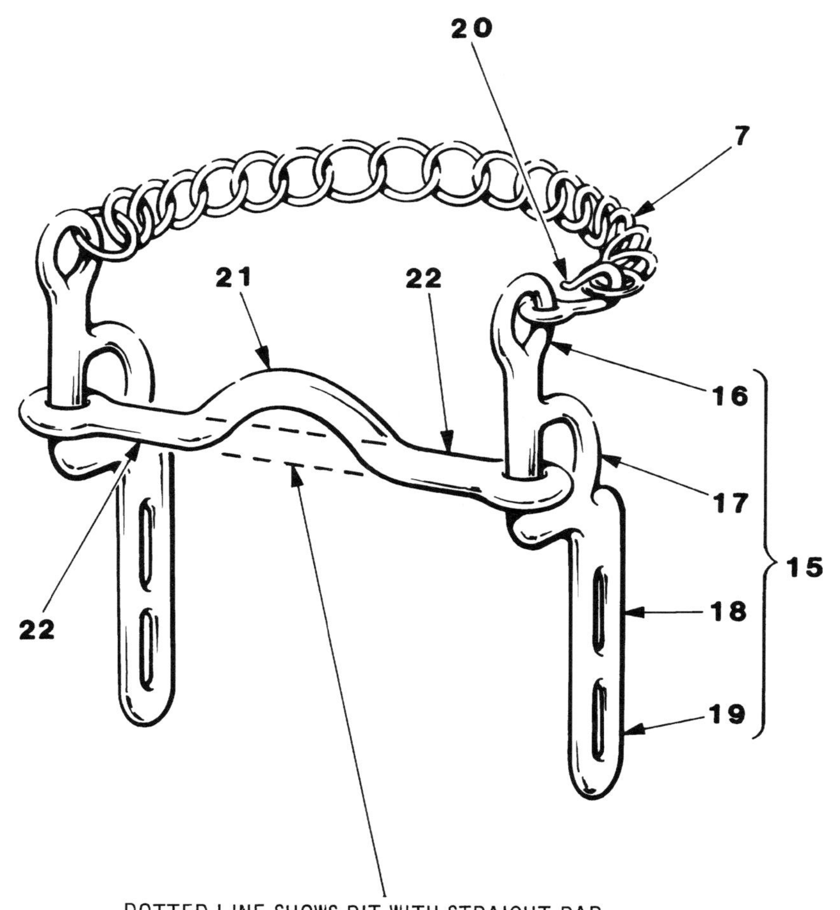

DOTTED LINE SHOWS BIT WITH STRAIGHT BAR

GLOSSARY OF TERMS

Axletree The pin or rod in the NAVE (centre) of a wheel on which the wheel turns: a pivot or support of any kind.

Cambric A fine, white linen manufactured from flax.

Draught pole A single shaft to which a pair of horses may be yoked.

Futchell A piece of timber or metal, lengthwise of a carriage, supporting the draught pole.

Hame One of the curved bars of a draught-horse's collar.

Marline A small rope, wound around a larger one to prevent wear.

Palembang cane Split from the stem of Calamus or Rattan palm. From Palembang, a town on the River Musi, Sumatra in the former Dutch East lndies.

Perch A pole joining the fore and hind gear of some vehicles.

Piasaba grass A coarse, stiff fibre from Brazilian palms. Used for making brushes.

Shalloon A light, worsted (woollen) yarn.

Swingletree (swinglebar, whippletree) The crosspiece of a carriage for the attachment of harness traces.

IMPERIAL MEASURES AND METRIC EQUIVALENTS

LENGTH

0.001 inch = 0.0254 mm
1/64 (0.0156 inch) = 0.3969 mm
1/32 (0.3125 inch) = 0.7938 mm
1/16 (0.0625 inch) = 1.5875 mm
1/8 (0.125 inch) = 3.175 mm
1/4 (0.250 inch) = 6.35 mm
1/2 (0.500 inch) = 12.7 mm
3/4 (0.750 inch) = 19.05 mm
1 inch (in) = 25.4 mm
12 in = 1 foot (ft) = 304.800 mm
3 ft = 1 yard (yd) = 914.400 mm
5½ yd = 1 pole = 5.029 metres
4 poles = 1 chain = 20.116 metres
10 chains = 1 furlong = 201.160 metres
8 furlongs = 1 mile (1,760 yds) = 1.61 kilometres
3 miles = 1 league = 4.83 kilometres

WEIGHT

1 grain = 0.065 gramme
27.34 grains = 1 dram = 1.77 grammes
16 drams = 1 ounce (oz)(437.5 grains) = 28.32 grammes
16 oz = 1 pound (lb)(7000 grains) = 0.453 kilogramme
14 lb = 1 stone = 6.342 kilogrammes
2 stones = 1 quarter = 12.700 kilogrammes
4 quarters = 1 hundredweight (cwt) = 50.802 kilogrammes
20 cwt = 1 ton (2240 lb) = 1.016 tonnes

LIQUID

1 fluid ounce (fl oz) = 28.413 millilitres
20 fl oz = 1 pint (pt) = 568.26 millilitres
8 pt = 1 gallon = 4.546 litres

Gnome rotary aero engines under test, mounted on artillery carriage test beds.
Photograph believed to be French, circa 1916.